Summer of Roses

LUANNE RICE

Summer of Roses

DOUBLEDAY LARGE PRINT HOME LIBRARY EDITION

BANTAM BOOKS

This Large Print Edition, prepared especially for Doubleday Large Print Home Library, contains the complete, unabridged text of the original Publisher's Edition.

SUMMER OF ROSES
A Bantam Book

Published by Bantam Dell
A Division of Random House, Inc.
New York, New York

Bantam Books is a registered trademark of Random House, Inc., and the colophon is a trademark of Random House, Inc.

ISBN: 0-7394-5574-5

Printed in the United States of America

This Large Print Book carries the
Seal of Approval of N.A.V.H.

TO ROSEMARY GOETTSCHE,
Willoughby Moon, the most beautiful rose of all

"In which Christopher Robin and Pooh
come to an enchanted place . . .

I
And all your friends
Sends—
I mean all your friend
Send—
(Very awkward this, it keeps
going wrong)
Well, anyhow, we send
Our love
END."

—CHAPTER X,
from *The House at Pooh Corner*,
by A. A. Milne

Acknowledgments

This is the Summer of Roses, but it is also the summer of wonderful publishers. Gratitude beyond words to everyone at Bantam, for all their kindness, patience, generosity, and vision: Irwyn Applebaum, Nita Taublib, Tracy Devine, Betsy Hulsebosch, Carolyn Schwartz, Cynthia Lasky, Barb Burg, Susan Corcoran, Gina Wachtel, Melissa Lord, Kerri Buckley, Kenneth Wohlrob, Jennifer Campaniolo, Igor Aronov, Mandy Lau, and Janet Rutledge.

Thank you to Deborah Dwyer and to Bantam's production staff, who work miracles: Anna Forgione, Kathleen Baldonado, Tracy Heydweiller, Virginia Norey, Christine Tanigawa, and Susan Hood.

Much admiration and affection to Jim Plumeri.

Boundless love and thanks to my agent, Andrea Cirillo, and everyone at the Jane Rotrosen Agency: Jane Berkey, Don Cleary, Meg Ruley, Peggy Gordijn, Annelise Robey,

Maggie Kelly, Hilary Demby, Christina Hogrebe, and Chris Ruen.

Epic gratitude to Ron Bernstein, who is nothing less than amazing.

In celebration of the Whale Trail sculpture event of southeastern Connecticut, with thanks to Diana Atwood Johnson and to Suzanne Mylar of K & M Productions. Amelia Onorato, my brilliant niece, is the artist for my beluga whale (for the Old Lyme–Phoebe Griffin Noyes Library), and I'm very proud of her work. Love and thanks also to Maureen and Olivier Onorato for all the support and celestial navigation.

Much love and thanks also to Rosemary's wonderful family—her husband, Roger Goettsche, and their brilliant daughters, Kate, Molly, and Emily.

Thank you, Lyn Gammill Walker, with much love and appreciation for such wonderful connection and insight.

Gratitude to SEA, the Sea Education Association of Woods Hole, Massachusetts, for that first voyage to see the whales, so long ago.

Thank you to E. J. McAdams, the poet of New York City nature.

Many thanks to Subhankar Banerjee for his brilliant, sensitive photographs of the Arctic National Wildlife Refuge.

Thank you to the staff at the Cape Hatteras National Seashore, the dolphins of Rodanthe, and protectors of the environment everywhere.

Unending awe to William Twigg Crawford,

Paul James, and J.M., for their wealth of knowledge about sharks.

Much gratitude to Susan Caruso, Mary Lou Cuccio, Ellie and Bud Ford, and the women at Domestic Violence Valley Shore Services.

Love and thanks to Sarah Walker, who is by far the most hilarious person in New York City.

Much appreciation to Carolyn Schwartz, for everything in Charleston, and to everyone at *Family Circle* magazine and the *Family Circle* Cup, for a wonderful event.

Thank you and love to the dauntless and inspiring Sam Whitney and Sadie Whitney-Havlicak.

With much love to Diana Atwood Johnson and John S. Johnson.

Love forever to Marta Curro and Mary Perrin.

Thank you to some wonderful musicians and artists, my friends: Mark Lonergan, Dore Dedrick, the Atwaters, Maura Fogarty, and Fletcher Buckley.

Much gratitude to Dr. Matthew Goulet.

I am grateful beyond words to Dr. Susan Robertson. Her support, vision, clarity, and insight have sustained me throughout the writing of this novel, and many others.

Summer
of
Roses

Prologue

My wedding was like a dream. It was almost everything a wedding should be, and when I think of it, even now, I see it unfolding like the kind of beautiful story that always has a happy ending.

I got married in my grandmother's garden, by the sea, on a brilliant early July morning at Hubbard's Point. The daylilies were in bloom. That's what I remember, almost as much as the roses: orange, cream, lemon, golden daylilies on tall green stalks, tossed by the summer breeze, trumpeting exultation up to the wild blue sky. But the roses were my grandmother's specialty, her pride and joy, and that year, for my wedding, they were all blooming.

Scarlet Dublin Bay roses climbed the trellis beside the front door of the weathered-shingle cottage, while Garnet-and-Golds and pale pink New Dawns meandered up the stone chimney. The beds by the iron bench bloomed with red, yellow, peach, and pink classic English varieties, while those along the stone wall, by the old wishing well and the steps up to the road, were low shrubs of white and cream roses. A six-foot hedge of *Rosa rugosa*—white and pink beach roses—lined the seawall, along with deep blue delphiniums and hydrangeas.

It was a perfect setting for a perfect wedding—something that most people, including me, never imagined would happen. I guess I thought I wasn't the marrying kind. Let's just say that I was a little on the guarded side. I had lost my parents very young. As a child I had been in love with our family. I know how dramatic that sounds, but it's true. We were so happy, and my parents had loved each other with wild, reckless, ends-of-the-earth abandon. I had watched them together, and taken it in, and decided, even at four, that nothing less would ever do for me. When they were killed in a ferry accident during a trip to Ireland, although I wasn't there, but home in Connecticut with my grandmother, I think I died with them.

So my wedding—and everything that had led up to it—the miracle of meeting Edward Hunter, and falling so madly in love with him, and being swept off my feet in a way I'd never expected or believed could happen—was a resurrection of sorts. A rising from the dead, of a little girl who went down to the bottom of the Irish Sea with her parents, twenty-seven years earlier.

Edward. He seemed to love me with everything he had, not wanting to let me out of his sight. His expression, his embrace, his presence—all had the intensity of a hurricane lamp turned up high. And when he poured that light on me, I was transfixed.

He was just over five-eight, but since I'm just under five-two, I had to stand on tiptoes to kiss him. A rugby player at Harvard, he was broad-shouldered and muscular. His red Saab bore three stickers: Harvard University, Columbia Business School, and a bumper sticker that said *Rugby Players Eat Their Dead.* The joke was, Edward was so gentle, I couldn't even imagine him playing such a rough sport.

When I go back to our wedding day, I see his red car parked in the road up at the top of the stone steps, behind the rose-and-ivy-covered wishing well. I can see the graceful arch curving over the well—with *Sea Garden,* the name of my grandmother's cottage, forged in wrought iron back when my great-grandfather was still alive—the black letters rusting away in the salt air even back then, twelve years ago. I remember the moment so well: standing there in my grandmother's yard, knowing that soon I would drive away with Edward in that red car—that I would be his wife, and we would be off on our honeymoon.

Can I say now, for certain, that I looked at that iron arch and saw the corroding letters as a reminder that even that which is most beautiful, intended to endure forever, can be corrupted or destroyed? No, I can't. But I do remember that the sight of it gave me my first cold feeling of the day.

My grandmother and Clara Littlefield—her next-door neighbor and best friend from childhood—had gone all out to make my wedding a dream come true. The yellow-and-white-striped tent stood in the side yard between their houses, on the very tip of Hubbard's Point, jutting proudly into Long Island Sound. Tables with long golden-cream tablecloths were scattered around, all decorated with flowers from the garden. A string quartet from the Hartt School of Music, in Hartford, played Vivaldi. My friends were in their summer best— bright sundresses, straw hats, blue blazers.

Granny stood before me, looking into my eyes. We were the same height, and we laughed, because we were both so happy. I wore a white wedding gown; she wore a pale yellow chiffon dress. My veil blew in the sea breeze; my bouquet was white roses, off-white lace hydrangeas, and ivy from the wishing well. Granny wore a yellow straw hat with a band of blue flowers.

"I wish Edward's family had been able to come," she said as we stood by the wishing well, ready to begin the procession.

"I know," I said. "He's trying to make the best of it."

"Well," she said. "Things happen . . . you'll

see them soon, I'm sure. One thing I know, Mara—your parents are with you today."

"Granny, don't get me started."

"I won't," my grandmother said, wriggling her shoulders with resolve. "We're staying strong as I walk you down the aisle, or I'm not Maeve Jameson."

"My parents would be proud of you," I said, because I knew she was thinking of them every bit as much as I was trying not to—and I gave her a big smile, just to prove I wasn't going to cry.

"Of us both," she said, linking arms with me as the quartet started playing Bach.

So much time has passed, but certain memories are still clear and sharp. The pressure of Granny's hand on mine, holding steady, as we walked across the grass; my beach friends Bay and Tara beaming at me; the smell of roses and salt air; Edward's short dark hair, his golden tan set off by a pale blue shirt and wheat linen blazer; his wide-eyed gaze.

I remember thinking his eyes looked like a little boy's. Hazel eyes. He had been so helpful all morning—taking charge of where the tables went, which direction the quartet should face. It was sort of odd, having a man "in charge," here on this point of land filled with strong women. Granny and I had exchanged an amused glance—letting him do his thing. But here he was, standing at our makeshift altar in the side yard, looking for all the world like a lost little boy as I approached him. But then I caught that blank stare—blank, yet somehow charged—and it made me hesitate, holding tight to my grandmother's hand.

Yes, I remember that stare, the look in his hazel eyes. It was fear—standing there under the striped tent, watching me approach, my betrothed was afraid of something. The years have gone by and told me all I need to know about his fear—but let's go back to my wedding day and pretend we don't have all this knowledge. Back then, in quick succession, I thought one thing and felt another. No—that's backwards. I felt first, thought second.

I felt cold—the same chilly primal shiver I'd experienced looking up at his car, seeing that salt-pitted, rusty metal arch. But I chased the unwanted, ugly chill with this thought: *Edward—hey, honey, Edward! Don't be afraid . . . please don't worry that it's too soon, or my grandmother doubts you. I love you. . . . I love you.*

I love you.

Words I had said so rarely up until that time—but since meeting Edward, I had used almost constantly. The old Mara Jameson had been too closed off and guarded to let them slip off her tongue; but the new Mara Jameson couldn't say them enough.

This was my home, my side yard, my family and friends—Edward was far from everything comfortable and familiar to him. His family hadn't been able to make it. These thoughts were flying through my mind as my grandmother passed my hand into his with the whispered words "Take care of her, Edward." Edward nodded, but the expression in his eyes didn't ease.

Memo to self and brides everywhere: if you're standing in front of a justice of the peace, about to get married, and all you can think about is why your husband-to-be looks very uncomfortable, it's a red flag worth paying attention to.

The ceremony occurred. That's how I think of it now: words and music. What did they all mean? It's hard to say, harder still to not be cynical. The ceremony disguised one basic truth: marriage is a contract. Let's put romance aside. First and foremost, marriage is a legal, binding contract, where two people are joined in partnership, their assets merged, their fates legally entwined through powers vested by no less than the state.

When I think back to the look in Edward's eyes, I believe that he was afraid that I might not follow through on the deal, might not sign on the dotted line. What would have happened if I hadn't? If I had listened to that tiny voice inside, if I had felt the cold chill and known that it meant something worth paying attention to?

But I didn't listen. I pushed my feelings aside and pulled other things out of the summer air: love, hope, faith, resolve. I held Edward's hand. "I do," I said. "I do," he said. He kissed the bride. People cheered, and when I looked out at my friends, I saw more than one of them crying and grinning at the same time. They were so very happy for me.

We stood there, husband and wife. Our brilliant summer wedding day, blue sky and sparkles on the calm water, Bach giving

way to Mozart and the sound of leaves flut-
tering in the breeze—everything was so
beautiful, so spectacular, it had to be a harbinger of a joyful life to come.

I turned to look at him. It's true, my
own eyes were moist, and my voice was
thin with wild and rising emotion. "Edward,"
I said, trailing off into all the hopes and
dreams and possibilities of our future
together. He stared at me—the fear gone
from his eyes, replaced by something
else. It was the first time I saw—well, you'll
hear about what I saw as my story goes on.
All I can say is, I felt the earth—the thin layer
of grass on granite ledge—tilt beneath my
feet.

He touched the flowers in my bouquet
and said, "You're so delicate, Mara. Like
a white rose. And white roses bruise so
easily. Is that what your grandmother
meant when she said I should take care of
you?"

His words took my breath away. Don't
they imply great tenderness? Show true
depth of caring, of understanding? Of
course they do. He could be so tender.
I'll never deny that. But do you also see,
as I do now, that his words implied a threat?

It was as if he'd been focused on Granny's gentle direction—just an offhand comment was how I'd taken it, a rather protective grandmother giving away the bride. Had Edward even heard the ceremony? Had he even *been* there? His hazel eyes flashed black as he mentioned Granny's words.

Just recently, I dreamed of a woman who lived under veils. Black, gray, white, silver, slate, dark blue—layers of veils covering her face. Take one off, there's another underneath. The woman lived in darkness, even when the sun was shining. She existed under cover. She could barely see out, and others could not see in. The question was: who put those veils on her? Did she do it to herself? In the dream, she took them off one by one—and at the very bottom, the very last, or first, was a white wedding veil. In my life, I had them torn from me. I wanted to keep them on—you have no idea how much I needed those veils.

Women learn how to hide the worst. We love the best, and show it to all who want to see. Our accomplishments, our careers, our awards, our homes, our gardens, our happy marriages, our beautiful children. We learn, by tacit agreement, to look away from—and hide—the hurt, the blight, the dark, the monster in the closet, the darkness in our new husband's eyes.

But in some lives, there comes a time when the monster comes out of the closet and won't go back in. That happened to me. He began to show himself. My grandmother was the first to see. Only the wisest people can observe a woman in such a relationship and not sit in judgment. Judgment is easy: it is black and white, as brutal as a gavel strike. It keeps a person from having to ask the hard questions: what can I do to help? Could that be me?

My grandmother didn't judge. She tried to understand—and if anyone could understand, it would be her, the woman who had raised me in her rose-covered cottage by Long Island Sound. A woman patient enough to coax red, pink, peach, yellow, and white roses from the stony Connecticut soil, to ease her brokenhearted orphan granddaughter back into life, could sit still long enough to see through the lies, see past the veils—and instead of judging, try to help, really help.

People said, "How could you have stayed

with him so long?" The true answer, of course, is that I had the veils. But the answer I gave was "I loved him." In its way, that answer was true too. My grandmother understood that.

It wasn't real love. I didn't know that for a long time. Real love is a boomerang—it comes back to you. With Edward, love was a sinkhole. It nearly consumed me, taking every single thing I had, and then some—until I, and everything surrounding me, collapsed.

I have Liam now, so I have learned the difference. And I have my daughter, Rose. The day Rose was born, nine years ago, I was on the run. I had left my home, my grandmother, my beloved Connecticut shoreline, where I had always lived, to escape Edward and try to save something of my life. The Connecticut motto is *Qui Transtulit Sustinet*—"He who transplants sustains."

Leave it to the founding fathers to say "he." Perhaps they knew that "she"—or at least "me"—"who transplants shatters." I left home, pregnant with Rose, and I fell apart. But Rose coaxed the love right from my bones. I built myself back, with the help of Rose and Liam. And, although she wasn't right there in person, my grandmother. She was with me, in my heart, guiding me, every single day while I lived in hiding, in another country, far from home.

You see, my grandmother let me go. She made the ultimate sacrifice for me—gave me and Rose, her great-granddaughter, the chance and means to get away from Edward. She was a one-woman underground railway for one emotionally battered woman. And it cost her so dearly, I don't know whether she will survive.

My name is Lily Malone now. It was my on-the-run name, and it has stuck. I have decided to keep it forever. *Lily* for the orange and yellow daylilies growing along the stone wall of my grandmother's sea garden, waving on long, slender green stalks in the salt breeze. *Malone* for the song she used to sing me when I was little:

> *In Dublin's fair city, where girls are so
> pretty,
> I once laid my eyes on sweet Molly
> Malone.
> She wheeled her wheelbarrow
> through streets broad and narrow,*

*Singing "cockles and mussels alive,
  alive-oh."*

Those lyrics are so sweet, and because my grandmother sang them to me when I was little and couldn't sleep, they seemed full of life and romance and the promise of unexpected love. I took the name Malone to honor my grandmother's lullaby, but also for a darker reason. The name helps me stay on guard—reminds me that someone once laid eyes on me too. And like Molly Malone, I was a hardworking woman; he liked that about me. He liked it very much.

I would like to explain my chosen name to my grandmother. I would like to see her again. To introduce her to Liam—and, especially, to Rose.

More than anything, I've come back from my nine-year exile to try to save my grandmother, as she once saved me. I am remembering all this for her. I want to recapture every detail, so I can appreciate exactly what she did for me—for the woman I was, and the woman I have become.

This story is a prayer for her, Maeve Jameson.

It begins twelve years ago, three years be-

fore I left Hubbard's Point for the most re-
mote place I could find—back when I was
Mara. Back when I was a rose that bruised
so easily.

Chapter 1

How does a person reenter a life she left nine years earlier? Knowing that there had been a relentless search for her, that her picture had been plastered on the front pages of every newspaper in Connecticut and beyond? Understanding that every local police department remained on the lookout for her? Realizing that all but one of her friends and family have given her up for dead?

The answer is, she walks right in the front door.

That's what Lily Malone did in the very-early-morning hours of August ninth. Just past one A.M., Liam Neill parked his truck in the turnaround at Hubbard's Point, lifted Rose—sleeping, after the long drive from Nova Scotia—and followed Lily down the stone steps.

Lily glanced at the arch over the wishing well—there was the house name, *Sea Garden,* its letters just a little more rusty, a bit more filigreed from the salt air, than they had been nine years earlier. The sight gave her a pang so deep, she gasped out loud. Lily was really home. A breeze blew off Long Island Sound—salt water, just like the Gulf of St. Lawrence in Maritime Canada, where she had lived and hidden these last nine years. But this night breeze was warm, gentle, filled with scents of marsh grass and sandy beaches—instead of the fjord's arctic cliffs and cold, clear water flowing straight off the pack ice.

"Oh my," she said out loud, alive with the thrill of finally coming home. The roses greeted her—their perfume filled the air, and if the ones growing up the trellis beside the front door were slightly less well tended than they'd been nine years ago, they were still profuse and extravagant. Lily reached up, through the thorns, to feel underneath the shingle just beside the dark porch light, and there it was—the key her grandmother had always kept hidden there, guarded by the roses' foliage and thorns. "She didn't move it," she whispered.

"Of course she didn't," Liam said in her ear, standing behind her with Rose. "She never stopped hoping you'd come back."

"Maeve is coming home too," Lily said, opening the squeaky screen door, holding it open with her shoulder, fumbling with the key in the rusty old door lock. "Right? Tell me she's going to be okay—"

"She will be, Lily," Liam said.

Lily felt the key turn. Nine years later, the door made the same bump as it opened, one of the hinges hanging just slightly. Stepping into the kitchen . . . smelling beach-house dampness encroaching from the absence of its owner. Yet someone— Clara, obviously—had opened a few windows. Lily walked through the first floor as if she were a ghost, haunting her most beloved, familiar place on earth.

Lily began to smile. "It's all the same," she whispered. The moon had risen out of the Sound, casting a gleaming white light on the calm water, its pale light flooding the room. Lily saw the familiar slipcovers, braided rugs, pillows she had needle-pointed for her grandmother. She ran her fingers over her old shell collection, books in the bookcase, moonstones gathered at low tide on Little Beach.

She had to see everything, yet she couldn't turn on a lamp yet. If she turned on a light, it would mean she was committed to this. "This" meaning that she was really here, that her exile was over, that she had returned to the land of the living. Neighbors would see the light and come over. People would know that she was back.

Edward would find out.

"Where does Rose sleep?" Liam asked.

"In my room," Lily whispered. She led him up the narrow stairs. The second floor had four small bedrooms—beach-cottage in size and feel. Lily's heart was racing as she entered her old room. Under the eaves on the north side, it had funny ceiling angles, a twin bed, and her old Betsy McCall paper dolls right there on the bureau. Pulling down the covers, she choked up to see the sheets—imprinted with tiny bouquets of blue roses—and a pink summer-weight blanket. She bent down to smell the bedding—it was fresh.

"My grandmother knew we were coming," she said. "Somehow, before she went to the hospital, she made up the bed for Rose."

Together they tucked Rose in. The little girl stirred, opening her eyes, glancing around the unfamiliar room in dream-state wonder. "Are we here?" she asked.

"Yes, honey. You'll see it all tomorrow morning. Good night."

"Night," Rose murmured as her eyes fluttered shut.

Lily and Liam went back downstairs. Moonlight was dazzling on the water in front of the house. Lily had watched countless moonrises from this room, through the wide, curtainless windows overlooking the rocks and sea. Everything seemed so open compared to the pine-shrouded cabin she'd lived in at Cape Hawk, Nova Scotia—she had hidden in a boreal forest, with hawks and owls as sentries.

Liam had been one of the first people she'd met, arriving in the distant, unfamiliar town—disguised by cropping her long dark hair, dyeing it light brown, wearing the old horn-rimmed spectacles her grandmother had given her. He had been her friend and savior, even though she had rejected him every step of the way. She had to, to protect herself and her unborn baby.

Lily's first weeks in Nova Scotia had been a dark fairy tale, complete with cabin deep in the North Woods, a bounty on her head in the form of a reward posted by Edward, and the benevolent presence of the fierce and kindly Liam—there for Rose's birth, delivering the baby on the kitchen floor, and swearing to protect forever this mother and child. And there had been plenty of protecting for him to do: born with complex heart defects, Rose had just completed her last round of surgery earlier that summer.

Brokenhearted baby, brokenhearted mother, Lily thought, gazing out at the moon on the Sound. Her arm was around Liam, and his around her. Gulls called from across the water, from their rookery on the rock islands half a mile offshore. Lily felt the sound in her heart, and thought of the annual Ceili Festival, just about to start in Cape Hawk, the Irish music as haunting as the gulls' cries.

She looked up at Liam—tall and lean, his blue eyes shadowed with his own private sorrows. Ravaged by the shark that killed his brother, Liam had one arm—and the childhood nickname, "Captain Hook," that had made him both a laughingstock and a tragic figure in his small town. Liam would have none of that—he blazed his way through university and graduate school, becoming a respected oceanographer and ichthyologist—studying great whites, the species that had torn apart his family and his own body.

Lily wasn't exactly sure what had brought them together. And she wasn't even sure she cared. They had found each other in that far-northern town. She had run so far from home, and found something like a replacement family. Anne, Marisa, Marlena . . . her friends and needlepointing club, the Nanouk Girls of the Frozen North, were like her sisters. And Liam. He had been present at Rose's birth, and he'd never gone away. Those nine years in Cape Hawk had strengthened Lily more than anything she could have imagined.

Her grandmother's illness had called her back to Hubbard's Point. Patrick Murphy, the lead detective on the case of Lily's disappearance, had finally found her in Cape

Hawk. The minute she heard of Maeve's illness, everything else fell away. Lily knew what she had to do.

She came home.

"I'm really here," she said, leaning against Liam.

"Are you ready for tomorrow?" he asked.

"I have to be," she said. "My grandmother needs me."

"I know," he said. His voice was low and calm. He touched her hair, and her skin tingled. They were still very new. Was it possible that just a few weeks ago they had kissed for the first time? After a whole lifetime of loving Rose, they were really together.

"I don't want Rose to ever know him," Lily said, and she didn't even have to say his name.

"Let me take her away," Liam said. "I'll hide her. Only you'll know where we are."

Lily's heart skipped, a stone scaling over the water's surface. What if he really could? What if she could hide Rose from Edward forever?

"Living in Canada," she said, "I've felt so powerful. I had complete control over her safety. Now that we're back in the States, what if he comes after her? He'll see her as a way to get to me. And me as a way to get to *her*."

She leaned back against his strong chest, as his one arm came around her from behind. They rocked against each other, staring at the moon's silver path across the water.

"I think you should go see your grandmother," he said. "But you should let me take Rose somewhere safe."

"We could ask Patrick for help," Lily said.

"We could," Liam said. "But I have an old friend at the University of Rhode Island. Graduate school of oceanography. He has a place near Scarborough Beach, on Narragansett Bay. He'd let us stay with him. It's not that far away."

"Rose has never been away from me," Lily said, feeling her heart tighten. "Except for going to the hospital."

"You'd be doing it for her," Liam said. "To keep her away from Edward, until you know what to expect."

"She'd love being with you," Lily murmured. Rose loved Liam with everything she had. For her ninth birthday, barely a month ago, she had wished for two things:

to see Nanny, the legendary white whale of Cape Hawk, and to have a real father like Liam. "How much should I tell Rose?"

"However much you think she can handle."

How could Lily begin to know what that was? Rose had just come through open-heart surgery. She was healing from what was supposed to be the final operation necessary to correct the last of the multiple heart defects—Tetralogy of Fallot—she'd been born with.

"I don't know," she said. "She'll have so many questions."

"It's going to work out, Lily," Liam said.

"You've made big promises to me before," Lily said, smiling. None bigger than the fact that he would always be there, never desert Rose—the heart-stricken baby he had brought into this world.

"And they've come true, right?"

"So far," she said, turning to tilt her head back, kissing him long and hard, feeling her blood tingle as it moved through her body. Every touch of Liam's was a promise, with the energy of magic. Outside, the waves hit the rocks, and leaves rustled in the breeze. Lily shivered, wanting more of everything.

"So the answer is yes?" Liam asked.

Lily closed her eyes, unable to speak. Everything had been happening so fast—from hearing about Maeve, to deciding to come out of hiding, to driving down from Nova Scotia.

"You don't have to decide right now," he said. "You need some sleep, Lily. You'll know what to do in the morning."

"Once the sun comes up," Lily said, "Clara will see your truck. She'll come over to investigate. If she sees you and Rose, there'll be no keeping it secret. Not that she means any harm—in fact, I can't wait to see her."

"I know," Liam said. "You're thinking it would be unfair to ask her to go along with something she might not understand. Let's go to bed—we have until dawn to decide."

"In just a few hours," Lily said.

Holding hands, they went upstairs again. Lily still hadn't turned on a light. She still hadn't let herself take that extra step. It didn't matter—she knew every inch of this house in the dark. Every draft, every creaky board, every piece of furniture. Her grandmother hadn't changed anything since Lily had left.

Yet here in this cottage she knew better

than any place on earth, Lily waited for
the answers. She couldn't help the joy
she felt—she loved the warm breeze, the
smell of her grandmother's roses. She led
Liam into the largest bedroom—the one
her grandmother had always saved for
guests—in the front of the house, where
dormer windows jutted out over the sloping
roof, facing the moonlit bay. Lily cranked
open the casement windows as wide as
they could go.

A gust of air fluttered the sheer white curtains and cooled Lily's hot skin. The sound
of waves, rhythmically splashing the rocks
down below, came through the windows.
Lily went to check on Rose. She bent down,
watched her daughter's chest rise and fall.
Rose's breaths were like the waves—
steady, sure, one after the other. Lily knew
that Rose would be in good hands with
Liam, but the idea of letting her beautiful girl
out of her sight was almost impossible to
bear.

"Lily," Liam whispered, in the doorway behind her, his hand on her shoulder. "Come
to bed."

Lily shook her head. She couldn't move.
How could something so peaceful fill her

with such fear? Rose was sleeping in Lily's own childhood bed; the summer breeze carried scents of honeysuckle and hundreds of red, pink, and white roses. The old words came back to her: *White roses bruise so easily.* Staring down at her daughter, she calmed herself with the hard-won certainty that Edward wasn't even aware that Rose existed.

As far as Edward knew, Lily was dead. She had died—everyone believed—nine years ago, when she was eight and a half months pregnant. Lily felt a rush, and she shuddered. It was as if she had just been granted a free pass by the gods. Edward didn't know about Rose. . . .

"I want you to do it," she said without turning around, not taking her eyes off her daughter's face, long brown lashes resting on delicate cheekbones, mouth ever-so-slightly open. Her left arm was bent at the elbow, fingertips on her neck, protecting the scar where she'd had open-heart surgery. "I want you to take her."

"I'll take care of her," Liam whispered.

Lily nodded. "I know you will. You always have."

She knelt by Rose's bed, staring at her for

a long minute—until Rose sighed and
turned. Not wanting to wake her up, Lily
kissed her sleeping daughter's head, and
followed Liam into the bedroom. She knew
that nothing in the world could make her
send Rose away, force her to take this action, except for one thing: a need to see her
grandmother, the woman who had raised
her, and make sure she got well.

Nothing else could do it.

Pulling down the white chenille bed-
spread, curling up beside Liam, she closed
her eyes. The sound of the waves merged
with the rise and fall of Liam's chest. She
counted the waves, felt his heartbeats. Outside the open window, the gulls on their island rookeries cried and cried.

Lily just stared at the moon, hanging outside the window, as she listened to the cries
of the gulls, Liam's breath on her neck. She
pulled his arm even tighter around her, and
she prayed that she was doing the right
thing.

Dawn came up like thunder, and Liam Neill
knew there wasn't much time. He knew he
had to get Rose away, and yet he didn't

know how to leave. He wanted to stay with Lily.

Lily made coffee and oatmeal, and then she got Rose washed and dressed. The sky went from deep purple to cerulean blue as the sun crowned the eastern horizon. Liam had heard so much about Hubbard's Point—it was almost mythical to him, the place where Lily had grown up, where her beloved Maeve had raised prizewinning roses and nurtured a strong, beautiful granddaughter. Liam stepped out on the side porch, drinking coffee and staring at the granite ledges sloping down to Long Island Sound. The cottage sat almost at the tip of a promontory—the Point of Hubbard's Point, as Lily had told him and Rose on the drive down from Cape Hawk.

Liam looked across the side yard toward a similar cottage—built of weather-silvered shingles, with turquoise shutters and door, white window boxes filled with red geraniums—and saw someone peering out a window.

He faded back, close to the house, then disappeared inside. Finding Lily and Rose in the kitchen, talking at the table, he tapped Lily's shoulder.

"Someone just saw me," he said. "Looking over from next door."

"That's Clara," Lily said. "She always gets up with the sun, in time for the *Hartford Courant.*"

"We'd better go," Liam said.

"But I don't get it," Rose said, her brow wrinkled. "I thought we just got here."

Lily took a deep breath. Liam knew what this was doing to her—he touched her glossy dark hair, stroking it for support. She looked Rose in the eyes.

"Honey," she said. "You and Liam are going to stay somewhere else for a few days. It won't be far away from here—not too far, anyway—and I'll know where you are every minute."

"Why aren't you coming?" Rose asked.

"I have to see about my grandmother."

"Your granny?"

Lily nodded. "Yes. You know she's sick—"

"That's why we came here, from Cape Hawk."

Lily stared at Rose, as if trying to decide how much to say. Liam kept watch out the side window, knowing that they didn't have much time.

"It is why we came," Lily said. "But long

ago, there was a reason why I left here. I
have to . . . take care of all that, before you
come back to stay."

"Mommy," Rose said, her voice breaking
with panic.

"Rose, it won't take very long."

"I want you to come with us."

"I will come find you," Lily said. "Very
soon, Rose—as soon as I straighten everything out. It won't be long—I promise
you. And in the meantime, you'll be with
Liam."

Rose hesitated. She still looked worried,
but she glanced up at Liam for reassurance.
He smiled down at her and squeezed her
hand. She raised her arms, and he lifted her
up. He leaned close to Lily—their eyes met
and locked.

"Take good care of her," Lily said.

"I will. As if she were my own," Liam said,
leaning forward, so Lily could embrace
Rose and Liam could hold them both at the
same time. Their bags were in the truck. Lily
had his cell phone number and he had left
her all the additional information he could—
addresses and telephone numbers for John
Stanley's home and lab, a hand-drawn map
of how to find his house in Narragansett.

"Bye, sweetheart," Lily said, her voice thin and her eyes moist.

"Bye, Mommy."

"I'll call you," Liam promised.

Lily waved him away. He glanced across the yard—the grass deep green, wet with dew—and saw the curtains fall again. Holding Rose, he walked up the sidewalk and stone steps, past the rose-covered well.

"What's that?" Rose asked.

"A wishing well," Liam said as he opened the truck door, buckled Rose into her seat. He strode around to the driver's side and started the engine.

"In my great-grandmother's yard?" Rose asked, sounding surprised.

"Yes," Liam said, putting the truck in reverse just as he saw the door to the house next door open and a gray-haired woman start hurrying down her sidewalk.

"I wish," Rose whispered. "I wish . . ."

Liam's pulse was racing as he backed into the cul-de-sac. The Sound spread out on both sides of the Point, blue water surrounding the land. Graceful cottages perched on rock ledges, gardens spilling over with beach roses and wildflowers. He couldn't take his eyes off Lily. She stood in the front yard, arms crossed tightly across her chest, hardly able to move.

"Who's that lady?" Rose asked, watching the white-haired woman stop in her tracks. Then the woman shrieked, and started running toward Lily.

"It's Clara," Liam said, although he had never met her himself. "You'll meet her someday."

"I hope so," Rose said, her voice thick. "She looks so happy to see Mommy."

"She sure does," Liam said. And then, with Lily holding out her arms to embrace her grandmother's oldest friend, he shifted into gear and headed for Rhode Island.

Chapter 2

It can't be true! I must be seeing things!"
Clara Littlefield said, stopping two feet from
Lily, just long enough to make sure she
wasn't staring at an apparition.

"It's me, Clara," Lily said. "I've come
home."

"Oh, darling," Clara said, breaking down
as she pulled Lily close in a hug. Lily held
her tight, feeling like a child. This woman
had been the closest thing Lily had had to
an aunt—Clara and Maeve had been as
close as sisters.

"Clara, tell me about Granny."

"I hardly know where to begin. I have a

thousand questions—what happened to you? Where have you been? How did you get here?"

"A friend dropped me off. I'll tell you the rest, but first I have to go see her."

"She's at Shoreline General."

"I know. Will you take me to her? I couldn't find the keys to her car."

"I have her purse at my house. I brought it back from the hospital, that first day. Of course I'll take you."

Lily took a deep breath. She'd made it over the first hurdle. She ran into the cottage, grabbed her bag, locked the door behind her. She stuck her cell phone in the pocket of her cotton pants—it was her lifeline to Rose and Liam. Then she and Clara climbed into Clara's blue Chrysler.

Driving through Hubbard's Point for the first time in daylight, Lily noticed how much had stayed the same—and how much had changed. Most cottages had retained their charming, nestled-into-the-rustic-landscape feel. But others . . .

"What happened there?" Lily asked as they passed the Langtrys' old property.

"Oh, dear. It's happening more and more. People buy a beach cottage and try to turn it into a showplace—frosted glass and all. How they manage to make a Hubbard's Point cottage look like a Meriden funeral home, I'll never know."

"I can just imagine what Granny says about it," Lily said.

"She says, 'They're embracing their nouveau richeness,'" Clara said. "Oh, I miss talking with her. No one makes me laugh like Maeve."

Makes. Lily heard the present tense and took hope.

"What do the doctors say?" Lily asked.

"They're confused. She's had some sort of what they're calling a 'neurological event.' Even that would give Maeve a chuckle. An *event.* She'd say they're making it sound like a lunar eclipse."

"But what sort of neurological event?" Lily asked, feeling frozen.

"That's what we don't know yet. They're running tests."

"Clara—Shoreline General? It's not exactly Yale–New Haven. . . ."

"Honey, it was an emergency, to get your grandmother seen to. You were born there, so was your father. Your grandfather died there—"

"Not exactly a testament—"

"Your grandmother is being treated very well. I didn't know what to do. You know, after all these years, she still has you down as her 'in case of emergency' person."

Lily took that in, the reality reverberating like an earthquake through her bones.

"It's as if she knew," Clara said, turning onto Shore Road. "That you were coming back."

"Hmm."

"Mara? Did she?"

"I'm not Mara anymore," Lily said. "I'm Lily now. Lily Malone."

"Lily. That will take some getting used to," Clara said. "Lily, Mara, this is very confusing. Can you tell me where you've been?"

"I ran away, Clara. From Edward."

"We thought he killed you."

"I know."

"It was a terrible thing to put your grandmother through," Clara said, sounding reproachful for the first time.

"There's a lot to the story that you don't know," Lily said, wondering how Clara would feel when she found out that Maeve had known exactly what Lily had done—and kept it from her best friend.

"Well, I'd like to know," Clara said. "And so would your grandmother, I'm sure. The stress built up in her, Mar—I mean, Lily. And everything changed after Edward showed up."

"What do you mean?"

Clara nodded. "Earlier this summer. Out of the clear blue, he just stopped by at Maeve's one day. He had a bag of things that had belonged to you—he wanted to give them to her."

"Just an excuse to upset her," Lily said.

"Well, he succeeded," Clara said. "She was so agitated. You see, she thought he had killed you . . ." she began again, glancing over at Lily.

Lily looked out the window. *No she didn't,* she wanted to say.

"I'm not blaming you," Clara said, her face growing flushed, her eyes red. "Please don't take it that way. Even before Edward upset her so—her grief has been unimaginable. Every summer day, she would wish you could be here, at the Point, enjoying it. She would imagine how old your baby would be. . . ."

Lily didn't reply.

"Your baby, Lily. What happened . . . ?"

"I lost the baby. A boy. Please don't ask me about it, Clara."

"No—I'm so sorry, dear."

Lily nodded, but said no more. Every word had to steer Clara, and anyone she might tell, away from the truth. Glancing over, Lily saw how she had aged: her hair was all white now, instead of just silver streaking the chestnut brown. Her face was wrinkled, and so were her hands on the steering wheel. Lily's stomach clenched, realizing how many years she had missed in Clara's life. In Maeve's. What would she find at the hospital?

Clara drove the back way, along the Shore Road, instead of taking the highway. Lily soaked in all the sights—old stores, new houses, fewer woods, a sense of the shore-line changing, becoming more suburban and homogenized. She felt a sharp, sudden longing for her far-northern refuge.

They approached the hospital, between Sachem and Seaside avenues, turning into the large parking lot. The day was early, be-fore official visiting hours, so there weren't many cars.

"Is she in the ICU?" Lily asked.

"She's on a medical floor," Clara said. "I'll come up with you."

Lily felt a burning need to see her grand-mother alone, but she held back the words. She couldn't hurt Clara. They walked in through the main doors, into the elevator, and went to the fifth floor. Lily's heart pounded as they walked down the long, sterile corridor.

"In here," Clara said. It was a private room. Sun slanted through the tall windows, rising over the Thames River. Lily blinked at the brightness. She heard the sounds of a monitor beeping. A yellow curtain was pulled partway around the bed. White blan-kets were pulled up, and Lily saw the shape of feet and legs underneath.

"Granny," Lily breathed, coming around the curtain.

"Maeve, darling," Clara said. "It's Mara. Mara has come home to see you. Darling, can you hear me? She's home . . ." Her voice broke, and she had to step away.

Lily stood by the bed. Her grandmother was right there, right there. She lay on her back, her long white hair spread behind her on the pillow. Her eyes were ever-so-slightly open—Lily saw their clear blue color as they flicked back and forth. Bending over, Lily took her hand. She pressed her lips to her grandmother's forehead.

The smell of sickness was in the air. It was perhaps that, almost more than anything, that brought hot, quick tears to Lily's eyes. Her grandmother had never smelled sick. She had always been followed by scents of roses, salt water, lemonade, orange tea, ginger cookies, and L'Air du Temps.

"Granny," Lily whispered, her lips still touching her grandmother's skin. "I came back. I had to see you. Please wake up. Please wake up."

"I thought," Clara said quietly, "that hearing your voice might get through to her. Oh, dear, she has to know you're alive. I can't bear this happening to her, with her not knowing."

Lily stroked her grandmother's hand. She knelt down so that her face was very close to Maeve's. She gazed at the familiar profile, lying there on the pillow. After her parents' deaths, she had been afraid to close her eyes and go to sleep. It was as if she couldn't bear knowing that she would have to wake up to a new day, knowing they wouldn't be there.

The last nine years had been like that. Every morning had been so hard to face— knowing that she had run away from someone just as close, just as dear, as her parents. Having to raise her daughter Rose never to know Maeve—depriving Rose of all the love that Maeve would have for them both—had been the hardest choice Lily had ever had to make.

"Did I do this?" Lily whispered, stroking her hair. "Did you just get too tired of waiting for us to come back?"

"Hello, Doctor," she heard Clara say.

"Hi, Mrs. Littlefield. The nurses told me that you were here with someone—"

"She's a relative," Clara said. "Maeve's next of kin."

"I'm Dr. Kirkland," he said.

"I'm Lily Malone, her granddaughter," Lily said, turning, rising. She saw the doctor standing in the doorway—he was tall, young, blond hair pushed back, wire-rimmed glasses. A nurse stood behind him, and at Lily's words, her mouth dropped open.

"It's you! But that's not the name . . ." the nurse said, her words trailing off. The shock registered in her eyes—she had just seen a ghost. Lily was returning from the dead, moment by moment.

"It's not the name she was born with," Clara said, always polite and trying to be helpful. "But it's the one she goes by now."

"I need to know about my grandmother," Lily said steadily, standing up, walking toward the door, then out into the hall with the doctor. "What's wrong with her?"

"The short answer is, we don't know," the doctor said.

"What tests have you done?"

"CT scan, EEG, EKG, blood panels . . ."

"Clara said you're calling it a neurological event. Did she have a stroke?" Lily asked. She was already preparing to call Rose's cardiologist in Boston. He was a specialist, preeminent in his field. They would transfer Maeve immediately—she would get the best cardiac care in the world, reverse the damage done, bring her back to consciousness.

"It's the first thing we thought of," Dr. Kirkland said. "She was brought here in a comatose state. But her EKG was normal. And almost immediately, she began having convulsions."

Lily struggled to maintain her composure.

She couldn't bear thinking of her grandmother having seizures.

"A brain tumor seemed possible. I'm her primary-care physician, so I called in a neurologist. Dr. Mead. I'm sure you'll meet her."

"You said 'seemed possible.' It's not a brain tumor?"

He shook his head. "No. It seems not to be."

"Then—what?"

"We did blood tests that showed, well . . ."

"Showed what?"

"This is odd. Her blood carboxyhemoglobin was very elevated. That's what we normally see during very cold winters, in people whose furnaces have been malfunctioning. Or in cars that are left running, with the heaters—"

"Carbon monoxide poisoning?" Lily asked. Living so long in such a cold climate, she had known to have the heating unit checked, install a detector, crack windows when the car was idling, to be ever vigilant about the odorless gas. But this was summer.

"Yes, but Ms. Jameson—er, Malone— we're really not sure. There is no obvious explanation, but the blood levels do seem to indicate—"

"I know what happened," she said.

The doctor just stood there looking intrigued, at least as much about her identity and sudden reappearance as about her theory of her grandmother's case. The first nurse had obviously told others, because a cluster of people stood down the hall, out of earshot, but looking on.

"Edward did it," Lily said steadily.

"What do you mean?"

"My husband," Lily said. "He tried to kill her."

"Kill?" the doctor asked, densely, forehead wrinkled as he tried to understand.

"My grandmother," Lily said, eyes filling with tears as she wished that Maeve had run away with her nine years ago, that they had gone to Cape Hawk together, that they had both run as far from Edward Hunter as they could.

Chapter 3

The days were long in Cape Hawk, Nova Scotia, with bright northern light lingering until well past nine at night, when fireflies would flash in the pines, and owls would begin their long hunts down from their mountain nests. A heat wave had settled over the area, and every morning dawned clear and golden, the bay's flat, calm surface unbroken by anything but whales coming up for air.

The whale-watching fleet would begin its daily trips at eight-thirty in the morning. Tourists flocked to the wharf, to board the Neill family boats. Many of them had spent the night at the Cape Hawk Inn, owned by the same family. Jude Neill captained the vessels, his wife Anne operated the inn, and his cousin Liam was the town's resident oceanographer.

Honeybees buzzed in the roses, but the real buzz took place in the hotel—where preparations for the monthlong Ceili Festival were fast and furious. Marisa Taylor walked along the harbor path, hearing strains of all the different Irish bands—fiddles, tin whistles, guitars, and accordions filling the air. She stared at the ferry coming across the strait, laden with vans full of musicians and their instruments.

When she got to the wharf, she reached for the brass key ring and unlocked the door to In Stitches, Lily's needlework shop. Marisa and all of Lily's friends had been taking turns keeping the shop open while she saw to things back home in Connecticut. The walls and baskets featured Lily's needlepoint canvases—of summer gardens spilling over with roses, lilies, delphinium, and larkspur; of Cape Hawk's blue harbor, bright with whale-watching boats; of Nanny, the famous and beloved pure white beluga whale, native to these waters; scenes of mothers, daughters, friends, and sisters.

Sisters, Marisa thought as the music drifted down from the hotel, through the shop's open door. Turning on the shop computer, Marisa instantly checked her own e-mail—although she had checked at home just thirty minutes ago, before leaving her kitchen. Still nothing.

Jessica, her nine-year-old daughter, came running down the dock, waving madly. She had come down to the harbor early, to look for starfish at low tide. Her jeans were rolled up, and her sneakers squeaked as they slapped the wharf slats.

"Did she write back yet?" Jessica asked, flying through the door.

"Whoa, wet feet!" Marisa called. "It's not our shop, remember?"

"I know," Jessica said, kicking off her sneakers. "Did she write back?"

"Not yet," Marisa said, watching her daughter's face fall.

"This is a sad summer so far," Jessica said. "Aunt Sam's not writing back to you, and my best friend went away."

"Not forever," Marisa reminded her. But when Lily left for Connecticut, she took her daughter Rose with her—leaving both Marisa and Jessica without best friends until they got back to Cape Hawk.

"It seems funny, to hear Irish music without you and Aunt Sam playing it," Jessica said.

"Seems that way to me too."

"Do you think she's coming?"

"I don't know," Marisa said. She didn't want Jessica to get her hopes up.

"You'd win the ceili contest," Jessica said. "Your band was good enough to put you both through nursing school."

"We got by," Marisa said. And they had. She remembered what the *Baltimore Sun* had said about their last performance together, at the Molly Maguire Pub just off the Johns Hopkins campus: "Fallen Angels play with holy ardor, sexy and thrilling, and somehow make traditional Irish music—as well as their original material—surprising and new. If you want a different kind of religious experience, head down to the Molly Maguire Pub to check out these fiddle-playing sisters."

"Did you send her the website?" Jessica asked.

"I did," Marisa said.

"Well," Jessica said, "maybe it's just because she hasn't seen your e-mail yet. We're so far apart, and Aunt Sam is in South America—right?"

"Peru," Marisa said.

"Well, that's why she hasn't written," Jessica said, sounding uncertain. "She's just busy. She's such a good nurse, like you were. I'm sure she's just caring for lots of sick people. She'll write or call us as soon as she gets back to Baltimore. We're just so far apart, that's all."

"I'm sure you're right, honey," Marisa said. She tried to smile, but Jess's words hit her like a lightning bolt: *We're just so far apart.* Jess was right, and it had nothing to do with miles. Her sister had ignored all Marisa's recent attempts to reach out. The breach between them seemed so deep now, and passing time only made it more so. Marisa had hoped the ceili contest would pique Sam's interest, so she would come north and they could talk.

"What if she's lost?" Jessica asked.

"Lost?"

"In Peru," Jessica said, looking worried. "What if something happened to her?"

"Oh, Jess—Sam travels all the time. I'm sure she's fine."

"But what if she isn't? Maybe you should ask that detective to help us find her," Jessica said.

"Hmm," Marisa said.

"The one who came up here, searching for Lily. Patrick. He was nice."

"He was," Marisa said. "He's also very far away."

"There's such a thing as planes, Mom," Jessica said.

"I know," Marisa said, hugging Jessica. Maybe Patrick *could* help. Marisa could call him—it would have nothing to do with his blue eyes, or the time they had spent together when he was up in Cape Hawk.

She could just ask him how a detective would go about finding someone who wasn't answering her e-mail. Someone who had once been Marisa's fellow nurse, music partner, and best friend. A sister who seemed to have fallen off the face of the earth . . .

Anne knelt in the inn's garden, transplanting Shasta daisies and gazing down the hill at

Lily's shop. While Lily, Liam, and Rose took care of business down south, Anne had set up a schedule for the Nanouk Girls to keep In Stitches running smoothly. The needlework shop had long been a gathering place for the women of the area, so Anne knew it wasn't really much trouble for them to keep it open till Lily got back.

Right now she spotted Marisa and Jessica standing in the doorway—looking across the water, like those women of old, watching for their men to come sailing over the horizon on whaling ships.

"What are you doing, hiding out here in the garden?" Jude asked, coming down the walkway from the inn, a coffee mug in each hand, a hammer stuck in his waistband. "When the whole place is going crazy in there?"

"You're a fine one to talk, about to get on board and go out in the bay all day. Thank you, love," she said, accepting a mug from her husband.

"Well, we have to find moments of peace while we can get them. Camille is in there, dealing with one band who forgot to book enough rooms, and another who wants to switch places on the roster with yet another, who lost its accordion player in Halifax. . . ."

"Oh yes. Had his nose broken in a fight with the mandolin player—apparently they were fighting over their new singer, a lassie from Dublin. I've heard all about it. That's why I'm out here. Shasta daisies are so much easier to take at nine A.M. than musicians."

"You've got the right idea, Annie," Jude said. "Flowers for you, whales for me— leave the craziness aside for a little while. At least till you go back inside. The music's nice to hear, though, isn't it?"

"It is," Anne said, listening as the uilleann pipes began to play, twining and weaving into a haunting rendition of "Minstrel Boy."

"Ah, that song . . ." Jude said.

"It's beautiful," Anne said.

"They played it at Connor's funeral," Jude said. "I'll never forget it."

"So long ago. You were only eleven."

"Aye."

Anne sipped her coffee, staring out over the placid bay. It was hard to believe that such a brutal attack could have occurred right out there, within sight of shore. The shark had taken Liam's arm and Connor's life—but it had taken something from Jude too. Anne had been in his class at school— one year behind his cousin Liam—and she remembered that when Jude came back after the funeral, his eyes were hollow and his shoulders were hunched, as if guarding his heart.

"C'mon," he said. "Wipe the dirt off your hands and help me out."

"Doing what?"

"The grandstand, my love. Camille says it's too rickety, and she wants me to tighten it up."

They took their coffees over to the gazebo, beside which had been erected a four-tier viewing stand. It was brought out of storage every year for the Gaelic music competition—and every year, Aunt Camille worried that the whole thing would give way, sending Cape Hawk's local dignitaries toppling down the hill.

Jude gave the wooden stand a good shake; although it seemed completely solid to Anne, he pulled some nails from his jeans pocket, began driving them in with the hammer. The sound effectively blocked out "Minstrel Boy"—which, Anne realized, may have been the whole point.

Anne climbed to the top tier, four rows up. A nail was sticking up from the bench—she gestured to Jude, and he handed up the hammer. She whacked the nail in, then made her way down the bench, making sure there weren't any more like it. The breeze was fresh, full of music and excitement—she had the feeling that this year's festival was going to bring something completely unexpected to the town.

"What do you think Liam is doing right now?" Jude asked.

"I think he's helping Lily, so she and Rose can get back home here."

"Did you ever think he'd find someone?"

"I know we all had our doubts," Anne said. "But then Lily came along."

"It's not sealed yet," Jude said. "She might still see the light—ask herself what she's doing with a one-armed shark researcher."

Anne looked down the hill, taking in the beautiful view. Life had a way of healing even the worst injuries. She gazed across the sparkling blue bay, ringed by rock ledges and tall pines. She had been in love with Jude since first grade, even before the shark attack—and she loved him still. She wanted to tell him that one-armed shark researchers didn't have the lock on being difficult, but she just held her tongue and hammered in another nail.

"Finally that song is finished," Jude said.

"So it is," Anne said.

"You're in charge of the festival and contest. Maybe you can make it a requirement that the bands leave 'Minstrel Boy' out of their repertoires next year."

"Hmm," Anne said, smiling out over the water again, as if she was giving his idea due consideration. She wasn't. She hoped every band would play it—this year and all years. When she heard it, she knew that Connor was close—and she suspected that Jude knew it too. It was what she loved about Irish music—especially the fiddles that played it. Fiddlers caught spirits and dreams whirling through the air, pulled them down to earth, where mere mortals could hear and see them. They brought the dead to life, and brought magic down from the sky, and made dreams more real than logic.

Down the hill, Marisa was back in the shop doorway, scanning the incoming ferry. Anne knew she was hoping for signs of her long-lost sister. Anne was saving a special spot on the festival bill for Fallen Angels, the fiddle-playing sisters. She knew that there were many ways of being lost, many ways of finding a way back to each other. She thought of Lily, down in Connecticut with Rose and Liam, a miracle story if ever there was one. She thought of Patrick, the cute cop who had so clearly taken a shine to Marisa. Her skin tingled as the piper hit his high note, as a salt wind blew off the bay. Cape Hawk was a magical place, and the music made it more so.

Even for residents who were hundreds of miles away . . .

Lily, sitting at her grandmother's bedside, felt like the girl who cried wolf. What did she really know? What proof did she have? What evidence had she had nine years ago? Seeing the doctor's blank expression reminded her of that day in the Berkshires, when she had been so hysterical—and the other hikers had, at first, just stared at her with disbelief.

She tried to shrug off that terrible memory, concentrating on her grandmother lying so still. The doctor had stepped back to talk to

Clara; Lily could hear their voices whispering, then fade as they walked down the hall
together. She could only imagine what they
were saying, what everyone was thinking.

The room was suddenly quiet—it was just
Lily and Maeve. Lily had been dreaming of
this moment for so long. She clasped her
grandmother's hand and felt like a little
girl. Holding this hand . . . walking to the
school bus . . . to swimming lessons . . . to
the post office . . . to Foley's store for penny
candy . . .

"Well, if it's not the prodigal granddaughter," a deep voice growled.

Lily blinked, looking over her shoulder.

Patrick Murphy stood in the doorway. He
pulled the door partway closed behind him,
then came closer, staring down at Maeve.
His curly red hair glinted in the sun. The expression in his bright blue eyes was grave,
as if it were his own grandmother lying in
the bed.

"You should hear what they're saying out
in the hall," he said.

"Did they tell you that Edward did this?"
she asked.

"We'll get to that in a minute," Patrick
said. "Cops are on the way. You make an

accusation like that, it's going to bring the heat."

"You're a cop," she said. "I want you to investigate it."

"I'm off the force, as you already know. Finished, *finito,* done. You did me in, Mara. Looking for you—well, for your body, actually—nearly an entire decade. I was positive Edward Hunter had murdered you. We found lime in his trunk. You know about lime? Makes things dissolve quickly. Yep, I thought he'd poured it on your bones."

Lily tried to hold back a shiver.

"I saw that," he said.

"He did this to my grandmother, Patrick. Did you know he came to see her recently? Clara told me."

"Yep, I know all about it. By the way, I think they're sending Clara down for a cardiac workup. You nearly gave her a heart attack."

"Don't joke about that," Lily warned, thinking of Rose and her long rounds of heart surgery.

"They're saying you're back from the dead. Much speculation is swirling out there—and it's not just Clara and the nurses, either. Nope. We've got doctors in on the guessing game—I'm serious. They're all gathered round the nurses' station. Let's see. You were kidnapped nine years ago. Your husband did it. No, wait—a cult did it. Satanists. Or—now, get this: you staged your own disappearance."

Lily ignored Patrick, but she felt herself trembling as she kept hold of her grandmother's hand.

"Never mind what they think," she said. "Edward put Maeve here, Patrick! He poisoned her."

"The doctors told me you think that."

"Then pay attention to that, and never mind about what happened nine years ago."

"Maybe you really don't know what you're in for," he said. "You're a phenomenon. Can you grasp the amount of interest there was in your disappearance?"

"No," she said. "And I don't care. It's my life—no one else's."

"Mara," he said. Catching her dirty look, he shook his head. "Lily. Sorry. I've thought of you as Mara Jameson for nine years. I retired in semi-disgrace over not being able to find you, and my wife accused me of being obsessed with you and divorced me, so I think you kind of owe me a little kindness, okay?"

"You did find me," she said. "That's why I'm here now."

"Took me nine years to find you," he said. "And your grandmother practically had to draw me a goddamn road map to get there." His eyes moved from Lily to Maeve. "Jesus, Maeve. I wish you'd wake up, so I could yell at you. Keeping it a secret all this time."

"She did what she had to do. We both did."

Patrick shook his head. "It must have killed her, to not know Rose."

Lily jolted at Rose's name. "Listen to me, Patrick," she said. "Edward doesn't know about her."

"Hiding Rose in Canada was one thing. But now you're back here—at home, in the United States. A kid is going to stand out, you know?"

"She's somewhere safe—help us keep it that way."

"Us?"

"Liam and me. Please, Patrick."

"The cops are going to want to interview

you," he said. "And me—because I found you."

"I know that," Lily said. "And I'm going to tell them the truth—about everything except Rose. I can't let Edward get to her."

"I'm trying to figure out why you're doing this," he said, peering at her, his blue eyes flashing in the sunlight streaming through the windows. "I'd really like to know the whole story. Did he beat you? Kick you? Were you battered?"

She paused, stared at him, wondered what he was capable of understanding. "Not in the way most people think of 'battered,'" she said, her heart racing.

"So, what did you do? The guy tried to kill you, you say now. What did you do about it? Did you call the cops?"

"No," Lily said.

"Why not?"

"Because I knew they wouldn't believe me. I didn't have any evidence, not really. Edward could be so charming, so persuasive. And I wasn't going to let him even lay eyes on my baby while I tried to convince them."

"You should have called the cops," he said stubbornly.

"I told my grandmother," she said. "Because I knew she'd believe me."

"And did she?"

"You know she did."

"So, you told Maeve—"

"And then I started making my plans to leave. *We* started, that is. Maeve and I."

"Christ," he said, staring down at Lily's grandmother lying motionless in the hospital bed. Lily saw a lot going on behind his eyes—thoughts and memories of the investigation, maybe. Ways Maeve had lied to protect Lily, to help her get away and stay hidden. "Why didn't Maeve go with you?"

"She had to stay behind, to throw Edward off."

"By lying to the police?"

"If that's what it took."

"And that's what you're about to do now?" Patrick asked as the sound of radios came from the hall, along with heavy footsteps. The police were here. Lily felt chills racing up her spine, desperate feelings of near-panic as she wondered what Patrick would say to them.

"If that's what it takes to protect Rose," she said.

"Jesus Christ, Lily."

"You don't know the whole story yet, Patrick. Please—don't give us away. Don't give her away. She's just gotten her life back—you have no idea what she's been through, so many surgeries to save her life—"

"I know," Patrick said. A knock sounded on the door. Patrick moved to answer it, but Lily grabbed his arm.

"Please, Patrick."

"Tell me this, Lily. Where is she? I have to know she's okay."

"She's with Liam Neill—that's all I can tell you. But she's with him. He's taking care of her, until I can be there. You know Liam from Cape Hawk—you and Marisa found us at his house. You must know what Rose means to him. Please, Patrick."

She saw something flicker in his eyes, as if he was making up his mind. Just then the door swung open, and a man and woman peered in.

"Hey, Murphy," the woman said to Patrick. "What're you doing here?"

"Ah, I just stopped by to see my friend Maeve. Come on in," Patrick said. "Let me make a few introductions."

Lily stepped back, leaning against her

grandmother's bed, reaching behind to touch her grandmother's hand. They were together in this. She and Maeve, protecting Rose. Lily felt strong enough to face whatever would come—but she needed her grandmother's presence to give her courage.

"Detectives Christine Dunne and Lance Sheridan, meet Lily Malone."

"We were told this was Mara Jameson."

"*Was* being the operative word," Patrick said. He glanced at Lily. "You're gonna get really sick of this Mara business, aren't you?"

"Yep," she said.

"Well, I'll let you explain," Patrick said, looking stoic as he stepped back.

He hadn't mentioned Rose. That was all Lily cared about. She gave him a grateful but guarded glance, and turned to face the two detectives. They both looked suspicious but curious; the woman was about thirty-five, with short blond hair and wide green eyes. Lily turned slightly, facing her directly.

"I told the doctor," Lily said, "that I think someone tried to kill my grandmother."

"That's why we're here," Detective Dunne said.

"One reason, anyway," Patrick said. Then, when the two detectives shot him a glance, he shrugged. "Call it what it is. You came to solve my case. As of this minute, it's officially on the books—you've found Mara Jameson. Congratulations."

The male detective, Lance Sheridan, smiled and nodded. But Christine Dunne never took her eyes off Lily, and Lily didn't look away. Lily felt that she was being studied and read, that all her answers would be filtered through the impressions Detective Dunne was filing away right now.

"Where have you been?" Detective Sheridan asked.

Chapter 4

Patrick Murphy faded back against the white hospital wall and listened to the two detectives put Lily through her paces. She ran through the story, or some version of the story, the one that Patrick already knew.

Nine years ago, pregnant with Edward Hunter's child, she escaped from him. She had lived with domestic violence. She couldn't stand the idea of bringing a child into that home—she refused. No, she didn't "stage" a disappearance—she just disappeared. Did anyone help her? No. Where did she go? Not prepared to answer that question. Where is the baby? He was born dead.

"He?" Patrick couldn't help himself.

"Yes." Lily was still and solemn. He gazed over at her, watching her stare back unblinking. The pulse throbbing in her throat was the only giveaway. She had pale skin, so striking against her jet black hair, cut sharply at shoulder length. Her cornflower blue eyes were pained and vulnerable as she made her case to the detectives about the carbon monoxide.

He almost snorted. Lily Malone was about as vulnerable as a ninja sword dancer. This woman was strength personified. Patrick's pride was still smarting from the way she'd outfoxed him every step of the way. He had to hand it to her.

Lily glanced over at him once or twice. He didn't say a word. The detectives were asking her again about the baby. Lily's voice shook as she told them it was too painful to talk about. Her distress was real—Patrick knew she was probably thinking about Rose, calling up to mind any one of her many surgeries, or the fact that she was somewhere hidden now. Her movements were small, careful. He watched the way she held her hands, gestured as she spoke.

Chasing her to Canada, he had met Marisa. Life had a funny way of unfolding.

"Now, if you'll all excuse me," Lily finally said, "I'd like to be alone with my grandmother."

Officers Dunne and Sheridan thanked her and said they'd be by Maeve's house later to look around. They headed for the door. Patrick hesitated. He thought maybe Lily would want to have a private word with him. But it was as if he were just a part of the unwelcome investigating team—she had turned her back on the three of them, ministering to her grandmother. Her profile was so delicate, bent over Maeve, smoothing the hair back from her forehead.

Patrick backed out of the room, came face-to-face with the other two. Down the hall, the crowd remained around the nurses' station. When police showed up at the hospital, word got around. And in this case—considering the fact that Mara Jameson had just reappeared— word was spreading like wildfire.

"What's going on?" Chris Dunne asked.

"What are you talking about?" Patrick replied.

"There's something between you—it's obvious."

"Between us?"

"You and Mara. Lily. Whatever the hell she calls herself. You two were exchanging looks as if you've known each other for years."

"I have known her for years," Patrick said. "I know her better than she knows herself. Her birthday, her blood type, her favorite dessert—it's blueberry pie, in case you're wondering—her favorite movies, the reason she likes needlepointing so much, and oh— the difference between needlepointing and cross-stitch. That's significant, when it comes to understanding the inner workings of her mind. You know why?"

"Shit, Murphy," Chris said.

"I'll tell you why," he continued as if she hadn't spoken. "Because her mother did needlepoint, see? Her mother was Irish. We're big storytellers, us micks, and if we can't get you to listen with your ears, we'll tell you stories any way we can. Young Lily was quite the genius with a needle and canvas when she was little, and her grandmother told me she used to get all her grief and pain out by stitching away."

"Maeve Jameson told you that?"

"Yep. During one of our many interviews."

"Do you believe her about the dead baby boy?"

Patrick thought of Rose—smiling, arms around Lily's neck, freckles across her cheeks, her brown braids, her big green eyes.

"Mmm," he said. "Why wouldn't I?"

"Well, the tabloids are gonna have a field day," Lance said. "Can you imagine, once they find out Mara Jameson has come back from the grave? The only thing that would make them happier would be if she had a tousle-haired little moppet with her—that and a nice custody tug-of-war with the father."

"The Sociopath Also Known As Edward Hunter," Christine Dunne said.

Patrick looked over at her, obviously with more than a little curiosity at her tone, because Chris blushed slightly.

"It's pretty clear, isn't it? The guy must have been some piece of work, to send Mara/Lily underground all this time."

"Maybe she's lying about that," Lance said.

"I believe her," Chris said.

Patrick let himself smile, just a little. He liked Christine Dunne better already.

Rose Malone sat on the rocks, staring at the water. In some ways, this was her favorite place to be. Right near salt water, with spray misting her face and a thick ribbon of silver fish swimming by, close enough for her to watch. Narragansett Bay wasn't as cold and clear as Cape Hawk Harbor, an inlet off the Gulf of St. Lawrence, but still—bending close, Rose could see lots of marine life under the surface.

"Dr. Neill, come look," she said.

"What have you got there?" he asked.

"Rock crabs," she said, pointing at the dark green crabs scuttling along the bottom. "And minnows. Why are there so many of them?"

"I'm not sure," he said. "They might be staying close to the shore to avoid bigger fish farther out."

Up in Cape Hawk, Dr. Neill was known far and wide as the person who knew more about sharks and whales than anyone in Canada. Maybe more than anyone in the world. Rose glanced at his face. Tan, with lines around his blue eyes, staring out at the water.

"What are you looking for?" Rose asked. "Nanny?"

"How'd you guess?"

"Because I was looking for her too," Rose said.

Nanny was the beluga—the white whale—who had swum down here to New England, far from her home in the Gulf of St. Lawrence, at the same time Rose's mother had found out about her grandmother. It seemed so magical to Rose, that the whale she had grown up loving would end up on this faraway coastline at the same time Rose and her mother did, almost as if she was following them—or leading them.

"Will you check on your computer?" Rose asked, scrambling up the rocks to look over his shoulder. Dr. Neill had a laptop programmed to follow the tracking devices on many sharks and whales and other marine species he and his friends had tagged. Rose loved to watch the lights blink—green for whales, purple for sharks. But right now, she could barely even see the lights.

She leaned against Dr. Neill's side. He hit some computer keys, but he mainly just seemed to be watching for Nanny the old-fashioned way—staring at the water's surface. A few seagulls flew low over the waves.

"I miss Mommy," Rose said suddenly.

"I miss her too, Rose."

"Is she coming soon?"

"She's looking after her grandmother right now. I'm sure she'll call us as soon as she makes sure everything is okay."

Rose nodded. If a person was sick, there was no one better in the world for looking after them than Rose's mother. Rose had been born with four defects in her heart. She had been a blue baby—her skin had actually turned indigo, her mother had told her—from not getting enough oxygen. It was why she hadn't grown as much as other kids her age, and why her fingertips were spatulate, clubbed.

Rose looked down at Dr. Neill's arm. Not his real one, but his prosthesis. It fit in his sleeve, but his fake hand was odd and club-like compared to a normal hand. The kids in Cape Hawk had whispered things their parents had told them—that when Dr. Neill was a boy, right after the shark had attacked him and his brother, killing Connor and ripping his arm off, he had had a hook.

The kids had called him Captain Hook, and the name had stuck. Rose couldn't bear to think of people teasing him. Rose loved him. Her mother had told her the story of how Dr. Neill had been her first friend in Cape Hawk. He had stopped by her cabin one day. Rose loved to picture this: the house deep in the woods, with no one around, and Dr. Neill heard noises coming from inside, and that was because Rose was being born. He had brought Rose into the world. . . .

"Why do you look so worried?" she asked, watching him gaze out over the water.

"I'm not worried," he said. "I'm just wondering about those menhaden—minnows."

"Do they have something to do with Nanny?"

"They could," he said, typing something into his computer, bringing up a whole new screen. It showed some graphs of currents and water temperatures. Rose watched him type in "Narragansett, Rhode Island," and the screen changed yet again. Outside, the seagulls screeched and started diving.

Rose heard some kids shout, and she saw them pointing at the water.

Dr. Neill grabbed her hand instantly. The kids were yelling, pointing at the surf. Dr. Neill gave her a look, and then he and Rose hurried across the yard.

Two boys had run all the way to the end of the rock breakwater that stuck out from the narrow, pebbly beach. They were calling to their friend, who was tearing along the sea-wall with a fishing rod in one hand and a net in the other.

"What are you fishing for?" Dr. Neill asked the young boy.

"Fins, man!" he called over his shoulder.

"Fins? Does he mean sharks?" Rose asked, worried.

"Yes," Dr. Neill said gently.

"Look!" the boy said, gesturing with his fishing pole.

And suddenly Rose saw what they were pointing at: huge black triangles zigzagging around the blue cove.

"Will they get Nanny?" she asked.

"She's not here, honey," he said, staring at the water. "We couldn't locate her on the computer, remember?"

Dr. Neill looked into her eyes then, smiled

to reassure her. He put his good arm around Rose's shoulders, and then they both looked back at the sharks swimming in the bay. Seeing them made her miss her mother even more. She knew that only something bad could keep them apart, something as bad as sharks, and she bit her lip to hold in the tears and threw both her arms around Dr. Neill's neck.

Chapter 5

As the day went on, the needlework shop got really busy. Jessica sat at the desk while her mother helped people choose yarn and pick out canvases to take home for souvenirs. The music festival was lots of fun for many reasons, and it was certainly really good for business. Cape Hawk was filling up with musicians and the tourists who had come to hear them, and everyone seemed to be stopping by to see what the shop had for sale.

Jessica was quiet, like a cat. She listened for clues to what was going on between her mother and aunt. They were sparse and few, and Jessica hoarded them when they came. Here was one right now.

"Oh, you're from Washington?" Jessica heard her mother ask a woman with a guitar case over her shoulder. "Do you play at the Golden Harp?"

"Yes, do you know it?" the woman asked.

"I used to play there, ages ago. My sister and I were at school in Baltimore, and we'd head into Georgetown on some weekends."

Jessica's ears perked up—and she looked over at her mother's face for extra clues. She saw one right away, the bruised look in her eyes that came from thinking back to that happy time in nursing school.

"All those lawyers and congresspeople," the woman said, laughing. "Looking for their lost Irishness and lost poetry."

"Their lost souls," Jessica's mother said quietly. "That's what my sister used to say."

"Well, we give 'em back their souls, don't we?" the woman asked. "That's why they come to hear us play. That's what ceili music is all about. Giving people back their hearts and souls. Aren't you lucky, living here in such a beautiful place? Does the music just pour out of you?"

Jessica watched her mother tallying up

the woman's purchases, pretending to concentrate on the numbers so she wouldn't
have to answer.

"Are you performing at the festival?" the
woman asked, after another moment.

"Well, if my sister gets here in time. But
she's out of the country right now."

"Tell her to hurry back for the Ceili Festival!" the woman said, gathering up her
things.

"I will," her mother said.

Jessica's heart fell like a stone. Looking
over at her mother again, she saw the bright
sheen of tears in her eyes. It pierced Jessica
to know how much her mother wanted Aunt
Sam to hurry back. Sitting by the big display
of needlepoint yarn, Jessica ducked her
head, to hide her own eyes.

"Honey?" her mother asked, after the
woman had gone. "You're being so quiet."

"The lady asked if the music poured out of
you."

"I know."

"It used to," Jessica said.

"The music never leaves," her mother
said. "Once you have it, you can't lose it."

Jessica's stomach ached. She wanted to
believe that that was true. When she was

younger, and so sad because her father had died, her aunt would come up from Baltimore to visit. She and her mother would talk softly, and their voices alone were music to Jessica. Later, after supper, they would take out their fiddles, and they would start to play. They had been doing it since they were girls, as young as Jessica. She would listen to the music—incredible, beautiful enough to destroy the pain of missing her father.

"Then why—" Jessica started to ask now.

"Why what, Jess?"

"Why do you never play it?" Jessica asked.

"I guess I need Sam for that."

Jessica nodded. She clasped her hands tight, so her mother wouldn't see the waves of emotion passing through her. Having taken recorder lessons in school, she had been secretly practicing—so her mother would have someone to play with in case Aunt Sam really didn't come back.

Just then, another musician walked in, and Jessica thought her mother seemed relieved to stop talking about everything.

"Mom, can I e-mail Rose?" Jessica asked.

"Sure, honey," her mother said. The new customer was friendly, and Jessica's mother asked about her guitar. The woman seemed happy to show her, so she opened the case. Jessica's mother seemed lost in the workmanship of the woman's Gibson guitar—Emmylou Harris edition.

"I went straight to the factory in Memphis to get it," the woman said, playing a few notes.

Jessica concentrated on the computer screen. No new e-mails. She tapped out a quick hello to her best friend, Rose: "I miss you. The summer music festival is starting, and my aunt will be here soon. . . ." She has to be, Jessica thought, hitting "Send."

Glancing up at her mother, she furtively went into the "Old Mail" folder. There were her aunt's e-mails. Her mother always saved them, as if they were precious, personal notes, instead of group e-mails sent out to a huge number of people. Jessica read one from last month—"Hola from Peru":

Hola everyone,
Made it to Peru safely! I'm in Iquitos, along the Amazonia—it's hot and humid and raining and colorful and poor and lively. . . .
Set up clinic in a school yesterday—there were hundreds lined up when we arrived—

gave out lots of anti-parasite medication, as the malnourishment is overwhelming. We have a pediatric surgeon and podiatrist, a dental team that has already pulled hundreds of teeth—and we have 2 more docs coming today—what we need is a dermatologist. . . .

I'm running the OBGYN clinic. Saw about 20 patients—lots of pregnant teens, half a dozen healthy women with normal pregnancies, one gal who looked as if she had some kind of hepatitis, a woman with a pelvic mass (with no money for referral), many worried well who just wanted TLC. Let's see what today brings.

It's invigorating to be in this world, for it sure expands mine.

Adios for now,

Sam

And then she read another, "Peru Update," written nearly two weeks ago—almost immediately after the reminder e-mail Jessica's mother had sent, telling Aunt Sam that the Ceili Festival was fast approaching, that she really hoped they could reunite onstage and let their music soften each other's heart.

Hola,

It's 7:30 a.m., I'm gearing up for another day in the jungle slums—We had an incredible day yesterday in our clinic—a school amidst shacks on stilts. Though this group has always had great experiences in this area—there was a little too much action yesterday . . . a stabbing and robbery by 8:30—we had to triage the stabbing—that was a first. So now we get police escorts everywhere.

I have 2 awesome med students as my translators—and we must have seen 40 people yesterday. Many worried well who needed TLC and vitamins and parasite meds. Some hypertension, lots of cataracts, lots of dermatology issues, 2 women with severe rheumatoid arthritis, every woman has back pain and headache. That is understandable, as many of them have birthed 6–10 babies at home alone, work in a market every day, and have nothing . . . These women are amazing— One woman yesterday had 7 kids—6 of whom have died related to accidents and infections . . . also saw many relatively healthy pregnant women—though they are 14–17 year olds—2 high risk, history of toxemia and were delivered at 27 weeks . . . women seem to go through menopause in their early 40's—with money these women can get good care . . . we have a great team, the pod guys have repaired club feet, the dentists have pulled hundreds of teeth, and peds surg have had many cases . . .

Anyway, my team is leaving now so I must run—we head up the river to work in a few small villages tomorrow. And then I'm heading home . . .

Life is good, more later,

Sam

Heading home, her aunt had written. What did that mean? Jessica read the e-mails over and over, looking for clues. Could her aunt really just return home to Baltimore without coming here to the ceili? Here to see her family? Jessica couldn't believe that was possible. Not the aunt she loved . . .

But as she stared at the screen, one clue was just too powerful to understand, and it made her stomach hurt even worse than before. The e-mail was to every single person her aunt knew. Jessica's mother's name was just part of a long list at the top of the page. It was as if Aunt Sam couldn't quite strike her from her life, but didn't care enough to write her something personal.

Closing her eyes, Jessica fought back the tears. They were coming hard and fast—not because she thought her aunt didn't care, but because she thought maybe her aunt cared too much. The hurt had been too bad for her to ignore. Jessica knew, because she had felt it too.

Glancing over at her mother, still admiring the woman's guitar, Jessica knew that her mother had been wrong about one thing. Sometimes the music *did* leave. Maybe it still lived somewhere, locked deep inside, but what did that matter, if you couldn't hear it play?

Jessica looked up, above her mother's head, out the open door of the shop. She looked past the inn, where the ceili was under way. Past the cliffs of Cape Hawk, up into the bright summer blue sky. She wished she could send a song through the air. Notes of music that had wings, just like tiny birds, flying south over the earth, asking Aunt Sam to come back to her family.

For the next two and a half days, Lily's life ceased to be her own. She yearned to be with Liam and Rose, but settled for the crackling, fuzzy connection of cell phone calls. Rose described the big house and wide blue bay, the excitement of something happening along the shore—lots more fish than usual, making Liam think it had something to do with why Nanny had come so far south.

Her old beach friends, Tara O'Toole and Bay McCabe, rode their bikes up the hill, leaned them against the old stone wall of the road's turnaround, running into the yard.

"You're back!" Bay cried. "It's true, it's true. . . ."

"Oh my God," Tara said, holding her, rocking her childhood friend back and forth, as if she needed to hold her to know she was really here. Lily held on tight, taking her friends' love right into her bones.

There were so many questions, so much catching up to do. It wasn't just that a few years had passed—Lily's life had changed entirely. She was Lily now, not Mara. The women had been children together, and now they had children of their own. The subject of Rose shimmered in Lily's mind and heart as she listened to Bay and Tara talk about their own kids.

"Maybe you underestimate what it was like when you disappeared," Bay said. She pointed at the yellow boots and watering can in the corner of Maeve's kitchen. "Those were on every news show in the state. You seemed to disappear into thin air."

"In a way, I did," Lily said.

"Tara and I were part of the search party that went out looking for you. Hundreds of volunteers—almost everyone from Hubbard's Point joined in, combing the beach and woods, Little Beach and the marsh and the Indian Grave. Then people from Black Hall came, and beyond."

"We wondered," Tara said, "whether you'd just decided to walk away."

"Oh, Tara . . ."

"Who could have blamed you?" Bay asked, holding her hand. "You never wanted to talk about it back then, but we knew . . ."

Lily just stared at her two friends, across all the years that had separated them.

"You were an expectant mother, about to have his baby," Tara said fiercely. "You must have been frantic to escape. Oh, Mara . . .

Lily . . . I understand. I'm glad you got away. Your poor baby."

Lily's heart seized with the words. She flushed, afraid her friends would look at her and see evidence of Rose all over her. Couldn't they see the truth written in Lily's eyes? Looking back and forth, she could hardly breathe. Was it safe? Did she dare? Keeping Rose a secret had seemed the only way, but she *couldn't* keep it from these two good women, her first best friends. They were mothers themselves, wonderful and loving and kind. Taking a deep breath, she decided.

"You have to promise not to tell, not a soul, not anyone," she said.

"Promise what?" Tara asked.

Bay's eyes gleamed, and Lily could tell that she already suspected. "Lily?"

"I have a daughter," Lily said quietly.

"Oh, Lily," Bay said. "That's wonderful."

"I can't wait for you to meet her, but she's in Rhode Island," Lily said. "Where Edward won't find her."

"That's good," Tara said. "You're so right to keep her from him. What's her name?"

"Rose," Lily said.

Bay nodded, smiling. "That's beautiful."

"It was for Granny. Granny and her garden. I missed her so much."

"Does she know?" Tara asked.

Lily nodded. "Right after Rose was born, I called her at my great-uncle's in Providence. I couldn't call her at home, because I wasn't sure whether the phones were tapped or not. It was his seventieth birthday—a party that had been planned for months. I knew Granny would be there—he was her only brother."

"Maeve must have felt such mixed emotions," Bay said. "Knowing she had a great-granddaughter . . ."

"But being unable to meet her or know her," Lily said. "I often wonder how she held it together, right after I left. It must have been so hard."

"For all of us," Bay said, squeezing her hand, gazing into her eyes as if she still couldn't quite believe Lily was really here. "We couldn't believe it, couldn't bear it."

"We had a candlelight vigil," Tara continued. "Down on the boardwalk. There were so many people, they filled the beach. It was such a warm night, so beautiful—we had all been searching for you, for days. Everyone was exhausted, losing hope."

"I'm so sorry," Lily said.

"Maeve spoke," Tara said. "At the vigil. I know it's crazy, but I wished you could be there—so you could know how much everyone loved you."

"We all had candles," Bay said. "We waited for Maeve, and I can remember her coming down the path behind the yellow cottage, wearing a long dress. It looked so familiar—and it wasn't until she came across the footbridge that I realized when I'd seen it before. She'd worn it to your wedding."

"Yellow chiffon," Lily said, picturing it.

"Her eyes were so red," Bay went on. "She'd been crying all day, it was obvious. Clara was with her—standing by her side. All your old friends, us beach kids, gathered around her. I was standing so close to her, Mar—I mean, Lily. She was just sobbing silently, as if her heart had just washed out to sea. I thought her tears would fill the creek."

"I'm so sorry I put her through that," Lily whispered. She pictured her grandmother weeping—not because she feared Lily was dead, but that she believed she would never see her again.

"Someone gave the signal—I'm not sure who. But suddenly one candle was lit, and then the flame passed to another, and on and on. After a few minutes, the entire beach was lit up by candlelight down below—and all the stars coming out above."

"She stood up on one of the white benches on the boardwalk," Tara said. "Bay and I stood right by her, to make sure she didn't fall. We thought she was going to beg everyone to keep looking for you, not give up—but she didn't. Instead, she just took this deep breath and stared over the crowd."

"Everything got so hushed," Bay said. "You couldn't hear a thing except the waves hitting the beach. Everyone was just waiting to hear what she would say."

"I still remember it," Tara said. "She said, 'You're all here because you love her so much, just as I do. My granddaughter is good, and sweet. She deserved only to be loved, not . . .'" And then she just broke down. Bay and I helped her walk back across the beach to the footbridge, and home."

"Edward must be going crazy, now that he knows you're back," Bay said. "You know he had you declared dead? And the marriage annulled for good measure?"

"I think he's the reason I'm back," Lily said quietly.

"What do you mean?"

"I think he did something to Maeve."

"Why now?" Tara asked.

"Edward is patient," Lily said. "His specialty is waiting. I think he's been waiting to punish Maeve all this time—and not just for speaking out about him. Her worst sin, to Edward, was in knowing about him—seeing through his act. Maeve was the first who did."

"We're going to make sure he doesn't hurt you," Tara said. "We'll take turns staying with you, or standing watch over you. He's not going to hurt you again."

"I'm sure Danny and Joe will want to help, too," Bay said of their husbands.

"You don't have to do this," Lily said, but inside she felt relieved.

"He's left a lot of wreckage," Tara said, her eyes dark and flashing.

Lily nodded. "Yes, he has. When I was in
Cape Hawk, I met someone who knows him
as well as I do. His next wife. The woman he
was with after me."

"You've met her?" Tara asked. "You're kidding. How?"

"Ironically, Edward gave us a road map to
each other," Lily said. "Without even knowing. She called him Ted, but everything else
was the same. We connected right away."

"I'm glad you weren't all alone," Bay said.
"That you had a friend."

"Cape Hawk is wonderful," Lily said. "I
missed you both so much, and I dreamed of
Hubbard's Point. But there are so many
strong, wise women up there, and Marisa
and I were really lucky to find them."

Her throat caught as she gazed out
the side window, at the pink roses brushing
the screen, and the wide blue Sound beyond. Seagulls wheeled and cried, and
something silver splashed at the surface.
Lily thought of the whales of Cape Hawk,
and the miracle of Nanny swimming so far
south this summer. She remembered
Rose's ninth birthday party, on one of
Liam's family's whale-watch boats, just
weeks earlier.

There had been so much love present that day. Rose had been surrounded by all her friends and Lily by all of hers. The Nanouks had gathered together, mothers and daughters, to celebrate Rose's birthday before her big surgery. Marisa had confided things she had never before told anyone. Lily had hugged her close, reassuring her that life got better.

Lily thought of Marisa now. They had both gotten away from the same dangerous man. Lily wondered whether Marisa would stay in touch with Patrick. There had been an obvious spark between them. Lily had thought she was too scarred to love again, but Liam had helped her to know that it wasn't true. She wished that for Marisa too.

A car backfired in the turnaround, and Lily jumped. The scent of roses filled the air. She had told Marisa that life got better, but what if it didn't? Lily wondered where Edward was now, whether he was watching, when he planned to reenter her life. As if sensing her unease, Bay took her hand.

"Everything will be fine," she said.

"Edward is a patient man," Lily whispered again.

"Then we'll wait him out," Tara said.

Lily heard the kitchen clock ticking, and hoped that her friends would be with her when he finally came.

Chapter 6

The fiddle case was all the way at the back of the hall closet, behind a pile of suitcases and winter boots. Digging it out, Marisa dislodged a box of mittens from the overhead shelf, bumped her head trying to avoid it. But finally she held the case in her hands, dusting the pebbled leather off with a red and white mitten.

Her hands were shaking slightly. Unlatching the top, she opened it up, looked in at her instrument. She'd had it a long time, and there were scratches to prove it. The fine, varnished cherrywood was nicked in places, and there was a small chip halfway up the neck. Lifting it out, Marisa rubbed the surface with her palm.

Oh, it felt so beautiful. She plucked the strings, began to tune by ear.

She had started missing her violin yesterday, when the woman in the shop had let her look at her guitar. All summer she had been fighting the urge, especially with Jessica asking her if the music had left. . . .

Living with Ted, Marisa had stopped playing. Not all at once. At first he had pretended to like hearing her, and he'd request specific songs when she'd practice. After a while, the opposite would happen; she would start playing, and he would tell her he needed to concentrate, or he had a headache, or he couldn't think through the music. Once he had said "through the noise," and that had shut her down.

Her love for fiddle music went back a long way before that, before him. She had started playing in fourth grade. She loved the tension of the strings under her fingers, teasing music out of them with the bow. Running through scales, she went straight into "O'er the Hills"—her and Sam's signature song.

Playing it pulled tears straight into her

eyes. There had been so many hurt feelings between them these last few years. The thing about a breach between two people who loved each other was that the longer it went on, the harder it was to go back and undo it.

The music came back now. So easily, it was as if she'd never stopped. She played her childhood songs, the ones she and Sam had learned together when they were in fourth and third grades, respectively— "Mary Had a Little Lamb," "London Bridge Is Falling Down," "Twinkle Twinkle Little Star," "Row Row Row Your Boat." She could almost believe Sam was with her now, urging her on.

As Marisa began to play a few notes of Mozart's Violin Concerto No. 3, she remembered how much awe she used to feel for her little sister as she'd fly through new pieces as if she'd written them. Even before they began to play violin, Sam had proven herself to be gifted with music. She sang before she could even talk. The two girls had shared a room, and Sam would sing herself to sleep every night—"Me, me, me, me . . ." she'd sing, always right on pitch, right in tune.

Marisa would sing harmony. She couldn't wait for Sam to learn to talk—and as soon as she did, the girls sang rounds, played musical games, wrote songs for their parents and each other. Sam sang like an angel, and she played like one too. At the age of four, she could pick out songs on the piano. Marisa taught her everything she knew, and before long, Sam was teaching her back.

The two sisters would sit on the back porch, practicing songs in the light of the moon, and sometimes it seemed they could continue all night, just to be together. Marisa remembered how their bows would move in unison, playing the tunes, and how she would feel so lucky to have a sister who loved doing the same thing.

"We can do this together for our whole lives," Marisa had said when she was nine, still called Patty.

"What do you mean?" Sam had asked.

"No one else will know all the same songs . . . we'll play these forever, the two of us, until we're old."

"What if we move apart from each other?"

"We won't."

"But sometimes sisters do," Sam pressed.

"Well then," she said, "we have to make a pact. If we do ever live apart, we'll always come back together every summer and play."

"Do you promise?" Sam asked.

"I do," she said. And they shook on it, right there under the rising moon.

For a long time, the promise never came up. They were so close, there wasn't a summer—or any other season—that they were apart. Marisa's first year of nursing school was the hardest, because Sam was still a senior in high school. But as soon as she could, Sam enrolled in Johns Hopkins just like her older sister.

Tuition was expensive, so at the end of every school week they would pack up their equipment and go to Irish bars, to play music and earn money to pay for their education. Their shows took them to places with names like Molly Maguire Pub, Blarney Stone, Galway Bay, Moran's Ale House. The crowd would be full of young people with bright eyes and open hearts, who would sing and stomp to the music, who would toast the sisters.

Their band was called Fallen Angels, because they both thought it was more realistic and fun to be sinners than saints. The truth was, Marisa thought Sam was a real angel. She was so bright and kind, always there for everyone. She gave so much to her patients, she needed those weekend shows just to play her heart out, purify all the pain she'd absorbed trying to help everyone. More often than not, it was just the two of them, with others sitting in as the spirit moved them.

Once, after they had both graduated and were working in a Baltimore clinic, they took a vacation to Paris, spent one afternoon drinking wine in a café along the Seine, near the Pont de l'Alma. A man had taken the table next to them. He was solid and tan, with a short dark ponytail and wraparound sunglasses, a black leather vest revealing bare arms so strong they were like iron. It was Bono.

The sisters fell in love with him on the spot. They bought him a drink. Then he bought them one. They started talking. It was all so Irish: words, heart, soul, and lots of wine. Bono smoked. Sam lit up, just because she had to keep him company. He was completely enamored of her desire to become a world health nurse.

They drank toasts to the poor, the rich, Ireland, America, Dublin, Baltimore, Elvis, music, poetry, sex, rock, and fallen angels everywhere.

"Here's to the Virgin Mary," Bono said, clinking glasses with the sisters. "May she bring us world peace and sold-out stadium shows."

"*Her* middle name is Mary," Sam said, pointing at her sister.

"That's the name you should go by," Bono said. "Mary. Or some version of it. Maureen, Muire, Maura, Marisa . . ."

"That's what I'm going to call you from now on," Sam said, eyes gleaming. "*Marisa.* No more Patty—" Years later, fleeing her life, abandoning her past, Marisa had made the name her own.

At the end of the night, Bono shook their hands. He smelled of cigarettes, sweat, leather, and St. Emilion. The pads of his fingertips felt hard and scarred, the stigmata of his guitar strings.

"I never want to forget this," Sam said, smiling into the ghostly gold light shimmering above the Seine and all Paris as he walked away into the night. The moment had seemed magical, almost as if they had conjured it.

"You sounded like you're really going to do it," Marisa had said. "Become a world health nurse."

"You know I want to," Sam said, hugging her. "But I'd miss you too much to go away for too long."

As it turned out, Marisa had been the first to leave. They both had jobs in Baltimore, and soon Sam began to travel with a world health organization—not full-time, but once or twice a year. But they kept playing music together in Baltimore, and until Marisa got married and moved to Boston, they shared an old row house just a few blocks from the harbor.

Now, holding her violin, Marisa thought of how easy their long-ago promise had been to keep—they would always get together to play, at least once every summer. Sam had loved Marisa's first husband, and she had been over the moon to become an aunt. Marisa knew that her daughter had made them closer than ever. It had seemed a bond that could never be broken, no matter what came along.

"That's pretty, Mom," Jessica said, coming in from the garden now. "What is it?"

"Mozart," Marisa said.

"That doesn't sound like fiddle music."

"It's not. It's violin music."

Jessica smiled. She looked so happy to hear her mother playing, Marisa felt a twinge in her heart.

"How do you know the difference?"

"Jess," Marisa said, "I think you know."

Jessica nodded, and her eyes filled with tears—because her aunt had been the one to teach her.

"They're the same instrument," Marisa said. "But it depends on how it's played."

"The violin speaks to the mind, and the fiddle speaks to the heart," Jessica said, but Marisa swore she could hear Sam's voice. Her sister had loved to quote Miss Tilly Lonergan, an old fiddle player from Baltimore.

"A violin has 'strings,' and a fiddle has 'strangs,'" Jessica said. "A violin is played sitting down, and a fiddle is played standing up." The differences usually made Jessica smile, but right now she had tears running down her face.

"Oh, honey . . ."

"Mom," she said, "why won't Aunt Sam come see us?"

"She's mad at me," Marisa said.

Marisa reached for her, and Jessica sobbed against her chest. Trying to console her, trying to help her, Marisa almost wished she had left her fiddle in the closet.

"She's not upset with you," Marisa said. "You can't think that."

"But I'm not enough to make her forget what happened," Jessica wept. "Or she would be here now."

Marisa's heart skipped several beats. Being angry at Marisa was one thing, but hurting Jessica was something else. She whispered that everything would get better, that Sam would probably call or write as soon as she got back to the States. But inside, she was shaking. Somehow she had to tell Sam what this was doing to Jess.

Easing away, Jessica picked up the violin and bow, handed them to her mother. Marisa saw the plea in her eyes, and remembered how comforted Jess had always been by their music—Marisa and Sam's—especially after her father had died.

"What would you like to hear, honey?" she asked.

"'O'er the Hills,'" Jessica said.

Somehow, Marisa had known that's what it would be. She drew the bow over the strings, began the sweet, sentimental tune. Jessica's eyes were closed. She looked so young and innocent. For a moment, Marisa saw the echo of her sister in her daughter's face.

What if something had happened? What if Sam had had an accident in Peru? Maybe Marisa was just grasping at straws, but she couldn't believe, any more than Jessica, that Sam would turn against them forever.

She thought of Patrick Murphy. He had seemed so stalwart, so steady, when he'd come up to Cape Hawk last month. She knew that he had spent many years trying to track down Lily. Maybe Marisa could call him, ask him to check on Sam and make sure she was okay. Could he do that?

Still playing the song, glancing down at Jessica, she knew she had to try.

Returning from visiting Maeve at the hospital, Patrick sat on the deck of his boat, *Probable Cause,* watching terns dive for minnows in the cove. The baitfish had been thick this week, and it was very unusual to see them in these numbers this far up the river. They swam in the estuary, but Patrick's dock was nearly seven miles inland. The water was brackish here, but right now it was a haven for fish and seabirds. Looking over the rail, Patrick saw a bluefish come to the surface, snapping at everything that moved. His phone rang and he didn't even check caller ID—he was too engrossed in the fishing ballet.

"Hello," he said.

"Patrick?" came the voice.

He knew it instantly. Patrick had a cop's instinct for identifying characteristics, and Marisa Taylor's voice had imprinted itself in his inner data bank.

"Marisa?"

She laughed, a quick, nervous ripple that made his skin tingle. "Yes, it's me. I'm surprised you knew—"

"I'm a detective, ma'am," he said. "It's my job to know."

"Ahh," she said, chuckling softly.

"How is life in Cape Hawk?" he asked.

"It's . . . well . . . it's fine."

Patrick listened, watching gulls circle overhead, waiting for her to continue, wondering why she sounded so hesitant.

"You must miss your friends," he said. "Lily and Rose. And Liam."

"Lily called me, and I do miss her—more than you can imagine." She paused. "It seems I'm missing everyone right now."

Patrick's heart jumped. Was she talking about him? He had promised himself to play it cool the next time he talked to her or saw her—meeting her at Cape Hawk had done something to his insides that hadn't been done since . . . well, since Sandra. He'd gotten all turned inside out. He was glad she couldn't see him right now—he felt his face turning bright red.

"Missing everyone?" he managed to ask.

"Yes," she said. "Well, one person in particular. My sister."

Okay, he told himself. That made more sense. He cleared his throat. She was calling him in his professional capacity. "Is she actually missing?" he asked.

"Well, I wouldn't say that," she said. "I hope not, anyway. She's a nurse, and her work takes her all over the world. Last I heard, she was in Peru. The thing is, I invited her up here for the Ceili Festival, and—"

"Whoa, stop a minute. The what?"

"The Ceili Festival."

"That's right, that's right," Patrick said. "Keep in mind, you're talking to a Murphy. The word 'ceili' makes my heart beat a little faster. It's in the genes. So, you're saying your sister is invited, but she hasn't replied?"

"Pretty much."

"That doesn't sound like angelic behavior to me. Even a fallen angel."

"You remembered," Marisa said, thinking about how Patrick's encouragement in Cape Hawk had fired her desire to play again.

Patrick's eyes narrowed as he stared at the birds wheeling over the smooth blue water. "That wasn't a band a good Irishman would forget hearing about. I'm still hoping to hear you play one of these days." He had the Chieftains on the CD player, and he turned it up. "So, go on. Your sister hasn't replied to your invitation. Have you been in close touch, in general?"

"Well . . ." Marisa said, trailing off.

"Not so close?"

"We were, always. But then I married Ted . . ."

"Edward Hunter strikes again," Patrick

said. He thought of Lily and Maeve, the years of separation between them. Such wonderful women, taken in by such a creep.

"What happened?" he asked.

"I ask myself that all the time. It wasn't any one thing. She just couldn't stand to see me losing myself. She's such a strong woman, the way I used to be. We became nurses because we wanted to help the sickest of the sick and the poorest of the poor." Her voice closed down, and she trailed off.

Patrick held the receiver, wishing he could comfort her. He'd seen the haunted look in her eyes up at Cape Hawk, and he recognized it from other women he'd seen.

"Abuse takes a lot out of a person," he said. "You should forgive yourself."

"I just wish Sam would forgive me," she said softly.

"You might have pushed her away," he said. "That's what seems to happen."

"I did," she said. "That's the hardest thing to live with. Jessica loves Sam so much—and the longer it goes on without hearing from her, the more it seems as if we never will."

"Are you worried about her?"

When she didn't respond, he went in another direction. "You say your sister is in Peru?"

"Yes. In the mountains, traveling around to poor villages."

"Do you know the name of the group she's with?"

"It's based in Baltimore, out of Johns Hopkins—Global Care."

Patrick wrote it down. "You're sure she's still in Peru?"

"Positive. She sent out a group e-mail recently, and she mentioned going to another area."

"What's her name—as it appears on her passport?"

"Samantha Joan Mahon."

"Would you like me to call some people I know? International law enforcement types? They could track her down."

"Seriously?"

"Yes."

Marisa was silent for a long time, wrestling with her own loneliness and Jessica's, but thinking hard about what Sam would want. "I don't think she'd like that much," she finally said. "I know that permits can be hard to get, visiting certain regions of the countries she visits. I wouldn't want to cause any problems for them. I guess it's better that I just wait to hear from her on her own."

"I understand. Has she been up to Cape Hawk?"

"No," Marisa said. "But I know she'd love it here. Especially now, with the music festival. Jessica's going to have a lemonade stand tomorrow, right by the gazebo. I can just imagine how Sam would love to see that. The old Sam, anyway."

Patrick held the phone, filled with sudden longing. He heard the love in her voice and knew he'd do just about anything he could to help. They were connected by something Patrick couldn't put into words.

Marisa broke the silence. "I want to thank you for offering that, Patrick."

"You don't have to thank me."

"I'm going to play you something. Our favorite song," she said. "Mine and Sam's." And then he heard her lay down the receiver, and a bow being drawn across strings, and then the most beautiful notes he'd ever heard issued through the telephone.

Patrick Murphy closed his eyes, feeling his boat rock beneath him. His world had felt so unstable, ever since his divorce. He had been feeling as if the earth's axis had slipped, set him on a course for falling off its surface. But right now, even with waves from a passing tug making his boat toss in the wake, he felt as if he was getting ground under his feet.

The music filled his ears and his heart. He wanted it never to end. He wanted the music to play all night. Marisa's playing was beautiful, and evoked the hills and the cliffs and the whales and the rocks of Cape Hawk. It made Patrick want to start his engines and steam north, through the Cape Cod Canal, straight across the wide water to Nova Scotia.

He contained his feelings, told himself that she was just playing him a song, not inviting him to visit. He listened to her play, his tense muscles relaxing as the music filled his body and spirit.

He swore he heard her heart pouring through the wire—nothing less than all that passion he'd heard earlier, coming straight at him. He couldn't believe it, but he felt something just like hope. Hope in what—it didn't even matter. He just listened to Marisa's music with his eyes closed and knew he'd do whatever it took to bring her sister back to her.

Chapter 7

A summer night at Hubbard's Point—the closest thing to heaven most people would ever find on earth. Waves splashed the shore, crickets rasped in the thick, tangled honeysuckle vines, and the spice of roses, wild thyme, and sassafras wafted through the salt air. Stars blazed overhead, and fireflies flitted through the yards.

Lily sat on the back porch, huddled in a blanket and listening to the waves. Her nerves crackled, and every sound made her jump. Lights on the Point had gone off one by one. She'd heard a whippoorwill calling across the swamp, and another answering.

Even nature seemed ominous, as if danger lurked in every shadow. She almost wished Edward would appear, because she couldn't stand the tension of waiting and wondering what his first move would be.

Now, staring across the water, she wondered whether Rose was asleep yet. They had spoken by phone a few hours earlier, and Rose told her Liam had read her a bedtime story, but she didn't want to go to bed.

Lily felt the same way. She saw a meteor shoot across the sky and held her breath. She wanted to reach for Rose—for Liam—but they weren't there. They were in Rhode Island, and Lily had been apart from them for three days now.

How could any of this have happened? Was everything in life like a meteor—blazing, sudden, out of her control? Or was there some pattern, some sense, to where she found herself tonight? It all seemed to hinge on Edward . . . and she found herself spinning back in time, to memories she had tried to put aside, to the day she met him, back when she was Mara.

What if she had been a starving artist, instead of a rising young designer? No one would suspect that there was a lot of money in designing canvases for upscale needle-work shops, but there was. And Edward had seen his opportunity.

Two weeks before Christmas 1993, Mara Jameson flew out of Providence's T.F. Green Airport for Washington, D.C. Larkspur and Ivy, a shop in Georgetown and one of her best customers, had invited her down for a tea, to meet their clients and her fans. Because it was snowing, because it was almost Christmas, because she had been working late every night, and because her grandmother told her to treat herself, she had used her airline miles for a business-class seat and booked a room at the Hay-Adams.

The flight was bumpy, but Mara wasn't scared. Whenever she had a rough flight, she would think of her father. He had flown during World War II—had been a hero for the twenty-five bombing runs he had made across the English Channel to Germany. She thought of all the bad weather he had encountered, all the attacks he had survived. After so much terror in the air, he had died on what should have been a peaceful cruise—a ferry excursion across a wide inlet, with Mara's mother on a trip to Ireland, when Mara was just four.

She had grown up believing that you can't predict your fate; you don't see death coming. You just do your best, staying as open to life's possibilities as you can. Worrying about rough flights was a waste of time.

On the final approach to National Airport, Mara realized that everyone on the plane was holding their breath; everyone but her. She turned toward the window and stared out. She felt an old ache in her chest—a hollowness that rang and echoed, as if she were a bell. The vibrations ran through her bones and nerves as the plane jostled against the headwinds. The person next to her was praying.

The plane shook, as if it might break apart. One person cried out sharply. Mara just watched the snow outside. Her eyes filled with tears; she wished she were afraid of dying. But she wasn't, and she hadn't been since the day her parents died. Sometimes she wished she had been with them on that ferry, instead of home in Connecticut with her grandmother.

She had built a life on work, needlepoint, and her grandmother. She was thirty-one years old, and she had never really been in love. Why fall in love, when it could all end on a summer day, on a peaceful ferry crossing in Ireland? When they finally touched down, bouncing hard on the tarmac, the other passengers cheered. Mara just gathered her things.

The business-class passengers were let off first. Mara noticed the other passengers waiting; a young man wearing a tweed sports coat stood at the front of the coach cabin, seeming to watch her as she gathered her things. Thinking she was holding everyone up, she gave him a quick smile and hurried off the plane.

The flight attendants and captain stood at the plane door, obviously shaken by the rough flight. She thanked them as she passed. The captain said, "Hope you'll fly with us again." "I will!" Mara said. She walked a little taller—shaken not so much by the flight as by her own emotional turmoil. Maybe she could make a New Year's resolution to try to open her heart a little.

Still troubled, she went to the taxi line. Standing at the curb, she noticed the man in the tweed jacket hurrying over. He had a stocky build; his shoulders looked very strong, straining the fabric. It was snowing, and she wondered whether he was cold without a topcoat. His briefcase looked a bit battered, as if he had had it since high school. His hair was brown and wavy, cut very short. She glimpsed the Harvard tag on his luggage, and that made her look away—a little too much advertising that he was an Ivy Leaguer, she thought.

A cab stopped, and Mara put her hand on the door to get in at the same time as the man. His eyes looked dark, charged—and for a minute she thought he was going to fight her for the cab. His energy frightened her, and she stepped back.

"It's all yours," she said.

"Want to share it?" he asked, seeming to regroup quickly.

"No. That's okay."

"Come on. Where are you going?" Suddenly the darkness in his eyes was replaced by one of the brightest smiles she'd ever seen. He looked sweet, charming, and insouciant—as if he was about to ask her to join some mad adventure in the nation's capital. In spite of her initial aversion to him, his smile was undeniably cute, and the tone of his voice was totally flirtatious.

Mara just smiled politely and ran for the next cab, telling the driver, "Hay-Adams, please," and climbing in as quickly as possible to get away from the man, who stood at the curb with a smitten look in his hazel eyes and—adorably—his hand over his heart.

She got to the wonderful hotel across Lafayette Park from the White House. Her grandparents had stayed here long ago, and Mara felt the blessing of her grandmother as she checked in at the grand lobby desk, rode upstairs in a burnished mahogany elevator, and entered a beautiful yellow room overlooking snow falling on the park and White House. She had just opened her suitcase—to unpack her dress and her latest needlepoint canvas designs—when she heard a knock at the door.

Peeking through the peephole, she saw someone standing with a big bouquet of red tulips. *Granny must have sent them,* she thought. Grabbing her bag for a tip for the porter, she threw open the door.

"It's you," she said, recognizing the young man from the cab stand.

"You needed tulips," he said. "It's snowing

out and you're beautiful, and all I could think was, I have to give that girl some red tulips."

"But how did you know where I'd be?"

"Fate led me here," he said.

She raised her eyebrows. The door was half open, and she was inside, and he was out in the hall. Her heart was pounding, and her mouth was dry. She felt scared, but also thrilled. Men didn't do things like this. Maybe they did in Paris, or Rome, or incredibly romantic places halfway around the world. But men flying from Providence to Washington didn't.

"Fate didn't know where I was staying," she said.

"A plane, a snowstorm, some tulips, I, and thou," he said, grinning wickedly, poetically.

"Hmm," she said.

She looked up and down the hallway. They were completely alone. If he had bad intentions, wouldn't he have already pushed his way in? As if reading her mind, he took half a step backward, away from her.

"Regardless of how fate brought us together," he said. "I know one thing. The tulips are for you. And you alone." Again, that grin. "I'll just take myself off to my room and dream about you."

"Your room? You're staying in the hotel?"

He nodded. "Okay—now you know my secret. I pulled up, walked in, and saw you just getting into the elevator. I thought—wow. We really *should* have shared that cab. Two coincidences in a row—same plane, same cab, same hotel. Whoa, that's three."

"So you jumped into the next elevator and guessed my floor?"

"Nope." Hazel eyes twinkling. "I bribed the bellman. I'm sorry. It's forward of me, I know. I ran to the florist, picked out the prettiest flowers I could find, and got back as soon as I could. Honestly, I didn't want to miss a minute of time with you."

She chuckled. He really was funny—and very handsome. He had sharp features that reminded her of a young Cary Grant, with bright eyes and a strong jaw and that quick, fun-loving smile. Lily felt herself smiling in his presence—after just five minutes. People were always telling her she was too serious, and she knew she was.

"Let me take you to dinner," he said.

"We don't even know each other's names," she said.

"I'm Edward Hunter," he said.

"I'm Mara Jameson," she said.

"Okay—now we know each other's names!"

She laughed. He handed her the tulips; she brought them up to her nose so she could smell them. Tulips in December—how extravagant, she thought.

"Please, Mara?" he asked. "I've come all this way. Don't send me away without letting me take you to dinner."

"All this way?"

His smile lit up his eyes, and he stepped so close, she could feel his warm breath on her forehead. Mara had come to Washington for work—she was very focused and ambitious, trying to get her business off the ground. She felt hesitant, afraid to say yes, but he was smiling at her with such bright eyes.

"Don't break my heart, Mara Jameson," he said, cupping the side of her face.

"I don't know you well enough to break your heart," she said hoarsely, mesmerized by his green eyes.

"Don't you be too sure of that," he said. "I've never bought red tulips in the snow for anyone in my entire life."

And then he kissed her.

She had literally kissed a stranger within minutes of meeting him. She had trusted his words, his smile, his warm eyes, the flowers he had bought her. How much had those tulips cost, after all? Ten dollars? Fifteen? When she thought back now, she wondered whether she had sold her entire life for the price of that single bouquet of out-of-season flowers.

Had he actually had a room at the hotel, or just followed her? She didn't know and doubted she ever would. She did know that she had been wearing an elegant black cashmere coat, her grandfather's thick gold watch chain as a necklace, a pair of emerald earrings—an outfit that she thought her Georgetown clients would appreciate. She had looked like a New England girl with money. He had heard her, she was positive, tell the driver of that cab her destination—one of the finest hotels in Washington.

Sitting on Maeve's porch, she pulled the blanket around her tighter. She stared across the bay, at the moon's path on the water. Her guarded heart—so easily softened by Edward's charm—had hardened as if frozen. The moon sparkled silver, breaking into a million pieces on the water. Lily had shut down after Edward—almost completely. There had been no quick romances, no sweeping her off her feet.

Her love for Liam had grown slowly. With every year of Rose's life, it had gotten truer and deeper. Lily hadn't even let herself feel or believe it. Very gently, he had melted her heart. Too quick a thaw might have destroyed her—Liam let her come around in her own time.

Three days without him and Rose was too much. It was after midnight, but she threw off the blanket and traded her nightgown for jeans and a sweatshirt. She fumbled for her grandmother's house and car keys, locked the door, and hurried up the stone steps.

The Point was deserted. All her neighbors had gone to bed. Her protectors—Bay and Tara—had been by earlier, and there had been no sign of Edward. Checking her pocket for the map and directions Liam had given her, she drove out Eight Mile River Road to I-95.

She had the car windows down, and she turned on the radio. Bonnie Raitt came on, and Lily sang along. The miles sped by, with warm air blowing through the car. Lily glanced in the rearview mirror. A car had pulled out of Hubbard's Point just behind her, and it was still there. Her stomach clenched—what if she was making a mistake, leading some reporter, or even worse, Edward—straight to Rose?

By the time she got to New London, the car was gone. A stream of trucks passed her, just normal traffic on this stretch of turnpike. Lily reached for her cell phone. Maybe she should let Liam know she was on her way. But it was so late—after midnight. Let him get some sleep—she'd wake him up soon enough.

She was so excited about the idea of seeing the people she loved, she didn't notice the car following her, three or four vehicles behind, about half a mile back. If she had seen it, she wouldn't have known whether it was friend or foe.

She hadn't given her protectors an itinerary.

And they hadn't given her one, either.

Liam had been tossing and turning for hours when he heard the footsteps on the porch. He hiked himself up on his elbow, glanced at the door of the small guesthouse

the Stanleys were letting him stay in with
Rose. He had turned off the outside light,
but he saw a moonlit silhouette pass the
window, and he knew—more than even recognizing her, he felt her coming toward him.

He pulled open the door, and Lily stood
there on the whitewashed porch, her dark
hair blowing in the cool breeze. Without any
words they reached for each other and
hugged, rocking, in the darkness. Now that
she was here, he was home. It didn't matter
that they were in a house they'd never been
before. Home was where Lily was. He felt
her hands on his back, sliding up under his
T-shirt, and he kissed the top of her head.

They were new at this. Liam had been in
love with her most of the nine years they
had known each other, but they had both
been so careful, being polite, appropriate,
and guarded. That had all ended at the beginning of this summer—on the way to
Boston, for Rose to have her last lifesaving
operation. Liam had known—there was
more than one life that needed to be saved.
He and Lily couldn't live without each other.
He had felt it for a long time, but he knew it
more deeply with every passing day.

"I couldn't stay away from you and Rose," she said.

"We couldn't stand not being with you," he said.

She tipped her head back, so that he could kiss her, and she tasted sweet and salty. When he closed the door, she pushed back the curtain, looking into the darkness. Her eyes looked worried.

"What's wrong?" he asked.

"I'm sure I'm just being overly careful, but I thought a car was following me when I left the beach."

"I'll go out and check," he said, but she caught his wrist and kissed him again. He wanted to carry her to his bed right then. But he looked down at her and smiled and took her hand as he led her through the small house to the yellow bedroom where Rose slept.

"My Rosie." Lily smiled.

"She misses you, but she's fine."

He watched Lily crouch, then kneel beside the bed. She kissed Rose's face, peeked down at her scar to make sure it was healing well, gently eased her daughter's left hand down from its protective spot across her collarbone. Rose slept through these

ministrations, sighing contentedly as if she
sensed her mother's presence through her
dreams.

They walked into the living room, and Lily
seemed to take in the old wicker furniture
with faded chintz cushions, the marine
charts of Narragansett Bay and Block Island
Sound, the brass telescope pointed at the
bay, and the bookshelves full of oceanographic journals and reference books. Then,
as if she'd absorbed as much as she
needed to know about the place that shel-
tered her daughter, she threw herself
against Liam's chest.

He held her with his one arm. He kissed
her, felt her skin moist against his. She
reached up to touch his face, and he felt her
fingertips light on his skin. He thought
maybe she'd want to talk—he started to
turn on a lamp, but she stopped him, finger
on his lips.

They walked into the bedroom. Liam felt
protective of Lily, and wanted to be
strong—he knew how hard it had to be for
her, worried about her grandmother, separated from Rose. But inside, he was shaking
with excitement. Being with her made him
feel seventeen.

The way she leaned against him, her breath hot on his neck, her pelvis pressing into his thighs. Her kisses were urgent, as if she couldn't wait. His heart was banging in his chest, and he tried to stay calm enough to remember to breathe. Her hands were at the buttons of his shirt, undoing them, sliding in and caressing his skin.

They had so much to say to each other, and they did it with their bodies. Words weren't enough for how he felt about Lily. They had lived a lifetime together—Rose's lifetime. Their shared dream had been to keep her alive, to give her a wonderful life. Liam's own heart was strong because of his love of Lily and Rose—he could and would do anything for them, to protect them.

That's what he wanted to tell Lily, and it's what he did tell her—with his lips, his tongue, his fingers, every bit of his body and soul. They were together tonight, and Liam knew that deep down they would never really be apart again.

"I don't want to leave," she whispered, lying under the sheets with him as the sky began to turn from black to deep blue with dawn's approach.

"I don't want you to," he said, kissing her hair as she lay on his shoulder.

"He hasn't called or showed up," Lily said. "I was sure he would, the minute the news got out."

"There's been a lot of news," Liam said. "I've kept the TV off, so Rose wouldn't see. But the Stanleys told me your return has been in the papers and on lots of programs. Are you sure that wasn't him, in the car?"

"I don't know. I've just gotten so jumpy," she said. "I know that he's waiting for the right moment, and I keep expecting him around every corner."

"I know we want to keep Rose away from him," Liam said. "But I think I should be with you—to keep you safe."

"Taking care of Rose is the best thing you can do for me," Lily said. "I wish we were all home in Cape Hawk again."

"Maybe we should go back home for a few days," he said. "You, me, and Rose. We could listen to some ceili bands—it would be good for us."

"Sssh," she said, kissing him hard. "You're tempting me, but I've got to see about Granny."

"I know," he said.

He took her hand, leading her across the room. His desk was piled high with books and journals from John Stanley's personal library. Liam had been amazed to find old editions of *Copeia,* the prestigious nine-teenth-century ichthyologic journal, dedi-cated to the study and conservation of sharks. He'd been looking for theories to explain the phenomenon he'd been observ-ing along the shore these past few days—the massing of baitfish in such unusual volume.

Lily drifted toward the open door. Liam fol-lowed her outside. The stars were white and brilliant in the dark blue sky. The night seemed to reflect the ocean, spreading out from the rocks all the way to the far horizon. The constellations made a canopy over-head, arching straight out of the sea. They illuminated the salt spray, fine and bright as snow.

"What's that?" Lily asked, pointing off-shore, at iridescence streaking through the water.

"Bioluminescence," Liam said. "Marine creatures that produce light."

"It looks like the northern lights, underwa-ter," she said.

"It's unusual, that's for sure," Liam said.

"Could it be Nanny?" Lily asked, sounding excited. "Maybe she really has followed us down from Nova Scotia!"

Looking at the white streaks, Liam could understand why Lily would think they were made by their favorite beluga whale, come all the way from Cape Hawk. Although Nanny hadn't shown up on his computer tracking screen, he was pretty sure the source of light was a marine mammal or another large sea creature.

As they approached the seawall, the roaring of distant waves grew stronger. The inshore waters were turbulent, and silhouetted in the breaking waves were filmy white jellyfish and hordes of silver menhaden, swimming parallel to the shore.

"It's so loud," Lily said, staring out at the water.

"It's a phenomenon called Ghost Hills," Liam told her.

"What is that?"

"There's a reef between here and Block Island. Normally, oceanographic activity there is fairly predictable. I've just been reading some old journals, and it seems that when the conditions are right—usually midway through hurricane season, like now—the winds and tides can conspire to send huge waves, 'Ghost Hills,' over the reef."

"It sounds more like galloping horses," Lily said, standing still, listening.

"I know. The waves can be sixty feet high—rogue waves. The surfers love them—they get towed out to the reef by motorboats or Jet Skis. The problem is, when Ghost Hills come, so do the sharks."

Lily hugged him. She knew about Liam and sharks. They stood close to the seawall, and felt the salt spray mist their faces. The beach smelled like fish, from the influx of bait. This was the food chain at work: Ghost Hills changed the whole marine environment. They pulled southern organisms in from the Gulf Stream and attracted northern species from the Labrador Current.

"Is this why Nanny came south?" Lily asked.

"I think so," Liam said. "Partly, at least. The rogue waves create a food source for large marine animals that wouldn't normally be there."

"Rose thinks Nanny followed us—that she was looking out for us."

"That can also be true—I'm sure it is,"

Liam said, smiling at Lily, wishing she would never leave.

"I just hope she's safe," Lily said, gazing out over the flashing, churning sea. In the distance, a large trawler made a long, slow turn, coming from the northeast. Silhouetted by the stars and the glowing waves, its familiar profile made Liam stare more closely.

"It's late," Lily said. "I want to go see Rose for a little while, but then I should be getting back to Hubbard's Point."

"I don't want you to go," Liam said, turning away from the dark boat, kissing her as star followed star through the night sky, as if holding her could make everything right, keep them safe and together. Then they both walked into the small house, to sit with Rose for as long as they could before Lily had to leave again.

Liam wished he could keep her from going back to the place where she'd been so afraid. Not even the dark waters where his brother had been killed had made him feel as powerless.

Patrick held himself back from calling his contacts in Baltimore. Marisa had asked him not to try tracking her sister. He told himself to stay out of it. As much as he wanted to take action, she had been very clear.

Instead, he began to have dreams of the North. They were filled with dark pines growing on craggy cliffs, mirror-smooth bottomless bays, ice blue skies, golden-eyed bobcats in the woods, broadtail hawks on the wing, and Marisa.

And now, for the third night in a row, he was dreaming of her again: they held hands in the snow and went swimming in a frozen cove, through a hole in the ice. The water was hot, and they held each other, kissing. . . .

Patrick moaned and woke himself up. He had thrashed the covers off his bunk. His chest and legs were soaking wet, his heart beating out of his chest. Swinging his legs out, he sat at the edge of his bunk, his head in his hands. Flora, his big black Lab, lay on her dog bed, watching him with huge eyes.

"Do you know what dreams mean?" he asked her.

She just thumped her tail.

The night was warm and still. He grabbed a bottle of water, headed up on deck. The air was cooler up here. He sat in the cock-pit in his boxer shorts, letting the breeze evaporate the sweat from his body. The dream was so vivid, even now—he looked around, almost surprised to be in this pro-tected Connecticut boatyard instead of lost in the northern wilds with Marisa.

He drank water, leaning his head back to look up at the sky. The stars were so bold, pinpoints of fire in the black night. Patrick grounded himself by finding the North Star. There it was, Polaris. He wondered whether he could follow it straight to Marisa. All he would have to do was cast off his lines—his boat was seaworthy enough to make the trip.

Sighing, he went back down to his bunk and waited for sleep to come again. His grandmother used to tell him stories about an angel who flew over the world at night, spreading her white wings to protect every-one, hold everyone together, bring the lost ones home. She'd point at the Milky Way, tell him it was the angel's shadow. Patrick hoped that she could bring Sam and Marisa together again.

"That's bullshit," he said out loud when he woke up the next morning. Maybe angels worked for grandmothers, but cops knew that the only way to get something done was to make it happen.

Picking up the phone, he got the number for Johns Hopkins, asked to be connected to Global Care.

"Hi," he said to the woman who answered the phone. "My name is Patrick Murphy."

"Yes?"

"I'm calling in regard to a nurse who is with your group in Peru. I need to get hold of her."

"Is this a family emergency?"

"No, no it's not," he said, frowning. He paused. This person didn't sound as if she'd be impressed by the phrase "retired detective." But he thought of Marisa and Jessica, and knew he had to go for it. "Listen, I'm a detective with the Connecticut State Police."

"Oh—what happened?"

"The woman I'm looking for is not in any trouble," he said quickly, mindful of what Marisa had said about Sam's work. "I'm trying to contact her because—"

"Sir," she said, cutting him off, "we are very protective of our health care workers, and I'm unable to give out any information about their whereabouts. If you'd like to send a letter to this office, I'll see if I can forward it on—"

"Thank you," Patrick growled. "That won't be necessary."

Flora needed to go for her morning walk. He let her off the boat, watched her prowl the woods around the boatyard's perimeter. That gave Patrick a chance to think. He could try calling Peru directly, try to get through to someone at the Global Care group. Or he could dial an old friend in the Baltimore PD, call in some old favors.

He didn't know the number by heart, had to look it up—but there it was in his old address book, written in years before. Patrick dialed, looking forward to hearing his pal's voice. Instead, he got Detective James Hanley's voicemail.

"Hey, Jim," he said. "It's Pat Murphy. A blast from the past, right? Listen, I'm trying to get some information on the whereabouts of a Baltimore woman, Samantha Mahon. . . ."

Patrick left him a long message about Global Care, Sam being somewhere in the wilds of Peru, her sister getting worried.

Then he hung up, wondering how long it would take Jim to get back to him.

He hoped it was soon. Because he knew how badly Marisa wanted to find her sister, and if it took too long, Patrick just might have to fly down to South America to bring her back himself.

Chapter 8

On her way back to Hubbard's Point from Rhode Island, Lily felt recharged and energized. Holding Liam had triggered even more desire, and seeing Rose had unleashed a hurricane of love—just like Ghost Hills, pounding the reef. When dawn broke, Rose woke up to find her mother sitting there, and Lily could still hear her cry of joy.

She drove under the train trestle that marked the entrance to Hubbard's Point and saw early-morning walkers out for their daily constitutional. There were the strollers, out to enjoy the gardens and scenery, and the power-walkers, out for exercise. They walked in groups, talking and laughing, or alone, just listening to the music of the waves and leaves rustling in the wind.

Driving around the bend and up the first hill, she saw Bay and Tara. Tara was pushing a stroller, with baby Joey inside, and she and Bay were winded and sweating and gave huge waves. Lily waved back, her heart lifting. Seeing Liam and Rose had done a lot to chase last night's demons away.

When she pulled up to the house, she came face-to-face with a man she didn't know. Tall, dark-haired, wearing a navy blue FBI T-shirt, he was sitting in the shade on Maeve's iron four-seasons garden bench.

"I'm Joe Holmes," he said, rising to shake her hand. "Tara's husband."

"I'm Lily Malone," she said.

"Nice to meet you," he said, smiling. "I've heard so much about you. Sorry about the intrusion—"

She shook her head. "No, I'm grateful. It's such a lot to ask you all to do this. In fact, maybe—"

"Don't try to talk us out of it," he said sternly. "You know Tara. Or—maybe you've forgotten. But trying to argue with her is like trying to convince a hurricane it should to go east when it wants to go west."

"I remember," Lily said.

"Besides, just from a professional stand-point," he said, "we'd like to get something right in your case. Protect you now, you know? You really pulled it off. Someday I'd like to interview you, to ask you how you did it. Hid for nine whole years."

"Can I ask you a question?" she asked quietly, remembering the headlights in her rearview mirror. "Did you follow me last night?"

"No," Joe said. "When I got up here, your car was gone. Tara figured you'd stayed at the hospital."

"I went to Rhode Island, to see my daughter. But I thought someone was following me for a while. . . ."

"Edward, you think?"

"God, I hope not," she said.

"He's bad news," Joe said. "I'll see what I can find out about where he was last night. Look—you just go about your business, do what you have to do. We'll watch your house."

"I saw Tara and Joey," she said. "Your

family has better things to do than stand watch over me."

"Better things to do than help a friend?" He shook his head. "I'm with Tara on that. Nothing's more important, Lily."

The summer day was warm. The grass tickled Rose's bare feet. She played outside while Dr. Neill did his work. A swing hung from a tall branch of one of the trees in the front yard, so she walked over to it and climbed on. The breeze ruffled the leaves overhead. A bird flew into the neat green hedge. Rose's mother had been there for breakfast, and Rose felt empty now, because she was gone again.

From the swing, Rose could look up and down the street. The family next door had older children; she had watched them climb into a blue station wagon and go driving off. Seeing kids made her miss Jessica. She glanced at the house. Dr. Neill was right there in the window. She waved, and he waved back, and that made her feel better.

Swinging back and forth, she watched a car drive down the street. It passed the house and kept going. She kept swinging, and after a few minutes, the car came back, driving slowly now. When it got to the drive-way, it came to a complete stop, but didn't turn in.

Maybe the man driving was lost, Rose thought. She glanced at the window; Dr. Neill was still there, looking down at his desk. Although the car was parked in the street, not the driveway, the man got out and stepped into the yard. He was much shorter than Dr. Neill, but heavier. He had short, sort of frizzy brown hair. At first, Rose felt alarmed, but then he smiled.

He looked so friendly and nice. Rose didn't move. She wasn't scared, but her mother had told her not to talk to strangers. Shade from the tall tree dappled his face, making it hard to see anything but his smile.

"Do you live here?" he asked.

Rose shook her head.

"Are you just visiting?" he asked, just a few feet away now. She could see his eyes now—bright but dead, like green marbles.

She nodded and stayed very still, glancing at the window. Dr. Neill was there, watching the man come closer. Suddenly he was on his feet.

"With your parents?"

The door opened. Dr. Neill started toward her, and something about the look on his face made her know she should run to him. She did, her heart galloping. When she turned around, the man was walking back to his car.

"You have such pretty green eyes," the man called. "And brown hair. I like your braids."

"Just a minute," Dr. Neill said, starting across the yard. "I want to talk to you."

The man didn't answer. He just kept staring at Rose as he climbed into his car. Slamming the door behind him hard, he began to pull away. The whole time, he just kept watching Rose. Then his car disappeared from sight.

"Who was that?" she asked Dr. Neill.

"Someone we have to be careful of," he said. "I won't let you outside alone again, okay?"

"Okay," she said.

He looked down into her eyes. Rose blinked, staring. She didn't know what had just happened, but she knew it made her heart beat too fast. The man had stared. He had smiled, as if he was nice. But his eyes had frightened her, flashing and hollow.

They had reminded her of a hungry animal, and she shivered.

Dr. Neill hugged her, and then he led her inside.

Liam sat at his computer, surrounded by early editions of *Copeia,* trying to shake off the disturbance he felt. He had no question about the visitor they'd just had. Edward had followed Lily last night, and he'd come back this morning to see the place in daylight. If only Liam hadn't let Rose go out by herself. If only he had told her to stay in the backyard, out of sight of the street.

He called Lily right away.

"What did he say? What did he do?" she asked.

"He didn't say much," Liam said. "He asked if she was visiting with her parents. Then he just stood there, staring at her."

"Oh no," Lily said. "He knows now—what are we going to do?"

"I think Rose and I should come to Hubbard's Point now," Liam said. "Why stay away if he already knows?"

"But what if it wasn't him? What if it was someone else, just a neighbor passing by, or—"

"Lily," Liam said gently.

"I don't know what to do," she said. "It seemed like such a good idea, for you to keep Rose away from here. Maybe that's still best—he doesn't know she's his. He has no idea."

"He mentioned her green eyes and brown hair," Liam said.

"Like his."

"Yes," Liam said.

"Oh God. I have to think . . ."

"Okay," he said. "But don't think too long. I want us all to be together."

After he hung up, Liam turned to see Rose sitting in a chair by the window, sunlight turning her brown hair shiny as copper. She had asked him for help braiding it that morning after Lily had left, and he had tried—tricky, with one arm. Now he saw it tumbling free to her shoulders—she had un-braided it after Edward's comment.

Hearing a knock at the front door, Liam's stomach clenched. He almost wished it would be Edward, so he could do battle. Rushing through the airy living room, he found his old friend John Stanley standing there—tan in a white polo shirt and faded Breton red shorts, wearing wire-rimmed spectacles and a Panama hat. John's grin evaporated at the look in Liam's eyes.

"Whoa," John said. "It's just me."

"We had an unwelcome visitor this morning," Liam said. He leaned around John, looked up and down the street. "Come on in."

"He found you?" John asked, frowning. Of course, Liam had told him all about the reason he and Rose needed to stay there. "Look, I have just the thing to take your mind off that. Have you noticed all the activity out there?" He pointed at the water.

"Hard to miss it," Liam said as he gazed at the cove churning and turning white with froth, fish in a feeding frenzy.

"Come take a boat ride. I'll show you something unreal."

"I have Rose with me. . . ."

"My kids used to love coming on oceanographic projects. We'll make her part of the team."

Liam nodded. Getting Rose away for the day would be the best possible thing to do. "Let me ask her," he said.

He hurried out, into the living room. Rose was curled up in a chair. She had a book open on her lap, but her gaze was troubled.

Liam could see that Edward's visit had disturbed her. "Rose," Liam said, "my friend wants to take us for a boat ride. Would you like that?"

"I want Mommy," she said.

Liam went to sit beside her. "I know," he said. "We're going to be with her really soon. But we can't today, so I thought maybe this would be the next best thing."

"I didn't like that man," she said.

"I know," he said.

"If we're on a boat ride, he can't come back and try to talk to me again, right?"

"Right," Liam said.

"Okay," Rose said, nodding.

Liam grabbed his laptop, cell phone, and binoculars, and stuffed them into his satchel. He put on his sunglasses and cap, then grabbed a snack and some juice for Rose. Leading John into the living room, he stood next to Rose.

"Rose, this is Dr. Stanley, whose house we're staying in."

"Thank you," Rose said politely.

"It's nice to meet you, Rose. Do you like boats?"

A smile began on her lips, spread to her

green eyes. Her face brightened, and she nodded. "Yes," she said. "I love them."

"Do you like science?" John asked. "Oceanography?"

"Yes," she said, her smile growing.

"Good," he said. "Because we have an oceanographic mystery going on right here, and it's pretty much up to us to solve it."

Liam rippled with excitement—the mystery of Ghost Hills. Generations of oceanographers had observed the phenomenon, pondered its cause. He gave Rose sunscreen to spread on her arms and legs, double-checked his bag to make sure he had everything. Then the three of them set off across John's yard.

A sturdy, thirty-foot stone breakwater jutted out from the beach. Liam could see that it kept the beachhead from eroding, pulling in crescents of sand and smooth seawashed pebbles from the waves. Two boats were docked alongside—*Respite,* a J-24 racing sloop, and *Blue Heron,* a thirty-six-foot down east lobster boat overhauled and refitted for oceanography work.

Rose was an old hand, from all her years aboard Liam's family's whale-watching fleet up in Cape Hawk. She jumped aboard *Blue*

Heron, standing back while John started up the engine and Liam walked along the breakwater, scanning once more for any sign of Edward, then casting off lines before leaping on board.

The water was calm as John steered south along the shore of the west passage of Narragansett Bay. The boat moved slowly, engines quiet, creating a lazy white wake rippling out behind. Two flocks of sandpipers flew low over the waves, just ahead of the big blue boat. Rose pointed, looking up to make sure Liam saw. He nodded and smiled, but his attention was fixed on larger birds—gulls and terns, swooping and diving along the beach.

"Birds working," Liam said, rummaging for his binoculars, lifting them to his eyes as he watched the shorebirds feasting on tiny silver fish—minnows, menhaden. All around them splashed fins and tails of larger fish.

"Yep," John said.

"What's running? Blues, stripers?"

"Everything," John said, and Liam gave him a look—he had already surmised the same thing. But John just continued steering the boat. They passed Narragansett Town Beach and Scarborough Beach, where surfers sat on their boards, staring out toward the open sea—toward the roar of Ghost Hills—while waiting for something worth riding amid the comparatively gentle swells. A pair of osprey fished along the shallows, wings gleaming white in the sun.

As they rounded Point Judith, the smell of fish became stronger. Liam wasn't surprised—this was home to the Galilee fishing fleet. Big diesel trawlers passed in and out of the breachway, to and from the Harbor of Refuge. These boats fished Georges Bank, the edge of the continental shelf, for haddock, cod, hake, whiting, flounder, and lobster, and they were every bit as hardy as the fleet out of Cape Hawk, Nova Scotia.

Liam had smelled lots of old bait and discarded fish in his day—but this was different. It was alive, and smelled of the sea, deep and blue and mysterious. It made the hair on the back of his neck stand on end. He looked at John, saw him frowning as he drove the boat. Instinctively Liam reached for Rose, drew her closer as they faced forward and the boat sliced through the water.

"Where are we going?" Rose asked.

"Not much farther," John said.

Liam glanced down the coast—Lily was just about twenty miles west of here. He wondered what she was doing right now, and he wondered whether the sudden, atavistic fear he felt welling up from inside had anything to do with Lily and what she was going through.

"This is it," John said, pulling back on the throttle, slowing the engine to a dull hum.

"Where are we?" Rose asked.

"That's the Point Judith Lighthouse," John said, pointing at the fifty-foot tower. Built of brownstone, the lower half whitewashed, it was crowned by a Fresnel lens that glinted in the brilliant sunlight.

"And seven miles out there is Block Island," Liam said.

"Six-point-four," John said. "From the tip of Point Jude to the north tip of Block. I remember, from when I got my pilot's license. Three-point-two miles to glide if I lost an engine. Three minutes of gliding is one afternoon of swimming. But I wouldn't want to swim in this water right now. Can you hear it?"

Rose frowned. With the engine down so low, the sound of small waves hitting the hull became more insistent. Only it wasn't waves at all: the sound was rapid and hard, almost like hundreds of hands clapping. Below, and more insistent, was a growing roar.

"What's that?" Rose asked, hurrying to the side. She gripped the rail, with Liam standing right beside her. They looked down into the blue water and saw silver everywhere. Silver tails, fins, scales. Thousands, hundreds of thousands, of small fish, right at the surface of the sea.

"Fish feeding," he said.

"We don't expect to see anything like this until September, if then," John said. "It's a rare year with this kind of activity."

The boat flushed ten, twenty herring gulls, black-backed gulls, laughing gulls, roseate terns—all rising in a screeching, cawing white cloud of wings. Liam looked over the side, saw the silver ribbon of fish extending in all directions. John drove out toward Block Island, across the Sound. The silver fish swam in a stream, a river of small fish weaving out to sea. And the oceangoing birds followed them in—more gulls and terns than Liam could believe.

"Is that—?" he asked, pointing up.

"A northern gannet," John said. "Spends most of its life at sea."

"Yet it's here in Block Island Sound?"

John's lips tightened. Liam knew that he had to be thinking the same thing—if these quantities of bait could pull in a northern gannet flying above the surface, what species of fish might there be swimming beneath? Liam thought of Nanny—whose whereabouts had been unknown these last days—and shivered.

A flotilla of motorboats—Boston Whalers, Grady-Whites, Aquasports—and Jet Skis towing surfers on surfboards passed by. Liam's attention was captured by another boat—a dark green trawler with a familiar low profile. Raising the binocs to his eyes, he felt his blood run cold. The ship was *Mar IV,* with its home port of Cape Hawk emblazoned in gold on the transom. There was its captain, Gerard Lafarge, standing at the bridge.

"A friend of yours?" John asked.

"Hardly," Liam said. "He's a fisherman I know from home. We've had a few run-ins, with him catching dolphins and selling them as tuna."

"We'll turn him in," John said, reaching for the radio transmitter. "If he's Canadian, he's not supposed to be fishing in Rhode Island."

"He's not fishing," Liam said, staring through the glasses. Lafarge was standing still, gazing at the waves. His outriggers were pulled in; the nets were rolled tight, the trawl doors up and inactive.

"So what's he doing here?" John said.

"That's what I'd like to know," Liam said as *Mar IV* steamed toward the action with the rest of the boats.

Just ahead, the giants were rising to life: Ghost Hills. Liam felt the water temperature rise—these ocean waves were straight off the Gulf Stream, brilliant cerulean blue, clear as sunshine. They rose fifty feet into the air, wild and thunderous, sliding over the reef, enormous and unbroken, then exploding into white foam.

"What are they?" Rose asked, sounding amazed.

"The biggest waves we've ever seen," Liam said, his arm around her.

"In the middle of the sea? I thought waves only broke on the beach," she said.

"They're breaking on an undersea reef," John said. "It only happens once or twice a century—when the wind and currents and tides are right."

Liam pulled his laptop out of the case, booted up, and waited for the predator program to load. He tapped in some coordinates, watching weather data flash across the screen. A tropical storm had swung east of Hatteras, north to Nova Scotia; a rare vacuum effect had been created, sending a whirl of monster rogue waves back in its wake.

"What we're seeing here is extremely rare on the East Coast," John said as a surfer made the drop and rode one wild wave to the screams and cheers of onlookers. "This sort of thing is seen on Maui's north coast in Hawaii, a notorious surf-towing spot—"

"It's called Jaws," Liam said. "For obvious reasons."

"Exactly," John said. "Just like Mavericks—a giant wave spot off Half Moon Bay, just north of San Francisco. Shark infested as well . . ."

"Just like Ghost Hills," Liam said. He had finally logged into the predator program and was looking at the incredible number of purple dots blinking in the immediate area.

"Green dots for whales, purple for sharks?" Rose asked, frowning.

"Yes," Liam said, giving her a reassuring hug.

"So, one of those green dots could be Nanny?"

"She's not here," Liam said, scanning the screen for MM122, Nanny's tag number.

"I'm glad," Rose said. "Because look at all those sharks."

It was true; Liam marked down the identities of all previously tagged sharks, swimming just below the surface: makos, tigers, two bulls, and, circling far beneath the others, two great whites. Some surfers dared the rip, oblivious to what was beneath their boards. Liam felt an adrenaline rush, as if he were riding a monster wave himself.

He thought of the car cruising so slowly down their street. With all the sharks down below in the tumultuous sea, he knew there were human predators much worse. They were just as hungry, just as vicious. Liam put his arm around Rose, held her close. There were fins all around the boat, but he stared past them, straight toward the road that meandered past their borrowed house, all the way back to Lily.

Chapter 9

Lily knew that something big had happened as soon as she stepped off the elevator on Shoreline General's fifth floor. Several doctors were huddled outside Maeve's room. They looked up fast, and her heart started thudding.

"Ms. Malone!" Dr. Mead said. "We were just trying to call you."

"What is it?" she asked, steadying herself against the wall.

"Good news," she said. "Your grand-mother has been responsive today."

"She's out of the coma?"

"Not completely," Dr. Mead said with a

touch of hesitation in her smile. "But she opened her eyes, looked around, and responded with marked improvement to some neuro tests."

"Did she say anything?"

"She said 'Mara,'" Dr. Mead said, smiling for real now.

"I have to see her," Lily said.

"Of course you do," Dr. Mead said, and she and the other doctors stepped aside for Lily to enter the room.

Maeve was having a white dream. She had had them her whole life, from the time she was very young and struggling to wake up from a very sound sleep. White dreams usually came on nights before exciting, wonderful days. For example, Maeve had had a white dream the night before she went to the statewide spelling bee in fourth grade, and won on the word "pyrometallurgical." She had had one the night before she won a tennis match her senior year at Black Hall High School. And very early in the morning of the day she married her husband.

White dreams were harbingers of great joy. They came in different forms—they might take place amid light-infused cumulus clouds, or in the sea foam of gentle waves off the west coast of Corsica, or in the softest white feathers of a dove's wings—but the feeling they imparted was always the same. They filled the dreamer with the most exquisite sensations of life— every particle of existence that filled a person's soul with love and light and wonder, and made getting up in the morning worth doing.

Today's white dream took place in a garden. Maeve stood on a path surrounded by white roses. She felt the weight of her clippers in one hand, and she heard the reassuring slap, slap of the waves on the rocks down front. It was her own garden, and she was pruning the White Dawns, climbing the trellis by the stone chimney. The air was brilliant and clear, softened with salt. Her hair was white, and so was that of the woman working beside her. Clara, of course.

They didn't even have to speak. They were a team. Oh, they had had their fights over the years. They didn't see eye to eye about everything, that was for sure. But in white dreams, all strife is secondary to love.

"Mara," Maeve said, clipping back some thorns and briars.

"That means 'sea,'" Clara said. "In Gaelic."

"Ard na Mara," Maeve said, "is where my son and his wife died in Ireland."

"But you sound so happy!"

"I am," Maeve said. "I'll see him soon."

"You can't leave now," Clara said cheerily. "Your granddaughter is here."

"Mara," Maeve said, and heard herself say, her voice echoing in her ears, as if she were half awake, as if the white dream were coming to an end, as if real life were calling her down from the bliss of it all. "Mara, Mara . . ."

"Granny," came the voice, and it wasn't Clara's. "Granny, I'm here!"

"Sweetheart," Maeve said. Someone squeezed her hand. Oh, it felt so wonderful and real. She would know that touch anywhere! It was the hand she had held on walks to school and the beach, the hand she had held at doctors' visits and dentist appointments, the hand she had held at the funerals of her son and daughter-in-law.

"Can you hear me?" the voice asked. It

wasn't Clara—this wasn't a dream. Maeve blinked—oh, it couldn't be. . . .

"Mara?" she asked.

"It's me, Granny!" she said, sounding so happy and excited. Maeve blinked her eyes, trying to focus and register. She coughed, and the chemical taste—that sweet syrupy air she had drunk down like a potion—came back, filled her senses, made her dizzy all over again. She couldn't quite do it, not now, not yet . . . soon, she thought. Don't leave, don't go away, just give me five more minutes. . . .

"Wake up, Granny." Mara's low voice. "Please, wake up. I want to see you, want to tell you about Rose. She's nine, Granny. She's so beautiful."

"Rose," Maeve murmured, back in the garden, the scent of flowers so heavy, pulling her back to sleep, away from the beautiful voice, Mara's voice. She struggled to open her eyes, look at the face of the person sitting there; oh, if only she could lift her eyelids, they were so heavy, and the smell was overpowering. . . . What had Mara told her he'd said once, so long ago: *White roses bruise so easily. . . .*

"Granny!" Mara said, her voice rising.

"Stay with me, wake up! I need you, Granny!"

White roses bruise so easily. . . .

The white dream dissolved into darkness, and Maeve knew—she had to warn Mara. She had to wake up, do whatever it took, warn her darling granddaughter that the danger was back, and that she had to do whatever she could to protect herself and her child.

But sleep was too strong to fight, and it bound her up and took Maeve deeper, back to where no one could reach her for now.

Lily's first instinct was despair, but Dr. Mead, the neurologist, tried to assure her that it was common for coma patients to go in and out of consciousness for a while before coming fully awake. Holding on to her words was very hard—her hopes had been so far up when she'd seen her grandmother's soft blue eyes—for the first time in nine whole years—and heard that familiar voice she thought she'd never hear again whisper her name.

Shaken, she decided to go down to the cafeteria for a cup of tea. She waited in line, aware of people whispering as she passed. Choosing the tea, filling a cup with boiling water, she tried to keep her hands from trembling and spilling the water. She found an empty table at the far end of the room, with windows overlooking the parking lot.

"Hello, Lily."

Her name was new, but the voice was old. She felt a trickle of fear run like an ice cube down her back. Her breath stopped cold—just like Rose's when she was a baby, unable to get air into her lungs. One word—her new name—and she felt the old familiar terror.

"Edward," she said.

"Well," he said, towering over her. He looked pale, older. He had lost his boyish sparkle. There were lines around his eyes and mouth. Or maybe it was just the moment—Edward had always been able to transform and morph, almost before her very eyes.

She held on to her Styrofoam cup. It was filled with boiling water. She held it in her hands, fingers wrapped around it, letting herself actually feel it. She thought maybe she was going into shock, and holding on to the hot cup was grounding her. She could throw it at him, she thought. Right now, and escape.

"My wife," he said. "I never thought I would see my wife again."

"What do you want?" she asked without looking up at him.

"What do I want?" he asked. "Hmm. That's a good question. I'd like to know what happened. Why you ran away from me. What did I do that was so terrible?"

"We're alone here, Edward," she said. "You know and I know the truth. Let's not pretend otherwise. We were both there."

"You humiliated me," he said. "No, worse than that . . . 'humiliated' doesn't really start to cover—you let me think that you were dead. And you let me be investigated for your murder."

She wanted to block her ears; she knew she had to stop him before he got going. Yet she couldn't help feeling curious, fascinated by his presence—just like staring at a shark's fin circling the boat on a summer day, or a copperhead sunning itself on a shady stretch of road, there was something irresistible about the most dangerous crea-tures. Almost as if normal people couldn't quite fathom sharing their existence with something so pretty and deadly and right there in the open.

"Edward," she said, "What are you doing here?"

"The newspapers said you came home because your grandmother was in the hospital. I've come to visit her. We've stayed in touch, you know, Maeve and I."

Lily wanted to jump up and scratch his eyes out. Her pulse shot up, her breathing went crazy, but she held on to her cup to keep herself steady. She could almost hear her grandmother's voice telling her to stay calm, not give him the satisfaction of seeing her true feelings.

"Did Maeve tell you I visited?" he asked pleasantly.

Lily stared into her cup. Why hadn't he mentioned Rose? Maybe Liam was wrong. Maybe the person in Rhode Island hadn't been Edward after all. If Edward knew about Rose, why wasn't he asking about her?

He chuckled slightly. "Of course she didn't," he said. "Maeve didn't know you were alive. You kept her in the dark, just like the rest of the world. So much for the close Jameson family."

"You put her here," she said.

He smiled, sending a chill down her spine.

"Guess who I saw this morning?" he asked.

Lily's mouth was dry. She sipped again, thinking *Don't react, don't blush, don't give him any clue that Rose exists.* Edward was the most instinctive person she had ever met. He had eyes in the back of his head and nerve endings that never quit.

"A girl with green eyes," he said.

She felt the blood coursing through her body, a rush that made her feel dizzy. She stared at him, and with the eye contact, his face turned cold and hard.

"You know what's the most unforgivable? The cruelest thing anyone has ever done to me?" he asked. "It was when you pretended to love me, and then just treated me like dirt. You don't know what's coming, Lily. Just like I didn't know that you were going to walk out on me."

Lily was shaking. Across the room, Patrick Murphy was coming through the door. He saw them and crossed the room in two seconds flat. At six-three, he towered over Edward. The tension between them was tight and ugly, but it gave Lily the first chance she'd had to actually study her onetime husband.

At five-eight, he was as muscular as ever. He was tan, and he wore chinos and a blue polo shirt with a New York Yacht Club insignia and the Rolex watch she'd given him while they were still together. His brown hair was longer, still wiry, gray at the temples. His hazel eyes were still bright and piercing, but there were bags and pouches underneath—he looked as if he'd done some drinking. He probably hung around with a swanky boating crowd, she thought. She thought of the lies he had told her about his sea captain great-grandfather.

"Well," Patrick said. "Look who's here. How's life treating you, Edward?"

"Fine," he replied in an absolutely clipped tone. He stared Patrick straight in the eye for no more than two seconds, then looked everywhere but at him.

"Doing a lot of golfing these days with all that free time? Sailing, maybe? Got yourself a big boat?"

"Big enough," Edward said. Then he smiled, as if he'd just thought up the best joke in the world. "Bigger than yours."

"Huh," Patrick said, glaring. "What are you doing here?"

"As I told Lily," he said, "I'm visiting Maeve."

"No you're not," Patrick said. "There's a police investigation."

"But you're off the police force," Edward said, smiling—with a hint of the old charm, the rippling delight he could bring to a statement. "I guess spending most of a decade trying to nail an innocent man for a murder that never happened didn't do wonders for your career."

"Stay away from Maeve and her family," Patrick said, staring steadily into Edward's eyes.

"Really? Do you plan to stop me?"

"Absolutely," Patrick said, smiling now. "They found your prints on Maeve's hot-water heater. You're going to have to answer some questions."

"I adjusted her thermostat," Edward said, glaring. "I'm happy to admit that. Her granddaughter wasn't there to help her, so I did!"

"My grandmother would never take your help," Lily said. "No matter what she needed, she would never ask you. You're lying."

Suddenly Edward's face turned bright red, the way it always did whenever she had challenged him. His lips thinned, and his hazel eyes turned black with rage. She saw the hate building in him, coming from that secret pool deep inside, and she felt a quick rush of fear.

"You think I'm lying? Why don't you ask Maeve?" Edward asked, stepping forward.

Lily felt as if he'd punched her in the stomach. He knew Maeve was in a coma.

"Come on, Lily. Let's go upstairs and see Maeve," Patrick said, taking her arm.

Lily nodded, still watching Edward. As she backed away, he tracked her with his eyes.

"Stay away, Edward," Patrick said. "There's an investigation going on."

"I think I *will* stay away," Edward said, staring at Lily. "I have something better to do. Someone better to visit."

Lily wanted to spring at him, but suddenly he turned and walked away fast. Lily made a small sound—something between fear and frustration—and Patrick looked down at her.

"What was that all about?" Patrick asked.

"He saw Rose today," Lily said. "This morning. He followed me to Rhode Island last night. I thought I saw a car, but then it seemed to disappear. I was so excited about seeing Rose and Liam, I just wasn't paying enough attention." She raised her hands to her head, twisted them into her hair. "After all these years I led him straight to her."

"How do you know he saw her?"

"Someone stopped to talk to Rose, out in the yard. Liam told me he thought it was Edward—and Edward just told me he'd seen 'a girl with green eyes.'"

"Playing a game with you," Patrick said, eyes narrowing.

"What's he going to do?" Lily asked.

Patrick shrugged. "I don't like this, that's for sure. It haunted me for years, wondering what he did to you. And now, knowing Marisa, I see it even more. There's something in that man that made two women like you run as far as they could."

"Is what you said true? About his fingerprints?" Lily asked.

Patrick shook his head. "Nah. But his reaction was interesting, wasn't it? The point is, the police don't want him anywhere near

Maeve. I'll call them." He looked down at Lily. "You know what I noticed? He called you Lily so easily."

She nodded, her pulse still racing.

"He knew you as Mara. It's harder for me to get used to your new name, and I wasn't married to you."

"I know," she said, staring into Patrick's bright blue eyes. "You see, he wouldn't have any problem with that. A changed name. Everything is interchangeable to him. Names, people, wives. Me, Marisa. Nothing is real to him, none of it matters. Not even Rose."

"No, I suppose not. He's left a lot of wreckage in his wake," Patrick said. "He got right in there, took what he wanted. Cops learn all about the statistics, all about emotional abuse, and how women who are more educated, or make more money than their husbands, are more likely to suffer it. But meeting you and Marisa . . . really woke me up."

"Emotional abuse," she said, an earthquake sending shock waves through her bones. The phrase—language—seemed so subtle, so polite, so *nothing,* compared to the reality of living through it.

"He took everything he could from you,"

Patrick said. "Got his hooks into you—heart, soul, and pocketbook."

"I know," Lily said. "I could never figure out where his paychecks were going. One night I dreamed he had a double life."

"Maeve had us check out that possibility," Patrick said wryly.

"Really?" Lily asked, remembering the desperate conversations she had had with her grandmother.

"Those trips he took," Patrick said.

Lily nodded. Hawthorne was an affluent town, and Edward had told her he had to cultivate business by visiting clients at their other houses. Some of them wintered in Naples or Palm Beach; the Ocean Reef Club in Key Largo; Aspen or Taos. Some had summer places in Edgartown, Sag Harbor, or Nantucket. "Edward was always flying off," she said.

"We never found much evidence of business he actually did in those places," Patrick said.

Lily glanced up, her heart kicking over.

"What?" he asked.

She looked away, wondering whether to tell him or not, remembering her state of mind back then.

"Go ahead," he said. "I want to hear."

"Once I was cleaning out the garage," she said. "I found an old pair of golf shoes. Really old, and mildewed, ones he never wore. He kept his good ones in a closet in the apartment. I started to throw them away, and something rattled inside. It was an earring."

"Not one of yours?" Patrick asked.

She shook her head, slowly, spinning back, as if in a dream.

"No. I held it in my hand. . . . It wasn't valuable or anything. Just cheap silver metal, with rhinestones."

"Did you ask him about it?"

"Yes. He said he had no idea where it came from. But his eyes—" She shuddered. "His eyes turned black, as if he had a monster inside. He was furious that I'd found the earring."

"What did you do?"

"I threw out the old shoe, and the earring." She dug her nails into her palms, so Patrick couldn't see. She had been so scared, at such a deep level. She had never let the thoughts come into shape until she got away from Edward, until she'd run away to Nova Scotia.

"Did you ever find another earring?"

"Yes. In the toe of the same golf shoes. He must have dug them out of the garbage after I threw them out. I came across them in the back of the closet, on his side with all his old sneakers. There were three mismatched earrings in there. The original one with rhinestones, and two others. All pierced, dangling. Only one of them was made of real gold. The others were costume jewelry."

"Did you think he was having affairs?" Patrick asked. "When he went away on those trips?"

Lily shook her head, tears flooding her eyes. "No," she said. "I thought he was killing women."

Patrick's silence was deafening, but his eyes were so kind. After a minute, he handed her his handkerchief.

"I'm so sorry," he said, "for how scared you have been."

Lily buried her face in her hands.

"He's very careful and methodical," Patrick said. "We looked into every trip he took, every city he visited. He had an explanation for everything."

"Everything?"

Patrick paused. "There was nothing we could nail him for, Lily. Let's just say he has a nasty history."

"Patrick, what if he comes after Rose?" Lily asked.

Patrick glanced over, surprise in his blue eyes. "What do you mean?" he asked.

"I mean, what if he decides he wants her in his life? What if he decides to try for custody?"

Patrick blinked slowly. His gaze was gentle, but he seemed to be looking at Lily as if he thought she were kidding, or half mad.

"It's not 'if,' Lily," he said softly. "It's 'when.' You know that, don't you?"

Chapter 10

Probable Cause rocked in the wake of a passing cabin cruiser, causing Patrick to bump against the chart table. He glared at the cruiser's transom, tempted to untie the lines and go charging after it and tell the captain to slow down. The truth was, he'd been feeling pent up for days.

Seeing Edward at the hospital had just made things worse—knowing what Lily had experienced and was still going through, and realizing that Marisa was still in exile so far north, far from her home and worried about her sister. He really wished he'd been able to nail that creep on something, years ago. He hated the fact that Lily and her family were in limbo, waiting for the other shoe to drop.

His cell phone rang, and he answered.

"Hello?" he said.

"Patrick Murphy, was I surprised to hear from you!"

"Jim Hanley?"

"You bet. How are you?"

"I'm great, Jim. Retired now."

"Catching fish instead of bad guys?" Jim asked, laughing.

"That's about the extent of it," Patrick said. "How about you?"

"Oh, working a fraud case," Jim said, and they talked shop for a while. They'd met eight years ago when Jim had apprehended a Connecticut robbery suspect. Patrick had been the lead detective, and Jim had done his best to get the suspect sent back to New London with as little fanfare as possible. The two of them had worked well together.

"Sorry it took me so long to get back to you on your message," Jim said finally, "but I wanted to check things out. To be honest, I thought I'd gotten it wrong the first time—

your message said Samantha Mahon was still in Peru—"

"That's right. Traveling with Global Care, from the university . . ."

"I called over there, they wouldn't talk to me," Jim said. "So I looked Samantha up in the phone book, took a ride over to her house. She lives in a two-family house, not far from the hospital."

"What do you mean—she was there?"

"That's right. Just came from seeing her today. She got back from Peru a week ago."

Patrick's stomach fell. That was before he'd talked to Marisa—her sister had returned home and not even told her. He thought of Marisa and Jessica checking e-mail, feeling excited about the possibility of Sam heading up to Cape Hawk when she returned to the States, and here she'd been back a week already.

"What did she say to you?" he asked.

"Not much," Jim said. "I pretty much had to tell her the truth, to explain why Baltimore PD cared about her whereabouts."

"Yeah? What'd you tell her?"

"That her sister was worried enough about her to send the cops. I told her she should give her sister a call."

"How did she react?"

"She said something strange," Jim said, pausing.

"What?"

"She said that her sister was lost. And then she closed the door in my face."

"Wow," Patrick said. "That's cold."

"Yeah. Family feuds are weird things. That's what it sounded like to me. You want her address and number, or do you just want to give it a rest?"

"Why don't you give it to me?" Patrick said, writing it down. "And while you're at it, why don't you keep tomorrow night free? We can go to some crab place on the harbor, and you can tell me about your fraud case."

"You've got a hankering for crabs?" Jim asked.

"I've got a friend who misses her sister," Patrick said. "And she isn't lost at all. See you tomorrow."

Lily sat at her grandmother's bedside. The air-conditioning hummed, the monitors beeped, and the lights were dim. The nurse had asked her to leave, telling her visiting hours were over, but something in Lily's face had made the nurse leave the room, gently closing the door behind her.

Holding Maeve's hand, Lily tried to will her awake. She needed her so much. She needed help in knowing what to do. One man had done so much harm to Lily and this woman she loved like a mother. And now he was setting his sights on Rose.

"Granny," Lily said, "please wake up. I need you."

Maeve stirred, her mouth twitching. Lily could almost believe she was listening, trying to come out of her deep sleep. What had Edward done to her?

Seeing Edward again had left her feeling frayed and raw. In spite of Patrick's assurance that he would not bother her here, that police were keeping an eye on him, she jumped at footsteps in the hallway, and when shadows fell across the door to Maeve's room.

He was so good at convincing people that he was good and kind, she could imagine him talking his way past the nurses. At one time, he had made her feel so safe. The way he had held her at night, stroking her hair, wanting to hear about her family, her upbringing, her terrible sadness at losing her parents.

She remembered lying in his bed in the apartment he rented in Hawthorne, the week after they'd returned from Washington, right after Christmas. He had listened, holding her. She'd talked about painting and needlepointing canvases with pictures that told stories.

Images of the shoreline—the Connecticut Impressionists at their easels by the banks of the Lieutenant River; children playing on the beach at Hubbard's Point; sailboats frostbiting in Hawthorne Harbor.

"I just love telling stories, and doing the work," she'd said. "Especially, I love the people I meet."

"I hope they pay you what you're worth," he'd said.

He'd drawn her out, getting her to admit she earned a good living, printing her canvases and selling them to fine gift shops up and down the East Coast, from Bar Harbor to Palm Beach.

He was a stockbroker at Connecticut–Wall Street Associates. Although he had worked at several places after graduating from Harvard, this firm was the best, he said. He had wealthy clients who treated him like a friend—or even a son.

"I coach Little League too," he said. "And basketball. Trying to give kids some of the . . ." He paused, kissing her forehead in a thoughtful way. "Let's just say, some of the advantages I never had."

"But you went to Harvard," she said.

He laughed. "On a baseball and rugby scholarship," he said. "My parents couldn't have afforded it otherwise. Believe me, the only college my parents ever saw was the one where my mother mopped floors. My father's institution of higher learning was Somers Prison."

"I'm so sorry," she said, shocked.

"Well, it taught me where I didn't want to go in life," he said, kissing her head again. "And my father's chaplain was a great guy—he used to sort of mentor me while my father was 'unavailable.' Showed me that service is the only way to go in life—helping others, you find your own way."

"That's such a wonderful attitude," Mara said.

"My life hasn't been easy," Edward said, rolling over so he could look straight into her eyes. She remembered the sweetness in his gaze, the all-consuming love she felt flowing from him into her. "I was beaten when I was young, Mara. I won't tell you the details—I want to spare you them."

"Edward!"

"I would never, ever hurt a soul," he said, stroking her cheek so tenderly, as if she was the most precious person in the world to him. "That's what my childhood taught me. To show love, and be gentle."

"You *are* gentle," she'd said.

He nodded. "I want to be even more so," he said. "Help show me how?"

"I don't have to," she said, so touched by his openness and honesty. She had always kept her own pain locked deep inside, but now she told him about her parents' drowning.

"We've both been through a lot," he'd said, his mouth pressed into her neck. She felt his cheeks, moist against her skin, and she sensed him trying to keep from breaking down. "I've never met anyone who understands me the way you do. It's as if we were meant to be together."

His words made her wonder. Was this what love was like? Letting your guard down and maybe beginning to have faith that the world was not such a bad place after all?

"I love you," he had said.

And the words were out before Mara could even think about holding them back—"I love you too." The first time she had ever said them to a man.

"I want to be with you forever," he said.

Mara felt a shiver—between thrill and fear—down her spine. Wasn't he moving a little too fast?

He had a photograph on his apartment wall—a beautiful old sepia-toned photo, of a whaling ship covered with ice. Tall cliffs rose behind it, everything glittering in ice. The ship's name, *The Pinnacle,* was lettered on the transom. Mara stared at the picture—this image of endless, brutal winter, and wondered whether two people could keep each other warm and happy in life.

"My great-grandfather's whaling ship," he said, following her gaze.

"Really?"

He nodded, gazing at the picture, as if it were a window into another, better world. "He was the captain—I'm named after him. Back in the early nineteenth century, our family was very wealthy, respected by everyone. Edward Hunter was an adventurer and an explorer. On some maps, it shows that there are straits near Tierra del Fuego named after him."

"That's incredible," she said.

"I let him be my guide sometimes," he said. "When I'm feeling overwhelmed, I just think of him at the helm, steering through terrible ice in the Arctic. I don't know what happened to our family. We were so respected—and then we crashed somehow. I actually feel sorry for my parents. But my North Star is him—Captain Edward Hunter."

"That's how I feel about my grandmother."

"Take me to meet her," he said.

She held him, trying to get her pulse to slow down. Granny had been saying the same thing. She'd been so thrilled to know that Mara had met someone—and relieved to know that he lived locally, in Hawthorne, just up the Connecticut River Valley from Black Hall, instead of far away.

"I'm not good enough for her, right?" he asked, pulling back.

"Of course you are."

"Because I'm a stockbroker and I went to

Harvard, and because my great-grandfather was a sea captain?"

She laughed, kissing his lips. "No," she said. "Because you're a good person."

His reaction rocked her—his eyes filled, as if no one had ever said that to him before. He held her so tight, she could hardly breathe.

"You believe in me," he said. "That means everything to me."

"I'm glad," she said, feeling overwhelmed and unsure.

"I want us to be together forever," he murmured. "Till we go into the ground together."

The phrase had chilled her. Yet she'd ignored her own inner sense of alarm, telling herself it meant that he loved her, that his feelings for her went beyond anything she had yet known.

There were so many ways she had sold herself out. Ignoring small things, telling herself they didn't matter, even that first day when she'd seen the cold fury in his eyes at the airport taxi stand.

Now, staring at her grandmother sleeping in her hospital bed, Lily thought of how quickly everything had happened, and how often she had pushed away big and small warning signs. Like how often he left his jobs, how the intervals between them grew longer and longer. How, after a while, it seemed easier to just put his name on her accounts than to keep giving him money to pay the bills.

Like his comment at their wedding: *White roses bruise so easily.*

Patrick had mentioned Edward's nasty history. Lily knew about his pattern of violence toward women all too well. On their wedding night, Edward told her about an old girlfriend, Judy Houghton. They hadn't exactly lived together, but he stayed with her most nights. She'd had a big old Victorian house in Haddam, inherited from her great-aunt. Judy had gone out one night, to the Hawthorne Inn. When she came home, Edward said he smelled another man on her. She got angry at him for accusing her, and he punched her.

"Oh my God," Mara said, covering her mouth with her hand.

"Her jaw was broken. Her mother called the police on me. It was between me and Judy, but her mother was always getting involved. She didn't understand, Mara. She never understood any of it, but she was al-

ways sticking her nose in. It was her inter-
fering that broke us up."

"But Edward—" Mara hardly knew where
to start. Why had Edward never even mentioned Judy until now? And why would he
tell her this story on their wedding night?

"I would never do that to you," he said,
soothing her, brushing her hair back from
her eyes. "Please don't worry, or be scared.
You're nothing like Judy."

"Edward—no matter what she did, she
didn't deserve to be punched!"

His eyes had flickered—she saw just a
hint of the blackness she'd spotted at their
first meeting. "She cheated on me," he said.

"But still. If a man ever hit me, ever laid
one hand on me—I would leave him," she
said. "In one second flat."

Edward had gazed at her, long and slow.
She felt almost like a fly being eyed by a
lizard trying to decide whether to eat her or
not. But then the spell broke. He smiled.
Thinking of his smiles now, she saw that he
had a repertoire—should he pull out the
flashy boyish grin, or the slow seductive
melting lip twist? This was somewhere in
between—détente. A peace accord.

The line in the sand had been drawn.

Edward had let her know that he had fists, and would use them if provoked. She had let Edward know that if he used them on her, she would be out the door.

Important information for both sides. Unfortunately for Mara, she had just put Edward on notice. Otherwise, she might have saved herself a lot of trouble. He might just have gotten mad one day and hit her—and Mara would have been out of there before he'd had the chance to do worse. As it was, she'd let him know he had to find subtler ways to break her spirit.

Gazing at Maeve now, in her hospital bed, Lily felt a lump in her throat. She had been married to Mr. Hyde. Dr. Jekyll had just been one of his masks. It had taken Lily years to figure out that Edward was chipping away at her—so slowly, she barely noticed. He'd found ways to buy time, keep her on the string, throw her little bits of hope so she'd stay another day, week, month, year. How had she ever stayed stupid for so long?

Lily knew that Liam was taking care, keeping watch over Rose. Patrick's words, *It's not "if," it's "when,"* rang in her ears. She had brought the people she loved into the same danger that she had known so long ago. And she didn't know what she could do to protect them. Especially Rose, her Rose.

Chapter 11

Driving down to Baltimore, Patrick kept the windows open and let the wind keep him cool. He had left Flora at the boatyard with Angelo, his friend and sometime dog sitter, because he wasn't sure how long his investigation would take, and he didn't want to leave her shut up in the car. But he missed her company, so when his cell phone rang, he was happy to hear Liam's voice.

"Any more signs of Edward?" Patrick asked.

"Not since that one time," Liam said. "I haven't let Rose out of my sight."

"Good," Patrick said.

"I want to be with Lily in Hubbard's Point," Liam said. "But she thinks that keeping Rose away is somehow safer."

"She might be right," Patrick said. "Edward can't be in two places at once. I think the reason he was at the hospital that day is that he's nervous about Maeve coming out of the coma. She's making progress, and he has to be afraid she'll talk."

"Is there any evidence he was involved?"

"One partial fingerprint on the hot-water heater. It will be interesting to hear what Maeve has to say about what was going on right before she collapsed."

"Do you think she'll wake up, Patrick?"

Patrick drove in silence for a few seconds. He pictured Maeve's bright, determined eyes, thought of the way she protected Lily's secret so selflessly these last nine years. "Don't count her out," he said quietly.

"I hope you're right," Liam said. "For Lily's sake."

"I know. They were very close; this has to be incredibly hard on her. Especially having to worry now about what Edward plans to do about Rose. I think you should stay where you are for now. Just keep a close watch on her. Don't let him near her."

"Don't worry," Liam said sharply. "He'd better not try. Besides, we've spent most of our time on the water, in a friend's boat. In fact, that's one reason I'm calling."

"What is it?"

"There's a guy from Cape Hawk," Liam said. "Gerard Lafarge. He's a fisherman with a bad reputation for netting dolphins and whales. There's an oceanographic anomaly going on here in Rhode Island—big ocean waves pulling in lots of unusual species, lots of activity. . . ."

"Not just in Rhode Island," Patrick said, thinking of how he'd seen thousands of small fish break the water's surface of his normally quiet cove.

"Lafarge isn't fishing, and there's no law against him cruising the area," Liam said. "But he's here for a reason, and I want to know what it is."

"Have you called up to Cape Hawk?" Patrick asked.

"Yes—I've asked my cousin, but he doesn't know anything."

As the Baltimore skyline rose into view, Patrick signaled to get off the highway. He glanced down at the seat beside him, trying to read the address Jim had offered up.

"Look," he said. "There's a chance I'll be heading up to Cape Hawk myself in just a few days. If I do get up there, I'll see what I can find out."

"I'd really appreciate that," Liam said. "Are you going to the ceili?"

"If things work out," Patrick said, following Jim's directions, "I'll be delivering one of the musicians."

Liam thanked him, and they said goodbye.

Once Patrick got off I-95, he began to smell the salt water. He thought about how Marisa had basically followed the Atlantic coastline her whole life. From Newport down here to Baltimore, then north again, through Boston, and up to Cape Hawk. Patrick was the same way, feeling most alive when he was breathing salt air. It spurred him on now as he wound his way through the narrow streets.

He found the address Jim Hanley had given him, drove around the block until he found a parking space. The neighborhood was behind the hospital, and he heard a siren in the distance, getting closer. The frame houses were two-family, neatly kept, with small yards and front porches. Kids played on the sidewalk, and older people sat on the stoops. Patrick walked up the front sidewalk of 64 Fish Street, up the steps, and knocked on the door.

Waiting a few minutes, he felt his heart pounding, just the way it always had when he was on a case and the stakes were very high. He tried to peer through a crack in the curtains at the door window. They were lace, pretty. Although many other houses on the street had gardens or window boxes, this one didn't. He figured that if Sam traveled a lot, she didn't have time to tend flowers.

When she didn't come to the door, he went back to his car. Jim had said six at the Crab Claw, and Patrick was a little early. He drove around the city a little, heading toward the hospital. This was where Marisa had gotten her start as a nurse, he knew. He looked up at the big brick building, wondering how many people she had helped in there.

Maybe Sam was back at work, here in the city. He wondered what had happened between the two sisters, what he was doing here—this was really none of his business. But he couldn't forget the look in Marisa's eyes, when he'd been up in Cape Hawk, and the sound of her voice, singing that song to him over the telephone line, and he just kept driving.

The Crab Claw sat right on the Inner Harbor. Patrick parked and walked down the cobblestone streets, into the raucous bar. He scanned the scene, saw Jim sitting with another man at a table on the deck. Making his way through the crowd, he saw who it was—Jack O'Brien, the assistant district attorney who had helped him with his case several years ago.

"Hey, Patrick, great to see you," Jim said.

"You too," Patrick said, shaking hands. "And, Jack—how are you?"

"Fine, Pat," Jack said. "Jim told me you were in town, so I thought I'd join in. It's been a long time. What's this I hear about you retiring?"

"The time had come," Patrick said, grinning. "Too much police work, not enough life." They caught up on the case they had shared, Patrick telling them that the suspect they'd caught was still in Somers, doing fifteen years for bank robbery. They asked him about Mara Jameson, and he filled them in on how she had returned as if from the dead. The waiter came and took their order, and Patrick sipped his Coke, watching boats in the harbor.

"So, you're retired," Jim said, "but you're still doing police work."

"Not really," Patrick said. "I'm just looking for a friend's sister."

"Yeah, Jim tells me you're looking for one of the Mahon girls," Jack said. "The Fallen Angels."

"You know them?"

"I did. And I remember their music even now—fifteen years later. They played in a pub just around the corner from the court-house. Half the cops and lawyers were in love with them. Sam went out with a friend of mine for a little while, right after Patty first moved away."

Patrick did his best to interview his old friend as subtly as possible. Sam Mahon had stayed on staff at Johns Hopkins after graduation, heading up a team of nurses that would travel to South America, Africa, and the Far East as they were needed and funding would allow.

"She missed her sister a lot," Jack said. "I remember that so well. They'd been insep-arable. Sam had come to Johns Hopkins because her big sister was already here. They were really close. So when Patty got married and moved to Boston, Sam had a tough time."

"She didn't play music after that?" Patrick asked.

"Not unless her sister came back to visit. They had a few reunion shows. Everyone loved them."

"What happened?" Patrick asked.

"I don't know. Patty's first husband died, and she married someone else—too soon, maybe. He was a jerk, I think. Sam didn't like him, didn't like what he was doing to her sister."

"Did he beat her?" Jim asked.

Patrick sipped his Coke. Cops always asked that—"Did he beat her?" As if the only damage could be done with fists. "No," Patrick said.

"That's right, you know her," Jack said.

"Yes," Patrick said. "She's the reason I'm here. She misses her sister. There's a music festival up in Nova Scotia, and she's trying to get Sam to come up and play with her."

"That's something I'd like to hear," Jack said. "I'm married now, two kids, happy and settled down. But there was something about hearing those two sing that made men turn stupid and go crazy. . . ." He slid a tape across the table to Patrick.

"What's this?"

"It's a bootleg tape of a Saint Paddy's Day show they did at the Blarney Stone, many years ago now. I've had it since then, but my wife doesn't like me to play it. She thinks the sisters sound too sexy for her husband to be listening to. Why don't you take it?"

"Thanks," Patrick said, slipping it into his shirt pocket.

As seagulls cried overhead, the waiter delivered their dinners. Platters of hard-shell crabs, baskets of french fries, and coleslaw. The three men cracked the crabs with mallets, talking about their lives, families, and cases. When they'd finished, Patrick thanked them for everything, said he hoped he'd see them sooner the next time.

He drove back to 64 Fish Street, listening to the tape Jack had given him. Beautiful, haunting notes played on a pair of fiddles . . . and then the sisters' voices singing "Cliffs of Dooneen."

God, his knees went weak. The breeze blew in his hair through the car's open window. Marisa's voice sang harmony with her sister's. It trembled with emotion, and he felt she was with him now, whispering the sweet, romantic lyrics right into his ear. The recording quality was pretty bad—someone must have taped it right there in the crowded bar. The sound of glasses clinking and people talking came through, but nothing could block that strain of pure longing in her voice.

She might well be singing about Cape Hawk—the cliffs, the mountains, the foam. He could almost see her standing in her cottage door, feel her in his arms. How would she feel if he was able to convince Sam to come? He wanted to do that for her. . . .

Finding a parking spot a block away, he popped the tape out and stuck it in his pocket for luck. Then he walked up the steps to Sam's house again. This time there were lights on inside. When he knocked, he heard footsteps.

After a few seconds, a woman opened the door. Her hair was soft, golden red, much lighter than Marisa's. But Patrick would have known her anywhere; the family resemblance was in the eyes—kind, curious, and full of good humor.

"Hello," she said.

"Hi," he said. "I'm Patrick Murphy."

"A good Irish name." She smiled.

"You're Samantha Mahon?" he asked.

"Yep, that's me. What can I do for you?"

"I was hoping you could play me some Celtic music," he said.

She laughed, but looked a little skeptical. "Time was, maybe I would have, but not now. Do I know you from somewhere?"

"You don't know me," he said.

"Then—" she said.

"I'm a friend of your sister's," he said.

"Is she okay? Is Gracie?" The question flew out, almost before she could think.

"They're fine," he said. "Although I think of Gracie as Jessica."

Her smile went away. She studied him, her green eyes narrowing. Her jaw was clenched, and she had one hand on the door, ready to close it.

"Why are you here?" she asked.

"Because she wants you to come up to Nova Scotia—Cape Hawk," he said. "She thinks you're still in Peru, and she's sitting by her computer waiting for you to send her an e-mail from the back of beyond."

"That's between me and my sister," she

said, emotion rising in her face. "You'd better go now."

"Please, Sam."

Her hand was firmly on the door, and she'd pulled it nearly closed. She was behind it, and he couldn't see her face. He heard her breathing, high and rapid. He could almost feel her trying to decide.

"Are you her boyfriend?" she asked.

Patrick felt surprised by the pointed question. "No," he said. "Just a friend."

She hesitated, but for some reason, that tipped the balance. She opened the door, and he walked in.

The living room was small, with a sofa and two chairs. She gestured for him to sit in one of the chairs, and she took the other. He watched her perch on the edge, as if she hadn't really committed to sitting yet. He gazed around the room, decorated with bright blankets and banners, obviously from her travels. A violin case lay on top of the bookshelf.

There were framed photos on one wall, and he scanned them and saw several of Marisa. Patrick took a deep breath and looked Sam in the eye.

"You and your sister used to live here together?" he asked, remembering what Jack had said.

"Yes. This was her apartment first." She pointed at a small mahogany table, some brass candlesticks, a crystal owl. "That was our grandmother's silver chest. The candlesticks and owl were Patty's—she bought them when she first moved in, to make her apartment feel grown-up and cozy. I moved to Baltimore to be with her. I became a nurse because of her."

"You were inspired by your big sister."

"Yes."

"She misses you, Sam."

Sam looked down at her feet; Patrick watched her composing herself and realized how much she resembled Marisa: the shape of her face, oval with high cheekbones and pale, freckled skin. Green eyes, a wide, expressive mouth. But where Marisa's hair was dark, reddish brown, Sam's was bright copper.

"I know you mean well," Sam said. "But you really don't understand."

"Can you tell me?"

She tilted her head, opened her mouth. For a second he thought she was going to tell him it was none of his business. But she didn't.

"How can I explain it," she began, "to someone who didn't know her before, who didn't know what she used to be like? She was like a one-woman high-wire act. You should have seen her—working the ER by day, bringing down the house by night. She was so talented—this'll sound weird, if you're not in the field, but she could get an IV line in a vein and the patient wouldn't even feel it. She could comfort the littlest kids, make them smile even while the doc was stitching them up. She loved everyone she treated, and they loved her."

Patrick listened. He pictured Marisa's smile, and he could believe it.

"She helped found Horizon House, right around the corner from the hospital. It's health care for low-income women and kids. People who can't afford the kind of help they need." Sam looked down, seeming to study her shoes for a long time. When she looked up, her eyes were glittering. "I was so proud of her for that," she said.

"Is that why you do the kind of work you do?" he asked.

"Someone has to," she said, letting the rest of the sentence hang in the air.

"Because Marisa doesn't?" he asked.

She let out something between a snort and a laugh. "'Marisa,'" she said. "That nickname used to make us smile. Bono gave it to her in Paris, one drunken night."

"But that's not why she uses it now," Patrick said.

"No, it's not," Sam said. "It's her alias. Want to know the biggest irony? A lot of what Horizon House does is geared toward helping abused women. My sister knew all about the dynamic, and it happened to her anyway."

"Is that what you can't forgive her for?" Patrick asked. The question sounded harsh, even to his ears, and Sam looked as if she'd been slapped.

"You don't know anything," she said. "You don't know my sister and me, the way we used to be." Her face was bright red, her eyes pooling with tears.

"Then tell me," he said. "Please?"

"We were so close," Sam said, her face still flushed. "We'd tell each other everything. If I needed her, she'd be on the next train. When Paul—her first husband—died, I took a month's leave, to go up and stay with her and Gracie. They needed me—and I needed them. I loved Paul as if he were my brother." She held in a sob, turning her head.

Patrick sat still, watching her walk over to the wall of pictures, taking down and handing him one of Marisa as a bride, Sam as her maid of honor. The man with Marisa had to be Paul—tall, blond, full of life and joy. Then Sam handed him another—of Sam and her sister holding a baby between them.

"My niece," she said, wiping her eyes. "I loved her as if she were my own. I'm her godmother, and no one ever took that role more seriously."

"I'm sure that's true," Patrick said, watching her stare at the picture.

"After Paul died, my sister was so vulnerable. She was really almost out of her mind—I know, because I was there. Everything was too much for her. That's why I had to stay for a month. She had this investment advisor—"

"Edward Hunter," Patrick said.

Sam looked up, shocked. "We called him Ted. You know him?"

"Yes. I was a detective, and he was a suspect in one of my cases."

"Then I don't need to tell you."

"Nope. You don't."

"He was a user. I held back from telling her what I thought—because she seemed so happy. He was there—right time, right place. She told me he was helping her pick up the pieces. Instead, she shattered into a million more."

"She wouldn't listen to you?"

"She wouldn't even *talk* to me."

Patrick watched the fire return to her green eyes. They flashed with anger as she stared down at the picture of her sister and niece. "He took her away from me," Sam said. "First she stopped calling me. Then she began dodging my calls. Grace would phone me, tell me that her mother was in bed crying. I'd say put her on, but Patty wouldn't take my call. When I'd finally get through to her, she'd say everything was great—she was fine, Ted was wonderful, they were all so happy. I wanted to throw up."

"You must have been really worried."

"Worried and frustrated. Angry. I actually

considered going up and getting Gracie out of there. I am her godmother, after all."

"Maybe that wouldn't have been such a bad idea."

"After a while, my sister wouldn't let me near her. She was so busy protecting Ted. It was a nightmare."

"I'm sure it was for her too," Patrick said.

Sam gave him a long, hard look. "She made her choices."

"That coming from you?" he asked.

"What do you mean?"

"A world health nurse," he said. "Who cares about the well-being of women. What about your sister?"

"The sister I knew and adored disappeared. She doesn't exist anymore."

"How do you know?" Patrick asked. "You haven't seen her in a long time."

"I can't stand to see her," Sam said. "It's too hard, seeing a woman who's afraid of her own shadow. And teaching her daughter to be afraid of hers."

"That's what trauma will do to people," Patrick said. "That's why they need their loved ones around, to help them get better. I hear that music is a really good way to get through to the other side."

Sam shook her head. Patrick recognized the stubbornness of a fellow redhead.

"The Cape Hawk ceili is supposed to be great. There's a fierce competition, and your sister wants to enter. Is that how a woman afraid of her own shadow would act?"

"I'm not going," Sam said.

Patrick took a deep breath. He could see that she was dug in to her position, and he knew better than to argue. Standing up, taking one last look at the picture of her sister, he looked up at her again.

"Got a tape deck?" he asked.

"Why?"

He just tilted his head, and she shrugged. He reached into his pocket, handed her the tape. She pushed PLAY, and suddenly the room was filled with music and fallen angels:

> You may travel far,
> Far from your own native home,
> Far away o'er the mountains,
> Far away o'er the foam,
> But of all the fine places I've ever
>   been,
> Oh, there's none can compare
> With the cliffs of Dooneen.

Patrick watched tears spill from her eyes, and he felt them in his own. He wondered if she was remembering the night she and her sister had sung those words. He knew she was hearing the harmony between them, and he saw her eyes slide to the photo, and then to her fiddle.

Clearing his throat, Patrick handed her his card.

"If you change your mind," he said, "I'm driving up in a few days."

"Thank you," she said, taking the card, placing it on the table. She didn't smile, and she didn't even glance at it.

Patrick wanted to ask her for the tape back, but she didn't offer. He figured she needed it more. They said goodbye, and as Patrick walked down the steps, he could almost feel her eyes on the back of his head. Behind him, the music rose into the night, and Patrick could still hear it, even as he drove away.

Chapter 12

Right after Lily got home that evening, she took a swim. The salt water washed over her, cooling her skin and easing her mind. In the bay, she felt connected to Liam and Rose. She bobbed in the small waves, imagining that they must have come from the east, from the Atlantic. They must have passed Rhode Island.

Small fish bumped her legs, but she didn't even flinch. Maybe they were part of the Ghost Hills phenomenon. Maybe they were harbingers of Nanny—Lily closed her eyes and thought that if only she could see Rose's beloved beluga, everything would be fine. She needed something as magical as Nanny to make her believe that all would be well.

She climbed out and toweled off, then sat on the porch steps. Hearing voices, she felt her heart skip. She knew that Edward would return—it was just a matter of time. But glancing through the trellis, she saw Bay and Tara coming down the steps, through the rose garden. They were dressed in shorts and sneakers, and they carried tennis rackets.

"Time to test that backhand," Tara called. "Do you still have your racket?"

"It's nearly dark out," Lily said.

"One of the big changes since you left Hubbard's Point," Bay said, "is lights at the tennis courts."

"Come on," Tara said. "No excuses. Let's go play."

Lily stared at the water. She felt so ragged tonight, after keeping vigil for Maeve, who just wouldn't wake up; she missed her child so badly, her bones ached. And she missed Liam, her only true love, with every breath in her body. She couldn't leave the house again.

"I can't," she said.

"Lily, if there's any change with Maeve," Tara said, "the hospital will call your cell phone. So will Liam, if Rose needs you."

If Rose needs you . . . Lily knew that Rose needed her all the time, just as Lily needed Rose. What was she doing, apart from the people she loved?

"We don't have to play long," Bay said. "Just half an hour."

"We'll wear you out, so you'll sleep better," Tara said, tugging her arm.

"Okay," Lily said slowly. "Let me get dressed and find my racket."

And she did.

The three women hurried down the road with their tennis rackets. Darkness settled on Hubbard's Point, and roses, honeysuckle, and pine scented the salt air. The breeze felt fresh, with a tiny chill to remind them that August was almost over, and September would soon be upon them. Stars twinkled through the branches overhead, and lights had started to come on in the cottages.

With every step, Lily felt younger. Walking the roads of Hubbard's Point, she was a child again. These were her best friends. Her grandmother loved her, and would be watching over her forever. Nothing bad could ever happen.

When they got to the tennis courts, they found them empty. They were old asphalt courts, nothing fancy. Because they were built at the far end of the sandy beach parking lot, they were constantly flooding. The tar would crack, and the beach crew would have to patch it. Tara walked over to a wooden box mounted on a tall pole. She opened the door and flipped a switch. Light flooded down, illuminating the courts.

"Let there be light," Tara said.

"I can't believe the beach sprang for lights," Lily said. "So much has changed from the days when we used to play in the dark. We couldn't even see the ball, but we'd be having too much fun to quit."

"So much has stayed the same, too," Bay said, giving her a quick hug. "We still have fun."

Lily pretended to tie her laces. She didn't want Bay to see her face. Having fun seemed very distant.

"Are we going to play Canadian doubles?" Tara asked. "You and I against Bay?"

"Sure," Lily said. "Whatever you want."

"That's what I want," Tara said, hugging her too, handing her a ball.

Lily jogged to the baseline. The light cast long shadows on the gray court. The lines had been freshly painted, and they gleamed white. Bay bounced the ball on the other side of the net. Somewhere across the swamp, a screech owl cried, a descending trill.

"Are you ready?" Bay asked. "Here it comes."

"Whack the hell out of it," Tara said. "Let the ball have it."

Bay hit, and the ball bounced, and Lily swung her racket. She connected, and the ball sailed back. Bay hit, now to Tara. *Thwack,* the ball returned. Lily's heart pounded. She crouched, ready for her turn.

Tennis came back to her in ten seconds or less. She hadn't played in over nine years, since before Rose was born. How many times had she and her friends played on this very court, hitting the ball until their arms were so tired they couldn't move? Lily had loved the game. She had played in the beach Labor Day tournament nearly every year. She had played in high school, been the number three singles player at Black Hall High.

Thwack, thwack.

She had been in discussions with a New York publisher about launching her own needlepoint magazine, and she had planned a tennis issue. A way to bring women readers, athletes, and needlepointers together. It would have been for spring, April or May. She had envisioned a racket and yellow ball. There would have been interviews with top women players inside. A story about women friends who'd grown up playing tennis together.

Thwack.

Lily stood on the baseline. The ball came, and she hit it hard. It returned, and she hit it harder. Her legs burned. Bay put the ball nearly in the alley, and Lily got to it, hit a backhand. It fired over the net like a bullet. She gritted her teeth, hitting the next and the next. Bay gave her a lob, she put it away. The ball came back, and Lily sent it to the far corner. Bay returned fire, and Lily stuck her racket out.

Tara had stepped off the court. It belonged to Lily now. She smashed every shot she could. She had power in her arm, and it flowed into her racket. *Whack the hell out of it,* Tara had said, and that's what Lily was doing.

She was whacking the hell out of everything Edward had done to her, taken from her. Every hit was for Rose and Maeve. For Liam. For every dream Lily had ever had. For the life that still beat in her body, in spite of everything he had done to quash it. Lily thought of her magazine that never was, of the years she had missed with her friends, of the fact that Liam and Rose were miles away.

"Go for it, Lily," she heard Tara say now.

Hitting the tennis ball, Lily felt sobs welling up from deep inside. The night was silent, except for the owl's call, the sound of the ball bouncing and hitting their rackets, and the breath tearing from Lily's chest as she fought her way back, trying to become that Hubbard's Point girl of long ago, who used to have so much fun.

Driving back from Baltimore, Patrick was all torn up about what had happened. He had failed on his mission. He felt more dejected with every mile he traveled. He knew he should call Marisa, let her know that at least Sam was safe at home, but he just didn't have the heart. When he got to the Black Hall exit, he turned off the highway and headed down the shore road. Picking up Flora at the boatyard, he drove toward Hubbard's Point—he'd check on Lily for Liam, buy some time before he broke the news.

But when he got to Maeve's place and knocked, no one was home. The car was in the turnaround, a light was on in the kitchen, but Lily didn't answer. Patrick's heart thudded—she had disappeared from here once before. He thought of the thumbprint on the hot-water heater and walked around the house, to try to get into the basement.

Maeve's house was almost like a ship; it sat right on the rock ledge, jutting out into Long Island Sound. Although it was dark, the sky was filled with stars, and the almost-full moon had started to rise in the east. Heading through the rose garden, he saw the damnedest thing. Staring at the dark water, he saw it again: a flash of white.

It rose up from the deep, crested the surface. In the moonlight, it looked shiny and hard, almost like a huge, glistening piece of driftwood. A massive tree trunk, stripped of its bark, polished by months in the waves. But as Patrick leaned closer, he saw that it had eyes. Large, liquid dark eyes that blinked at him.

"Holy shit," Patrick said, jumping back.

Flora started to growl. She ran down to the seawall, just above the tidal pools, pacing back and forth. The sea creature didn't move. Unperturbed by one large Labrador retriever, it just rested on the surface of the water twenty yards out, gazing straight at Patrick.

Flora barked. She dug in her front paws, pointing at the leviathan, barking and howling. Patrick was a fisherman; he often took *Probable Cause* out to the Race, to go after stripers. He had once hooked a prizewinning bluefish that weighed in at close to forty pounds. This monster put anything Patrick had ever caught to shame. It had to be four meters long. And he knew, from having been to Mystic Aquarium and having visited Nova Scotia, that it was a beluga whale.

Beluga whales were native to Cape Hawk. While there a month ago, when he first found Lily and Rose, he had heard the whole story about Nanny. Supposedly she had swum down to Boston while Rose had her heart surgery. Could this be the same damn whale, here in the waters of Hubbard's Point? Was this part of the oceanographic anomaly Liam had spoken about?

Wherever it had come from, it didn't seem in a big hurry to leave. Patrick's heart was beating like a snare drum, so fast he could hardly breathe. Flora, on the other hand, seemed to have made her peace with the whale. She lay on the seawall, panting. The whale rose to the surface, eyes on Patrick.

As Patrick followed the whale, he felt his heart start to calm down. In fact, he felt an ease spread through his body that he hadn't felt in a long time. There was something very beautiful about the animal; its eyes looked almost human, as if there was a soul deep inside. It gave him a sense of peace, and he suddenly knew what he had to do.

Almost without thinking, Patrick reached for his cell phone. He dialed a number that he had rarely called before, but that he had somehow committed to memory.

"Hello?" she said.

"Marisa," he said. "It's Patrick."

"Hi, Patrick," she said.

"I had to call you, Marisa," he said. "I took a drive today."

"Really?" she asked. "Where did you go?"

"Baltimore," he said.

"Oh!" she said, sounding excited. "Where I used to live with Sam. She'll be back there soon, unless she comes straight up here, to the ceili."

"Marisa, I went to see Sam," he said.

"But she's in Peru," Marisa said.

Patrick stared out at the whale. Her dark, sweet eyes gazed out from the gentle waves. He wished he could somehow soften what he had to say. He held the phone with both hands, just as he would have held Marisa's hand.

"She's home," he said.

Marisa was silent for a few long moments. "No," she said.

"I'm sorry," he said. "She got home last week."

"Why didn't she call me?" Marisa whispered.

Patrick heard the shock in her voice. He pictured Sam's face, the emotion in her eyes as she'd talked about how her sister had changed. He couldn't bring himself to tell Marisa. He couldn't stand to think of her being so hurt. "I think she's been pretty busy," he said. "The traveling and all . . ."

"What about Gracie?" Marisa asked, slipping up for the first time since Patrick had met her. "Jessica . . ."

"She told me she's her godmother."

"The only person I would ever trust with my daughter," Marisa said, her voice low and lost.

"I know she loves her," Patrick said. "Loves you both."

"Did she say that?"

"She didn't have to," he said. "Her house is full of you. Pictures everywhere. Your brass candlesticks and crystal owl."

"I thought . . ." Marisa said, then paused for a long minute. "I thought she might have gotten rid of them. I think she wants to forget about me—about me and Jess."

"How can she?" Patrick asked, wishing he could hold her. "No one could forget you, Marisa."

He waited for a few seconds, hearing his words sink in. Did she know how much he thought of her? He wanted to tell her that he wanted to listen to her sing all day and night; that he dreamed about her . . . and that he had wanted so badly to bring her sister back to her.

"It was so kind of you to try . . . you didn't have to do that, go see her," she said. "It means a lot to me. Even if . . ."

"Don't give up hope," Patrick said. "Give her a chance to think things over. She's a redhead, remember? We're stubborn as hell."

She laughed a little, and he felt a smile come to his lips, the happiest he'd felt in days. "What do you think I'm looking at?" he asked.

"I can't imagine."

"A white whale," he said. "Right here, off the coast of Connecticut. Not twenty yards away from where I'm sitting."

"Is it Nanny?" Marisa asked, sounding shocked and thrilled.

"I think so," Patrick said. "But why would she be here?"

"Well, probably because of Rose."

"Because of Rose . . ." Patrick repeated. He watched the whale watching him. It was the oddest sensation, as if she actually knew him. Her eyes blinked in the liquid light. They were dark and eloquent, as if the whale somehow knew what Patrick didn't.

"Yes," Marisa said. "What other explanation could there be?"

"I wonder what Liam would say," Patrick said. "He seems to think there's some kind of oceanographic mystery going on around here."

"Well, I agree with him there. Love is always a mystery," Marisa said.

"Love?" Patrick asked, his heart beating harder.

"Why shouldn't it be love? Whales are mammals. They make connections and feel bonds, just the way we do."

Patrick couldn't quite speak, listening to her gentle voice.

"I'm a nurse," she said. "I've studied anatomy. There are plenty of physical similarities. Why not emotional ones?"

Patrick frowned. He had seen the kind of connections humans made. He'd been at many crime scenes where husbands had killed wives, wives had killed husbands, parents had killed children. He had seen every possible permutation of hurt and evil known to mankind. His divorce had left him bitter and afraid to believe in love, yet talking to Marisa filled him with the strangest feeling of peace.

"You don't believe me," she said.

"I want to . . ." he said, trailing off.

"Is she still there?" Marisa asked.

"The whale? Yes," he said, peering into the dark water. There she was, just resting on the surface. The waves and incoming tide would move her toward shore, and she would circle around, just so she could stay facing him. The rising moon cast a silver net all around her, but she was unfettered and free, and just rode the waves.

"Patrick?" Marisa asked after a few seconds.

"I'm here," he said. He stared out over the water. A few fine clouds had blown in, covering the bright moon with gossamer folds. He was afraid the whale might be too hard to see, with the light slightly dimmed, but she was still there.

"Thank you for today," Marisa said. "For going to see Sam."

"You're welcome."

"I just wish . . ." Marisa said.

"What?"

"I just wish you were both coming here," she said. "You and Sam. To the ceili." Then, as if she couldn't speak anymore, she said goodbye quickly, and hung up the phone.

Patrick sat on the porch steps, trying to catch his breath. She had just said she wished he were coming . . . Sam, but him too. He bowed his head, staring at the phone. He hadn't wanted the call to end; he wasn't ready for the connection to be broken.

He took a deep breath. He took a picture of Nanny with his cell phone and sent it to Marisa. He hoped that she would like seeing the whale, that it would remind her that wonderful, unlikely things could happen.

Then he stood up and moved to Maeve's wicker rocker, watching the whale swim in the moon's silver path. He had Marisa's voice in his ear, and he felt it in his pounding heart. He thought of Liam, too far away. Talking to Marisa had made certain things clear to him, so he sent Liam a picture too, along with a quick message. Just then, he heard a puff of air, saw the whale arch her gleaming back and disappear into the black sea.

Patrick sat back, wondering what had just happened.

Chapter 13

As night fell, Liam worked at his desk, collating reports from oceanographers in the field. Rose was out on the screen porch, reading *The Lion, the Witch, and the Wardrobe.* It was her favorite book, reminding her of her best friend, Jessica, and she never got tired of it. Liam knew that the familiar story probably comforted her, and it made him feel good to think of how often Lily had probably read it to her.

His laptop was open, the screen filled with a picture of Nanny sent to him by Patrick Murphy. The picture was a silver blur, with one clear dark eye. Patrick's message read:

Look who dropped by to see the Malone girls. Too bad only one of them is here. Why don't you pack up Rose and bring her home? It's a mistake to stay apart from the people you love—take it from one who knows. Lily really needs you.

Liam stared and stared. All day he'd been amassing data on the Ghost Hills phenomenon—cataloguing all the tagged sharks and whales he and John had been able to identify—but right now he had another project under way.

More than anything, he wanted to take Patrick's suggestion. He couldn't sleep, because all he could think of was Lily. She had been right here, in this house, in his bed. When he lay down on the sheet where she had been, he felt on fire. The pillow smelled like her. Every day the scent faded a little more.

Was Patrick right? Should Liam and Rose return to Hubbard's Point? He needed Lily as much as Patrick said she needed him. But he had to really think this over—he didn't want to underestimate Edward. And Patrick didn't know Lily the way Liam did.

Liam had been there when Lily had given birth to Rose. He had showed up at her cabin in the woods, far down a logging road from anything close to civilization. She had run nearly a thousand miles to get away from her husband, and she was so scared of being found, she would rather give birth in the middle of nowhere than risk going to a hospital.

Liam had boiled water and gotten towels, just like in the movies. Lily was lying on her kitchen floor, bathed in sweat and tears. Liam was little more than a stranger, but he was all she'd had. He remembered how she'd squeezed his hand with every contraction, crying with anguish.

Somehow he'd known that her pain was deeper even than childbirth. She howled, and he heard echoes of terror. He knew he'd never seen a person more alone, and he knew that someone had scared her half to death. She was without a husband, without family, and even before Liam knew her whole story, he knew that he would love her forever.

It didn't matter to him that she had been married before, that she'd never gotten divorced. He didn't care. Liam knew that there were ways of being connected that went beyond ceremonies and licenses. He loved Lily with every part of himself. She owned his heart, and so did Rose. No matter what happened, they were his life.

So time didn't really matter to Liam. His desire for Lily had no bounds. He knew he'd sell his soul to be with her for ten minutes. But that would be as true tomorrow or next year or in twenty years as it was now. She made his skin tingle, and his heart pound, just to think of her.

As much as he wanted to take Patrick up on his idea, Liam knew they had to be very careful. The person who had scared her half to death had been her husband, her baby's father. He had had Lily declared dead, so he could collect on her insurance and cash in her stocks and bonds. Patrick had filled Liam in on all the details.

Lily had existed merely as a food source to Edward Hunter. Liam understood the dynamic very well. Although he studied whales, they were collateral to his main academic focus.

Sharks.

Liam's brother Connor had been killed by the same great white shark that had taken

Liam's arm. Liam knew that sharks ate to live. They patrolled the oceans, always in search of prey. They didn't attack out of any sense of hate. They were emotionless in their quest for food.

Liam knew that Edward Hunter was like a shark. He had targeted Lily because she was a good prospect. He had probably thought he'd live off her for the rest of his life. But unlike sharks, human predators possessed great capacities for rage when thwarted. Liam knew that when she walked out on him, Edward had been viciously angry—and people were still paying for it.

Liam had been quietly researching, and he believed that Edward Hunter was a very specific type of personality. He looked and acted like other people. He knew just what to say and do to get people to trust him. He "groomed" people—Lily, Marisa—even before he'd made his move: listened to them talk, figured out what moved and motivated them, and then appeared to give them what they most wanted.

As Dr. Robert Hare stated on page one of *Without Conscience,* "Everybody has met these people, been deceived and manipulated by them, and forced to live with or repair the damage they have wrought. These often charming—but always deadly—individuals have a clinical name: *psychopaths.* Their hallmark is a stunning lack of conscience; their game is self-gratification at the other person's expense. Many spend time in prison, but many do not. All take far more than they give."

If Liam couldn't literally be with the woman he loved, protecting her with his presence, he would do what he did best—study and learn. Maybe he would find something that would be helpful to her in dealing with Edward. He sat hunched over the books, itching to rip the guy apart.

He knew one thing: he had never felt this way about a shark.

Picking up the phone, he called Lily. The phone barely rang, and then she answered it.

"I want to bring Rose home to you," Liam said without preamble. "We're letting this idiot dictate our lives."

Lily was silent. Liam felt her, a million miles away, lost in her old life. He wanted to reel her back, remind her of what they had, show her how much he loved her, how strong they would be together. Strong enough to face anything.

The rumble of monster waves came through the open window, shook the cottage. Ghost Hills were alive tonight. They pounded the beach, and he felt the rhythm in his body.

"Lily?" he asked.

"I want that," Lily said, her voice so quiet, it was nearly drowned out by the roar of the waves ten miles out at sea. "But I'm afraid for Rose. I have to think, Liam."

"And I have to see you, Lily," he said.

When she hung up, all he could hear was the sound of his own heart. It was pounding, like the carrying echoes of Ghost Hills crashing on the reef. It swamped him and pushed him under, made it impossible to breathe. Liam shut down the computer, walked through the small house, and stood at the open porch door.

Stars flashed overhead. He hoped that Lily could see them. The constellations rose out of the sea, as if living creatures glowing with bioluminescence had flown into the sky. The stars told stories of myth and love. The sea was full of Ghost Hills and white whales. Didn't Lily know what a miracle it all was? He hoped that Nanny was watching over her—because Liam couldn't be there to do it.

Marisa had never seen a Cape Hawk evening like this. The normally sleepy streets were bustling with people, some carrying instrument cases, some running to make their performance times. People picnicked on the lawn of the inn, and down along the wharf. The Nanouk Girls had all come into town to listen to the night's ceili offerings, and Marisa tried to enjoy it all.

They spread their blankets in a row beside the stone fisherman in the village square. Marlena had brought grapes, bread, and cheese, Cindy had brought wine for the grownups and lemonade for the kids, Alison had made a big salad, Anne had raided the inn's kitchen and supplied lobster rolls for everyone. Marisa and Jessica had made Toll House cookies for dessert.

While the others talked, Marisa sat back and watched the musicians. There were so many women, from all over. She wondered how many of them were sisters, traveling all this way to Nova Scotia together. She looked for family resemblances, saw them everywhere. She felt happy for all these women, and she felt a terrible hollow hurt inside, for Sam.

Anne Neill saw Marisa sitting outside the circle, and she edged over. She had big blue eyes, chestnut brown hair pulled back in a French twist. She wore a peach cable knit sweater over lime green slacks—Marisa thought her bright clothes reflected her spirit. Anne was an innkeeper in every sense of the word, and her hospitality showed even when she wasn't at the inn's desk.

"How are you?" Anne said.

"I'm fine," Marisa said, trying to smile. "You've done a wonderful job with the ceili."

"Thank you," Anne said. "It's the most fun part of the year, but it does keep me busy. It's nice to sit down and listen to the music for a while."

Marisa nodded. "I've been to so many. In Newport, and on the Eastern Shore of Maryland, lots in Boston . . ."

"Always with your sister?" Anne asked.

Marisa nodded. She didn't want to cry, so she swallowed hard and looked away.

"We're holding a space on the bill for the two of you," Anne said.

"I don't think," Marisa began, "we'll be needing it."

Anne didn't say anything, but her blue eyes were so warm and kind, her smile so steadying, Marisa felt her heart crack. She heard the women on stage playing "*Taibreamh.*" It was sweet and traditional, and meant "Dreams" in Gaelic, and had always been Sam's favorite lullaby. Tears popped into Marisa's eyes and spilled over, and she thought she might break in two.

"Where's your sister now?" Anne asked gently.

"In Baltimore," Marisa said. "I'd thought she was in Peru. But she came home last week."

"And didn't tell you," Anne said.

Marisa shook her head, picturing Patrick going to the little house on Fish Street, talking to Sam. "A friend of mine found her," she said.

"Are you and Sam very close?" Anne asked.

"We were."

"Sisters," Anne said. "You grow up knowing everything about each other, living in the same house, sharing the same secrets, having the same feelings."

"That was Sam and I," Marisa said, suddenly knowing that Anne had to have a sister. "We were exactly like that."

"When we were young, my sister Emily and I were so close, we did everything together. You and Sam played fiddle, Emily and I did step dancing."

"At ceilis?" Marisa asked.

Anne nodded. "Until she went to college. And then took a job in Toronto, and then moved to Vancouver. It was never the same after that. I felt so abandoned. How could someone I'd spent every free moment with, loved more than anyone—my best friend in the world—just leave me that way?"

"But she wasn't leaving you," Marisa said, remembering how she had left Sam at home first, going to school in Baltimore. And how she had then left her in Baltimore, to marry Paul and live outside Boston. "She was just living her life."

"I know that now," Anne said. "But back then . . ." She shook her head.

"I think it's different for me and Sam," Marisa said. "She always celebrated my choices, no matter what. We'd miss each

other, but we always found a way to be together. This time, though . . . I let myself be
treated badly by someone, and I wouldn't
let Sam help me."

"Are you the oldest?" Anne asked.

"Yes."

Anne's smile was loving and wise.
"Younger sisters," she said. "Always want
their older sisters to be smarter than they
are. They want them to know more than
they know. They want them to show the
way."

"Are you the youngest?" Marisa asked.

Anne nodded. "Yes, I am."

"And you and Emily . . . ?"

"We're closer than ever. It took me a while,
but I came around. She was patient, right
there waiting for me. I think sometimes sisters have to rebel against each other, just
the way teenagers do with their parents. It
doesn't mean they don't love each other.
Sometimes you just have to go apart, to
come back together."

Marisa nodded, wishing it could be true.

"Who's the friend?" Anne asked.

"Excuse me?"

"The friend who went to Baltimore to find
Sam," Anne said. "Who was that?"

"Patrick Murphy," Marisa said.

"The detective who came—?"

Marisa nodded. "Yes," she said. "The one who came here to find Lily."

"Maybe," Anne said, "you should invite him to the ceili."

"I mentioned it to him," Marisa said. "But he won't come. I don't . . . I don't even really want him to. I'm not ready." She thought of Ted, of the damage between her and Sam, of Jessica. "I don't think I'll ever be ready again."

"You know," Anne said gently, "I heard Lily say the same thing. But there was Liam. . . . Life had hurt them both. Lily's marriage to Edward—and Liam's brother being killed by that shark, Liam losing his arm. His family fell apart after that. They were both so closed off, but somehow they helped each other to live again. You and Patrick—"

"No," Marisa said. "It's different. We hardly know each other."

Anne tilted her head. "I think people look for each other. That's what ceili music is all about—so full of heart and love. We're all out at sea in our storm-tossed boats, getting washed clean of life's pain, making space for love to come in."

Just then, Jude hailed Anne from the steps of the inn. She gave him a wave, then looked Marisa in the eyes. "I'm not giving up on Sam," she said. "I'm saving you that spot in the program."

"But—" Marisa began.

Anne shook her head, her smile wide. Giving Marisa a hug, she went back to work. "If she comes, we'll be ready for her," she called back over her shoulder.

Telling her friends she was taking a walk, Marisa headed down toward the harbor. The water shimmered, blue and silver under starlight. She looked out at the fishing fleet, tugging at their moorings in the flood tide. Gazing south, she imagined Patrick on his boat in Connecticut, Sam in her apartment in Baltimore. It seemed so easy to imagine them both coming to Cape Hawk, yet impossible at the same time.

She pulled out a paper and pen and wrote the words "storm tossed." She knew they were the beginning of a song. She even thought she knew who it was for.

Chapter 14

Maeve had been dreaming of her granddaughter, the two of them working in the
garden, tending the roses. The sea air was
so fresh and clean, the fragrance of roses
so sweet. She heard her own voice in her
ears, calling for someone to come. Blinking,
her eyes blurred as a man approached. Was
it Patrick? An angel down from heaven? Or
someone else? Maeve wiped her eyes, and
she saw.

Edward Hunter stood over Maeve's bed.
He stared down at her with cold eyes.
Maeve felt her mouth drop open. Sweat
sprang out on her brow, and waves of nau-

sea passed through her. She never felt afraid, or at least never let people see her fear. But she couldn't help it now. She must have been making sounds, because he leaned down, put his ear near her mouth.

"You're babbling," she heard him say. "You're not making any sense at all. That's why you're in here. Because you're losing it. You're an old lady, and no one cares about you. Even your precious granddaughter can't be bothered with you."

Maeve felt like shrieking, but instead she just closed her eyes. She heard his voice and knew his cruelty. It reassured her in some small way. She wasn't crazy, wasn't crazy at all. Edward was being Edward. It was one thing she had always been able to count on.

She went deep inside. His voice continued, but she no longer heard it. She saw his vicious face, but then honeysuckle and roses emerged from the darkness to crowd him out.

The roses were beautiful. They grew in a tangle, deep in the garden. The sound of the waves was a lulling shush, shush, shush against the sun-kissed rocks The wishing well was cool and deep. Maeve dropped a penny down, as she had so many times over the years. She made a wish. Her eyes closed, she waited for the wish to come true.

"I want my granddaughter," she wished silently. "Mara, Mara . . ."

Rose felt better every day since her last surgery, except for one thing. She missed her mother. She didn't think there were any four words in the world worse than "I miss my mother." Although she didn't say them out loud very often, because she didn't want to upset Dr. Neill, the words were inside her, more with every breath, and embroidered on her heart.

The beautiful summer days just seemed sad and strange, here in the salty old beach house by Narragansett Bay. Dr. Neill had appointed her official whale watcher, and when they weren't out in the boat with Dr. Stanley, Rose spent a lot of time by the wide window, the brass telescope trained on the water's surface.

She'd seen fish jumping, their backs silver and blue, some of them marked with dark stripes, their tails and fins delicate as hammered metal. She'd watched seagulls flying overhead with crabs hanging out of their yellow bills. And Rose had even seen a sea turtle paddling by.

But no whales at all. No Nanny.

"Can I see her picture again?" Rose asked, going over to stand by Dr. Neill at his desk. He had lots of books and papers spread out. There were pictures of blue, tiger, mako, basking, Greenland, great white sharks; marine mammals, including humpbacks, minkes, blue, fin, sperm, and beluga whales, Atlantic bottlenose dolphins, harbor and harp seals. The documents reassured Rose because they reminded her of his office in Cape Hawk. He pushed some of them aside so she could lean closer to see Nanny's picture on his laptop screen.

"There she is," Dr. Neill said.

"Who took the picture again?"

"Patrick Murphy."

"The man who came to Nova Scotia to tell Mommy her grandmother was sick?"

"Yes."

"He took Nanny's picture in Hubbard's Point, in front of Mom's grandmother's house?"

"Yes."

Rose raised her eyebrows and wiggled them. Didn't Dr. Neill know how ridiculous it seemed? She and he were in this house where they didn't really know anyone, and the person they loved most, Rose's mother, was in Hubbard's Point. Even Nanny was there. He sat at his computer, entering information about all the different species they had seen out at the reef.

"Dr. Neill," she said.

"You know, Rose," he said, "I've been thinking. You should call me Liam. Don't you think?"

She shook her head. He had tried telling her this before. But she didn't want to. It didn't suit the way she felt about him. "Liam" was a name for her mother to call him. It was a grown-up name. Rose wouldn't feel right calling him that. Besides . . . she swallowed, thinking about the name she wanted to use for him. It made her blush to think about, and she felt the blood making her face hot.

"No?" he asked.

"Nope," she said stubbornly. "Dr. Neill's fine. So, Dr. Neill, why don't we go there?"

"Well, because your mother has to take care of some things," he said. "And she thought it would be better for you to be here while she does them."

"We could help her," Rose said.

"I know," he said. "I agree with you, and I'm working on it." Rose leaned comfortably against his side. She rested her head on his shoulder, not because she was tired, but just because she wanted to. They just stayed like that for a few minutes, looking at Nanny's picture on the screen, and Rose imagined how happy they could be if they could all be together.

"When will things be . . ." She searched for the word. She was thinking that so much happened in life. She had had heart defects, and Dr. Neill only had one arm, and her mother's grandmother was in the hospital, and they were in different places. "When will things be right?" she asked finally.

"I think they are now," Dr. Neill said.

Rose frowned. She knew what he was thinking. Her mother had always told her to be grateful, to count her blessings. Even when Rose couldn't breathe right or play with her friends, even when she had to stay in the ICU because her heart had too much fluid, even during those hardest times, her mother would press her lips to Rose's ear and whisper, "We are so lucky, because we love each other."

"You think things are right, now?" Rose asked. "But how can you say that? When we're here, and Mommy and Nanny are at Hubbard's Point?"

Dr. Neill turned away from his computer screen to look her straight in the eye. She knew how important his work was, how much he had been learning about those big waves and strange fish. She knew that he had seen a fishing boat from Cape Hawk, and that he was worried about it. But right now, he was giving Rose every bit of his attention.

"Rose," he said, "I know that none of it makes sense."

"Even to you?" she asked.

"Yes," he said.

"Because you miss her too?"

"More than I've ever missed anyone or anything."

"But I thought you liked working here— going out to Ghost Hills on Dr. Stanley's boat. . . ."

"That's my job," Dr. Neill said, smiling. "You and your mother are my life."

Rose nodded. She knew that it was true;

she had felt it for a long time, maybe since the day she was born. He was like her father, in every important way. When other kids talked about their dads, Rose knew deep down, somehow, that she had a father somewhere in the world. But she'd never cared, or asked about him, because Dr. Neill was enough for her.

Just then, Dr. Neill raised his eyes, looked over her head. Rose saw his expression change, and she felt a little thrill—as if a mysterious wind had just started to blow, as if the weather had just changed in some wonderful way.

"Rose," Dr. Neill said, glancing down at her, his eyes shining, "I think that things just started to make sense."

And Rose looked, and she saw what he meant—a blue car pulling into the driveway, beside the tall boxwood hedge.

"Mommy!" Rose shouted, as she flew out the front door and went tearing barefoot across the manicured lawn, straight into the arms of her mother.

Chapter 15

It didn't take long to pack up and get on the road for Hubbard's Point. Liam had been ready ever since the night before. He had pretty much made up his mind the minute he read Patrick's message. When an idea was right, it was right; the important thing was that Lily felt good about it too.

"What changed?" he asked, driving along Route 1, holding hands with Lily across the seat.

"I came to my senses," Lily said. "Everything was happening so fast, I hardly had time to think."

"He can't do anything to us," Liam said.

"Who can't?" Rose asked from the back seat.

"Rosie, Rosie," Lily said, turning half around, sidestepping the question. "Wait till you see who's waiting for you at Hubbard's Point."

"Nanny!" Rose said. "Dr. Neill has her picture on his laptop!"

"Patrick took it," Liam said, glancing at Lily. Spotting a service station up ahead, he turned in. The gas gauge was down below a quarter full.

The three of them got out of the car. While the attendant filled the tank, Rose wanted to go into the store. Liam and Lily followed her, arms around each other. The shop was odd and quirky, a wood frame building that looked as if it had once been a house. Several boats were parked out front on trailers, some with For Sale signs.

The building's front porch had benches and rockers, racks of local papers, and a bulletin board covered with business cards, notices, and pictures of boats for sale. Another board was filled with pictures of fishermen holding up prize catches—ten-foot makos, fifty-two-inch stripers, a fourteen-foot blue shark.

Inside, the wide floorboards creaked under their feet. A soda fountain ran along the
right-hand wall, and the front of the store
was filled with bushel baskets of local produce. Lily grabbed a cart and loaded it with
fresh tomatoes, basil, corn, and squash.
Rose ran toward the back of the shop, and
suddenly squealed.

"What is it?" Liam asked as he and Lily
hurried back.

"Look!" Rose said, pointing.

A faded red curtain divided the store in
half. Rose had peeked behind; looking over
her head, Liam saw that the room was filled
with shark jaws hanging on every inch of
wall space. A rack of jars leaned precari-
ously against a table—they contained tiny
sharks in formaldehyde. Their eyes were
clouded, their snouts sharp, their shark
shapes unmistakable. A pile of ragged
hacked-off shark and dolphin fins lay on the
rickety blue table. Everything had a price
tag. After a quick look, Lily hurried Rose
back into the grocery area.

"Can I help you?" a man asked, coming
through a door at the back of the room. He
had a dark five-o'clock shadow, salt-damp

hair, and a T-shirt that said "Captain Nick's Sportfish Charters."

"Are you Captain Nick?" Liam asked.

"You got it," he said. "Interested in a charter? There's plenty to go after right now, twenty-foot great whites up from the Bahamas and even bigger white whales down from Nova Scotia."

"Belugas are an endangered species," Liam said.

The man laughed. "Oh, I know," he said. "We're not going to hook them—just see them. I have to admit, I get a little carried away. There's never been a summer like this one—pure fishing madness, thanks to some gigantic waves rolling in from out at sea. You should've seen what we bagged yesterday—purple back, pink sides, and bright red fins, five or six feet long, swimming zigzag like a sea snake. Had to be straight up from the tropics."

"An opah," Liam said.

"Whatever it's called, it was something else. Check it out on the board in front—got a whole gallery of my customers' catches out there."

"I'm actually interested in your catches here," Liam said, getting ready to blast Captain Nick for the baby sharks and boiled jaws and ruined fins. But just then Lily called his name, and he backed away. It was just as well. His emotions were running so high from seeing Lily again, he wasn't quite in command of himself.

She stood on the porch, right in front of the board Captain Nick had just mentioned. While Rose rocked happily in one of the wooden porch chairs, Lily pointed at a blurry photo.

"Is that who I think it is?" she asked.

Liam focused on the board. There was the photograph Nick had mentioned—a six-foot opah, brilliant colors sparkling. His eyes swept over the gallery of trophy fish—marlin, sharks, swordfish, and tuna. The pictures had been taken dockside, with the fishermen standing proudly by the hanging scales. Lily was pointing at a photo of a fifteen-foot Atlantic bottlenose dolphin, hanging upside down, caught in a net.

"Don't get bent out of shape or anything," Captain Nick said, coming up behind them. "That fish isn't dead."

"It's not a fish," Liam said. "It's a mammal."

"Who caught it?" Lily asked, her voice trembling.

"Oh, never mind who caught it," Captain Nick said. "The important thing is, it's still alive. We kept it alive, according to any regulation you want to name."

"Why do you want to catch dolphins?" Lily asked, glaring at him.

"With all due respect," he said, "that's not your business."

"Come on, Lily," Liam said, putting his arm around her, gathering Rose, heading toward the car. He was shaking inside, but he didn't want to show it. Lily had been through enough and now they were bringing Rose home. Liam would call John later—Jude and Patrick too. Something was going on, and he needed help to figure it out.

He took one last glance back at the bulletin board. The camera must have moved, because it was impossible to read the name of the boat just behind the netted dolphin. But Liam would know the boat anywhere, because he recognized the grinning skipper.

The ship was the *Mar IV.*

"Did you see that?" Lily whispered.

"Gerard Lafarge," Liam said.

And in spite of what Captain Nick had said, the dolphin was dead.

Getting out of the car at Hubbard's Point, Liam knew they were home. The three of them stood there holding each other for the longest time. He couldn't let go of Lily, and she couldn't let go of him. Her eyes were as blue as the summer bay. He kissed her, hardly able to believe they were together again.

They broke apart, and Liam saw people coming from around the house. Lily had asked her friends to be there. She grabbed his arm, making introductions: Bay McCabe and Dan Connolly and Tara O'Toole and Joe Holmes, two of Lily's oldest childhood friends and their husbands and children. Liam shook hands with everyone. He couldn't quite get over how normal it all seemed, after the long days and nights of their enforced separation, and then the shock of that strange roadside shop.

Watching Lily introduce Rose to her friends, Liam's heart pounded. Her slim fingers protectively on Rose's shoulder, the pride and joy in her eyes—her friends' eyes welled up, gazing down at Rose, then up at Lily. Liam knew what a momentous day this was for all of them, and he stood back smiling.

"Bay and I have known your mom forever," Tara said, crouching down. "We were all best friends when we were your age."

"What did you do together?" Rose asked.

Tara had a wonderful, wicked smile that filled her eyes with mischief. "We rowed boats out to Gull Island, and went to the Indian Grave, dug for treasure at Little Beach, collected sea glass and moonstones, made necklaces out of jingle shells, played tennis till the middle of the night, went to movies on the beach, left notes for each other in the drawers at Foley's Store. . . ."

"Sounds fun," Rose said. "A lot like what I do with Jessica."

"Your best friend?"

Rose nodded. "At Cape Hawk."

"Well, that's the kind of stuff we'll all do at Hubbard's Point," Tara said. "I think you're really going to like it here."

"We're just so happy to meet you, Rose," Bay said. "We love your mother, and we already love you."

Rose blushed, and smiled shyly.

Liam watched her, feeling as proud as any father. She had her mother's kindness and curiosity. Her natural desire to learn pushed her to try new things and read books beyond her school level; two days ago, Liam had found her on her knees by the bookcase, pulling out old copies of *Cetacean Journal,* looking for articles about belugas.

"They're toothed whales," she'd announced to Liam. "They eat a diet of crustaceans, cephalopods, and sea worms. Crustaceans—that's crabs and lobsters! No wonder Nanny likes it down south here. I've seen so many seagulls flying by with crabs in their bills."

"Yes." Liam had smiled, overflowing with pride. "You'll be quite an oceanographer, Rose Malone. You proved it on the boat at Ghost Hills."

"Like you," she'd said, beaming.

Evening breezes blew off the Sound, salty and warm. The sun began to set, casting gold light on the waves and long ledges of glacial moraine. Tara and Bay had brought over pizza, keeping it warm in the oven. Lily steamed corn and sliced tomatoes. Bay and Dan's kids—Eliza, Annie, Billy, and Pegeen—gathered with Tara and Joe's little boy, Joe Jr., around Rose, obviously thrilled to welcome the latest addition to a long line of Hubbard's Point children.

Liam sat beside Lily on the porch swing, his arm around her shoulders. With the kids around, the talk was very general—summer weather, tennis plans, back to school, the latest on Maeve. Liam opened his laptop, logged onto his whale program, felt a wave of relief to see the familiar green light.

"Where's Nanny?" Rose asked, scanning the bay.

"She's out there," Liam said. He pointed at his screen, at her light registering in a spot just about two hundred yards offshore.

"Maybe she's looking for crabs to eat," Rose said. "Beluga whales eat crustaceans."

"We could go crabbing down front," Billy suggested.

Lily set them up with strings and sinkers, and Annie and Eliza led all the younger kids down on the rocks. The sound of rocks clicking as they broke open mussels for bait chimed through the air. The minute the coast was clear, all the adults started talking.

"I can't believe you're all here now," Bay said to Lily and Liam.

"I can't believe it took you so long!" Tara said.

"It's so great to meet you after hearing so much about you," Dan said.

"Liam, it's official, you're now a Hubbard's Pointer," Tara said.

"Thanks for the great welcome," Liam said. And then, directing the question at Tara's husband Joe—Lily had told him Joe was in the FBI—"Are we making a mistake? Coming back here with Rose right out in the open for Edward to see?"

"That's a tough question to answer," Joe said. "It depends."

"On what?" Lily asked.

"It's probably more of a mistake to give him the power he's been getting, having you hide out all this time, Lily. That makes him feel like a big shot. For a narcissist like Hunter, he gets off on any reaction he can get out of you. If he makes you swoon, he likes that. If he makes you cry, he likes that too."

"Did Edward know Lily was still alive?" Liam asked.

"He knows he didn't kill her," Joe said. "So I suspect that, yes, he knew she was alive."

"Was he looking for me? Us?" Lily asked, gazing down at Rose, crouched by the tidal pool.

"He may have been," Joe said. "I suspect he was keeping a low profile. He was under investigation, and even though he knew he hadn't killed you, he had other things to hide. During a murder investigation like that, he had to behave himself. There were areas of his life he wouldn't want us looking at."

"Like what?" Liam asked.

Joe shrugged. "He's a con man. The fact that he does most of it legally—through stockbrokering and marriage—doesn't minimize the fact that he tricks people into giving him their money."

"And their hearts," Lily said.

Hearing her say that was like a punch in Liam's stomach. Lily had given this man her love, her heart. He looked over, saw the worry and hurt in her eyes, wished he could erase every bit of pain. She had told him some of the details about her life with Edward; he knew she had buried some of it so deep, she hoped never to think of it again. Her nine years in Cape Hawk had been a time of healing; the fact that she was ready for this confrontation said a lot about her strength and the passage of time.

"We were at your wedding," Tara said. "And we watched you go farther and farther away from us. The longer you were married to him, the more you hid out from us."

"We were very isolated," Lily said. "He didn't even like *me* to be with my friends." She shivered, wrapping her arms around herself.

Liam moved closer, wishing he could keep her warm. But he knew that the chill she felt had nothing to do with the evening air, the sea breeze. It came from deep inside, from memories of living with a man who had crushed her dreams and sent her fleeing from everything she loved.

A demon had come out. Lily had brought him out for all to see. Talking about him a little bit at a time, she was exposing him for what he was. Liam felt shaken by the group's emotion as they talked about the old days and truths about Lily's life with Edward that they had suspected but never really known.

Lily stood up abruptly, craning her neck, checking on Rose playing on the rocks. The summer night was warm and peaceful. The children laughed and talked, splashing in the shallow tidal pool halfway down the rock ledge. Although the sun was down now, the rising moon spread white light on the Sound, the granite, and the rock pool. Bay called for Annie and Eliza to bring Joey up to the porch.

Liam expected Lily to call Rose, but she didn't. She leaned over the porch rail, watching her daughter crouch by the pool's edge. The dark surface rippled with moonlight. Rose seemed mesmerized by the life she could still see in the dim light, the deep green seaweed, silver-blue periwinkles, purple mussels, and speckled crabs. Liam remembered his own young fascination with the sea, and he whispered in Lily's ear, "Our marine biologist in the making."

"Yes," Lily whispered back, her eyes shining.

Liam hugged her, loving how happy she was here. She took it all in: her daughter, the moon, her great friends, her grandmother's house. Lily could never be kept down for long. Her spirit was too naturally buoyant.

Just then, Rose sprang to her feet. She

jumped up and down, pointing out to sea. "Nanny!" she cried.

Liam had seen a lot of whales in his life. He had grown up on the northwest coast of Nova Scotia, where whales were a way of life. But he never remembered feeling such excitement and joy at the sight of a whale as he felt right now—spotting Marine Mammal 122, the St. Lawrence beluga also known as Nanny, right here in the water in front of the house.

"Do you see her?" Rose called.

"We do," all Lily's friends called back, stunned and delighted by the rare sight.

Liam took Lily's hand. They ran down the steps, down the grassy hill, to the seawall. They jumped down, climbed across the rocks to be with Rose. Just offshore, the beluga gazed at them with her dark eyes, the most expressive of any whale's. Liam felt as if his heart were on display for the whale, and anyone who might look, to examine.

"It's really her," Rose breathed.

"It really is," Lily said.

"Everything is going to be fine now," Rose said.

"We're together," Lily said. "That's what matters."

They heard the phone ringing inside the house and Lily ran to answer it. Liam heard her shriek of joy.

He jumped up to grab her as she flew back down the bank and leapt into his arms.

"It's Granny!" she cried. "She's awake!"

Chapter 16

Maeve wanted a drink of water. She was so parched. It had been like being lost in a desert, with nothing but heat rising from the endless brown sand. Waking up was like stumbling into an oasis.

"May I please have some water?" she asked one of the doctors, hovering above her with a light shining in her eyes. She realized that they were the first words she'd spoken in some time. The image of the desert was still with her, and her mind flickered with mirages of Mara.

"Sure thing, in just a minute. Can you tell me your name?"

"Maeve Jameson," she said.

"Do you know how old you are?"

"I'm eighty-three years old."

"Very good," he said. Now he took her pulse, holding her hand for a maddeningly long time. Didn't he know what it was like to be terribly thirsty? And to boot, Maeve had an awful, chemical taste in her throat.

"Do you know where you are?"

She pursed her lips. He had her there. Last she remembered, she'd been at the Point. She had been in the garden, clipping roses. Clara had been there, and someone else. But then the wind had picked up, and the rain had started, turning into one of those blustery nor'easters when there was really nothing much to do but stay inside, warm and dry, while the storm battered the coast. She remembered pulling on a shawl because she was chilly. She'd gone to pick out a good book to read by the fire, but then she'd noticed how dusty the shelves were, and she'd started to dust. . . .

She looked around now. White walls, fluorescent lights, sterile environment. She decided to take a stab in the dark. "The hospital?" she ventured.

"Yes," he said. "One more question. Do you know why you're here?"

She couldn't help herself; she nearly began to cry. Suddenly she remembered the dreams she had had of Mara. It was as if Mara had been right here, beside her. Holding her hand, whispering in her ear, giving her a sponge bath. Maeve thought Clara had been here too. But that was probably real. Of course Clara would come.

The dreams of Mara, though . . . such sweet dreams of love. Their special bond, as close as can be, all the secrets they'd shared through life, all the gardens they had planted, the years when Maeve had watched Mara growing up. The most beautiful feelings Maeve could remember having, right here in this hospital bed, dreaming of her granddaughter. But that's all they were—dreams.

"Young man," she said, and her throat was so dry she sounded raspy and horrible, like a witch in the movies. "You're treating me as if I'm crazy." She felt a terrible wave of fear. She probably was out of her mind. In and out of dreams, such longed-for reality, trying to pull Mara out of thin air. Had Maeve

gone round the bend without knowing it?
She could think of almost nothing worse.

"No. I'm sorry if it seems I've been vague.
I'm giving you what's called a mental status
test. You see, you've been in a coma."

"A coma!" Maeve blurted out the word,
somewhat marveling at the thought. How
dramatic and rather glamorous. It was certainly better than losing one's mind.

"We've been worried about you. It's been
over two weeks now."

"My goodness," Maeve said. She felt a
combination of elation, to know she was out
of the coma, and weakness, to know she'd
been in one at all. Those dreams of Mara
made a little more sense now. Perhaps she
had gone "into the tunnel." She'd been
walking toward the light, into the love she
had felt for her granddaughter. It had kept
her going all these years, worried and missing her.

She felt herself shrink into the bedclothes
now. "What happened to me? Was I in a car
wreck?" She asked the question, but didn't
remember anything about a car. No squeal
of brakes, no swerving to avoid an animal,
nothing.

"No, Mrs. Jameson. You had carbon monoxide poisoning."

The taste in her mouth, she thought. She tried to lick her lips, but her tongue was too dry. This young doctor was being very thorough; she watched him now, consulting with another doctor, a woman, and two nurses. They were huddled at the end of her bed, talking earnestly, glancing at the door. They sounded excited. Maeve figured it wasn't every day that someone came out of a coma in their hospital.

She cleared her throat.

"Water . . ." she asked.

"Mrs. Jameson," the other doctor, a woman with curly dark hair and a soft smile, said. "I'm Dr. Mead. I have some good news for you. It's very good news, but I just want to make sure you're ready for it."

"I'm always ready for good news," Maeve said, accepting the plastic cup with the straw, sipping thirstily.

"It's about your granddaughter," Dr. Mead said. Suddenly the doctor's smile grew radiant, and she glanced at the door.

Maeve handed the doctor her glass. Oh, it was better than any water, better than any well or spring or river, better than every drop of rain that had ever fallen upon any garden. It couldn't be true, but it was. It had to be a dream, but it wasn't. Maeve sat up tall and held out her arms.

"Mara!" she gasped.

There were more doctors standing at the door to the room, trying to hold her back, but Mara would have none of it. She had a man and a child at her side, and together they broke through the hospital personnel, and Maeve heard Mara start to sob before she was even halfway across the room.

"Granny!" she cried.

"Oh, my darling!"

"I'm home, Granny," Mara said, flinging herself into Maeve's arms, holding on to her so tight, with those hands Maeve knew and loved so well. Maeve held Mara as if she were still her baby granddaughter, with all the love she had always had, every minute of the time she had been gone, holding on and knowing that she would never let her go again.

Lily sat on the edge of Maeve's bed, with her arm around Rose. She had introduced her grandmother to Liam, but this was one of the greatest moments in her life, bringing Maeve and Rose face-to-face, a meeting she had imagined for nine long years. And it was exactly as Lily had known it would be: Maeve acted as if she'd known Rose since the day she was born, and Rose was quiet and shy, but immensely curious, and unable to stop smiling at her great-grandmother.

"You turned nine years old this summer," Maeve said smiling.

"Yes. On June twenty-seventh," Rose said. "How did you know?"

"I've kept track of you," Maeve said. "Every second."

"Even though we weren't together?" Rose asked.

"Yes. Even though."

Lily loved the way her grandmother was taking Rose in. Gazing at her sun-lightened brown braids, her green-gold eyes, her pink mouth. Rose was very small for her age, because of her heart defects, but Maeve would never mention it, just love her all the more.

"I have a scar," Rose said.

"You do?"

Rose nodded. She glanced at Lily, to see if it was okay to show her. Lily's throat tightened. Rose's heart condition had always been such a big part of who Rose was, and Lily was touched to see Rose wanting her great-grandmother to know it all right away.

Lily helped Rose pull her shirt down below her collarbone, so Maeve could see the newest scar, from the latest operation.

"Rose had open-heart surgery early this summer," Lily said. "But she's fine now."

"That's so good to hear," Maeve said. She didn't frown or look worried. She just smiled calmly at Rose, as if she knew that some people have open-heart surgery and go into comas, but that life just flows on. "Does the scar hurt?"

"It itches," Rose said.

"Ahh," Maeve said, as if she understood. She held Rose's hand, shaking it gently.

"I love your name. Rose."

"Thank you. We're both named after flowers. Me and Mommy."

"Your mother is named after a flower?" Maeve asked, looking up, meeting Lily's eyes.

"Lily," she said. "That's the name I've used since I left. I took it, to remind me of your garden. All those daylilies, so bright in the sun."

"My garden missed you," Maeve said, eyes glittering.

"I missed it, and you, so much. I needle-pointed so many canvases of Sea Garden. The wishing well, the cottage, the roses growing up the door, the four-seasons bench."

"It's a beautiful place," Liam said.

"Thank you," Maeve said, smiling and squinting at him, as if trying to be friendly while still taking his measure. "Have you known my granddaughter long?"

"Since a few days before your great-granddaughter was born."

Maeve blinked, taking that in. She seemed to be resting in the knowledge that she was really awake, her family was really with her. She suddenly looked so old and tired, as if the weight of the last nine years had just caught up with her. Lily watched the way she held Liam's gaze. She felt safe with him, Lily could see.

"You've known them a long time," Maeve said.

"Known and loved them," Liam said, smiling.

"Granny," Lily said, "we don't want to tire you out. You need lots of rest."

"Darling, I feel I could dance right now," Maeve said. Lily knew what she meant— she felt the same way. But her grandmother looked frail, her cheeks sunken and pale. The nurses seemed to be edging into the room, giving the signal that it was time to go.

Lily held her grandmother's hand. It seemed almost impossible to leave, even though she knew she could come back in the morning. Being apart for so long made their time together seem rare, precious, and fragile. If Lily let go, who could guarantee that she would ever have a moment like this again? She felt her hand start to tremble, and her grandmother felt it too.

"It will be all right, darling," her grand-mother said.

"How do you know?" Lily asked.

"I just know. Please tell her, Liam."

"She's right, Lily," he said, putting his hand on her shoulder.

"There's a prayer," her grandmother said. "By Julian of Norwich. She was a wonderful saint, a mystic. All my favorite saints are mystics, because they have so much faith. They can see the most impossible things, because they see with the eyes of the heart.

I prayed Julian's prayer every day, while you were away. It goes, 'All will be well, and all will be well, and all manner of things will be well.'"

"I like that prayer," Rose said.

"So do I," Liam said.

"It's a very good one," Maeve said. "Will you try it, darling?"

"I'll try," Lily said doubtfully. She still couldn't let go of Maeve's hand.

"When can I go home?" Maeve asked the only doctor still remaining, making notes on her chart.

"We'll have to see," he said. "We'll send you down to neuro tomorrow for some tests, and we'll know better after that."

"Don't worry, Granny," Lily said, kissing her. "We'll get you home as soon as possible. Your house is waiting for you."

"I can't wait," Maeve said. Then, smiling at Liam: "Take care of her till I get back there, okay?"

"You can count on it," he said.

Lily hugged her grandmother, then held her face between her hands, looking into her soft blue eyes. It had seemed an eternity since she'd been able to do that, and she felt that tears were imminent again.

Maeve kissed them all, long and hard. When they started to leave the room, they walked backwards, waving. Maeve blew them kisses.

"Goodbye, darlings," she said. "Goodbye, Lily and Liam and Rose."

Lily smiled, turning away as the tears really began to flow. Her grandmother had just called her Lily. Mara was gone forever.

It was past ten o'clock at night. Across the Gold Star Bridge, on the other side of the Thames River, they went to Rosie's, an old silver diner, with turquoise leatherette booths. Rose was thrilled to go to a place with her name, and about getting to order blueberry pancakes late at night.

Lily sat beside Rose, and she and Liam held hands across the table. They talked about Maeve, and Rose asked what she should call her, should it be Granny? Lily said they'd better ask Maeve.

"I like the name Maeve," Rose said.

"Maeve was a warrior queen in Irish legend," Lily said. "She was from the Connaught, in the west of Ireland."

"Named for a queen, wow," Rose said.

"A warrior queen, no less," Liam said,

nodding his head to Lily. "Granddaughter of Maeve."

"Do I seem as if I have the blood of a warrior queen?" she asked.

"Totally, Mommy," Rose said. "The way you boss people around in hospitals, when they're not paying attention to me."

"I've done that," Lily agreed.

The waitress came over with their blueberry pancakes. She knocked over Liam's water glass, and a small amount spilled on his lap. He cleaned it up quickly, smiling, and Lily felt a small, quiet, unexpected sense of safety. A memory arose: Edward going into a rage because a waiter spilled his water. The evening had been turned upside down over that one small thing. He had stopped speaking, eaten in silence, slammed the money down on the table without leaving a tip.

That had been crazy, Lily thought now, watching Liam and Rose happily eat their pancakes. Lily took a deep breath, feeling how safe and normal her life had become.

"I could call her Maeve," Rose said between bites.

"Your great-grandmother?" Lily asked.

"Yes," Rose said. "I like the name a lot. I'm

glad she's named after Queen Maeve. I want to call her that."

"But I thought you didn't like to call adults by their first names," Liam said.

"I didn't say that," Rose said, frowning.

Lily sipped her milk, wondering what conversation she had missed.

"Well, when I asked if you wanted to call me Liam."

Rose instantly turned bright red.

"What is it, honey?" Lily asked. "Do you think it's too impolite for you to stop calling him Dr. Neill and start calling him Liam? Is it because he's our friend instead of a relative, like Granny?"

"It's not because of that," Rose said, her voice falling to a whisper as she dropped her fork on her plate. Her eyes got big, and tears pooled on the bottom rims. "It's just that I want to call him something else."

"What do you want to call him?" Lily asked.

Liam already knew. Lily could tell, because she felt him squeeze her hand.

"Daddy," Rose said.

Chapter 17

Patrick Murphy went to the hospital as soon as he heard. When he first got there, Maeve was not in her room. They had taken her down for some tests, and then she had physical therapy. So he sat in the chair by the side of the bed where she had lain so long, waiting for her to return.

He thought of Marisa and Sam, the nursing sisters. He thought of how many people they had helped, and it stung him to think he'd been unable to bring them back together. As Patrick stared at Maeve's hospital bed, he knew that these were all casualties of the same man; he blamed Edward Hunter for all of it.

On the Major Crime Squad, he had investigated many comas. Blunt-force trauma, poisoning, falls from high places, the gamut. He had observed coma patients go through stages. When they got to the place of drawing inward, trying to move into a fetal position, Patrick had seen very few of them come back. So, waiting for Maeve, he knew that her waking up was a miracle. But he didn't know what she had lost, whether she'd still be the same Maeve he knew.

When he heard the wheels coming down the corridor, he jumped up. He expected to see her on a gurney. Honestly, he expected to see a shrunken old woman who had aged a lot, who had lost ground. When he saw her in a wheelchair, sitting up, her white hair neatly brushed and her blue eyes sharp and bright, he felt himself start to grin.

"Well, if you're not a sight for sore eyes," he said, grinning wider.

"Patrick Murphy," she said, smiling just as much.

He bent down to peck her cheek, but she put her arms around his neck and gave him a long hug. Good thing too. He buried his face in her shoulder for a few seconds, so she wouldn't see tears in his eyes.

"What was that for?" he asked when she stopped.

"You found her," Maeve said.

"Mara?"

"Her name is Lily now," Maeve said.

Patrick chuckled. "Maeve, Maeve, Maeve," he said. "You sure do get with the program faster than any other eighty-three-year-old I know."

"Well, she doesn't want to live in the past," Maeve said. "Who can blame her? Have you met Rose?"

"I sure have. Your great-granddaughter."

"She's beautiful. I can't wait to get home to Hubbard's Point, so I can watch her swimming and crabbing on the rocks. And Liam? You've met him?"

Patrick nodded. "He's a good guy. I checked him out, of course. No priors, never been married, lots of publications and awards in his field, ichthyology. That's the study of—"

"Fish—sharks. I know, dear. Is that what happened to his arm?"

"Yes, as a matter of fact," Patrick said. "How would you know that?"

Maeve stared past his head, at clouds going by the window. The expression on her face was beatific, like Saint Theresa or the Mona Lisa. Patrick had seen that gaze a million times during the years he was investigating the case. It jostled him slightly now. She was a wise woman. The aide asked if she wanted to get into bed, but Maeve just shook her head. She wanted to stay sitting up, in the chair.

"I guess I know because of something in his eyes," Maeve said. "He's a very handsome man. He loves Lily—that's obvious to anyone who looks at him. But there is sorrow in his eyes. I think he is very reserved, except with Lily and Rose. He has the look of someone who has been terribly wounded."

"You can tell all that just by looking in his eyes?" Patrick asked. "Jeez, Maeve. You should have been the detective, not me."

"Oh, teachers have to be detectives," she said, peering at him. "Don't think I don't see the same thing in you."

"The same?"

"My darling, tough detective. Wounded by life and love and this investigation."

"Maeve, let's leave it at 'tough,' okay?"

She sighed. "I had a boy in my class once, thirty years ago now. Peter Liffey—he came to school with his arm in a sling one day. All we were told was that he had a broken arm."

Patrick listened, seeing infinite compassion in Maeve's eyes.

"His schoolwork suffered. I had him come after school, for extra help. Little by little, I began to find out about him. Small things he'd let drop. Like, his mother had a black eye. His father got mad when Peter forgot to take out the trash. Or when Peter asked too many questions. You get the idea."

"Domestic violence back in the day," Patrick said. "Back when guys could beat their wives and kids behind closed doors, and the cops would look the other way. It used to be called 'family business.'"

"Yes."

"What happened to Peter? Did you turn him around? Or did he go the way of his father? Is he somewhere beating his own wife right now?"

"He turned around," Maeve said. "He went to college, and then to medical school. We stayed in touch the entire time. He became a psychiatrist, and he has written many papers and books on the subject of family violence. He studies the very thing that hurt him the most in his young life."

"That's why you guessed the ichthyologist had been attacked by a shark?"

"Yes. Liam has the same haunted look as Peter. Some people have to understand the things that scare them most."

Patrick grabbed a chair and pulled it over right next to her wheelchair and sat down. "Maeve, I have to ask you something. Do you remember Edward stopping by the cottage?"

She frowned, gazing out the window. "Yes. Clara and I were out in the garden. He said he was in the area on business."

"Did you ask him to check your furnace?"

Maeve snorted. "Of course not. Why?"

"Lily has made some allegations. And we're taking them very seriously."

"What are they?"

"She thinks Edward messed around with the heating system, poisoned you. Maybe he suspected she was alive. And he knew the only way to get to her was through you."

"She would come home if she thought I

needed her," Maeve said, her eyes open wide.

"We think maybe he did something to your furnace, under the house. There's access from outside, through the door above the seawall. It's possible he blocked the out-flow, or stuffed something into the ventila-tion ducts. We've checked, and there was a partial fingerprint, but no signs of tamper-ing. We suspect that he did something to cause carbon dioxide to build up. You couldn't smell it, you couldn't see it."

"It's summertime; I wouldn't even have thought of carbon monoxide," Maeve said. "But I'm old, and I get cold. I'm always chilly, even when other people are warm. I turn the heat up on cool nights. Or I light a fire."

"Edward might have taken advantage of that. Did anything seem different? Anything you can think of? Anything at all, Maeve. It would help. . . ."

"I can't remember," Maeve murmured, and Patrick could see that he had upset her. She was suddenly paler than before, slump-ing slightly in her chair. He held her hand. It was cold.

The hospital's air-conditioning was humming. He didn't see a thermostat to turn it down. But he got up and pulled the white cotton blanket off Maeve's bed. He tucked it around her shoulders, down over her knees. Then he sat down beside her and held her hand again. After all the time they'd spent together, Patrick loved her almost as much as his own grandmother.

"At least two good things have come of all this," Maeve said. "Lily had Rose. And she met Liam."

Patrick nodded, and he caught Maeve looking at him with a worried gaze.

Maeve dabbed at her eyes with a tissue, smiling slightly. "I once hoped you and my granddaughter would fall in love. After your marriage broke up, and during all the years you were looking for Lily and I could tell how much you cared . . . I wondered. You were so fascinated by her. . . ."

Patrick folded his arms over his chest, staring out the window.

"Oh, I used to dream that you'd find her," Maeve said. "And love her and the baby. I'm so happy that she's found Liam, of course. But what about you? How do you feel about it?"

Patrick stared at the clouds for a minute, then looked down at Maeve.

"I've met someone," he said.

"Patrick!" she said, her eyes shining.

He shook his head. "She's wonderful, but she's far away. And not just in miles—she's been through too much. She's—well, she's been very hurt. You're not going to believe this, Maeve. She was Edward's wife, after Lily."

"The one from outside Boston? Patty, wasn't it? With a daughter who'd be about Rose's age . . . Grace?"

Patrick nodded, feeling a tingle run down his spine. "She ran away from him too, up to Nova Scotia—Cape Hawk—just like Lily . . . because of a picture Edward had, an old photograph of a whaling ship in the Cape Hawk harbor. She goes by the name Marisa Taylor now. Her daughter is Jessica."

"And you . . ."

"I met her, when I went up to find Lily. She's beautiful. Plays music, and used to have a band with her sister. They're estranged now—because of what happened with Edward. He kept Marisa from seeing her sister, and a lot of damage was done. I tried to help, to convince her sister to forgive her, go up to Cape Hawk and reunite. But she wouldn't listen."

Maeve stared at him with such light in her blue eyes. "Oh, Patrick," she said. "You've done so much to pick up the pieces of lives shattered by that man. Lily's, mine. And now these other women . . . what about you?"

"What do you mean?"

"Your marriage, dear. I know you're 'tough,' as you said earlier. But I also know how that wounded you. Why don't you go up to see Marisa? Even if she can't reunite with her sister just yet, she would be a lucky person indeed to have a friend like you."

"I don't know, Maeve."

"Darling, if there's one thing this experience has taught me, it's that life is so short, and so precious. I feel so sorry that the sisters are losing time, and the chance to be together. Don't you lose it too. Go to Cape Hawk."

Patrick looked at her as if he were her grandson and she was the wisest woman on earth.

"Please, Patrick," she said, her eyes gleaming. "Don't let Edward Hunter take one more thing from any of us. Take back your life, and give Marisa back hers. Don't give up."

He couldn't speak, but he nodded. Maeve squeezed his hand, pulled him closer for a hug. Maeve had said *Don't give up.* Patrick let the words play in his mind, and he knew he had to try once more—if that didn't work, then so be it. Either way, he had a trip to make, and it was time he got started.

Of course it had to happen. Liam and Lily both knew it was just a matter of time. Still, when the confrontation came, it was both worse and less eventful than Liam would have expected.

Lily was in the kitchen, making dinner. She had been at the hospital for most of the afternoon, and Liam and Rose had gone to the fish store to get lobsters. They'd stopped at the vegetable stand for corn, picked up a blueberry pie from a bakery in Black Hall, some fresh peach ice cream from Paradise Ice Cream. Liam enjoyed getting to know the area where Lily had grown up, and Rose seemed to love driving around and doing errands with him.

"Are there lobsters here in the Sound?"

Rose asked as they walked down the rocks to fill the big pot with seawater.

"Definitely," Liam said. "This is a perfect habitat for them, with all the rock ledges to hide in."

"And there are lobsters up in Cape Hawk?"

"Yes. A lot of the fishing boats down in the harbor actually go out for lobsters. It's a big part of the fleet's catch."

"Could we catch them ourselves here?" Rose asked, helping Liam hold the pot steady so the water would flow in. When they had enough, they righted it, and then picked tufts of rockweed. Liam's family had always steamed lobsters with seaweed, and Lily wanted to try it. Rose had bare feet; she navigated the rocks with no trouble. The air was chilly, so she wore a sweatshirt. The sleeves were pushed up, and the legs of her jeans were rolled up to her knees. Liam loved watching her be a kid, so carefree on a summer night.

"We could," he said. "All we'd need is a boat and some pots."

"Can we get a boat?" Rose asked, her eyes sparkling with excitement.

"If your mom says so."

They gathered some mussels to cook with the lobsters. Liam couldn't help telling Rose the Latin names for everything—*Homarus americanus* for lobster, *Mytilus edulis* for blue mussels—for her future career in oceanography. They scanned the waves for Nanny, although it was still a little early for her to appear. She wasn't there, so they scrambled up the rocks to the yard.

As they rounded the corner of the house, Liam saw him. He recognized his stocky, muscular build, his intense smile, those gleaming green eyes from his brief appearance in Rhode Island.

Liam held the heavy pot, filled with water, in the crook of his arm. He wanted to grab for Rose, to pull her back, but he was not dexterous with his prosthesis, and he didn't move fast enough. She walked straight into Edward's path. Liam felt as if he saw a Mack truck bearing down on her, when it was just a man getting out of his Jaguar.

"Rose," he said quietly.

She seemed transfixed by the man coming down the stairs to stand beside the wishing well.

Edward crouched down, smiling at her. He had eyes only for Rose. Liam put down the pot, grasped Rose's hand, and pulled her toward him. It was instinctive, one-two-three, like pulling her away from a snake. She looked up at him with surprise. Liam's heart was racing, and he didn't want to take his eyes off Edward, but he registered Rose's shock at Liam's rudeness.

"Go inside," he told her. Liam knew he sounded sharp, but he couldn't stop to think. He pushed Rose toward the door, then stood between her and Edward.

"My daughter," Edward said, meeting Liam's eyes. "That's my daughter, isn't it? My kid. She looks like me. I'd know her anywhere."

"You have no place here," Liam said.

"Oh, really? Her mother and I got married in that side yard, right there. Who are you?"

"Liam Neill," he said, rising up, towering over Edward Hunter, standing between him and the house, just wishing Edward would make a move to get by him.

"That's my baby," Edward said. "And I have every right to her. Get out of my way."

"You're not welcome here," Liam said. His voice was deep and held violence. He had become an ichthyologist because a shark had killed his brother, and right now, facing

Edward Hunter, he felt primal hatred surging up for the predators of all species.

"Liam." The door slammed as Lily came out to stand beside him. Liam glared at Edward. He wanted the fight to be between them, but he respected Lily too much to keep her out of it. This was her battle, all hers. But Edward had to know that if he faced Lily, he was facing Liam too.

"Mara, you're a liar," Edward said. "You put me through hell, do you know that? I was investigated for *murder.* Do you know what that was like? It was a nightmare. You lied about our baby. That is my daughter. She has my face, my eyes. She's like looking in the mirror! She's mine."

"She's not *yours,*" Lily said. "She doesn't belong to you or anyone. She is her own person, beautiful and true, and she has nothing to do with you."

"She has my blood!"

"How dare you come here?" Lily asked, sounding calm. "After what you did to me? Your act might work for new people, who don't know you. But not here, not with me. I see who you are."

"You're crazy. I was a wonderful husband. Ask anyone. You had no right to take my child away. She's mine! I'm going to have her, I swear to you. I'm going to get what's mine!"

"Did you hear Lily?" Liam asked. "She just told you the child doesn't belong to you. Can you grasp that concept? You don't own people. Lily doesn't want anything to do with you. Leave now."

"One-armed wonder," Edward said, smirking.

It's funny, Liam thought. That was the moment he knew. He had seen Edward's glittering hazel eyes, he had heard his possessiveness about what was "his," he had seen the arrogance and aggression in showing up here. But it was in that small comment, that throwaway cruelty, that Liam saw the man for exactly who he was.

"Don't you dare!" Lily shouted, her outward calm dissolving. "Liam is the most wonderful man in the world. He loves my daughter! *Our* daughter," Lily said, gazing up at Liam with sheer panic, making his heart pound, because he knew she wanted it to be true, that she finally accepted the way Liam had felt all along—that he had always loved Rose as if she were his own.

"What?" Edward asked. "She's *his* daughter?"

Lily was shaking too hard to answer. Liam held her, rocking her in the front yard as the sun set, its orange rays making all the roses look as if they were on fire.

"I don't believe you," Edward shouted. "She looks like me. She's the right age. I swear to God, I'm going to take her from you. I swear you'll be sorry for this."

Liam tried to shield Lily with his body. He felt her quivering against him, her body trembling with sobs.

Edward's words, *I'm going to take her from you,* rang in Liam's ears. He wanted to take two steps and kill Edward with his bare hands. But he had to take care of Lily right now. He turned his back on the monster and led the woman he loved into her grandmother's house.

Rose was standing inside the kitchen door, her expression pure shock. She had never seen her mother like this. Liam doubted she had ever heard her mother raise her voice. He could see Edward through the kitchen door window, standing right by the wishing well, laughing.

"Why is that man laughing?" Rose asked. "While Mommy's crying?"

"Rose," Lily said, falling to her knees and pulling Rose into her arms.

"Mommy, what's wrong?" Rose asked, her words muffled by Lily's shoulder—Lily was holding her so hard.

Liam had to get them away from the door. He shepherded them into the living room, sat beside them on the sofa. He held Lily while she cried, and Rose just looked up at him with confusion in her eyes. Edward was wrong. Rose looked nothing like him. Yes, her eyes were green, but they were warm, deep, crackling with lively intelligence. Looking into the eyes of Edward Hunter, Liam had had the cold sensation of a reptile, primitive and undeveloped.

"Tell me what's wrong," Rose repeated. "That's the man from Rhode Island. Who is he?"

"His name is Edward Hunter," Liam said.

"He's my real father," Rose said. It wasn't a question.

"I'm so sorry to put you through this," Lily said. "I don't think of him as your father. He doesn't know you at all. I took you away from him before you were born. I've only wanted good for you, my sweetheart."

"I didn't like him in Rhode Island, and I don't like him now," Rose said. "The way he smiled at me." She shivered. "Even before he started yelling. It wasn't a real smile."

Liam nodded at her, struck by her perception. No falling for Edward's glib charm—not Rose. The sun went all the way down, and the room grew dark. No one moved for a long time. They had no appetite anymore.

When the moon began to rise, Liam stood up and went into the kitchen. Edward had left. His Jaguar was gone. Rose stood at Liam's side, gazing out into the shadows. The moon cast a cold, blue light on all the rocks and roses. The beauty of Hubbard's Point suddenly seemed sinister.

Liam asked Rose if she wanted her lobster, but she didn't. She asked if they could let them go, on the rocks. Liam got the plastic bag out of the refrigerator, and he heard the lobsters scratching inside. The sound made him feel sick. Holding hands, he and Rose walked down to the water. Nanny was there, swimming in a circle of moonlight.

"We've fed her crabs," Rose said, "but I don't want to feed her the lobsters."

"I know," Liam said.

He took the rubber bands off their claws. Showing Rose how to hold them by the carapace so she wouldn't get pinched, he helped her to set them free in the tidal pool. They had plenty of life force, instantly swimming to safety, to hide in crevices under the seaweed.

They stood looking at Nanny for a long time. Liam knew Lily was in the window, up above. His mind was racing, thinking of what she had said to Edward. Rose waved at Nanny, and then it was time to go to bed.

Liam lingered in the hallway, looking at them. Lily sat on the edge of Rose's bed, reading from *A Wrinkle in Time,* one of her own favorite childhood books. Liam didn't want to let them out of his sight. He wanted to give Lily this time alone with Rose, and he wanted to get his words straight.

When Lily came out, she looked drained and tired. He took her hand, led her back downstairs. They went onto the porch, where they could see both Nanny and the tidal pool, both bathed in moonlight.

"Rose wanted to let those lobsters go," Lily said.

"She did," Liam said. "Do you know why?"

Lily shook her head.

"I think it was a completely gentle instinct. She had seen someone being controlling and cruel, and even though she didn't completely understand, she wanted to express herself by doing something kind."

"She is kind," Lily said, her eyes quickly filling with tears. "She's nothing like him."

"I know," Liam said. He held her hand, stroking it, trying to soothe her. "Lily, I heard what you said to him."

"The whole Point heard," Lily said.

"No. I mean, I heard what you said about me. About Rose being ours."

Lily's tears spilled over. "Do you think he'll believe that? Will it keep him from coming after her? I should never have come back here. In spite of how I feel about Maeve . . ."

"Lily," Liam said, holding her, making her look him in the eye. "She *is* ours."

She shook her head. "But she's not . . . if he forced her to have a blood test . . ."

"In every way that matters," Liam said, "she's our daughter. I was with you when she was born. I helped her come into the world, and I put her on your stomach for you to hold. I felt like a father that day, Lily. And I've never stopped feeling like one ever since. Rose's father."

"You've been there for her," Lily whispered.

"I've tried," he said. "All I've ever cared about was being there for you and Rose."

"You promised us you'd look after us," she cried. "Liam, I tried to push you away for so long. I didn't trust you, didn't trust the world. But I've never forgotten that promise, or that you were there at the beginning. Yours were the very first eyes Rose ever looked into."

There were stars burning in the sky, so bright they couldn't even be dimmed by the white moonlight, and he felt they were shining for Lily and Rose now. "You're my family," he said, kissing her hand. "You and Rose."

"You're ours," she whispered.

"That's what you were getting at, when you said to Edward that Rose is our daughter. I knew that was what you meant. No matter what the obstacles, we've been a family since that first day."

"You've been with us at the hospitals. You've paid Rose's hospital bills," she said.

"I never thank you enough for that, because, in so many ways, it's been the least of what you do. You look over us, Liam. Even when I haven't let you be close, you've stayed right there. I've always known that all I'd ever have to do is call you. And you'd come."

"Even more than you know," he said.

"I used to think she was born with heart defects because I let *my* heart be broken," Lily said.

"I've always known you had a broken heart," Liam said. "And I've wanted more than anything for you to let me try to help you heal it."

"You have," she whispered.

Liam's own heart was pounding, a feeling of giant waves in his chest. He pulled Lily closer, kissed her. Stars flashed in the sky, in his eyes. Her body was so hot, as if she had a fever. When they stopped, he still held her tight, their gazes locked.

"Lily, I want to marry you," he said.

"Oh, Liam—"

"I always have. Don't you know that, Lily?"

"We've loved each other for so long," she whispered. "Even before I knew it."

"Do you know it now?"

"I do," she said.

Her eyes were shining, and Liam swore he saw happiness for the first time that night. It gave him the hope he needed, reinforced the ineffable connection they had had for so long.

"Lily, I want us to get married right away. This weekend, as soon as we can get the license. I want to adopt Rose. So he can't come after her at all."

Lily led him down the porch steps, around the house, to the grassy strip between the cottage and the seawall. The grass was cool beneath his bare feet, and she pulled him down and slid on top of him, her body firm, hot, and glistening with sweat. Liam could hardly breathe, his mind on fire with everything.

She ran her hands down his body, sliding them up under his shirt, untucking the tails from the waistband of his jeans. He felt her undo the button, start to tug the zipper down. Her mouth was on his, open and ravenous. He held her with his one good arm, letting her work her way down his face, his neck, kissing his collarbone.

Liam's thoughts flew out of his head. They had spent too much time operating with their minds—every step of the way had had to be negotiated, navigated, calculated. Lily had been on the run, and that had been her prison: so far from home, trapped by the need to stay hidden. He felt her breaking free, and he was right there with her.

They made love with their bodies, and maybe for the first time ever, they weren't thinking at all. Liam just felt their bare skin on the cool grass, Lily's body hot from running and his aching for her touch. A chilly breeze blew off the water, signaling that August's end was coming.

He held her afterward, their heartbeats slowing to something close to normal. Seagulls cried out on Gull Island. He remembered when their sound had made Lily break down, with all her worry and fear bottled up over Maeve and what Edward might try to do. Right now she lay flat on her back, staring up at the sky, holding out her arms as if she could catch all the stars.

"Liam," she said.

"Lily," he said back.

"How many stars are there?"

"More than anyone can count."

"That's not a very scientific answer," she said, laughing.

"Well, there are about one hundred billion stars in our galaxy."

She smiled, as if satisfied. What's the scientific name of Nanny?"

"Delphinapterus leucas," he said, raising himself up to watch Nanny swimming close to the shore. "Rose already knows that."

"What does that translate to?"

"Delphinapterus, without fins, *leucas,* white. Why?"

"You're an oceanographer. Can oceanographers predict what the weather will be in September?" she asked.

"I don't know," he said, his pulse kicking over. "Why?"

"Liam," she said. "Maeve is home, Rose is well. You and I—it's just so wonderful. I never thought we'd have all this. I was just thinking . . . why should we wait? September is almost here."

"Lily," he said, pulling her close. Her eyes were bright blue, even in the dark.

"I love you, Liam," she whispered, their gazes locking. "I want you. *Yes,* Liam."

"Yes?"

"I want to marry you. A September wedding . . ."

He stared into her eyes so deeply, and he

saw the smile come to her lips. His own heart was pounding. He thought of every-thing he knew about what Lily had been through, and he pictured Ghost Hills, monster waves crashing over the reef. They were sixty feet tall, capable of killing anyone in their path. He knew that Lily had nearly been swept under once; Liam was going to make sure it never happened again.

Chapter 18

The late afternoon held golden light, spilling it down the rock cliffs, into the fjord, across the calm bay. Fiddles and tin whistles played, inviting the town to dance, calling everyone from their houses for the last days of the ceili. Marisa and Jessica sat by the stone fisherman, listening to the music.

"Mommy, why don't you play?" Jessica asked.

"I can't play without Sam," Marisa said.

"You wrote your new song and everything. . . ."

It was true. Inspired by Anne's phrase, and by knowing Patrick Murphy, Marisa had written a new song, "Storm Tossed"—it was ready to play, but she knew that it would have to wait until she had her partner and fellow Fallen Angel, her sister Sam, with her again.

A group of young girls, Irish dancers, ran along the wharf in their green dresses; a van from Prince Edward Island rumbled down the cobbled street, band members jammed in, singing at the top of their lungs. A quartet from Yarmouth sat on stage, two fiddle players racing through "Maureen's Reel," the tin whistle and accordion players tapping their feet for percussion.

Marisa lifted her head for every car that drove through town. She watched as the ferry slid across the strait, its white wheelhouse glinting in the butterscotch light. A single whale arched its back, a glossy black island that disappeared in the ferry's wake. Night would fall soon, and another day would be over. Another chance to play gone . . . Marisa tried to concentrate on the band playing. They were very good, but Marisa knew that she and Sam could beat them.

Jessica went down to the water's edge to watch for the whales to reappear. They always did—after diving, fishing down below in the plankton-rich waters flowing in from the Gulf of St. Lawrence, whales always resurfaced to take a breath. Marisa had learned that it was something to count on.

She had lost faith over her years with Ted—there hadn't been much to count on, including herself. Her music had stopped, and even Sam had given up on her. After years of always meeting at the Blarney Stone for Saint Patrick's Day—no matter where in the world Sam was working, she would travel back to Baltimore, and Marisa would take the train down from Boston, and they would take the stage and set the bar on fire with their fiddles.

Marisa had gotten lost in a bad relationship—the kind of thing she'd never thought could happen to a woman like her. She was strong, tough, and brave. She'd managed to run a clinic for low-income families in Baltimore. She had opened another in South Boston—and kept working even while taking care of her first husband, Paul, after he was diagnosed with lymphoma. If only she had stayed strong after his death—instead of falling for the stockbroker Paul had trusted with their investments, the man who had trashed her, driven her apart from her sister, and killed her daughter's puppy before she finally found the courage to get herself and Jessica away from him.

"Mom, look!" Jessica said, pointing as the whale surfaced. A spout of fine mist shot up, gold in the last light of day. Marisa smiled, to let Jessica know that she saw. But as she gazed across the bay, something on the ferry caught her attention.

The vessel was midway across the passage, the narrow strait leading between the fjord's high, granite cliffs. Its deck was filled with cars and trucks, more people coming to Cape Hawk for the ceili. Some of the drivers and passengers had left their vehicles, to stand along the ferry's railing, to breathe the clear sea air and catch their first notes of the Irish music. A pair of hawks circled overhead, and most of the people looked up to watch them disappear into the thick pine forest.

All except one person—who had caught sight of Marisa, and was standing at the rail, grinning and waving. She gasped at the sight of him.

"Jess, come on!" Marisa called.

She grabbed her daughter's hand, and

they ran along the wharf. The fiddles soared into "Geese in the Bog," and people in the grandstand and on blankets spread over the Cape Hawk Inn's wide green lawn began to clap in time. Marisa spotted Anne and Jude Neill, standing in the gazebo, leaning against the rail. Anne saw what was happening and called to Marisa.

The ferry's engines roared into reverse, and the water churned white around the dark red hull. One dockhand manned the controls, gears shifting as the metal plates creaked into place. Thick lines were thrown and tied. Car engines were started. Marisa held out her hands, as if she could touch the person standing at the rail.

People waiting in their cars began to toot their horns. Only one car remained unmanned, and it was Patrick's. He leaned against the rail right across from them, the setting sun making his red hair shine like copper, his blue eyes sparkle. His black Lab stood beside him, wagging her tail and seeming to grin with her red tongue hanging out.

"You came," Marisa said.

"I had to," he said.

"Had to?"

"I'm on a mission."

Marisa tilted her head, and Jessica reached out, as if she could touch the dog from across the narrow gap that separated them.

"My aunt goes on missions," Jessica said. "To places like Peru. That's where she is now."

"Jess," Marisa said, because she knew how wound up her daughter got on the topic of Sam, and she felt her disappointment that the ferry had delivered someone else.

Patrick's smile widened.

"She's coming," Jessica said stubbornly. "She's on her way—she has to be! She knows it's the ceili, and she knows we're waiting. She wouldn't miss the chance to play fiddle with you, and she wouldn't let me down!"

"Jessica," Marisa said, wondering why Patrick looked so happy; his blue eyes locked onto hers, and he wouldn't look away, his smile growing.

"I think you're right," Patrick said. "Your aunt wouldn't let you down."

"Patrick," Marisa said. He didn't know

how much Jess loved Sam, how crushed she would be when Sam didn't come.

"You'd better get off the ferry," Jessica said, still holding out her hand toward the friendly dog. "Whatever your mission was, you're here now."

"My mission . . ." Patrick said, staring at Marisa.

"You beat Aunt Sam here," Jessica said.

"Not by much," a voice rang out from above.

Marisa raised her eyes. The wheelhouse was a tall rectangle, right in the middle of the deck. Wide windows looked in all directions, so the captain could see anything coming at him from any direction—whales, dolphins, fishing boats, seabirds. Maybe even fallen angels . . .

Because he seemed to have met one along the way, somewhere between the other shore and the Cape Hawk landing. The captain stood grinning, waving through the open window. Standing beside him was a tall, freckle-faced vision with bright green eyes and a halo of wild red hair, lifting her fiddle case high above her head in greeting, and her voice in song—sounding like anything but a fallen angel, sounding as if she had wings:

"I'm here!" she called.

"Aunt Sam!" Jessica cried back.

Once the ferry had docked, and Patrick had driven off and parked his car, he'd stood there quietly with his dog, watching the sisters and Jessica reunite. Marisa had been hugging Sam, pulling Jessica into the embrace. They cried, holding each other. Marisa looked into her sister's eyes, hardly able to believe she was here.

"You came," Marisa said. "Oh, Sam . . ."

"With a little help," Sam said, her eyes glinting as she looked at Patrick.

"Patrick. Thank you so much," Marisa said, turning to smile at him. Only then did he step forward, give Marisa a surprisingly shy glance and a quick hug. Marisa felt him in her arms, and her heart jumped. He kissed her lightly, and she reached up to touch his cheek.

"I'm so glad it worked out," he said, his blue eyes burning into hers.

"What happened?" Marisa asked.

"I called your sister," he said. "And she

had already made up her mind. She was on her way—all she needed was a ride."

"You were on your way?" Marisa asked Sam.

Sam nodded, tears spilling down her cheeks. It had been over two years since Marisa had looked into her eyes. They were bright green, with fine lines radiating out at the corners. Marisa wanted to touch her face, wipe her tears away. She held back, trembling.

"I *was* on my way," Sam said, her voice throaty and low. "Patrick's visit . . . well, it helped me realize how much I needed to see you."

"We needed to see you too," Marisa said.

"We did, Aunt Sam," Jessica said.

"You've grown so much," Sam said, crouching down. "I can hardly believe it." She shook, sobbing. "I've missed two years of your life."

"I never stopped thinking of you," Jessica said, staring at her with wide eyes.

"Oh, honey." Sam wept. "I thought of you and your mother every day. No matter where I was or what I was doing."

"We love you, Sam," Marisa said.

"We do, Aunt Sam," Jessica said.

"It's time we'll never get back," Sam said, looking at them both. "Can you forgive me?"

Oh, what a question. Sam's eyes were so hopeful, beseeching. Marisa gazed into them and saw the little sister she had always loved, to whom she had read *The House at Pooh Corner,* and with whom she had studied biochemistry and epidemiology.

"Sam," Marisa whispered.

"I didn't know," Sam said, holding her hands, "that you had left him for good. You always went back. I just couldn't watch you do it anymore."

"I'm so sorry," Marisa said.

The sisters embraced. For Marisa, all the years melted away. Wherever in the world Sam had been, whether they had been speaking or not, they had never lost touch. They were sisters, connected forever.

"It's over now," Jessica said, "and we're all together."

Marisa looked up at Patrick, her gratitude so deep it was beyond words. This reunion had happened only because of him, yet he was standing apart. Their eyes locked; she wanted to reach out her hand, to invite him over, but she felt stunned with emotion. His eyes were filled with such a gentle expression, one she hadn't seen for so long—she shivered, because it reminded her of how Paul used to look at her.

"Patrick," she said again. "Thank you."

"You don't have to thank me," he said, his voice soft and gruff.

"How can I not?" she asked. "After what you've done for us?"

"You needed to find your sister," he said. "And she needed to find you."

"I know," Marisa said, wanting to say so much more.

"You should let Sam settle in," Patrick said, stepping back. Marisa opened her mouth to speak, but she faltered. Maybe he had just delivered Sam—and didn't plan on staying. Perhaps she had the wrong idea . . . but there was still that look in his blue eyes, reminding her of the only real love she had ever known, watching her as if he never wanted to look away.

"Aunt Sam, you brought your fiddle," Jessica said.

"I did," Sam said, glancing at Marisa. "We're going to clean up at the competition, knock those other bands right off the stage."

"Are we really going to play together?" Marisa asked, almost unable to believe it.

"I think we should, don't you?" Sam asked softly. "After Patrick went to all the trouble to get me here?"

"It's good to see you all together," Patrick said, his eyes still locked on hers. Her heart beat fast in her throat, and she swayed slightly.

"I love your dog," Jessica said as she crouched to hug and pet the black Lab.

"Flora, meet Jessica," Patrick said, finally turning away from Marisa. He stretched after his long drive, looking around, possibly looking for a way out of the family reunion. "I hope the inn takes dogs. I probably should have called first, to check." So he *was* planning to stay. Marisa smiled with relief.

"Anne and Jude are over at the ceili," Marisa said. "I'm sure they'll find a place for you and Flora. Let's go over and see. . . ."

"Yes, and check out who's playing," Sam said. Then she glanced back at the ferry. The captain, a man Marisa had often seen but never met, had just loaded up the next group of cars, preparing to cross back to the other side. He was lean and lanky, with short brown hair under a Greek fisherman's cap, and a sexy way of leaning over the controls. He smiled straight at Sam.

"You know him?" Marisa asked.

"That's T. J. McGuinn," Sam said, giving him a last wave as the horn sounded and the ferry pulled away, into the strait.

"You took a twenty-minute ferry ride and you got to know the captain? I've lived in town for months, and I didn't even know his name."

Sam smiled, her dimples showing, looking half-embarrassed as she shrugged. "T.J. and I hit it off—what can I say?"

"Can we please find Flora a hotel room?" Jessica asked. "And make sure there's a spot on the ceili schedule for Fallen Angels?"

"Sounds like a great plan," Patrick said, grinning at Marisa.

Then Sam linked arms with her and began to march toward the inn. Glancing over her shoulder, Marisa saw Patrick handing Jessica one end of Flora's red leash, showing her how to slip her hand through the loop.

"I had a puppy once," Jessica said.

"You did?" Patrick asked. "So, you like dogs?"

"I love them," Jessica said.

"Me too," Patrick said.

And Marisa was glad she was walking ahead, with Sam, because she wouldn't have wanted them to see the look in her eyes, realizing what it meant to Jessica to encounter a man who loved his dog.

Chapter 19

On the day Maeve finally came home from the hospital, Lily and Liam and Rose went to pick her up. The nurses pushed Maeve down to the lobby in a wheelchair, and Liam helped her into the car. All the way home, Maeve kept exclaiming about how wonderful everything was: the greenness of the marshes, the blue of the sky, the brightness of the day, the smell of salt in the air. She kept leaning forward to touch Lily on the shoulder, as if she couldn't quite believe they were together again. Then she'd pat Rose's hand, sitting next to her.

"I can't believe this," she said. "We're all together."

"I tried to call Patrick, to invite him to join us," Lily said. "But he's gone to Cape Hawk."

"Ah," Maeve said. "That's my dear boy."

As Liam pulled under the train trestle, into Hubbard's Point, Lily fell in love with the place all over again. Could a landscape actually be in a person's blood? The summer wind blew through the open car window, bringing the essence of roses and the sea, soothing her more than anything she'd ever known. Yet a strong longing for the wilds of Cape Hawk surged within her as well.

Clara was waiting by the wishing well. Rose had made a sign saying WELCOME HOME, MAEVE! Liam had hung it over the front door. When Clara came forward to embrace the friend she'd known and loved for the whole eighty-three years of their shared life, Maeve began openly weeping.

"I'm so sorry, my dearest," Maeve cried, gripping Clara's hands. "I wanted to tell you the truth, but I couldn't."

"You were desperate to protect our girl. I understand, darling. I do, and I'm so grate-

ful you've come home safe. I don't think I'd
be able to live without you!"

In honor of all the summer's blessings,
Liam and Rose had caught lobsters. Liam
had bought a rowboat with a small engine
and three pots, set them just off the rocks
with buoys marked with white and green
stripes. That morning at dawn, while Nanny
swam in the waves—her white back and
dorsal ridge pink in the light of the rising
sun—Liam and Rose had rowed out to haul
their first catch.

Ten lobsters came up in the pots. Lily had
watched from the porch as Liam showed
Rose how to measure the carapace, and
then how to throw back the undersize ones,
and the egg-bearing female. All but three
were keepers. Rose still seemed hesitant
about eating lobsters, but she wanted to
celebrate for Maeve's sake.

Maeve walked through her house, checking out everything. Rose stayed by her side,
pointing out pictures she had drawn, flowers she had picked, asters she had pressed
in the family Bible, just as Lily had done as
a child. Maeve in turn had pointed out the
doorway in the downstairs bedroom where
she had measured Lily's growth every sum-

mer, the blue ribbons Lily had won in beach swim races, her first tennis trophy, and her very first needlepoint pillow—of a rose garden.

"See?" Maeve asked. "Your mother has always loved roses."

Rose beamed.

"Let's measure you," Maeve said, rummaging through her dresser drawer for a pencil.

"I'm short for my age," Rose said, standing against the door. Her head came up to where Lily's had been when she was six, three years younger. Lily, watching from the hall, felt a pang.

"That doesn't matter," Maeve said, making the pencil mark. "It's no use comparing yourself with others. Not just in height, but in life. It's how you grow inside—how you try and how you learn from your mistakes— that counts. That's all that matters, sweetheart."

"Thank you," Rose said, looking up at her great-grandmother with grave eyes. She turned to look at the mark and smiled.

"I used to imagine us doing this," Maeve said. "I've always saved a place for you on this door."

"Even though you didn't know me?"

"Oh, Rose. I've always known you," Maeve said, hugging her. "Right where it matters."

"Where?"

"In my heart," Maeve said.

Rose nodded. That was something she understood very well.

Liam called to say the lobsters were almost done. Lily put out corn, melted butter, and tossed the salad with tomatoes freshly picked from Clara's garden.

They sat around the kitchen table. Everyone joined hands, and Maeve said grace. Lily bowed her head. She could barely look up—all of them together at one table: Maeve, Liam, Rose, and Lily. This was a day she had so often thought would never come.

One morning while Maeve was resting and Liam and Rose were out in the boat, Lily took her coffee into the garden, to read on the iron bench. The weather was changing; the end of summer was near. A cool fog hung over the Point, softening the contours of rocks and rosebushes. The bell buoy tolled in the channel, and foghorns mourned in the distance.

"Hello, Mara."

Just like that, she thought, her hair standing on end: nine years away from him, and he just walked in as if he owned the place. Edward came out of the fog and stood before her. She glanced around for his car.

"I parked down at the beach and walked up," he said.

She stared at him without speaking. She was shaking, and she didn't want him to see. Nine years, and this was the first time they were completely alone together. He was stocky as ever, heavier than he used to be. There was gray in his brown hair. Only his eyes were the same. Bright hazel-gold, piercing in the fog.

"Why are you here?" she asked calmly. "We've asked you to leave us alone."

"'Us'?" he asked. "The only 'us' is you and me, Mara. You're my wife."

"You had the marriage annulled," she said, "and me declared dead."

"You wanted that, didn't you?" he asked, anger already starting to leak out, like steam. "Do you know what you put me through? Police grilling me as if I were a criminal. I was treated like a dog, taken in for questioning, hounded by the press."

Lily gazed beyond him, to the cottage. She didn't want to look at his eyes. His tone was quiet, but his eyes were burning with rage.

"You don't know what it was like, staring into camera after camera, knowing that the whole world wondered whether I had killed you, chopped up your body, and thrown it into the Sound."

Lily held back the shiver so he couldn't see. He sounded as if he had given the grisly scenario some careful thought. *Chopped up your body.* The words reverberated.

"The only reason you were upset about my disappearing," she said, "is that it made you look bad. Your feelings had nothing to do with me, or the baby. You didn't want the baby, Edward. You barely spoke to me the whole time I was pregnant, except to tell me how unhappy you were about our lives changing."

"You *did* make me look bad!" he said, as if she hadn't even mentioned the baby. But Lily stayed focused.

"You'd bump into me, hard, every chance

you got. You spilled things on me. When I passed you, you tripped me. How many times did I fall when I was pregnant?"

"I can't help that you fell."

"You were too much of a coward to come out and hit me. But you made sure I felt your force. You beat me in every way but with your fists."

Again, the smug look touched his eyes and mouth. His lips twitched in a smile. Maybe he was remembering his old cruelties. Maybe it gave him pleasure to know that she had figured him out.

"You were clumsy, Mara. You always have been."

Lily's muscles rippled. She thought of herself on the tennis court, getting to the hard shots, putting the ball away. She thought of herself carrying Rose as a baby, a toddler, a small child—Rose in one arm, groceries or bags of yarn or rock salt for the icy walkway in Cape Hawk balanced in the other. She had never fallen, not once, in the years since she'd left him.

"It's over, Edward. I see you now."

"What does that mean?" he asked.

"It means that I get who you are. You can't

hurt me the way you used to, because I understand the kind of person you are."

He took a step forward. They were very
close, touching toe to toe. Lily felt his breath
on her forehead. He was just a few inches
taller than she was, but he seemed as aggressive as a giant. His skin gave off violence.

"I'm getting to you right now," he said, his
teeth gritted, his face hot red.

"Leave," she said.

"You. Can't. Get. Away. With. What. You.
Did," he said staccato, with his fists
clenched. "You humiliated me."

"Edward, I was trying to save my own life,"
she said. "Do you remember the mountain?
Think of that the next time you wonder why
I ran away."

Their eyes met, and now Lily couldn't look
away. Nine and a half years ago, she had
seen him for exactly who he really was, and
he knew it. Bringing it up now felt powerful,
vindicating. But seeing the blood in his face,
dark red and boiling, made her stomach
drop.

"You didn't call the police that day," he
said, eyes glinting, because he knew that

her mistake in not calling for help had given him the upper hand.

"You were my husband," she said. "I tried to tell myself I was wrong."

He stared, fists clenched.

"I was pregnant. I couldn't bear to face what I was actually married to."

"*'What'*? You say that as if I'm a *thing,*" he said. "You treat me as if I'm a nothing, and you always have. That's the problem, Mara. You don't like men. You don't respect us. I feel sorry for what's-his-name. The one-armed wonder."

She started to back away. Edward was so ugly, in his words and heart. She just wanted to go inside, gather her family to her, remind herself of the light and goodness in her life.

"You should have told the police that day," he said. "You realize that, don't you?"

She didn't answer.

"It would have been your best chance." He smiled. "Found any earrings lately?"

Lily started to tremble, feeling wrenched inside, just like when she had lived with him, feeling twisted like a skein of yarn.

"There's no one to hear you. Don't worry—I checked before I let you see me.

My daughter is out in the boat with your freak, and Maeve is napping on her bed. I looked in the window. Having her bedroom on the first floor really comes in handy."

"You leave her alone," Lily said, her voice rising.

"I don't waste my time with people like Maeve," he said. "She means *nothing* to me. Did she stand up for me after you walked out? No. She knew you were alive, and she let me suffer through all those police visits." He reached into his back pocket, took out a rolled-up piece of paper.

"See," he said, tapping the paper on the palm of one hand, "you really don't know. You don't *know* whether you were imagining what happened on the mountain. You've always had such a good imagination, Mara. You're so *creative.* Seeing things that aren't there, thinking I mean one thing when I'm saying another. You doubt yourself, don't you? Even now, you're asking yourself, 'Was I right? Or was I wrong?' Right?" He smiled, as if he'd just told a great joke.

Lily's heart was pounding. "I don't doubt myself, Edward, not now. And neither does your other wife. We both know what you did, who you are."

"What?" he asked.

"Patty," she said. "Grace's mother."

He looked shocked. "Where are they?"

"We all run away from you, Edward," she said. "She's a wonderful woman. I'm just sorry she had to go through what I did. You'll be happy to know that she's thriving—just as I did."

Lily had gone too far. She saw his expression change—from anger, to shock, and now white-hot fury. He smacked the rolled-up paper down on the arm of the bench. It flew into the low cedar growing just behind the bench as a windscreen.

"Read *that,* Mara," he said. "Then let's see you *thrive.* I hope you enjoy every minute of it."

Lily shook her head. She began to walk slowly toward the cottage.

"Pick it up!" he shouted. "Read it!"

She just ignored him. Her body was quaking from the inside out, but she made herself walk erect and steady, one foot in front of the other. She felt the glass doorknob, cool under her palm. Turned it, pushed the door open, quietly closed it behind her.

Edward stood in the yard, staring at the house. She saw him gazing straight through the kitchen window, shadowy in the fog. Lily's heart was in her throat. She backed away, so she was in the dark hallway, where he couldn't see her. He looked immobile, hands on his hips, as if he might stand there forever.

After a while, he walked over to retrieve the paper that was lodged in the cedar branches. He smoothed it, brushing away needles. Then he folded it. She watched him walk toward the front door, but her view was blocked by the rosebush growing up alongside. He seemed to pause for a minute, and then she heard the screen door screech open. Her heart was racing, and she looked wildly for the portable phone, ready to dial 911.

Then the screen door slammed, and she saw him walk past the wishing well, up the stone steps, and out of sight toward the beach. Lily went upstairs, to the bedroom overlooking the front yard and dead-end road for a better view. He was nowhere in sight. Maeve was still dozing, and Liam and Rose hadn't returned from their boat ride. Lily walked down the stairs, through the first floor, and into the kitchen.

Hands trembling, she opened the door.

The paper was wedged in the crack. As she reached for it, she pricked her finger on a thorn; he had slid a white rose into the paper's fold. She let the rose fall to the floor. Blood from her finger smeared the paper as she spread it open.

It was a subpoena:

THE CONNECTICUT STATUTE
Sec. 46b-168. (Formerly Sec. 52-184).
Genetic tests when paternity is in dispute.
Assessment of costs.

(a) In any proceeding in which the question of paternity is at issue, the court or a family support magistrate, on motion of any party, may order genetic tests which shall mean deoxyribonucleic acid tests, to be performed by a hospital, accredited laboratory, qualified physician or other qualified person designated by the court, to determine whether or not the putative father or husband is the father of the child. The results of such tests, whether ordered under this section or required by the

IV-D agency under section 46b-168a, shall be admissible in evidence to either establish definite exclusion of the putative father or husband or as evidence that he is the father of the child without the need for foundation testimony or other proof of authenticity or accuracy, unless objection is made in writing not later than twenty days prior to the hearing at which such results may be introduced in evidence.

Lily sank into a chair. She stared and stared at the paper. Patrick's words had just come true. The minutes passed, and she had no sense of time at all. She heard voices outside. Looking up, she saw Rose's face in the window. Happy, carefree, just back from her boat ride. She held up a hand in greeting, her eyes elated and full of joy.

Such pretty green eyes. Lily smiled through the window. She picked up the rose and the subpoena. Going to the door, she couldn't stop gazing at her happy daughter. Eyes are the window to the soul, she thought, smiling at Rose's. They revealed what a person had inside, and what Rose had was beautiful.

This can't be happening, Lily thought. She felt wild, overwhelmed, as if she'd just gotten off a dangerous flight. Her feet were on solid ground, but her body was still rattling, from all the fear and bumps. From the minute she had decided to return to Hubbard's Point, she had known in her heart that this day would come. That didn't lessen the impact of now confronting the reality of a no-holds-barred battle with Edward—with Rose, precious Rose, in the center of it all.

Opening the door, she felt her daughter charge into her arms.

"Do we have any old bread?" Rose asked. "The swans are swimming by, and I want to feed them."

"Sure," Lily said. She rummaged through the bread box.

"Want to come down on the rocks?" Rose asked. "And feed them with us?"

Lily started to say no. She had to call a lawyer, she had to research Connecticut law, she had to pack all their bags and get ready to go into hiding again, slip out of Hubbard's Point, Black Hall, Connecticut, the United States. Her veins were flooded with adrenaline, literally compelling her with fight-or-flight instincts. But Rose was staring up at her, eyes sparkling, chest rising and falling from the everyday exertion of being nine years old.

"Of course," Lily said. She grabbed the bread, and Rose's hand. Rose led her down the hill beside the cottage, past the cement medallion embedded with shells and a sand dollar that Lily had made when she was a young girl. Liam stood on the rocks. Rose scrambled down to him, bread in hand. The swans were swimming out of the silver mist, around the Point. Liam stared at Lily, and she knew that he knew something was wrong.

The swans glided up, graceful white birds with orange bills. They looked so lovely and serene. The babies they had had at the beginning of the summer had grown; their feathers were still dark, but getting whiter.

"Mom," Rose said. "Dr. Neill told me swans are like belugas. They're born dark, as a way of staying camouflaged from predators. Then they get lighter as they grow up, until they turn pure white when they're adults."

Lily nodded, unable to speak.

"Aren't they beautiful?" Rose asked. She

held out her hand, and the mother swan got close enough to almost nip her fingers. Lily cried out as she lunged forward to grab Rose and hold her tight. They lost their balance slightly, and Lily scraped her bare foot on the barnacles.

"Mommy!" Rose said, alarmed.

"Be careful," Lily said, holding back tears as she gripped Rose. "I just don't want you to get hurt, honey."

"Okay, Mom. I'll be careful," Rose said looking surprised. "I'm fine."

"She's fine," Liam said, steadying them both.

Lily nodded, but he just didn't know. He didn't know that *none* of them was fine, that everything had changed. The fog seemed so soft, and it drained color from the landscape. The water was silver, the rocks were gray, the weathered cottage was silvery brown, the roses seemed bleached of life. Nothing felt familiar, nothing at all.

It was a different world.

Chapter 20

They had the subpoena out on the kitchen table, taking turns reading it. Only Lily couldn't pick it up again. She knew that no amount of staring at it would make it go away.

Clara had invited Rose over for a tea party, which was really just an excuse to get her out of the house while Lily, Liam, and Maeve tried to figure out what to do. Fog had settled on the landscape, contributing to the uneasy feeling inside.

"He's going to try to take her away from me," Lily said.

"That will never happen," Liam said.

"This is all my fault," Maeve said. "If only I hadn't gotten sick . . ."

"Oh, Granny," Lily said.

"You shouldn't have come home," Maeve said. "Darling, why don't you just leave? Just take Rose and go back to Canada. Hide her even deeper than before."

"We couldn't leave you," Liam said.

Lily felt stunned by how quickly a feeling of well-being could evaporate. Even knowing that Edward knew she was back, she'd been lulled into a sense of safety. Being home with her grandmother, reuniting with her friends, getting even closer to Liam and seeing how much he loved it here, saying yes to his proposal, all had given Lily a feeling of her own power.

But now Edward was going to enlist the courts to help him play his games. Lily remembered seeing him with children when they were married. Bay's kids were little, and they would often run up from the beach, to ask if they could play on the rocks. Sometimes Lily and Edward would be visiting from Hawthorne, and Lily had loved their visits.

She'd get bread for them to feed the swans, drop-lines so they could go crabbing, fishing poles so they could see what was biting. There were two girls and a boy, and Lily had imagined what it would be like when she and Edward had their family. How many children would they have? Would they love the beach and the sea, like Lily? Or the mountains and the woods, like Edward?

She had expected Edward to join in. Bay's kids were adorable, bright, and funny. They loved to joke and laugh, and they weren't the least bit squeamish about seaweed, crabs, or bait. But Edward would never even talk to them.

"Come on," Lily would say, tugging his hand. "Let's take them swimming. We can go out to the big rock."

"It's covered with bird shit," he would say, sitting on the porch, absorbed in his laptop. He barely even looked up, so he didn't see the looks of first exasperation and then resolve pass across Lily's face.

"Okay then," she said, patiently trying another angle. "Let's take them snorkeling. I saw some lobsters in the cove yesterday."

"I'm trying to get my resumé together," he'd snap. "Can't you see that?"

Lily didn't believe him. She knew that he was playing computer games, because she could see his screen reflected in the cottage window behind him. She thought of asking him why he never seemed to care about getting his resumé together except when the kids were over. He seemed completely unconcerned with finding a job he really liked, just coasting from brokerage firm to brokerage firm, never really getting entrenched anywhere, sometimes leaving even before his commission checks came in. Lily took a deep breath, determined to salvage the day. She grabbed his hand.

"Edward," she said.

He didn't reply.

"Please?"

"Go have fun with your little friends," he said.

"I will," she said. "I hope you'll play with our kids when we have them."

He just kept tapping on the keyboard, and she shook her head, feeling frustrated. The kids waited on the rocks, faces turned up toward the cottage. They had seen this same interaction before; Lily could see they weren't expecting much from Edward.

She was halfway down the small grassy hill to the seawall, when Edward said,

"Hey." Lily turned back, shielding her eyes against the sun to look at him.

"You look good," he said, smiling. She was wearing a blue tank suit, and her body was thin and strong.

"Thank you," she said, wondering if this was supposed to be a peace offering. In case it was, she smiled.

"Women ruin their figures when they get pregnant," he said. His smile widened.

Lily had reddened, stopped in her tracks. Why did he have to say that, with the kids right there? Her eyes stung with hot, sudden tears. Down on the rocks, she went through the motions of tying on sinkers, baiting hooks, helping the children cast into the bay. She had felt numb, though. Edward's words could do that to her.

That night, in bed, he had seemed so avid, as if he wanted to make it up to her. Edward's ardor was really rare, so she fought to push her hurt aside, wrapping her arms around his neck, arching her back, trying to work up feelings of passion.

She had started feeling unconnected to her body. Her heart and soul seemed to be in a completely different place than her bones and skin. She ached to really be touched, in a way she could feel it. But his hand on her skin was rough, hurtful—harsh and abrasive, as if making her flinch was more the point than giving her pleasure.

Was this what marriage was like? Once the thrills and excitement of early courtship were over, was this what everyone did? She couldn't even remember the last time he had wanted to have sex with her. Usually he slept with a wall of pillows between them, flinching when she'd run a tentative hand down his spine.

Before they got married, he had told her he wanted to be a father. But after the wedding, she heard only how much he didn't want to be a parent, wanted her to keep her figure, wanted her all to himself.

But right now, here they were in their bed, having sex. There was no eye contact; he stared at the headboard, and Lily felt tears come to her eyes. The friction hurt. It was as if he had forgotten he was inside a woman, inside the softest place in her body. She gripped the rails of the headboard, bracing herself.

Lily's tears began to leak out because she used to think *Maybe tonight we'll make a baby, maybe I'll get to be a mother.* She cried because this felt like destruction, not creation.

Lily remembered that now, shivering at Maeve's table. She closed her eyes. She had a collection of worst moments in her life, and that was one of them—the night she had conceived Rose. She had wept inconsolably afterward.

Lily remembered driving over to Maeve's house the next day. She hadn't told her grandmother that she was upset. By then, she was practiced in the lie: smiling, laughing, acting as if everything was great. She was always "fine."

"How are you, darling?" *Fine.*

"Would you like some tea?" *Yes, that would be fine.*

"How was your weekend?" *Just fine, thank you.*

It was always worst after a fight. In fact, after one of the worst yelling matches—with Lily losing it totally, screaming so loudly she hurt her throat, and Edward looking at her with the smug victory he always seemed to feel when he made her that angry—she felt like she was about to collapse. He huffed into bed, covers pulled over his head. Her chest hurt, and she felt afraid.

She was young. Her family had no history of heart trouble. This was just stress, she told herself. She took her own pulse, but she was too upset to count her heartbeats.

Not wanting to overreact, she went into the bedroom. "Edward," she said.

He didn't reply.

"I think I might be having a heart attack."

He ignored her, as if she had just said she was tired, or cold, or had a stomachache. Lily's thinking was very skewed. She didn't want to dial 911. It would just call attention to their chaotic life and marriage. Neighbors had called the police a few weeks earlier, after they'd been yelling into the night. "Everything is okay, Officer," Edward had said. And Lily had done her part—smiling at the cops, both of whom she'd seen around their small town. "I'm fine," she said. "Everything is fine."

Domestic squabblers, she'd heard the neighbor woman whisper to a friend in the hall one day after that, while Lily stood on the other side of her apartment door, cringing with shame.

So, not wanting another siren to come to their apartment, she'd pulled on her coat and driven herself to the Shoreline Clinic.

The closer she got, the worse she felt. The pain seemed hot, as if someone had stuck a piece of blazing coal right in the spot where her heart should be. She touched her sternum and felt pain radiating into her ribs. It felt as if someone had punched her, as if someone's knuckles had come slamming into her chest.

By the time she got inside the clinic, she could barely walk. Quivering, hand on her heart, she'd sat at the triage desk, silently weeping. She had been coming to this clinic since she was a baby. Her parents had brought her here for croup when she was a year old. She had come here at four, when she'd stepped on a rusty nail and needed a tetanus shot. She'd come here to get her blood test, the week before marrying Edward. They had her records—and they knew her by sight.

The desk nurse had bought needlework supplies from her. The ER attending had ordered several needlepoint pillows for her dining room chairs. They all knew Maeve, from years of living in the area. As she sat at the nurses' station, Lily thought she should have gone somewhere else. She should have driven to another clinic, where no one knew her, no one would recognize Edward and look at him with judgment the next time they saw him at the IGA.

"I think," Lily said, trying to get the words out, "I'm having a heart attack."

They were so kind. They took her right in—to a doctor she'd never met. She wanted to ask them to give her a woman doctor, but she didn't have the strength. She was afraid of a man laughing at her, thinking she was making something out of nothing. The doctor did an EKG. He sat beside her the whole time. He just gazed at her with kind eyes, and his presence was so restful and gentle, it made Lily cry all the more.

He listened to her heart. His touch, one hand on her shoulder, the other on the stethoscope as he moved it over her chest, was softer than her husband's. It told her that she mattered, she was worth caring about, her heart was worth listening to.

When he reached her sternum, he pressed it gently with two fingers. Lily nearly shrieked with pain. "There," he said. "That's where it hurts?"

"Yes," she sobbed.

And deeper inside, where he couldn't get

to with his examining touch. She just sat there on the table, while the doctor read her tests, took her blood pressure, waited for her to stop crying. He asked her about stress. Shaking, she said she was under some. At work? He asked. "At home," she said, and they might have been the two hardest words she'd ever spoken. He nodded.

"I haven't found anything cardiac," he said when he had finished.

She waited, listening.

"That doesn't mean there's not something there. But I've found no evidence of a heart attack, or heart failure, anything like that."

"But my heart hurts so much."

He nodded, taking her so seriously. She remembered how much that meant to her, the way he was really believing her, not thinking she was crazy or overreacting. It made it possible for her to take a deep breath.

"I'm going to order a stress test," he said. "I'll recommend a cardiologist for you. But I don't think it will show anything wrong."

"Then what?" she asked.

He stared into her eyes. He was young, tall, thin, with big blue eyes and thinning blond hair. He wore a white coat. As he spoke, he took her hand, as if it were the most natural thing in the world.

"I think you have a broken heart," he said.

The words unleashed new tears. Lily sat there crying softly, just holding the hand of this doctor she'd never met. Deep down she knew he was right; she just never thought she'd hear a doctor say it. He gave her the name of a cardiologist, written on a sheet of notepaper. He also wrote down the name of someplace else he thought she should call: Shoreline Domestic Violence Services.

"He doesn't hit me," she whispered, shocked by seeing the words.

"Emotional and verbal abuse can be just as bad."

"But it's not domestic *violence.* Is it?

"Ask your heart," the doctor said quietly. He patted her shoulder, then left the room.

Lily got dressed. She was shaking as she pulled on her clothes. The contact jelly from the EKG stuck to her bra and shirt. She wondered whether Edward would be up when she got home. Maybe he would be worried, shaken up by the fact that she had actually left.

Or maybe he wouldn't. Her mind was racing, and her heart still hurt. She was worried about what she would find at home, the kind of mood Edward would be in. Domestic violence? She shook her head. The doctor had been so nice, but he didn't understand after all. Edward never laid a hand on her. They fought; they had problems. His terrible childhood had left him with so much anger.

Lily had read about the cycle of violence. She knew that men who were beaten as children often beat their wives and kids. Edward had hit Judy, but he had resisted hitting Lily. Wasn't that a sign of his willingness to be different, to treat her well? Lily should have explained that to the doctor.

She had been too shy to tell him about their sex life, how painful it all was. Leaving the clinic, she had taken care of the paperwork on the way out. The doctor was busy with another patient, but he nodded to Lily as she passed by. She mustered a smile for him. *Look,* it seemed to say. *I'm fine now.*

She dropped the sheet of notepaper in the garbage on the way out, in the pail in the parking lot, but only when she was sure he wouldn't see. And then she drove home. Little did she know, she was already pregnant.

Now, so many years, so many miles later, she looked out the window, at her beautiful Rose playing in her grandmother's garden.

"We have to get a lawyer," Lily said.

The August day was cool and misty, the contours of every tree and cliff blurred, Cape Hawk's dark pines and black rock ravines painted soft gray by the weather. Only the inn's long red roof remained vivid, visible even across the water, pulling everyone to the ceili.

It was Marisa's day to work at In Stitches, so she and Sam had to practice right there in the shop, doors flung open to the foggy wharf and bay. The two sisters hadn't played together in a long time—over two years. Marisa, dark-haired and tall, sat on one stool, while Sam, redheaded and even taller, perched on another, running through scales on their fiddles.

They were so happy to be together again, and in some ways it was as comfortable as ever—Marisa had brought Sam coffee on the couch that morning, Sam had brushed and braided Jessica's hair—they all had that bone-level comfort that comes from being family. Practicing their music, Marisa wondered when they'd start to talk.

She gazed out the shop door, and she watched as Jessica took Flora for a walk across the inn's lawn. It was too damp for people to picnic on blankets, but nothing could keep them away from the ceili—some had set up folding chairs, others stood in clusters, and all were dressed for the weather in raincoats, slickers, and plastic sheets. Marisa knew that Patrick had told Jess that she could walk Flora anytime. She kept her eyes peeled for him, but he was nowhere to be seen.

"Want to take a break?" Sam asked after a few minutes.

Marisa nodded. "I was thinking the same thing."

They went into the back, poured glasses of iced tea from the small refrigerator Lily kept in the workroom. Clinking glasses, both sisters smiled.

"I'm so glad you're here," Marisa said. "I never thought you'd come."

"I almost didn't," Sam said.

"When Patrick told me you were back in

Baltimore," Marisa said, "I was so shocked."

"I didn't mean to hurt you," Sam said.

Marisa felt so tight; they had been building to this for so long, after the years of Ted. Her chest ached, and she stared into her younger sister's eyes. She flooded with emotion, just as she had at their reunion. "My terrible marriage," she said.

Sam took her hands. "Ted," she said.

"I was so lonely," Marisa said. "It was after Paul had died, and you went back to Baltimore. He was there—he seemed to love me. And he seemed to love Jessica."

"I know," Sam said. "I was happy for you at first—I was. But I just watched you disappearing. You were losing yourself, and I was losing you."

"Sam," Marisa said. She swallowed, thinking of how she had always wanted her little sister to look up to her. She wanted to be a good example, wanted to show Sam the way. "I didn't know what to do. It's so hard to explain—"

"You don't have to," Sam said.

"But—"

"You ran those clinics. You treated so many battered women. I thought you would know—I never thought it would happen to you."

"I never did either. I thought I knew the signs—but he was so charming at first. He seemed to love me so much."

"Isn't that what all the women tell us?" Sam asked softly. "When we ask them what's going on?"

Marisa nodded, remembering the many hands she had held, the tired and confused and terrified faces she'd looked into.

"The worst part," she said, "was what he did to Jessica's puppy. I still can't believe I put her in a situation like that."

"I know," Sam said. "When you told me, I wanted to come kill him myself."

"That was the last thing I did tell you," Marisa said. "You seemed so disgusted with me. That's when I finally got out. How could I have let it go so far?"

"I just felt so helpless. You know what the worst part for me was? It was hearing you stop realizing how wonderful you are," Sam said.

"What?" Marisa asked, shocked.

Sam blinked hard, her green eyes glittering. "I just watched you giving in so much to him," she said. "You were such a star in nursing school. Who, in our whole class, would volunteer every spare minute she had, to vaccinate little kids in the worst sections of town? My sister."

Marisa listened, spellbound.

"Who would practice her fiddle every night, after her labs and homework were done, just so she could put on a fabulously terrific performance Friday and Saturday nights—to make sure the tip jar overflowed, so we could pay the next semester's tuition? My sister."

"Oh, Sam," Marisa said.

"You played like an angel, and I'm not talking *fallen*," Sam said. "You were never a fallen angel—that was me. I rode my big sister's coattails all through nursing school. I was the one with too many boyfriends, not enough A's."

"No, Sam," Marisa said. "You were always wonderful. You have the most compassionate heart I know. That's what makes you such a great nurse . . . and sister, and aunt."

"Well, I don't think the family compassion has ever been an issue," Sam said. "You had love to spare with him. You have a solid-gold heart, and he cashed in."

Marisa chuckled, wiping away tears as

she reached for a pen. "That's a great line," she said. "I think we could sell it in Nashville. . . ."

"'She had a solid-gold heart,'" Sam sang, making up a tune on the fiddle as she went along.

"'And he cashed in,'" Marisa harmonized.

"'He was a solid-gold jerk,'" Sam continued.

"'With a heart of tin,'" Marisa sang.

Sam cracked up. They improvised the music, playing together as if they'd never stopped. The notes flew out of their fiddles, their rhythm was suddenly in sync, their toes tapped time, and Marisa knew that everything was going to be okay. The sisters had always worked out their lives in music. They had started off more than one show worried about exams, or a patient, or so many other things, and ended the night toasting and hugging and dancing with joy.

It had always been that way, and it was still. They ranged from their brand-new, just-written song straight into "Galway Lasses," and from there into "Geese in the Bog." Then for something sweeter, "Maudabawn Chapel."

"I wrote a new song," Marisa said eventually.

"Really?"

"Yep. It's called 'Storm Tossed.'"

"A little autobiographical?" Sam asked, grinning.

"Slightly," Marisa said, glancing out the door again, looking for Patrick. "It's pretty easy—it's in G."

"Ooh," Sam said, after listening to the first few bars. "Pretty. Love that E minor."

"Heartstrings, right?" Marisa asked.

"Oh yeah."

Nursing was the sisters' way, every bit as much as music. *Heartstrings,* Sam had said, and Marisa knew that they were what counted. Playing fiddle with her sister, Marisa stared out the door as the Cape Hawk ferry crossed the water. She was concentrating on her rhythm, on keeping time with Sam, but she was also looking for the big redheaded Irishman who had brought them back together, who had tugged Marisa's heartstrings and inspired her song.

Chapter 21

The lawyer's name was Lindsey Grant Winship. She was a partner in a Hartford firm, with offices in Constitution Plaza. Tall windows overlooked the Old State House, red-brick and gold-domed, an austere reminder of Connecticut's colonial beginnings. Lily sat in her office with Liam, her heart hammering as if she had just finished a race—instead of being about to begin one.

Lindsey was about fifty, tall and lean, with softly streaked brown hair. She was warm and welcoming, instantly comforting and understanding and somehow maternal—yet her brown eyes were filled with the curiosity and enthusiasm of a young girl. Her office was filled with color: paintings by her daughter, wonderful abstract portraits and landscapes, touched with gold leaf. Photographs of her daughter, from babyhood up until the present, graduate school. And shells and rocks picked up from the many beaches Lindsey and her family had visited over a lifetime of vacations.

Lindsey listened carefully, filling a yellow legal pad with notes as Lily gave background on her marriage, escape, Rose's birth and life, up until the present.

"He delivered the subpoena himself, instead of having a process server do it. That was very aggressive of him," Lindsey said when Lily was finished.

"Edward was never lacking in aggression. He never hit me, though. . . ." Lily said.

"The sophisticated ones never do," Lindsey said. "They use threats to instill fear, just like Edward did when he told you about Judy. He made sure you understood the potential for future consequences—that if you stepped out of line, you might very well have been beaten, just like Judy. That's one way he tried to control you."

"What can I expect now?"

"He will try to use Family Court to attack you. Men like him use custody battles to destroy their mates, while also maintaining a connection with them. Lily, I'm sorry . . . but many women experience the most brutal abuse during this process."

"But won't the judge see through him?" Liam asked.

Lindsey grimaced. "He'll play a role—the part of someone unfairly accused. Not only will he not admit his behavior, he'll deny it. He'll highlight his volunteer work, presenting himself as kindhearted and caring. Just as he did with Lily, during the marriage."

"He kept me off balance for so long," Lily said. "I was so confused about what he was really like. He would tell me he was one way, but he would behave another. He'd tell me he loved me—but he acted as if he hated me. It took me over two years to realize that I had to pay attention to what he *did*—not what he *said*."

Lindsey nodded. "Edward is a textbook case. He's controlling, manipulative, feels fully entitled, and massively disrespectful. He really believed he owned you, Lily. Once you married him, you became his. His outrage over your escape, your seeing him for who he really is, will fuel him now."

"Fuel him?" Lily asked.

"Any attempt you make to stand up for your rights he'll take as an act of aggression against him. And Edward's propensity to see you as his personal property will no doubt extend to Rose," Lindsey said. "What was his reaction when you first told him you were pregnant?"

"When I told him," she said, "he threw a lamp against the door. He kicked a hole in the wall. I never saw him so violent. He said, 'Don't I have any say in this?' His eyes went blank, the way they always did when he raged."

"Lily," Liam said, taking her hand.

"Was that when you decided to leave him?" Lindsey asked.

"Almost," she said, not wanting to remember.

"What happened, Lily?"

Lily closed her eyes. "Once his anger passed, he put his arms around me, rocked me, told me that everything would be different. I thought, Maybe this will be the turning point. Maybe he'll finally 'get it.' He told me he had made a picnic for us."

She opened her eyes, watching Lindsey as she took notes.

"We got into the car, went for a drive. It was late fall, and most of the leaves were off the trees. But it was a beautiful, bright, sunny day. When Edward was good, he was really fun. He put in a CD, and he held my hand. I felt so turned around—I just wanted to believe that we could make it work. I thought maybe a baby would make every-thing different."

Lindsey nodded.

"We drove north, up into Massachusetts. Edward had been born in Springfield, and he said he always felt happiest, rejuvenated, when he went to back to his home state. In spite of his bad childhood, his favorite teacher and aunts lived up there. I thought maybe we were going to visit his family."

"But you weren't?"

Lily shook her head, remembering. "No," she said. "We drove into the Berkshires. There was a little ski area, where he had learned how to ski as a boy. The road was so pretty. It wound into the hills, through the woods. Edward told me that he loved the forest—trees made him feel closest to his roots. The sea belonged to me, but he loved getting lost in the woods. We drove up the mountain trail . . ."

"Which ski area?"

"Mount Blantyre," Lily said. "There were just a few yellow leaves left on the branches, but we climbed the mountain, into the darkest pines. Suddenly we emerged—at this amazing overlook. We parked in a lot filled with other cars. The day was quite warm. People had come to hike."

"And you were pregnant?"

"Yes. But by then I wasn't sick anymore. I really wanted to stretch my legs, get some air after the drive. He got the picnic basket out . . ."

Liam looked away, as if he couldn't bear to hear about a day with Edward. Or perhaps he knew what was coming next.

"We headed up the trail," Lily said. "We passed a few people, everyone smiling and saying hi. Edward was telling me how when the baby was born, he'd teach him or her how to ski. We'd come here every weekend in the winter—and maybe even in the summer or fall, for hikes. Hubbard's Point would be for summer, of course."

"Did you pass a lot of people?" Lindsey asked.

"At first," Lily said. "But they began thinning out." She breathed steadily, remembering. "Everything was fine. I was getting hungry, thinking we should stop soon. The trail wasn't steeply pitched. He had chosen a long, lazy hike, and I remember feeling touched by his care. Edward liked extreme hiking—almost rock climbing. That day we took the easy route—but even so, there were some serious drop-offs. I remember feeling a little vertigo, but not too bad. I'm a New Englander—good and hardy when it comes to the outdoors."

"Lily . . ." Liam said. He gazed at her; he could feel what she was about to say.

"Suddenly Edward stopped. We were on a long straight stretch of trail, at the head of a rock face. It was such a simple thing he did . . . he looked left, then right—" Lily said. "And I knew."

Lindsey and Liam just stared at her.

The hair still stood up on the back of Lily's neck when she remembered. Edward had been looking to make sure no one would see him push her off. "The look on his face was all-business. His eyes were black, focused. He stepped toward me, grabbed my wrist."

Lily swallowed, cringed, reliving it as she so often had in her dreams, nightmares of Edward. The coldest, most fearful part was also the seemingly most innocent: when he had stopped, looked oh-so-casually back and forth.

"He tried to push you off the cliff?" Lindsey asked. "Tried to kill you?"

Lily nodded.

"He didn't want the baby," Liam said.

"Or me," Lily said.

"But he probably would have inherited everything you had," Lindsey said, tapping the financial documents Lily had brought.

"My instincts kicked in," Lily said. "I heard myself scream, and I started scrambling up the bank. He began tugging my arm, yelling at me. Almost immediately, someone came running—a young man, hiking alone. I was hysterical. I grabbed him and begged him to walk me down to the base lodge."

"What did Edward do?"

"He said I was just afraid of heights, making the whole thing up. The young hiker looked at me as if I was crazy. He believed Edward, I could see it! I was babbling. Some older couples came along; I'm not sure what they thought, but they helped me get down the mountain. Edward just stalked off. Lindsey, I know he wanted to kill me—do you believe me?"

"I do, Lily," Lindsey said.

In that moment, Lily knew in her soul that she could completely trust Lindsey Grant Winship. The lawyer's eyes were steady, her voice resolute.

"I wouldn't let him drive me home," Lily said. "I called my grandmother, and she came to get me."

"Good for you."

"I never went back to the apartment in Hawthorne," Lily said. "And on that ride home with my grandmother, I began to think of how I would get away. I had just seen how convincing he was. I was the crazy one—he was sane. That's what it would be like. He'd never let me get away. My grandmother and I began to plan."

"And then you ran away."

"To Cape Hawk," Lily said. She tried to compose herself. She stared out the window at the Old State House.

"He's not on the birth certificate," Liam said.

"That's why he's filed this motion to compel a DNA test," Lindsey said.

"Can we fight it?"

"Yes. We can stall, but he will win. The judge will force you to have Rose tested. You have to prepare yourself, Lily. Edward is going to present himself as the victim here—you took his child away for nine years. You'll see him in court as a hurt, sensitive man, trying to work things out for the good of Rose."

Lily's heart began to race—she could see him already, his puppy-dog eyes, his boyish grin, his false humility. She tried to imagine the way the judge would view him—as a wronged man.

"What does he want?" Liam asked.

"That's a very good question," Lindsey said. "Because what he says he wants and what he really wants are two different things. Lily, you'll need all your strength for this. Edward will probably claim to want full custody."

"Oh God!"

"He doesn't, of course."

Lily held on tight, stomach muscles rigid as she steeled herself to sit still and hear Lindsey out.

"He sees this as a game—the whole point is beating you. He's going to use the courts to attack you, and he's going to use Rose as a pawn. He doesn't want full custody. He probably doesn't even want shared custody. If the court grants him visitation, he will most likely not even keep to the schedule. He'll miss every date and appointment. There is one very serious weapon that we have in our arsenal."

"What's that?" Liam asked, because Lily was too sick to respond.

"Child support. If he is found to be Rose's father, we can ask the court to order that he pay child support."

"I wouldn't take his money if I were broke and penniless!" Lily said.

"Lily, I know," Lindsey said. "It's just the way this kind of litigation is played."

Played—was this some kind of game? Lily bowed her head—she was in a nightmare beyond imagining. She felt dizzy, completely overwhelmed.

"The court will appoint what's called a 'guardian ad litem,'" Lindsey said. "Someone designated by the court to look out for the child's best interests, during the pendency of the case."

Lily felt the world tilt. She was skidding off the earth, into space, into the void. A person designated to look after Rose's best interests? Someone other than Lily? She felt Liam take her hand.

"I can't believe this," Lily said. "I don't want Edward in her life at *all*!"

"I know," Lindsey said.

"Let's not even let it get that far. Fight the paternity test for as long as you can," Liam said. "No matter what it costs. If it takes everything we have, it will be worth it, to keep him away from Lily and Rose."

"The hearing is scheduled for next week," Lindsey said. "We're ordered to appear before Judge Porter, at Family Court in Silver Bay, and I plan to play Rose's medical history strong and hard."

"We'll be there," Liam said. "And we'll tell him exactly who Edward Hunter is."

Lindsey was gazing at Lily, as if assessing her strength, her capability for withstanding the prolonged court battle that lay ahead.

"I should have stayed hidden," Lily whispered. "Shouldn't I?"

Lindsey didn't reply.

Chapter 22

From the top deck of the *Redtail*—the Cape Hawk ferry—Patrick could see forever, or almost. A fine mist obscured only the very tops of the massive cliffs lining the great fjord, pine trees clinging to ledges, branches dotted with the white heads of adult male bald eagles; Cape Hawk harbor and bay, silver in the fog, sliced with the white wakes of fishing and whale-watch boats, rippled by the black backs of diving whales; the long, red-roofed inn, where Patrick and Flora were staying, nestled into the town; and the wharf, where Marisa was currently tending Lily's shop.

He leaned over the rail, as if he could hear the music over the ferry engine's roar as the vessel pulled away from the Cape Hawk wharf. He could still see the look in Marisa's eyes the moment she'd caught sight of her sister. Nothing had ever made him feel better than bringing Sam north. As he stared at the shop, he imagined telling Marisa how it had all come to pass.

On the other hand, maybe he should just head back to Connecticut. He'd find out what he could for Liam, then drive home. After what he and Sandra had gone through in the divorce, trusting wasn't easy. Maeve had called him on it, telling him to take this chance with Marisa. He stared toward the shop, and his heart raced just knowing that she was inside.

"Sorry it took me so long," the voice sounded behind him. "But I had to make sure my copilot was up from below."

"No problem," Patrick said, turning toward T. J. McGuinn, coming out of the *Redtail* wheelhouse.

"So, you're a friend of the Mahon sisters?" T.J. asked.

"Yes," Patrick said.

"I've noticed Marisa around town, and my

buddy Liam Neill sees her friend Lily," T.J. said. "She keeps to herself. I'd never guess she and Sam are related."

"No?" Patrick asked. "Why not?"

T.J. laughed. "That Sam's a hot ticket. Yesterday, first time on the ferry, she walked straight up to the wheelhouse and asked to come inside. It's sort of against regulations . . ."

"Yeah, the Coast Guard tends to frown on flirting while operating a hundred-ton vessel," Patrick said, chuckling.

"Don't report me," T.J. said. "But anyway, I let her in. How do you say no to green eyes like that?"

"What did she want?"

"She asked me to show her the sights as we approached the town—she wanted an overview. I guess she spotted that—" He pointed at a sticker affixed to the wheelhouse window. Patrick peered more closely, saw that it was from the Peace Corps. "She told me she knew a kindred spirit when she saw one."

"Good line," Patrick said.

"Turns out it's more than a line. We've worked in some of the same places. I learned how to drive a ferry in South Amer-

ica, building a school for a village on the
other side of a river from where she just
helped set up a hospital. Anyway, I pointed
out the main landmarks of town—the inn,
the grandstand for the ceili, the docks, the
whale boats. When people come to Cape
Hawk, it's fairly predictable what they hope
to see."

"Not much going on up here?"

"Nope. Just the way I like it," T.J. said.
"The world's too crazy a place. I like the
peace and quiet of Cape Hawk."

Patrick nodded. He looked back across
the water, toward the wharf. T.J. was right—
it looked very peaceful from out here. A
sleepy little town right at the base of a seaside mountain. So why did Patrick feel anything but at peace? There was Jessica
walking Flora—he saw them on the inn
lawn. The shop door was open, but Marisa
was still nowhere in sight.

"So, do you live in town?" he asked, narrowing his eyes at T.J.

"Yes—an apartment just above the ferry
office, by the dock. Why?"

"I figured you might know some of the
characters who hang around the waterfront."

T.J. laughed. "Most of them are Neills. That's the family that owns half the town. Anne's the innkeeper, Jude operates the whaleboats, and Liam runs an oceanographic program. He's away, though."

Patrick nodded knowingly, in his seasoned-cop way. "I know Liam," he said. "Actually, the person I'm interested in is Gerard Lafarge."

T.J.'s expression changed, his guard suddenly up.

"What about him?"

"I'll be straight with you. I'm investigating his whereabouts."

"What for? What do you want to know about a lowlife like him for? What's he done? And—for that matter—why are you asking me?"

Patrick had clearly lost some of his edge. During his years of following the Mara Jameson disappearance, none of his interrogation subjects would have asked more questions than he did.

"Look," Patrick said. "I'm just a retired cop, doing a favor for Liam."

"Oh," T.J. said, relaxing again. "For Liam, no problem. Liam's a great guy, a true conservationist. The opposite of the Lafarge bunch. Those guys think natural resources were put on earth just for their personal use. They're the most unethical fishermen I've ever seen—and making my living on the water, I've seen lots of fishing practices."

"Do you have any idea where Gerry might be right now?"

T.J. peered out, seeming to gaze over the flat, pewter bay. "Funny you should ask," he said. "I've heard things lately."

"Like what?"

"Someone said he was down south, fishing a reef in Rhode Island."

"That's pretty far to go, isn't it?"

"Not for Lafarge—not if there's money in it."

"What kind of money could there be there?"

"I don't know. I've heard about some monster waves, driven inshore by the tail end of a hurricane. They began breaking over the reef, bringing lots of unusual fish into the area."

"Yeah, Liam mentioned that," Patrick said. "But half the species are from up here— northern waters. Lots of sharks, I guess, plus a bunch of marine mammals that are off-limits to fishermen anyway."

"Lafarge doesn't care what comes up in his nets," T.J. said, shaking his head.

Just then the ferry began to slow her engines. They were pulling into the slip on the other side of the strait. T.J. excused himself, went into the wheelhouse to take the controls. Patrick drifted toward the back of the deck. He watched people getting into their cars.

The whole operation took about fifteen minutes—the deckhands directed cars and trucks off quickly, and then loaded up the Cape Hawk–bound vehicles. Patrick breathed in the sea air, feeling the ferry rise and fall with the easy onshore waves. He found himself staring across the narrow passage, eyes on the shop door. And he made up his mind. When he got back to Cape Hawk, he'd head right over and ask Marisa out to dinner. He couldn't leave without talking to her, taking the chance.

Just then, out of the corner of his eye, he noticed a white van driving onto the ferry. White vans were anything but uncommon, especially during the ceili—lots of bands were still arriving, and many of them needed vans and panel trucks to hold all the musicians and their instruments. Their vehicles had windows and passenger seats, and were decorated with the band names and il-lustrations of shamrocks, harps, guitars, maps of Ireland.

But this particular van, the one that had Patrick's attention, was quite different. It had no windows in the back, but it con-tained a refrigerator unit; Patrick saw the vents above, and the trail of water dripping on the ferry's metal deck below. Its logo, far from being Irish or musical, showed a lone dolphin: smiling, standing on its tail, balancing a beach ball on one flipper. Patrick reached into his pocket, pulled out the picture he had printed out from the po-lice website. He checked it to be sure, and he felt that click he always felt when police work yielded something interesting.

Most interesting of all: Gerard Lafarge was in the driver's seat.

After such a short time of rehearsing with Sam, Marisa felt they were almost ready to play. They ran through all their old favorites, and by the end of the afternoon, Sam knew "Storm Tossed" by heart.

Marisa felt so tender toward her sister, so

glad they were together again. She remembered starting the violin in fourth grade,
coming home from her lessons and teaching her younger sister everything she had
learned. The next year, when Sam was
ready for music lessons, she had amazed
the teacher by already knowing how to play
vibrato—while the rest of her class was dutifully plucking, pizzicato, the notes to "Mary
Had a Little Lamb."

After so long apart, it seemed amazing to
have Sam here now. Marisa thought of what
Anne had said, about sometimes sisters
needing to separate for a while. Although
she never would have believed it possible, it
seemed they had come back stronger than
ever. And she knew she had Patrick to
thank for it.

"What did Patrick say to you?" Marisa
asked now. "To make you want to come see
me?"

"He said a lot," Sam said. "But what really
got me was a tape of us playing."

"Us?"

"Fallen Angels," Sam said.

"How did he get it?"

"A friend of his in the Baltimore DA's office. An old fan of ours, apparently."

"And Patrick had it?" Marisa asked, gazing out at the harbor.

"Yes. He seemed to know it by heart, the way he cued it to the spot of you singing 'Cliffs of Dooneen.'"

Marisa shivered to think of Patrick listening to a tape of her singing.

"He said the two of you were just friends," Sam said.

"That's true," Marisa said.

Sam nodded, holding back a smile. "Okay," she said.

"What do you mean?"

"Just," Sam said, taking her older sister's hand, "maybe you've forgotten how to read your own hearts. Both of you."

"Both of us?"

"You and Patrick," Sam said softly. "He reminds me of Paul, you know, when you first met. He really went all out to get me here."

"He wanted us to be together," Marisa said.

"That wasn't for me," Sam said.

Marisa gazed out the door, feeling a tingle go down her spine.

"You haven't stopped watching for him," Sam said. "Not once, all day."

"I just want to thank him," Marisa said. "For bringing you back to me and Jessica."

"Here comes the ferry," Sam said, waving.

"Are you going to see T.J.?" Marisa asked.

"He said he might stop up at the inn for a drink later," Sam said. "I'll probably drop in too."

"Well, let's head up there now," Marisa said. "We'll talk to Anne and find out when we're playing."

The two sisters walked across the wharf, then up the long, grassy hill. Late-day sun had burned off the remaining mist, turning the afternoon bright and golden. Even the lawn was dry, so people had spread blankets and were starting to picnic. A twelve-member band from Dublin had taken the stage, and their music was lively and joyous. Jessica and her friend Allie were on the gazebo with Flora, who faced out to sea as if waiting for her master.

The sisters walked up the steps, across the broad porch, and into the inn's lobby. Anne stood at the front desk, making notations in the guest book. She looked up, smiling.

"Hi, Marisa. And let me guess—you must be Sam!"

"And you must be Anne."

"Welcome," Anne said. "We've all heard so much about you. We'd begun to think you'd gotten lost in the Andes."

"I almost did," Sam said, squeezing Marisa's hand.

Marisa and Anne exchanged a glance, and Marisa felt grateful to have such a good friend.

"Well, you made it in time for the ceili," Anne said. "We're waiting with bated breath—nobody's heard Marisa play yet, and we can't wait to hear the two of you together. How does Sunday night sound? It's the last night of the festival and we should have a great crowd."

"Great," Sam said.

The side door opened, and a bunch of men walked in. Marisa recognized them— the day shift of *Redtail,* the Cape Hawk ferry. They were just off duty, heading into the bar.

T. J. McGuinn was among them, his Greek fisherman's hat pulled down over one eye— a slow smile coming to his lips as he caught sight of Sam. "Hi," he said. "How are you?"

"I'm great," Sam said. "I'm with my sister."

"Could I buy you both a drink, to celebrate your reunion?" he asked.

"I think I'll wait for Patrick," Marisa said.

"Patrick? I talked to him on the ferry," T.J. said. "He came back with us and I saw him drive off, going up toward the cliffs."

Marisa's heart fell. She glanced at Sam, saw her look of concern. Sam had always been able to read Marisa's emotions, and she knew she could see how disappointed she felt.

"Are you sure you don't want to join us?" Sam asked.

"Yes," Marisa said, trying to smile. "Go ahead. Have fun."

Sam squeezed Marisa's hand. "See you later," she said, and headed into the bar with T.J.

"You bet," Marisa said.

Then Anne got busy, with people just off the ferry wanting to check in. Marisa wandered over to the door. She stood on the front porch, listening to the band from Dublin, watching Jessica and Allie playing fetch with Patrick's Flora.

Marisa sat on the top step, facing the band, the long lawn, and the bright blue bay spreading out between the two rocky headlands. The water was so calm . . . there was nothing storm-tossed about it. The song played in her head, though, and she thought of how funny it was to have written such a song for a man she hardly knew.

Chapter 23

By the time Patrick had finished following the white van, it was nearly eight o'clock. He returned to town and drove past In Stitches, afraid that Marisa had gone home, and sure enough—the shop was dark and locked for the night. He had missed his chance to ask her out for dinner. His truck window was down; hearing a familiar bark, he glanced up at the inn and saw Flora. She was playing ball with Jessica, so he parked and headed across the grass.

A band called the Seven Harps was playing some music that reminded him of the Chieftains and got his blood flowing. He paused to listen, and that's when he spied Marisa. She hadn't seen him yet—sitting on the top step of the inn, she was watching her daughter and gazing over the bay, seemingly lost in thought. Patrick hung back.

This was the moment he'd been waiting for. He'd come all the way from Connecticut to spend time with Marisa. She had been so friendly, encouraging him on the phone. So why did he feel so nervous?

Her dark hair was so pretty, the way it fell across her eyes. He took a deep breath. His heart was racing as he walked slowly up to the inn, sat down beside her. They didn't speak right away, but just looked at each other, smiling. Patrick couldn't quite believe that he was here, in this hidden little northern town, with this quiet, careful woman who had haunted him since he first saw her.

Without knowing he was going to do it, he reached over and brushed the hair behind her ear. He let his hand linger for just a minute, then dropped it to his side.

"Oh," she said, sounding surprised.

"Your eyes are too pretty to hide," he said.

"Thank you," she said.

"You probably thought I disappeared," he said.

"Well, a little," she said.

"I wanted to give you and your sister some time to reunite," he said.

"I appreciate that," she said. "But I was just starting to miss you."

He couldn't take his eyes off her, shocked by how happy her words made him. The evening was cool and clear, with every trace of mist gone from the air. Stars had started to come out, glowing in the deepening blue sky over the rippling bay.

"What have you been doing?" she asked.

"Detective work," he said.

"For Liam?" she asked.

"Yes," he said, and smiled. "I was on a stakeout." He'd been hot on the trail of Lafarge, and the only thing that could have pulled him away was the idea of seeing her—too late for dinner, just for a few minutes, sitting on the steps of the Cape Hawk Inn.

"I wouldn't want to hold you back from an investigation," she said.

He glanced over at her.

"In fact," she continued, "I was thinking you might like some help."

His smile widened. "Really?"

Marisa nodded. "I think my sister would sit for Jessica and Flora if you wanted me to keep you company. I can imagine that stakeouts can get really boring without someone to talk to."

"They can," he agreed.

"Then let me check with Sam," Marisa said. "And I'll be right back, okay?"

"Okay," Patrick said, hardly able to believe it as he watched her run into the inn, toward the pub. Sandra had hated when he had work to do; she had never wanted to hear about it, and she'd sure never wanted to tag along on a stakeout. Marisa probably wouldn't either, once she saw what it was like.

Flora ran over, with Jessica right behind her. Patrick petted his dog behind the ears, just the way she liked it, smiling at the little girl standing by her side.

"It sure is nice of you to take such good care of Flora," he said.

"She's wonderful," Jessica said. "She's the best dog I've ever met, except for one."

"One?"

Jessica nodded. "Tally," she said.

"Who's Tally?" Patrick asked.

But Jessica turned and threw the yellow tennis ball again, and Flora went bounding away. Jessica followed, tearing across the grass. A Frisbee game was in progress, but she and Flora ran around it, toward the gazebo. Patrick watched Flora snatch the ball, then gallop up the steps of the small, round structure right in the middle of the inn's lawn.

"Hi, Patrick," Sam said, coming out onto the porch.

"Hi, Sam."

"That's been their spot all day," Sam said, gazing at Jessica and Flora. "First with Jess's friend Allie, and then just the two of them."

Patrick looked at the way Jessica sat there, her arm looped around Flora's neck, whispering in her ear.

"She's been really nice, looking after my dog," Patrick said.

Sam glanced at him with surprise. "Don't you know?" she asked. "Your dog is looking after her." Something in her voice was so tender, almost sorrowful, Patrick wanted to ask her what she meant. But just then Marisa came out the inn door, with T. J. McGuinn behind her.

"Are you sure you don't mind?" Marisa asked.

"Hanging out with my niece?" Sam asked. "Never."

"I might keep you company for a few more minutes, if that's okay," T.J. said. "Then I'll head home—I've got the dawn ferry shift tomorrow."

Sam smiled and nodded, and Marisa gathered up her jacket and bag. She called to Jessica that she'd be back before too long, and Jessica waved to show she'd heard. Glancing up at Patrick, Marisa let him know she was ready.

The two of them crossed the lawn to Patrick's truck. With so many people spread out on the grass on blankets and lawn chairs to listen to the ceili, he felt eyes on them, and it gave him a feeling of pride to be seen with Marisa. The Irish music played, carried on the evening breeze. Patrick opened Marisa's door, then went around the truck to get in and start it up.

They drove along the wharf, and then turned onto a road that took them winding into the pine-dark Cape Hawk hills. From here, looking down at the bay, everything was shades of dark blue. Shadowed by the cliffs, the water blended into the land across the strait. The twilight sky was clear, deep blue, sprinkled with silver stars. They seemed to hang in the tree branches, sweeping low over the narrow road.

Patrick traced the route he had come earlier, following Gerard Lafarge in the white van. There weren't many houses on this stretch, only old unpaved logging roads that reached into the forest.

"Can you tell me what we're doing?" Marisa asked.

"Of course," he said. "Liam saw someone from Cape Hawk down at the Block Island reef last week. Canadian fishermen can't fish in U.S. waters, for one thing. But Liam said not only was the guy fishing, he was catching dolphins. I just happened to see the person in question driving off the Cape Hawk ferry today."

"So that's good news, right?" Marisa asked. "If he's here, he can't be in New England, bothering dolphins."

"Seems that way," Patrick said. "But from what Liam and T.J. say, Gerard Lafarge is a slippery customer. He was driving a reefer truck, and I want to get a look inside."

"Gerard Lafarge?" Marisa asked, sounding surprised.

"Yes," Patrick said, turning right onto a gravel road that wound down into the valley, just alongside the fjord.

"But he doesn't live up here," she said. "I don't know him well, but I've seen him coming out of a house on the other side of town—behind the post office. His driveway is right next to the parking lot, and I often see him or his wife driving out when I go to get the mail."

Patrick narrowed his eyes. That was odd information. He'd watched Lafarge pull in behind a small red house, get out of his van, and be met by a woman. Patrick had assumed he was watching a poacher's homecoming—but maybe it was something more seedy. Maybe Lafarge had a girlfriend on this side of town.

The woods were so thick on this stretch of road, Patrick had to turn on his headlights. Darkness would hide his truck once they got to their destination, but having to use lights made him nervous. Residents wouldn't expect much traffic out here—there really wasn't anything but a handful of houses, a few logging roads, and a smoke-house or two.

"Do you know his wife?" Patrick asked.

"Not really. But I've seen her."

"Is she small, light-haired, athletic-look-ing?" he asked, picturing the woman he'd seen meet Lafarge at the door.

"No," Marisa said. "She's as tall as I am. Red-haired like Sam."

"Hmm," Patrick said.

When they got close to the red house, he doused the truck lights. Cruising past slowly, he saw that the van was still there, and that there were lights on in the house. The front curtains were drawn, and smoke wisped from the chimney. Blue light flick-ered from a TV in the room on the left. Patrick went a quarter mile farther, then turned into the unmarked road he'd spotted earlier. It snaked through the thick woods, stopping just beyond the clearing around the red house. From here, he and Marisa had a perfect view. He turned off the truck engine.

Branches interlocked overhead, and pine boughs formed a natural screen. Patrick couldn't have a chosen a better place from which to watch Lafarge. Or to sit with

Marisa. Enclosed by the trees, they were completely alone. The realization made his heart pound in a way that had nothing to do with the stakeout itself.

"I love the smell of the woods," Marisa said.

"Me too," Patrick said. "Did you grow up in the country?"

"No, Newport, Rhode Island. Right on Spring Street, across from Trinity Church. It's like a small city."

"I know Newport," Patrick said. "Growing up on the Connecticut shoreline, we went there a lot on weekends. It was always fun—but I didn't sail, and my father wasn't rich, so I felt pretty out of place."

"I didn't sail, and my father wasn't rich either," Marisa said. Patrick took his eyes off the red house long enough to see her smile at him.

"Really?" Patrick asked. "I guess I thought all the girls down on Bannister's Wharf were sailors. I imagined them all going to private schools, having trust funds, things like that. And I was just a cop's son, about to become a cop myself."

"My father was a teacher," Marisa said. "And my mother was a nurse."

"Is that why you and Sam . . . ?"

"Yes," Marisa said. "We went to public school, where our father taught, and we used to hear our mother talking about the people she treated in the emergency room where she worked. She really cared about everyone—we could see she loved her work, loved making a difference. She saved a lot of lives over the years—car accidents, near drownings, little kids choking, or with high fevers . . . she really inspired both me and Sam."

"Who inspired the music?" Patrick asked.

Marisa laughed. "There were a lot of musical people in Newport. One family had ten kids, and they used to give concerts at our church. Everyone played an instrument. Sam and I wanted to be like that—so I took up violin in fourth grade, and she followed the next year."

"And you got good enough to put yourselves through nursing school," Patrick said.

Marisa nodded. "We loved doing it too. We'd be working so hard all week, we'd barely even have time to see each other. But when weekends came, we'd jump into our car and head for Georgetown, or one of about twenty bars in Baltimore, wherever we were booked to play. We'd hit the stage together, and even if we hadn't rehearsed once all week, we'd just play our fiddles and sing in harmony, as if we did it every single night."

"You two were something to hear, that's for sure," Patrick said softly. "I'm sure you still are."

"How do you know?" Marisa asked.

"I made Sam give this back to me," he said, reaching into his door pocket, sliding the cassette into the tape deck. He pushed PLAY, made sure the volume was low, and watched Marisa's face as the sweet sound of her and Sam singing "O'er the Hills" came lilting out of the speakers.

"Sam and I never made any recordings," Marisa said.

"It's a bootleg." Patrick smiled. "Rare and valuable."

"She told me this tape is what convinced her to come up here," Marisa said.

Patrick shook his head. "She might say that," he said. "But it wasn't."

"No?"

"No," he said. "It was you. The way she feels about you."

"How do you know?"

Patrick held the words inside. He listened to the beautiful music, smelled the pine forest, glanced across the front seat. Marisa was right here with him, singing softly along to her own voice on the tape. His skin tingled with the excitement of being so close to her. He hadn't felt anything like this in a long time. And he'd felt it from the moment he met her, when he was still on the trail he'd begun to follow all those years ago, searching so doggedly for Mara Jameson. Maybe he'd been looking for Marisa all along.

"I love your voice," he said quietly.

She shook her head. "Sam has the best voice," she said. "Wait till tomorrow, when you hear us sing at the ceili. When you hear her hitting those high notes . . ."

"I'm listening to *you* hit them," he said, reaching for her hand. "Right now."

Patrick looked into her eyes. Clear emerald green, sparkling in the starlight. He had never seen eyes like them, and he never wanted to look away. He put his arms around her, and kissed her.

They held each other for a long time, and then Marisa leaned her head against his chest. Patrick wondered whether she could hear his heart thumping. Her shoulder dug gently into his side, and he wished she would never move. After a long time, a few minutes, he remembered that they were supposed to be watching the red house. But he no longer cared.

A tree branch jostled, and a big gray bird flew out. Patrick barely felt startled; all he could think about was Marisa, pressed against his body. He held her more tightly, thinking she might have felt afraid. But she tilted her head up, smiling and looking him in the eyes.

"That was an owl," she said.

"It was?"

She nodded. "They sleep all day, and fly out at night, just after twilight. The woods around my house are filled with them."

Patrick had never thought of owls as being particularly romantic before, but suddenly they seemed wildly so. Everything seemed like a harbinger—the twilight owl flying out of the tree above them, straight up to the stars. The whales in the bay surging up from the depths, bringing mystery and magic to Patrick's tired old soul. Mostly,

Marisa—her voice on the tape, and her in his arms—the most beautiful nature of all.

Reaching up, she caressed his face. He kissed her again, sliding deeper down the seat to hold her closer. Her skin was the softest thing he'd ever felt. He wanted the moment to go on forever, but after a minute, she pulled back a little.

"Can I ask you something?" she asked.

"Sure," he said.

"Why have you helped us so much? Why did you bring Sam up here?"

"Can't you tell?" he asked.

She gazed up at him, her green eyes huge, watching him as if she was in total suspense, waiting for him to tell her something that would shock her. He felt her hand on his forearm, and he wanted to raise it to his lips and kiss it. But he suddenly couldn't move. All he could do was stare into her eyes.

"I think so," she said. "But I have to ask you anyway. See, I have Jessica . . ."

"I know," he said. "Your daughter."

"Whatever I do," she said, "whatever I feel, I worry about what it will mean to her. I could never . . ."

Patrick waited, watching her get her thoughts together.

"Never put her in a position to be so hurt again."

"No," Patrick said. They didn't even have to say his name: Edward Hunter.

"I've been watching Jess with your dog. She loves Flora. Loves all dogs—so much. That's just how she is, full of love for everyone and everything. But Flora is the first dog she's really known, played with—in a long time."

"She mentioned she had a puppy," Patrick said.

Marisa nodded slowly.

"Can you tell me what happened?"

"Ted kicked her," Marisa said. "And my daughter saw. She watched as I tried to save her, but Tally died."

"I'm so sorry," Patrick said.

"See, I brought that pain into Jess's life. I know you're a wonderful man—I can tell. Anyone can tell. But because of Jess, I have to be careful. Do you understand?"

Patrick nodded. He wanted to tell her about his marriage. How he had believed in his vows, how he'd thought that being a husband was the most important thing he'd ever do. He wanted to explain to her that he'd made the worst mistake of his life—not paying enough attention to the person he'd held most dear in the world, how his police work had cost him his wife. But his throat was too tight to say all that.

"Marisa," he said.

"Jess loves your dog," she said.

"I'm glad," he said. "That's good."

"It is?" she asked, gazing up at him, waiting for what seemed like forever, before he could swallow, could get rid of the lump in his throat.

"It is," he said. He wanted to say, *because she's going to be spending a lot of time with her.* He'd been on his own for four years now, hadn't even come close to falling in love with someone else. But now, sitting with Marisa, he felt that changing.

They kissed again, and he felt her run her fingers down his forearm. He shivered in spite of the warm thawing right in the center of his chest, where his heart had been frozen for so long.

Outside the truck, the night burst into tiny red stars. They sparkled in the sky, coming out of the chimney. Marisa saw them and sat up straight, and Patrick suddenly remembered what they were actually doing here, parked in the woods.

"What's that?" she asked.

"They're burning something in the fire-place," he said, watching sparks fly into the night. "It's dry—maybe paper. I'm going to try to look through the curtains, see what they're doing."

He started to open the truck door, and Marisa did the same.

"I want to come with you," she said when he glanced across the seat.

Patrick wanted to tell her to stay here, where it was safe. But he saw the determination in her eyes, so he nodded. They closed the doors silently, began cautiously covering ground. Fallen pine needles formed a soft cushion under their feet, muffling their steps. The smell of wood smoke mingled with the fresh sea air and an unpleasant smell of dead fish.

When they got to the van parked in the driveway, Patrick gestured for Marisa to hang back. She nodded, edging into the van's shadow. He moved forward, closer to the red house. The yard was almost totally clear of trees and bushes, but the surrounding woods were so thick and tall, they blocked much light from moon or stars. Patrick reached the structure, crouched as he walked under the two front windows.

He could hear the TV blaring inside. One voice rose above it, and Patrick raised his head slowly, to look through the window. Although the dark green curtains were pulled tight, he could see through a crack underneath. The room was small and square, stuffed with furniture.

Two people sat on the couch—the woman Patrick had seen earlier, eyes glued to the TV, and Lafarge, talking on a telephone. He tried to listen, but the TV was so loud, it made the words unclear. Lafarge suddenly jumped up, phone to his ear, to stir the fire with a poker. Patrick saw the logs crackle, and when he looked up, he saw another geyser of sparks come out the chimney.

At least Lafarge had moved closer to the window, so Patrick was able to hear a snatch of conversation: ". . . won't last much longer, since the waves are already dying down . . . yes, of course I know that . . . last chance before she comes back and becomes the star tourist attraction again . . . why not, money for us?" Patrick heard him say three more words: "get the white . . ." Then Lafarge went back to the couch, sat down beside the woman, and continued talking into the phone.

Just then, Patrick heard a door hinge creak. He wheeled around, and couldn't believe his eyes: Marisa had opened the van's door, and was climbing inside. Running across the yard, he reached the van in time to see her disappear between the two front seats, into the compartment in back.

"What are you doing?" he whispered.

"Get the back doors open," she said, sounding frantic.

Patrick raced around back. He jiggled the door handle, found it locked. Glancing at the house, he made sure no one was coming. He paused for a second—entering someone's vehicle was against the law, and he didn't have a warrant or probable cause or anything that would give him the right to enter the van. But Marisa was in there, and she needed his help, so he reached for the keys—still in the ignition—and went around back to unlock the van door.

The odor nearly bowled him over. The back of the van had no windows, so the darkness was almost total. He heard a faint barking—almost like a puppy whimpering for its mother. Crawling in, he knocked over a bucket of herring—dead and rotting, from the smell of it.

"I heard them crying," Marisa explained.

As Patrick's eyes got used to the darkness, he saw that she was crouched over an animal crate, trying to tug it toward the open door. Without seeing inside, Patrick grabbed the handle and pulled it free.

Standing in the yard, he looked in through the wire grate. Four enormous eyes stared out at him out of two white faces, two black noses, two thatches of whiskers catching the very faint light from a rising moon.

"What are they?" he asked.

"Seal pups," Marisa said.

Patrick stood, staring at their dark eyes in that soft white fur, and he thought of Lafarge's words: *Get the white.* Baby seals, he thought. That's what they're poaching now. He reached up to help Marisa out of the van. She jumped down, then bent to look inside the cage.

"We have to get them out of here," she said.

"You're right," Patrick said. He had no idea why Lafarge had them, whether he had any sort of right or permit—but he remembered raiding a dog breeder once, where the conditions were unimaginably inhumane, and this scene was even worse. The seals lay on their sides, panting, their sides rising and falling in quick breaths.

If the cops came, Patrick would be arrested for stealing, but he didn't care. He carried the crate to his truck, placed it in the back. Marisa began to climb in over the side, and he grabbed her arm.

"You can't ride back here," he said. "Come in front with me—I'll drive slow, they'll be okay. Better than they were in the van . . ."

She shook her head, her eyes flashing with wild emotion. "I have to ride with them," she said.

Patrick started to argue with her, but he suddenly knew she was thinking of Tally. It wasn't her fault that Jessica's puppy had died, but Patrick knew the feeling of wanting to make up for the pain and mistakes of the past. So he kissed her and handed her his jacket to sit on, promising he'd drive as carefully as he could. She stuck a few papers in his hand, telling him she'd grabbed them out of the van.

Backing the truck out of the narrow road,

he kept the lights off. He felt every rut, every root across the track, hoping Marisa and the baby seals weren't being jostled too badly. His adrenaline was surging as he thought of Lafarge's words and the squalor in which he'd kept the seals. He wondered about that dolphin in the picture Liam had seen, trying to figure out what was going on.

Once he hit the open road, he turned on the truck lights, including the one in the cab. The papers Marisa had handed him were scattered on the seat beside him, and he glanced down as he drove. One envelope bore the same logo as the one on the side of Lafarge's van—a smiling dolphin standing on its tail. The letterhead said "Sea Canyon Resort."

Patrick wanted to read the letter, but he knew he had to drive—and he knew he had to call Liam. His eye had caught the name of the addressee and suddenly one thing fell into place.

But Marisa was rapping on the window behind Patrick's head, telling him to hurry, the seals were dying. So he called to her to hold tight, and he drove out of the fjord's valley and down the other side of the mountain toward the village of Cape Hawk, as fast as he dared. And then his cell phone rang.

It wasn't until after everyone went to bed and Liam had the cottage to himself that he made the phone call he'd been waiting to make all day. His heart was heavy with worry over the look in Lily's eyes after their meeting with the lawyer. He took his cell phone out onto the porch and dialed Patrick's cell phone number.

"Hello?" came the deep voice.

"Hi, it's Liam," he said.

"You read my mind," Patrick said. "I was just about to call you."

"You sound as if you're driving," Liam said. "Are you in Cape Hawk?"

"Yes," Patrick said. "I'm in my truck, with Marisa in back trying to keep two seal pups alive. We took them out of Lafarge's van."

"Lafarge's van? What are you talking about? He has a black pickup truck. And besides, he's not in Nova Scotia—he's still here in the area."

"I know," Patrick said. "More on that in a minute. You're the oceanographer—where do I go for a seal emergency?"

"There's a wildlife rehab about ten miles east of Cape Hawk. Head out of town, take a right at the lighthouse, and it's on that road. I'll call my friend Jean Olivier—he runs it, and I'll make sure he's there waiting for you."

"Great," Patrick said. "I see the lighthouse from here."

"Tell me about this van."

"It seems to be owned by a place called Sea Canyon Resort—at least it has their logo stenciled on the side. There were letters inside, on their stationery, addressed to Gilbert Lafarge."

"Gerard's brother," Liam said. "So he's in this too. And I've heard about this resort. It's a big development near Digby."

"I heard him talking to someone on the phone," Patrick said. "Something about the waves dying down."

"Ghost Hills," Liam said. With the shock of Edward's appearance, and the court order for Rose's blood test, he had barely had time to register the fact that the oceanic phenomenon was dwindling faster every day. John had told him the pelagic species were getting back to normal, with the more rare visitors returning to their home waters.

"He said 'Get the white,'" Patrick said. "I guess he meant the seals—their fur is almost pure white, with these black spots on their backs. He said something after that, but the TV was too loud for me to hear."

Liam could barely listen or think about the Lafarge brothers, or even the white seal pups. He was too focused on Lily, and what would happen at court.

"How are you doing?" Patrick asked. "Why did you call, by the way?"

"It's about Rose," Liam said. "We're really worried. Lily's beside herself."

"Rose's heart?"

"No," Liam said. "Edward has gotten a court order. He's making Rose get a DNA test."

"We can't let him near Rose," Patrick said. "That's for sure."

"I know, but court's in two days. We need an eleventh-hour miracle."

"Like what?"

Liam had been thinking all night, and he had a plan. "Do you know where I thought we could start?" he asked.

"Talk to me," Patrick said.

And Liam did.

Patrick listened carefully, and then he offered his own ideas. He gave Liam the name he needed, and they agreed to get Joe Holmes involved too, so he could do the necessary tracking to find the witness they needed for court.

"I'll be there myself," Patrick said.

"Are you sure you'll be able to?" Liam said.

"I'll do my best. Marisa's playing in the music competition the night before, so it would mean getting a late start. But I'll drive all night, and get there when I can."

"Thank you," Liam said.

"Okay," Patrick said. "Let me go now—I don't want to miss the wildlife place."

"I'll call Jean," Liam said.

They said goodbye and hung up. Liam dialed his friend's number, caught him working in the office, and told him to expect visitors with two sick seal pups. *Get the white,* Patrick had quoted Gilbert Lafarge as saying.

The words shimmered in Liam's mind, troubling him like a disturbance under the water's surface. He couldn't quite make out the source of what was bothering him—he had too much to concentrate on, plotting what had to happen at the court hearing. So he just stared out at the calm cove, taking some deep breaths.

Looking around, he realized that he couldn't see Nanny. He peered into the darkness, listening for any sound she might make—her tail slapping the surface, an exhalation before diving—but there was nothing.

Get the white.

It couldn't be, could it? Liam's heart thudded, scanning the sea. He leaned against the porch rail, watching for a few minutes more. Feeling an undercurrent of worry, he decided to go upstairs and try to forget the white whale, try to forget the weeks ahead, try to forget everything except holding Lily.

Chapter 24

Sitting on the porch of the Cape Hawk Inn the next morning, Patrick made one very long phone call. It was to Joe Holmes, of the FBI's Connecticut Field Office—but since it was Sunday morning, Patrick caught him at home, in Hubbard's Point.

They talked for nearly an hour, covering everything Liam had mentioned last night. Patrick gave Joe the address he remembered from the Mara Jameson case file, and Joe told him he would take care of it. Almost as an aside, he also gave Joe the details he knew about Gilbert Lafarge, as well as the name of the Sea Canyon Resort.

"Oceanographic rescue work isn't exactly my area of expertise," Joe said. "But if it helps Liam, I'll do what I can."

"I figure there's someone you can call in Canada," Patrick said. "To see if they can stop what's going on. If you could have seen these two seals . . ."

"I'll do my best," Joe said. "But the main thing is to track down the witness for Lily, hope she's willing to cooperate."

"It's a long shot, and very last-minute. If it works, it'll be a home run for Lily," Patrick said. "And Liam came up with it. I wish I had."

"Me too," Joe said. "If it happens, that is."

"Big if," Patrick said, hanging up.

There was a time when Patrick would have needed to leave immediately, to return to Connecticut so he could be in the thick of the action that was brewing down there. He would have turned on his lights and sirens, gotten there by late tonight. But court wasn't until ten tomorrow morning, when he'd told Liam he'd be there. So for now, he just walked inside the inn, told Anne that he was reporting for duty.

"Are you sure?" she asked. "Because to-day is going to be the biggest day of the ceili. We're expecting a busload from Halifax—and with our very own Marisa on the bill, all the Nanouks will be arriving in droves."

"I'm positive," he said.

Anne gave him a hammer and a tool belt, and he joined the team of workmen out on the lawn. Throughout the monthlong music festival, the entries had been winnowed down to just a few finalists. Today the big bands, quartets, and duos would be competing for the grand prizes and bragging rights. Patrick and the others were adding another row of reviewing stands, to make room for all the judges and fans.

He lifted planks, hammered nails, carried two-by-fours on his shoulders. Working up a sweat, he pulled off his T-shirt and threw it on the grass. He'd volunteered for the project the day he'd checked into the inn, as his way of supporting Marisa and Sam. Although Fallen Angels hadn't entered any of the previous levels of competition, Camille Neill, the family matriarch and founder of the festival, had granted them special dispensation—because of Sam's work as an international nurse, and the fact that she'd traveled the longest distance to compete.

At about noon, he looked up to see Marisa, Sam, Jessica, and Flora coming across the lawn. He wiped his face and put his shirt back on, bending down to pet Flora as she came bounding ahead of the others, with Jessica running right behind.

"Did she behave herself last night?" he asked.

"Yes!" Jessica said. "She slept right at the end of my bed."

"And that was okay with your mom?" he asked.

"It was fine with me," Marisa said, smiling. They had shared a long, sweet kiss when he had finally gotten her home last night. He held back now, not sure of how she wanted to be in front of her sister and daughter, but he was thrilled when she came forward and stood on her toes to kiss his cheek.

"How are you today," he asked, "after the eventful time we had last night?"

"I'm great. I called Jean this morning, and he said the seals are going to be fine. They were dehydrated, but other than that, they're healthy. He's going to try to introduce them into a colony of harp seals as soon as they're ready."

"I'd like to lock that Lafarge guy in the back of a van without fresh water and feed him rotten herring," Sam said. "See how he likes it. T.J. told me he was on the first ferry this morning, looking apoplectic. I can just imagine what he must have thought when he opened the door this morning and found them missing."

"Maybe he thinks they escaped!" Jessica giggled.

"When actually they were rescued by your mother," Patrick said, wondering where Gilbert Lafarge was going in such a hurry. He hoped that Joe would be able to connect with his Canadian counterpart, to check in on the Sea Canyon Resort and figure out what the Lafarges were up to.

They all walked around the grandstand, the sisters and Jessica admiring the work Patrick and the others had done. Patrick linked his hand with Marisa's, and they strolled a few steps behind Sam and Jess. He thought of the conversations he'd had with Liam and Joe, and as he looked her in the eye, he knew he had to tell her.

"There's something you have to know," he said.

"What?" she asked, glancing up.

"Lily's facing a court fight this week. Edward is forcing Rose to take a DNA test."

"Paternity?"

Patrick nodded, and he saw her face fall.

"She can't let him win," Marisa said.

Patrick saw how determined she looked, how bright her green eyes were. She was a different woman from when he'd met her, just weeks earlier, when he'd first come up to Cape Hawk in search of Mara Jameson. As he felt the cool breeze blowing off the bay, swirling in from the Gulf of St. Lawrence, he knew that he was a different man too.

"What can we do?" Marisa asked.

"I'm going to go down there, after the ceili," he said, looking straight into her eyes. "To be there when they face him in court."

"I don't want Ted to hurt Rose," Jessica said, holding on to Flora.

"I've been worried about seals," Marisa said. "When it's my friend that really needs my help."

Patrick nodded, and waited for her to say more. He could see the thoughts just behind her eyes; he knew that she'd want to head to Connecticut, to help Lily, but he knew she had made a life for herself and Jessica here, far from Ted. Patrick started to speak, when Jessica interrupted.

"Rose is so worried about Nanny, and she doesn't even know what could happen with Ted. She sent me an e-mail, saying no one has seen Nanny in two days. It's not exactly easy to lose a white whale, but now she seems to be lost," Jessica said, and Patrick stopped dead in his tracks.

"Patrick?" Marisa asked. "Are you okay?"

"I am," he said, giving her a hug and a kiss. "I know you've got to get ready for your big moment, and I have to make a couple of calls. I just want you to know, I'll be here in the crowd when you take the stage, rooting for you with all I've got."

"And I want you to listen especially," she said, staring into his eyes as she grabbed his wrist, "to the last song in our set."

"The last song?"

She nodded, her green eyes glinting. And as he turned to go into the inn to call Liam, he knew that everything she wanted him to hear and everything he needed to know would be in that song, and he would be sitting right here on the stand he'd just built, listening.

Ghost Hills had all but died down. The only evidence that they had been there at all were the large swells rolling over the reef, the surfers waiting in vain for another killer wave breaking with a sixty-foot drop, the seabirds cruising the skies as if hoping for a resurgence of the rich marine life that had populated these waters this last summer month.

Only two trawlers remained to survey the area. One, operated by Captain Nick Olson out of Galilee, and the other, a rust red vessel from Cape Hawk, Nova Scotia, its nets and trawl doors hauled fast, to prevent any passing Coast Guard vessels or aircraft from suspecting it of fishing outside Canadian waters.

While the two fishing boats drifted hundreds of yards apart, the two skippers drove hard-bottom inflatable dinghies toward each other, to meet in what was basically the middle of the open ocean. Money was exchanged—twenty-five thousand U.S. dollars, in cash.

The two boat captains were nervous, but for different reasons. Captain Gerard Lafarge had a deadline to meet, and he was already several days behind. The big fancy resort was scheduled to open on Labor Day weekend, and he knew that many important people had booked their rooms, that the resort owners were planning to put on a show for them unlike anything they'd ever seen.

Captain Nick Olson was nervous because he had already gotten in trouble with Fish and Wildlife once this summer, and he had the feeling they were watching him. He'd made his crew stay extra vigilant, reporting to him any suspicious activity, or people asking questions about ship business. Not only that, but he wasn't all that thrilled about what Lafarge was doing. The waves rose and fell, and although he had never felt seasick a day in his life, he felt mighty queasy.

"So the place opens in what, a week?" he asked Lafarge.

"Yes. Just think of it, all those rich people having their last holiday of summer, swimming with marine mammals supplied by us."

"What do they have?" Nick asked. "A big

tank with dolphins instead of a pool with a waterslide?"

"Basically," Gerry laughed. "Everyone wants the next thrill. People swim with sharks in Australia and South Africa, they dive with moray eels in Cancún. Now they don't even have to leave the Northeast. Instead of paying their hard-earned money to go on whale-watch cruises, they can actually swim with them."

"This place cost a lot to stay at?"

"It's a luxury resort," Gerry said. "As fancy as it gets. That's why I just paid you twenty-five grand. Sea Canyon thanks you."

Captain Nick grunted. He glanced over at *Mar IV.* He wondered how long the dolphins could last out of water. He wondered whether they'd catch the beluga, and if they did, what kind of drugs they'd give it to keep it calm for the voyage up the coast.

"Seriously," Lafarge said. "If you hadn't used your contacts to figure out where the thing was, we'd never have known where to start trailing her. It's perfect—swimming right in front of Neill's house. That know-it-all idiot. Treating me like shit since we were kids."

"Huh," Nick said. He had seen that look of

derision in oceanographers' eyes before. They always thought they were the good guys, while Nick and Gerry were just fishermen trying to make a living. He tried to tell himself that now—so why did he feel so bad?

"Look," Gerry said. "My brother fucked up the seals we were supposed to deliver, so I'd better get going, catch the damn thing."

"Fine," Nick said, stowing the bag of money under his seat. "See you round."

"Yeah," Gerry said. "Call me next time Ghost Hills appear. This was great—we wouldn't have had a chance at the whale up home, that's for sure. She was the biggest tourist attraction Cape Hawk ever had, and if things go right, she'll do the same for Sea Canyon. And we'll be the richer for it."

Nick didn't even reply to that. He was remembering a time thirty years ago, when he was a boy. Whales had been rare in Rhode Island waters, then as now, but one winter a humpback whale had swum up Narragansett Bay, all the way north of the Newport Bridge. His grandfather had taken Nick on board his sturdy lobster boat, and they had followed the whale, trying to get it to turn around and swim out to sea.

"Why are we doing this, Grandpa?" Nick had asked, his fingers frozen inside his gloves.

"Because whales are mammals," his grandfather said, standing at the helm. "They are warm-blooded and breathe air, just like people."

"They're not like fish?"

"They swim like fish," his grandfather said. "But that's all. When whales lose their mates, they sing underwater until they find them again. If we don't help this one turn around, there might be another whale out there, singing and searching."

His grandfather told Nick to pound the surface with his oar, to make the biggest ruckus he could. They drove the lobster boat around and around the spot where they'd last seen the whale dive, where air bubbles came to the surface from her breath. His grandfather stared, driving the boat and following the whale, while Nick made noise—until they saw the whale make a wide turn, her shape a submarine-like shadow under the icy waves, and head back out to sea.

Nick remembered that now. He waved goodbye to Lafarge, then pushed the throttle open and drove across the open water to his fishing boat. Even though he made his living on salt water, hooking and netting and slicing open fish all day long, he'd never felt sicker about a catch. And the whale wasn't even caught yet. He imagined his grandfather looking down, ashamed of him.

He couldn't imagine her surviving the trip north. His stomach upset and churning, in a way he couldn't understand and couldn't quite believe, Nick Olson wheeled back to the ship, leaving *Mar IV* in his wake.

The day had seemed endless, waiting for the concert to begin. Jessica stared at the computer screen, knowing that she wanted to write to Rose, but not knowing what to say. What Patrick said had scared her a lot, as she thought of Ted in Rose's life. Jessica thought about Nanny, because it was easier than thinking about Ted. She knew how it felt to be so worried about an animal. Jessica had felt that way last year, when she'd watched Tally so hurt, lying on her mother's lap.

Petting Flora, Jessica looked into the Lab's dark, deep eyes. She felt the smooth fur under her hand, warm and soft. Flora dipped her head, edging closer to Jessica. Somehow it seemed as if the dog knew how much Jessica missed her puppy; or maybe it was Patrick who knew that. For some reason he had let Flora sleep here last night, instead of with him at the inn. Jessica knew it was partly because he had gone out with her mother—but she knew it was also because Patrick seemed to understand that Jessica needed Flora.

Walking into the living room, she found her aunt standing in front of the mirror, fixing her makeup. Jessica stood still, watching for a few seconds. Her heart skipped a beat—and she suddenly felt so happy, her heart almost hurt. She hadn't felt this way in a long time, since before Ted had come into their lives.

Back then, life had been different. She had missed her father, but she'd known that he was in heaven looking over them; she'd known that the world was good, and people loved each other. Her aunt would send postcards from all over the world, and sometimes she would come to visit—for Christmas or summer vacation, or to surprise Jessica's mother for her birthday. After

Ted came along, he seemed to drive Aunt Sam away. And once he killed Tally, Jessica had stopped believing that the world was a good place after all.

"Who's that standing so quietly over there?" Aunt Sam asked, putting on her eye shadow.

"It's me," Jessica said, coming forward.

"Where's Flora? I've seen her around so much in the last two days, it seems as if I have another niece!"

"My sister Flora," she said.

"Oh, it's great having a sister," Sam said. "I don't know what I'd do without your mother."

"Even though you didn't come to visit us for a long time?"

Aunt Sam lowered her hands, turned to face Jessica. She was dressed for the ceili in black jeans and a black ballet top, with bright blue Incan beads around her throat and a green ribbon in her curly red hair.

"Even so."

"I thought you were mad," Jessica said. "It was so different than before, when you used to visit all the time."

Aunt Sam sat down on the loveseat, pulled Jessica to sit beside her. "You and your mother are the most important people in my life," she said. "Sometimes sisters have disagreements. Or one sees the other doing something she thinks might be bad for her . . . if she speaks up, there might be hurt feelings. And if she stays quiet, well— she worries that something bad will happen."

"Like Mom and Ted?"

Aunt Sam hesitated, and Jessica's stomach hurt. She didn't like it when adults didn't tell the whole truth, when they held back hard thoughts because they thought kids couldn't take them. But Aunt Sam made up her mind and nodded.

"Yes," she said. "But your mother was very brave to get away, come all the way up here to start a new life. I'm so proud of her. I like seeing her fight back."

"Thank you," Jessica's mother said, coming into the room.

"I heard what Patrick said," Aunt Sam said. "I don't like to see people like Ted get away with hurting others."

"I know," her mother said in a funny, thoughtful voice.

"Didn't Patrick say your friend has a court battle coming up?" Aunt Sam asked.

"He did say that."

Jessica looked from her mother to her aunt. They looked so much alike, yet were so different. Aunt Sam was tall and thin, with full, wavy red hair and fun-loving green eyes. Her mother was tall but not quite as thin, with straight dark hair cut chin-length. Her eyes were the same sea green as her sister's; for a long time, Jessica had wondered where the fun had gone. There had once been fire there, and mischief, and excitement—as if she believed that something wonderful was about to happen.

Her mother's eyes had lost that, for a long time. But now, watching the two sisters putting on their cowboy boots, gathering up their fiddles, Jessica could see the fun and fire coming back.

"You could go down to Connecticut after the concert," Aunt Sam said. "And help Lily in court. You have a few things you could tell the judge that would keep Edward out of Rose's life."

"About Tally!" Jessica said.

"And other things," her mother said.

"I want to go too," Jessica said. "To be with Rose."

"He would be there, Jess. We'd have to see him."

Jessica thought of Tally, and she thought of the baby seals, and she thought of Lily and Rose and Nanny—she would help them all if she could. "Mom," Jessica said, "they're our friends, and we love them. I want to go."

"So do I," her mother said.

"We could all go," Sam said. "I'd like to be there too."

"Oh, Sam . . ."

Jessica's mother was smiling so wide, and Aunt Sam looked so fierce and protective, sparks glistening in her eyes.

"First," Aunt Sam said, "we have a ceili festival to win."

"Look out," Jessica said. "Here come the Flying Angels."

"It's Fallen—" Aunt Sam started to say, but Jessica's mother stopped her.

"I think we need a new name," she said. "And I think Jessica just gave it to us."

The excitement had built all week, and now, on the last day of the ceili, the moment had come at last: for all finalists to take the

stage and play the best music of their lives.
The inn's lawn was completely packed, with
not even an inch of grass to spare. Blankets
were side-by-side, and people sat in beach
chairs with their knees drawn up. The
Nanouk Girls had commandeered a prime
spot between the gazebo and the stage.
The two grandstands were filled with dignitaries from the town and province, contest
judges, and the Neill family—Camille, Jude,
Anne, as well as some distant cousins.

Gazing down the long hillside, Marisa saw
the sun's rays illuminating the wide blue
bay. Mountain shadows turned the surface
dark silver, rippling with the wakes of returning fishing boats. She listened to the band
playing—a quartet from Ingonish, the uilleann pipes haunting and mystical, their
notes hanging in the clear northern air.

Sam stood beside her, quietly tuning her
fiddle. Although they hadn't played together
publicly in years, they spent these minutes
before taking the stage in perfect ease.
Sam's way of dealing with any preconcert
nervousness had always been to concentrate on her instrument. Marisa's was to
search the crowd for the faces of the people
she knew best.

There were the Nanouks, sipping wine and drinking in the beautiful music. Anne had to sit with her family, but Marisa knew that her heart was with the group of friends on their blankets by the gazebo. Marisa saw T.J. leaning against the rail fence.

And there, right in front of the stage, sitting side by side, were Patrick and Jess. Flora lay at their feet. Marisa's heart began to thump. She breathed in the clean air. For so long, she had never even imagined a night like this. Seeing her daughter with a man she trusted was more than she had let herself dream. She glanced at her sister, rosining her bow, and wondered what she'd say if Marisa told her she thought she was in love.

The band from Ingonish finished, and everyone clapped. Then Anne stood up from the grandstand and climbed the stairs to the stage. Marisa nudged Sam. She knew that they were about to get their cue. Anne smiled out at the crowd, thanked everyone for being there, and then turned toward the inn.

"We have a special entry in the contest," she said. "They are nurses, they are sisters, they are my friends. Please give a warm

Cape Hawk welcome to—" Anne glanced down at Jessica, as if she needed a reminder of the new name, "to the Flying Angels!"

Marisa grabbed Sam's hand, and they ran down the path together. Their fiddles seemed to whistle in the wind blowing through their strings. How many times had they done this? Hurried along, on their way to somewhere important—school, a concert, a birthday party, a wedding—together, each one knowing that the other was there?

They climbed the makeshift stage. Sam looked at Marisa, and Marisa nodded. "One, two," Sam said, counting them in, and they began to play.

They both wore black. Sam's cowboy boots were scuffed yellow, and Marisa's were scuffed turquoise. They stood so close together that when the breeze blew Sam's hair, a few strands caught in Marisa's mouth. She barely noticed. Their bows moved in unison, fast and precise.

They played a jig, a reel, and a ballad— "O'er the Hills," their signature song. When they started that one up, a voice from the back of the crowd whooped—Marisa was tempted to look out, see if she might catch a face from the past, maybe an old fan from the Baltimore days. But the truth was, tonight she was playing for two people—the little girl out front, who had always had Marisa's heart, and the man next to her, who had begun to open it up again. She and Sam sang in harmony, playing along.

When it was time for the fourth song, Sam got ready to start, but Marisa lowered her bow. Surprised—her rhythm thrown off, Sam glanced over.

"Everything okay?" she whispered.

"Yes," Marisa said. She just had to look up for a minute. The sky was blue, just starting to darken. Soon the stars would appear, silver sparks, bursting in the velvet sky. Marisa imagined a cat's cradle, threads in the night, connecting the stars and holding everyone together. She thought of Lily, sent her love and hope, wished for her to hold on tight until help—Patrick, Marisa, Jessica, and Sam—arrived. Then she looked at Patrick and her daughter, sitting side by side.

"This is the last song," she said out loud, looking straight at Patrick. He nodded, and she suddenly had such a lump in her throat, she wasn't sure she could sing.

"Ready?" Sam asked, bow poised.

"Ready," Marisa said. She tapped her toe, one, two, three, four . . . And then the sisters began to sing.

There was a storm at sea,
With killer waves,
And my little boat,
So far from shore,
I couldn't see the land,
Sea was so rough,
I was sailing to you,
In my storm-tossed boat,
I'd forgotten that love
Is the only thing,
That can save a girl
From drowning alone.
You're my life preserver,
You're my star in the sky,
You're my port in the storm,
You're my light in the night. . . .

The sisters sang harmony. Everyone in the crowd was silent. Maybe they knew they were hearing a private love song, and maybe they didn't. Marisa played her fiddle, gazing down at one face in the crowd. His hair was red. His eyes were so blue. Even in the gently falling darkness, his eyes were so blue.

When the music ended, the silence was deafening—and suddenly the crowd erupted in thunderous applause. People jumped up, gave them a standing ovation. Marisa and Sam locked hands, took a deep bow.

Now the judges had to consult among themselves, to make their decision, but Marisa could barely think about that. This night had already given her everything she wanted. Still holding her sister's hand, she climbed down off the stage, into Patrick's and Jessica's embrace.

"You were great, Mommy!" Jessica said. "Aunt Sam too! You are definitely going to win."

"I don't know," Marisa heard Sam say. "We're such late entries, we're the festival's dark horse."

"Patrick," Marisa said, holding him and looking up into his clear blue eyes.

"You were amazing," he said.

"Thank you," she said.

"That song was the most beautiful I've ever heard. . . ."

Marisa gazed up at him. She wanted to tell him how *he* had made the words and notes flow.

But for now, they had something much more important to do. Singing the song, staring down the hill at Lily's shop, knowing that loyalty and friendship were what had saved Marisa and Jessica these last months—everything had built up like a tidal wave in Marisa's chest.

"Patrick," she said. "We have to go."

"What do you mean?"

"To Connecticut," Marisa said.

"To help Lily and Rose," Jessica said. "Is there room for all of us? Me, Mom, and Aunt Sam?"

"Of course," he said, his eyes glinting.

"We'll take my car. Let's leave right away, this minute—so we can get there in time," Marisa said.

Patrick kissed her, drowning out the roar of the crowd, letting her know that they were on their way.

Chapter 25

Early Monday morning, Liam, Lily, and Rose went to stand on the rocks in front of the house. Liam and Lily were both dressed for court. Rose stood in front of them, then crouched by the edge of the bay. No one spoke for a few minutes, but they were all scanning the blue surface, rippled with the butterscotch light of the early-morning sun, looking for Nanny.

"She's not here again today," Rose said sadly.

"Not that we can see," Liam said.

"But if she was here," Rose said, "she'd have to come up for air."

"She might come up for air at the very minute you turn your back."

Rose peered over her shoulder at him for a long minute, taking him in. Then, as if in those seconds she feared she'd miss Nanny, she whipped her head back.

"Did I miss her?" Rose asked.

"No," Liam said.

"But she's *not* here, is she?" Lily asked, her voice low and worried. "If she were, she'd show up on your tracking screen, right?"

"Her transmitter might have gotten lost," Liam said, taking his eyes off the water just long enough to gaze into Lily's eyes. "The battery could have died; I've known that it was time to replace it, but I don't have my equipment here. It's all back in Cape Hawk."

"So she really could be right here?" Lily asked. "And we've somehow not seen her the last five—"

"Six," Rose interrupted.

"Six days?" Lily asked.

"It's possible," Liam said, scanning again.

He knew that other things were possible as well. Nanny was getting older. Her immune system could have become compromised, living so far from her native arctic waters. She could have picked up a parasite. Her normal food source, capelin, was unavailable. The boat traffic in Long Island Sound was very busy, especially in near-shore areas. Perhaps she had been injured by a propeller. Her journey south from Nova Scotia, seeming to follow Rose along the way, had been an extraordinary one.

Liam prayed that Patrick was wrong.

He couldn't bear to think of the proud white whale in captivity—he hoped that Patrick was mistaken, that the Lafarge brothers had nothing to do with Nanny's disappearance. Liam had alerted John Stanley and Peter Wayland, the Fish and Wildlife officer, and by now he was sure that the Coast Guard and every oceanographic research vessel in the area were on the lookout for the *Mar IV.*

In spite of Patrick's suspicions, Liam continued to look out. Just like his ancestors, who had stood in the crow's nest of the *Pinnacle,* watching for whale spouts so they might kill the whales for profit, Liam stood on the rocks, scanning for Nanny, so he and his beloved Lily and Rose might continue their summer of faith. That's what it had been, he realized.

He knew that Ghost Hills—as amazing and unbelievable as they were—provided a scientific explanation for why Nanny had come south from Cape Hawk. Liam knew what his oceanographer colleagues would say. But deep down, he knew differently. Nanny had come to Connecticut out of love. Whales are mammals, and life is full of mystery. Not everything could be explained by logic and science. There had been nothing logical about Nanny's behavior this summer.

But looking down at Lily and Rose, Liam realized that there had been nothing logical about his, either. He had spent most of his life in a fortress of his own making. In a stone house on a hill, surrounded by boreal forest, surrounded by books and journals instead of people to love. He had lost his arm to the shark that had killed his brother Connor. And he'd spent every year since then trying to make sense of the loss, trying to understand tragedy with his mind.

From the minute Lily and Rose had entered his life, he had loved them. Yet because Lily was so protective and closed off, Liam had kept his feelings mostly to himself. He hadn't wanted to scare Lily or drive her away; he had understood that something terrible had happened to her, and that she needed to stay behind her walls as much as Liam had needed to stay behind his.

Over time, he began to realize that Lily was just like him. She had been attacked by a shark too. She had gone into the water one fine day, and after that, nothing would be the same. Liam suspected that she ran the same thoughts through her mind as he did through his: *What if I had been a minute earlier? A minute later?* Maybe the shark would have gone swimming by, and she wouldn't have been attacked.

Edward might not have noticed her. He might have set his sights on the next woman to walk by—someone else wearing expensive shoes, a cashmere coat. The shark might have swum on to other waters, to menace someone else. But then she wouldn't have had Rose. And Liam wouldn't have met either of them.

Liam put his arm around Lily now. As they scanned the bay for Nanny, he knew that she was worried about court. They had to be there in an hour. Life as Lily knew it was hanging in a very precarious balance; she was about to enter into the court system, where men in black robes would soon be making decisions that would affect the way she raised her daughter.

Although a respectable scientist, Liam was also a northern renegade. He was descended from Cape Hawk whalers—Arctic explorers who had sailed from the Gulf of St. Lawrence around Cape Horn and the Cape of Good Hope, had survived shipwrecks and subsisted on rainwater and vegetation. They had gone one-on-one with the sea, and lived to tell about it.

What Lily didn't know was, Liam would do anything for her and Rose. And "anything," to a man who'd had his arm ripped off by the shark that had killed his brother, was a big word. If Edward tried anything today— raised one hand to Lily . . . well, Liam would almost welcome it.

His cell phone rang, and he reached into his pocket to answer it.

"Hello?" he said.

"Liam, it's Pete Wayland."

"Hi, Pete," Liam said. Although he was on the way to court, immersed in all of that, he was grateful for the distraction. He stepped away from Lily and Rose to take the call.

"Did John tell you what was going on? Patrick Murphy, a retired detective, thinks that maybe Gerard Lafarge is after a beluga—"

"Your friend's right," Pete said. The connection was terrible, but even through the static, Liam could hear the excitement in his voice. "You'll never believe who came through."

"Who?"

"Nick Olson—Captain Nick. He contacted me yesterday, told me that there was a beluga whale in the hold of—you guessed it— *Mar IV.* He gave us the ship's coordinates, and we went right out. Lafarge had a hold full of marine mammals—sick or dying dolphins."

"What about a beluga?" Liam asked, his heart falling.

"No," Peter said. "She wasn't on board. We're keeping an eye out for her, but there've been no sightings. If it's any consolation, Lafarge is in custody for violating the Marine Mammal Protection Act."

"Thanks," Liam said. "Let me know if you see her."

"I will," Pete promised, and they hung up.

Liam's heart kicked over. He hadn't realized how upset he felt about Nanny—even in spite of what was going on with the people he loved—until now. Rose stood on the rocks, pointing out to sea.

"That's a school of blues," he said as the seagulls began to wheel and dive on the slick of bluefish, silver and gleaming at the surface.

"It's so shiny, just like Nanny's head," Rose said, disappointed.

"Rose, try not to worry," Lily said, crouching beside her daughter, taking her hand. "You know that Nanny always takes care of herself. She found her way down here, to Hubbard's Point. I'm sure she's making her way somewhere else, right now. We'll hear about her soon."

"But I already miss her," Rose whispered.

"So do I," Lily said.

"Do you think she's swimming back to Cape Hawk?" Rose asked.

Lily and Rose both turned to look at Liam.

"I don't know, Rose," he said.

Worry lines creased her brow. Holding her mother's hand, she turned back toward the bay, gazing into the unknown.

Liam stared at the backs of their heads, this mother and daughter he loved so much.

He and Lily were dressed in the dark, con-servative clothes they had brought along from Cape Hawk. Although they hadn't dis-cussed it, he knew they had brought them fearing that something would happen to Maeve—that her coma would prove to be ir-reversible. They had been prepared for the worst—and it hadn't happened. That could be true for Nanny too.

"Have faith, Rose," he said now.

"Faith?" she asked.

"We've got to trust that everything is going to work out," he said.

"For Nanny?" Rose asked.

"For everyone," Liam said, staring straight into Lily's blue, questioning, worried eyes.

Rose, her mother, and Dr. Neill were making their way up the hill, away from the rocks. Nanny hadn't shown up, and now it was time for the grownups to go to court. Rose was going to stay with Maeve and Clara. They had plans to plant four new rose-bushes right beside the wishing well. Maeve had even bought Rose her own straw hat, trowel, and garden gloves. But the funny thing was, when Rose looked into the bag, she saw *two* new hats, *two* new trowels, and *two* new pairs of garden gloves.

"Who's the other one for?" Rose had asked, but Maeve had just smiled with that great-grandmotherly twinkle in her eye.

Now, coming around the side of the house, Rose saw Maeve and Clara by the wishing well, starting to dig. The garden smelled of fresh earth. Rose clung to her mother's hand. She didn't want her to leave.

"Stay," Rose said. "Maeve got new gloves for us, you and me."

"Honey," her mother said, bending down to look Rose in the eyes. "I have to go to court. I don't have a choice. But I want you to know—you don't have to worry about anything. You're here with Maeve and Clara, and I'll come home as soon as I can."

"I don't want you to go," Rose whispered, with a big lump in her throat. She knew that *court* was a place where important things happened. Gripping her mother's hand, she stared into her eyes for answers.

"I know you don't," her mother said. "But I'm going for *us.*"

"What do you mean?"

"I'm going to tell the judge how much I love you."

"Really?" Rose asked.

"Really," her mother said. "There's nothing in the world more important than that."

"Why do you have my hospital records?" Rose asked, because she had seen her mother going through them on the table last night, putting them into a folder that she told Dr. Neill she was taking to court.

"Because I want to tell the judge how much you've been through . . ."

"Been through *together,*" Rose emphasized.

"Yes, honey. I want him to understand that you have heart defects that have taken a lot of healing. A lot of time, and doctors' visits, and trips to the hospital."

"With you," Rose said. "You are always with me, Mommy."

"Yes," her mother said, her eyes gleaming as she smiled. "Always."

"Rose," Dr. Neill said now, his hand on her shoulder—almost as if he knew that Rose's heart had just started jumping and banging, going crazy inside her chest. She hadn't had any blue spells in a long time now—not since the last surgery. But right now she was getting breathless.

He picked her up. She put her arms around his neck, leaned her face against his cheek. It felt smooth but just a little scratchy, from his shave. He smelled like shaving cream and shampoo. His dark hair curled around his ears, and he had gray in his temples. She closed her eyes, letting him hold her, calming her down. Even though he didn't say anything, she felt better.

"Rose," Maeve called, "will you come and help me and Clara plant these rosebushes?"

Just then, a car pulled into the cul-de-sac. Still in Dr. Neill's arms, Rose craned her neck to see who it was. The car was familiar, but she wasn't sure. A door opened, and a black dog jumped out. The dog was sweet and friendly, with a red collar and pink tongue hanging out—Rose recognized her as belonging to Patrick, the red-haired policeman.

"Flora, darling!" Maeve said, sounding shocked and happy just as the back door opened all the way, and Rose saw who was inside.

"Jessica!" she cried out, wriggling as Dr.

Neill put her down. Rose tore up the stone steps.

Her best friend jumped out of the car and came flying down the road. They met halfway, hugging and laughing. Rose's heart was in her throat, but in a good way—the best way ever. Jessica had tears in her eyes, and so did Rose. She wiped them away, laughing so hard, feeling all the sadness of missing her best friend melt into the summer sky.

"I can't believe you're here!" Rose said.

"I can't believe I am, either!" Jessica said.

Rose held her hand, tugged her down the steps into her great-grandmother's beautiful yard. She was so proud to show her friend where her family came from—the cozy shingled cottage, the stone wishing well with the magical arch spelling out *Sea Garden,* roses everywhere, and the sparkling Sound spreading out from the long, sloping rock ledges.

"Hi, Dr. Neill," Jessica said.

"Hello, Jessica," he said. "It's nice to see a friend from Cape Hawk."

"It's nice to see *you,*" she said.

And then Rose's mother came around the car with Marisa and another woman—both as tall as Rose's mother was tiny. Patrick walked beside Marisa, and Rose noticed that they were holding hands.

"Well, you must be Marisa," Maeve said.

"I'm so glad to meet you, Mrs. Jameson," Marisa said. She reached out her hand, as if to shake Maeve's—but Maeve pulled her close in a hug.

"This is my sister Sam," Marisa said.

"Hello," the redheaded woman said.

"Thank you both for coming," Maeve said. "It means so much to us."

"I wouldn't miss it," Sam said. "He did the same things to Marisa and Jess as he did to your granddaughter. . . ."

"Jessica," Maeve said, turning toward her. "Do you like gardening?"

Jessica nodded. "I planted a rosebush in Cape Hawk. It's like the one we had in our garden back home, in Weston."

"Well, that's wonderful," Maeve said. "Clara and I thought Rose might like to help us plant these rosebushes while her mother takes care of business . . . would you like to help us?"

Jessica glanced at her mother a little anxiously. Rose knew that she was probably feeling the same way she felt about her mother's going to court, so she squeezed Jessica's hand. That made her friend smile.

"Sure," Jessica said. "I want to help."

Rose ran into the house and got the gardening gear her grandmother had bought. Now she knew who it was for! She put one of the straw hats on her head, and stood on tiptoe to put the other on Jessica's. They waved their trowels, shiny silver spades with glossy wooden handles.

"Ready!" Rose said.

"I'm ready," Jessica piped in.

The adults all looked at each other. The two older women, dressed in their messy garden clothes and straw hats, and the five grownups in their court clothes—Patrick and Marisa and Sam, and Rose's mother and Dr. Neill.

"Are we ready too?" Patrick asked with his big Irish grin.

"Yes," Marisa said.

"You bet," Rose's mother said.

"Let's go get him," Dr. Neill said.

"I can't wait," Sam said.

Then Rose's mother and Dr. Neill leaned down to give Rose the biggest hug she'd ever had in her life—both of them looking at her with love and bravery in their eyes. She felt a giant swell, almost as if Nanny had just come up for air, sent a huge wave flooding over her. She closed her eyes, letting the wave and their hugs hold her aloft.

Rose watched as her mother stopped in front of Maeve. They looked at each other for the longest time, arrows of strength and love shooting from their eyes. Rose felt almost like crying, even though she didn't know why. Her great-grandmother's gaze was so ferocious—she looked charged up, ready for battle. She kissed Rose's mother. And then she did the oddest thing. She shook her hand—just as if they were in a business meeting instead of a rose garden.

"Godspeed, my darling," Maeve said. "You will prevail."

"Granny," Rose's mother said, her eyes huge and wide open, looking almost as if she were a very little girl, and in that second Rose could see her mother at Rose's age and even younger, turning to Maeve for everything.

"Right is might, darling," Maeve said. "He has gotten away with so much for so long. You're going to end that with the truth. Today . . ."

"What if he wins?"

"He won't," Maeve said, hands on Rose's mother's cheeks, gazing hard into her eyes. Her touch left two small streaks of dirt on her cheekbones, like war paint. Dr. Neill brushed them away, and Rose's mother turned, and she and Dr. Neill walked up the stone steps.

"I love you, Mommy!" Rose shouted out.

Her mother looked directly at Rose. Their eyes met and held—her mother's were as bright blue as the sky. They smiled at each other. Her mother held up a coin and threw it into the Sea Garden wishing well. It sparkled in the sunlight, turning as it flew through the air, jingling against the rocks inside.

Rose's mother had thrown the coin, but Rose made a wish anyway.

Chapter 26

Lily and Liam sat together in front, while Patrick, Marisa, and Sam rode in back. Marisa and Patrick seemed so happy and close, even though they had to be exhausted from their long drive. The conversation was quick and lively, catching up on the weeks since they'd first met in Cape Hawk, hearing about Patrick driving Sam up from Baltimore for the ceili, and it reminded Lily of good friends, out for a summer drive—instead of on the way to Family Court.

"You should have heard Marisa and her sister," Patrick said. "They were the best at the festival."

"Even though we came in third," Marisa said.

"Wait till next year," Sam said.

Talking with Marisa, listening to her calm voice and irrepressible laugh, made Lily forget the butterflies in her stomach for a minute or two. But then her mind would turn to what might happen next—and she'd feel cold and clammy and so nervous she couldn't think straight. Liam held her hand. She kept glancing across the seat, as if to make sure he was really there.

Pulling into Silver Bay, past the beach shops and children's museum, it was easy to think that this was just another summer day. The drugstore still had bins of beach balls and colorful rafts out front, along with signs for school supplies in the windows. Mothers and kids, shopping for school shoes, came out of Sutherland's in a hurry to get back to one of the last beach days.

When they got to the courthouse parking lot, Patrick spoke to the guard, who leaned into the car to shake his hand and asked him where he'd been.

The building itself was white brick, nondescript architecture from the sixties. Lily had driven past here countless times, on her way to the IGA, or the bookstore, or the record shop, or the garden center—life's little everyday journeys. How often had she come by, not even turning her head to watch the men and women on the way inside, to battle over the very things they each held most dear?

"I don't want to go inside," she said, grasping Liam's hand.

Everyone turned to look at her. Only Marisa spoke, reaching forward over the front seat to touch Lily's shoulder.

"You can do this," she said.

"I can't!" Lily said, filled with panic.

"Lily," Marisa said, their eyes meeting. "You've got to believe me. I know you can do this. You're my role model. You're going to go in there and stand tall, and you're going to be heard. And we're going to be right there rooting for you."

"All of us," Sam said.

Lily closed her eyes, feeling the world spin.

"Yes," Liam said softly. "All."

Something in the way he said the word . . .

Lily slowly opened her eyes. She looked out the window and saw her friends coming toward them: Tara and Joe, Bay and Danny.

They surrounded the car. "Is he here?" she heard Patrick ask Joe.

"Oh yeah," Joe said. "All shiny and prepped."

"Creep," Patrick muttered.

Liam climbed out and reached back into the car for her. Lily stared at his hand. She knew that she could wait in here indefinitely, until the judge called and someone came to get her. She could stay till the court closed for the day, skip the proceedings entirely.

She'd tried flight already. Now it was time to fight. She grabbed Liam's hand, and let him pull her out of the car, into his embrace.

Joe's cell phone rang; he answered it, then covered the mouthpiece. "Excuse me," he said. "I'll see you inside."

Walking around the building, they heard radios squawking and the sound of a crowd. Emerging on the front sidewalk of the courthouse, she blinked as reporters rushed forward. They had microphones and cameras. She remembered to hold her head high.

"Lily," some of the reporters called. "Mara!" shouted others.

"The idiot called the press," she heard Patrick say.

"Well, isn't he in for a surprise?" she heard Tara retort with a chuckle.

Lily didn't know what she meant, but she was surprised by her friend finding humor in such a scene. She felt herself pushed and shoved, borne forward like someone at a warped Mardi Gras. There was a festive tone in the air, a feeling of anticipation yet at the same time resolution. When she raised her head, she saw many of the reporters smiling at her.

"Go for it, Lily," one of them, a young woman with short blond hair, called. "Don't let him win!" called another, a man with dark glasses.

"We're right here rooting for you," said a print reporter, her notebook open, as Lily walked by. "Can I have a comment?"

Lily couldn't reply, but Marisa did. "We're together in this," she said.

"Ask her name," Lily heard Sam direct one of the TV anchors, the pretty dark-haired woman from the Hartford station. Lily turned, saw Sam pointing at Marisa.

"What's your name?" the anchor asked, microphone in Marisa's face.

"My real name is Patricia Hunter," Marisa said, standing tall and proud.

The crowd began to buzz, and then to

roar. "It's his second wife!" someone called, and then they were all pressing forward, asking questions, ready with their microphones. Lily looked at Sam, tears running down her cheeks, her throat tight with emotion and pride for her friend. She knew that Marisa had much more to say, but for right now it would have to wait.

The courthouse door swung open, and Joe stood there smiling—no, grinning—beckoning Lily and her entourage inside. And, glancing at Liam for strength, with her arm linked with Marisa's, Lily walked forward into the Silver Bay Family Courthouse, ready to meet her and Rose's destiny.

No cameras were allowed inside, so the hall was relatively empty. A cluster of state marshals stood off to the side, talking and watching. Like the guard out back, they waved at Patrick.

They made it through the line for the metal detector in just a few minutes. Walking down the corridor toward the courtroom, Lily and Marisa clasped hands. Coming around the corner, they saw Edward.

Or more importantly, he saw them.

In that moment, Lily watched the skies open up. The look in Edward's golden-hazel

eyes, when he saw his two ex-wives together, was a full-fledged thunderstorm.
Dark clouds, torrential rains, thunder, and
lightning. His face went bright red, looking
ready to explode.

"Hello, Ted," Sam called.

"Oh boy," Tara said.

"Do you see that?" Lily whispered to Marisa.

"I'd almost forgotten what it was like to
watch him lose it," Marisa said. "But now
it's all coming back to me."

Liam put his arm around Lily's shoulders.

Edward's rage was so blatant, everyone
saw it. Lily's stomach clenched. This is what
Rose will face, she thought, if Edward wins
today. She shook off her emotions and felt
her spine stiffen.

"He called the press, but he didn't count
on Marisa showing up," Patrick said.

"Hello, everyone," Lindsey Winship said,
joining them.

"Lindsey," Lily said, and began making introductions. She saved Marisa for last. "This
is my wonderful friend Marisa Taylor. She
came all the way down from Nova Scotia to
show up today."

"It's so good of you to be here," Lindsey
said warmly to Marisa. "He might easily deny

the allegations of one woman—but your story will make that much more difficult."

"I want to be called by my real name today," Marisa said. "So he doesn't figure out my alias. I want to be able to leave again, and not have him find me and Jessica. So it's Patricia Hunter."

"Patty," Sam said, putting her arm around her sister's shoulders.

"Good idea, Patty," Lindsey said, her eyes shining. "Although perhaps that won't be necessary."

"Heads up," Liam said, tightening his arm around Lily as Edward left his lawyer and walked over.

"Well," Edward said sharply, looking back and forth between Lily and Marisa. "Isn't this something? You couldn't win on your own, Lily, so you had to get another liar to help you?"

Lily and Marisa faced him together, Liam, Patrick, and Sam standing right there. Lily didn't know what the judge would say, or what the reporters would report, but she knew in that moment that she was the most blessed person ever—to have such wonderful friends.

"We don't lie, Edward," Lily said softly.

"No, Ted," Marisa said. "And you, of all people, know that . . ."

"We were good and loving and true," Lily whispered.

"And you just trashed them," Sam said.

"You're deluded," Edward said. "And I'm going to prove to the judge exactly that."

Lily just shook her head. Standing in the courthouse corridor, she felt her strength building, as if every angel in her life had come to earth, to be with her now. Her father and mother were here. Liam's brother Connor . . .

Lily felt the courage of her convictions. She felt the warmth of her humanity, and her big, loving heart. She felt the energy of being a woman. She felt the tenderness of Liam's love for her, and hers for him. She felt the flow of friendships, some old, some new. She felt the respect of strangers—the reporters who had come to witness, and the marshals who guarded the courthouse. She felt the strength that came from being Rose's mother.

A door opened, and Lily looked down the hall behind Edward. It was almost ten o'clock, the time court was scheduled to begin. Two women were coming down the hall, one of them with an armload of files. Court clerks, Lily thought. But Edward didn't turn around. He had eyes only for Lily. It was as if everyone, even Marisa, had just melted away. She was his opponent. He was here to defeat her and no one else.

The crowd began to rustle a little. Lily felt an electric buzz coming off Liam. She wanted to look at him, but she was mesmerized by Edward. She had loved him once; even now, she wanted to ask him, couldn't he just see reason and go away? They both knew that he cared nothing for their child. . . . His eyes were black holes, burning with hate.

Joe cleared his throat, and Lily's attention was torn away from Edward's eyes. Joe was grinning, and as Lily looked around, she saw that so were Patrick, Tara, Bay, and Danny. Marisa too. Lindsey. And even Liam.

"What is it?" Lily asked Liam.

The two women got closer, right behind Edward. As they approached, Lily saw Joe raise his eyebrow at one of the uniformed marshals, giving him the high sign. The marshal acknowledged it with a nod, but didn't move.

"Liam?" Lily asked, looking up at him.

"Getting nervous?" Edward asked, smiling.

"She has no reason to be," Patrick said.

Edward just stared him down.

"You know," Patrick said, "there's someone else that Joe and I thought Lily and Marisa should meet."

Edward just stood there, his face red and smug.

"Who's that?" Edward asked.

"Hi, Ed," said one of the two women behind him. Midway between Lily's and Marisa's height, she had the same dark brown hair. Her eyes were soft, warm, blue. She had a long thick scar all the way up the right side of her face.

Beads of sweat popped out on Edward's forehead. A few reporters pressed forward, and the other woman—younger, in a business suit, looking very much a lawyer—opened one of her files and handed them some photographs.

Lily saw the pictures flash by: a woman bruised and broken, head and face bandaged in some shots, cut and stitched in others, one with her broken-toothed mouth hanging open as if she had no jawbones.

Suddenly, Lily knew.

"Judy?" she asked, her eyes filling with tears.

Judy Houghton smiled and nodded, and with blue eyes gleaming stepped forward to give Lily a big hug.

Chapter 27

Judy Houghton," Lily said. "The one before me." "Yes," Judy said. "I'm so sorry for what you've been through."

"Judy, this is Patricia," Lily said, and the three women stared at each other, smiling and holding hands.

Edward had wheeled around back down the hall, where he was deep in conference with his lawyer, a tall, older, stooped man in a three-piece suit. The reporters were examining the photos. Lily's eyes were drawn to one photo in particular—a mummylike figure in a bed, hooked up to tubes.

"Is that you?" Lily asked.

"Yes," Judy said. "That was the night Edward beat me for coming home late. He accused me of being out with another man, even though I was at my sister's."

"I'm so sorry," Lily said, tears welling up with compassion for what Edward had done to her.

"He broke my nose and shattered my cheekbone," Judy said. "With just one punch, he broke my jaw in three places. All my front teeth, and the ones in back on the right, were broken. I went flying across the room and smashed into the window. That's how I got this." She touched the long scar on her cheek.

"Oh, Judy," Marisa whispered.

"He didn't hit us," Lily said.

Judy glanced down the hall, where Edward was hunched with his lawyer, talking and gesturing.

"No," she said. "He learned not to. The police came. He got arrested."

Lily remembered Edward telling her about hitting Judy. He had made it seem so long ago, a fleeting incident, almost unreal. She had been disturbed even then about his seeming lack of remorse. Looking back, of course, she knew that he had told her about his previous violence to put her on notice. But now, to meet this real woman, to know that he had disfigured her face and put her in the hospital, literally made Lily sick.

"We knew about Edward's record of assault," Patrick said, stepping forward. "It's one of the reasons we looked at him so hard when you went missing, Lily."

"And one of the reasons we went looking for Judy again now, for this hearing," Joe said.

"Liam really pushed us," Patrick said, and Lily glanced up, saw Liam blushing.

"Judy wasn't so easy to track down," Joe said. "It was touch and go, and we didn't say anything because we didn't want you to be disappointed, and you needed to be prepared to go forward without her if necessary."

"I left Hawthorne," Judy said. "After everything that happened. And after Ed, well, he wouldn't fulfill his obligations to me."

"Obligations?" Lily asked.

"I remember reading about your disappearance," Judy continued. "At first I was sure he'd killed you. But I always hoped that you'd just gotten away."

"I did get away," Lily said. "I ran for my life. And my baby's . . ."

"How is she?" Judy asked with a smile.

"She's wonderful," Lily told her, smiling back.

Just then, Edward came back over. He was pale and drawn, and his voice shook as he stood there, staring from Judy to Lily to Marisa, and he said, "You can't hurt me now."

"Hurt you?" Judy asked.

"I've paid my debt for those," he said, pointing at the photos. "You had me arrested, and I did all the time I had to do. You can't do anything more to me."

"Anything more to *you*?" Lily asked, incredulous, wanting to scream at him. Her heart was racing, and Judy had to put her hand on her wrist to gentle her down.

"He doesn't get it," Judy said calmly. "He never did. And he's certainly never paid his debts."

"I'll see you in court," Edward said to Lily.

"He worked for my father," Judy said. "That's how I met him. My father had a seat on the New York Stock Exchange. Ed did maintenance work at my father's boatyard. But he was smart, and funny, and my father liked him. Ed used to read the *Wall Street Journal,* asking my father for stock tips. My father was impressed with some of his picks, and he offered him a job as an assistant. That's how he got started."

"Your father gave him a job. . . ." Marisa said.

"Ed was smart. He made connections very fast and easily. He made up an Ivy League background. It was the boom eighties, and he got a job as a stockbroker right after I left him." Judy laughed lightly. "Unlucky, in some ways, for him."

"Why?"

"Well . . ." Judy began.

"Very unlucky for him," said the other young woman, and for the first time, Lily turned to smile at her. She was obviously a lawyer—in her gray striped suit and black patent leather pumps, her arms full of files, her dark hair pulled back in a neat French twist. She and Lindsey had had their heads together while Lily and Judy talked.

"I haven't met you yet," Lily said. "I'm Lily Malone. Are you Judy's lawyer?"

"I'm Rebecca," the young woman said,

laughing. "So sorry not to have introduced myself first. But I've been a little mesmerized by this whole thing. Yes, I consider myself her lawyer."

"And a very fine one," Judy said proudly.

Just then, the court doors swung open, and a marshal signaled everyone to start filing in. Edward and his lawyer had started arguing again. His lawyer was advising something, and Edward was shaking his head with vehemence, shaking his finger. Lindsey came forward, tapped Lily on the shoulder.

"Are you ready?" she asked.

"Yes," Lily said, smiling at Judy. "I am."

Liam and Marisa and Judy and everyone from Hubbard's Point were right with her, and they all filed into the courtroom.

Liam watched Lily in action, and she was incredible. All through the last days, he had wanted to tell her what Joe and Patrick were doing—trying to put together a case for the judge, bringing together the other two women in Edward Hunter's life—so that Lindsey Winship could argue against forcing Rose to take the DNA test.

Now, as the courtroom filled up, he kissed Lily on the cheek as she went up to the table. He felt the change in her mood. Having everyone's support made such a difference—especially the support of Marisa and Judy. He glanced at the two women, sitting between him and Sam, in the row directly behind Lily, and wondered what kind of man could do so much to destroy such wonderful spirits.

If there was one thing that made this moment almost pleasurable, it was seeing Edward Hunter squirm across the courtroom, at the plaintiff's table. He was still whispering insistently to his lawyer. The elderly lawyer's face was lined and gaunt, and he had a haunted, worried look.

Just then a marshal banged the gavel.

"Family Court of the State of Connecticut is in order, the Honorable Martha D. Porter presiding. Please be seated." The judge was in her mid-fifties, tall and slender, with frosted brown hair and a very slight tan. She gazed out over her courtroom with dark, wise eyes that had perhaps seen more than their share of pathos.

"Judge Porter is a woman?" he heard Bay whisper.

"Excellent," Tara whispered back.

"Hearing arguments in the matter of Hunter versus Malone," the court clerk read. "Motion to compel—"

"Excuse me," Lindsey Grant Winship said, rising from her seat. "If I may, Your Honor, I would like to address a matter of pressing urgency."

"Yes, Ms. Winship . . . you're attorney for the defense?"

"Yes, Your Honor. Until this moment, I have represented Lily Malone and the minor child Rose Malone in the aforestated action. However, I must recuse myself, due to conflict of interests."

Lily's gasp was horrible to hear.

Across the courtroom, Edward was alert and on guard. His lawyer whispered something, explaining what was happening, and a slow smile began to seep across Edward's face like molasses—it touched only the surface, didn't come from deep inside, as if there were no deep insides to come from. He was responding to the sound of pain. Liam saw, and felt revulsion.

Lily's face was a mask of confusion and anguish as Lindsey marshaled her papers and faced the judge. Lindsey leaned over, hand on Lily's shoulder, whispered something into her ear.

"Your Honor," Edward's lawyer said, "this is highly irregular, and I must object. To leave Ms. Malone without legal counsel at this moment is unacceptable. My client has waited nine years to meet his daughter."

Rebecca, Judy Houghton's lawyer, snorted and let out a wildly exuberant laugh.

"Judge Porter," Lindsey Winship said, "I wish to offer these affidavits and court orders in support of my new client. As you can see, there's already been a judgment entered in this matter, with a rather serious problem in terms of compliance. May I approach?"

"Yes," the judge said, and Lindsey stepped forward to lay one document on the clerk's table and another on the plaintiff's—directly in front of Edward.

Watching from the second row, Liam saw Edward blanch. He turned gray-white, the color of a shark's belly. Edward's lawyer fought him for the paper, which Edward clearly didn't want him to see. Once the old lawyer won the tug-of-war, he too turned shark-belly white.

"As you can see, Your Honor," Lindsey said as the clerk marked the document and handed it to the judge, "Mr. Hunter is already in serious arrears for child support."

"Your Honor," Edward's lawyer said in stentorian tones, "this order is many years old. It was entered for a minor child, who not only is not the concern of this court at this time, but is no longer even a minor!"

"I'm twenty-one," Rebecca said, standing up.

"Your Honor!" the old, stooped lawyer said as Edward inched lower in his seat and began to look for the exit sign.

"He was ordered to pay child support," Rebecca said, "beginning the day I was born, when my mother was still in the hospital. She'd been at my aunt's, making curtains for my nursery, and he thought she was having an affair instead, and beat her so badly, she went into early labor."

Liam saw Lily's mouth open and her eyes fill with tears. They were both remembering the day Rose was born and Lily's anguish.

"Too bad for him," Rebecca said, "I was born three months premature—three months more that he owes."

"Your Honor," Lindsey said, "Mr. Hunter

was ordered to pay two thousand dollars a
month child support for his daughter. To
date, he has never willingly paid one cent.
Ms. Houghton had his salary attached for a
time, but she lost track of him when he
moved nine years ago."

"That's a lot of unpaid child support, Mr.
Hunter," Judge Porter said.

"Your Honor, the order states that the support ceases after the end of schooling," Edward's lawyer said feebly. "At twenty-one,
the young lady must be finished with college, so I submit—"

"I'm in law school," Rebecca said. "He's
never wanted to meet me, so he doesn't
know that. But I've helped my mother file legal documents against him for so long . . ."

Liam smiled up at the young woman,
fierce and bright and shining, facing the
judge and her father. She was straight and
tall, with dark hair—like Lily's, Marisa's, and
her mother's. Liam suspected that if they
were to track down Mrs. Hunter, Edward's
mother, she might turn out to have dark hair
too.

"And I want to become a Family Court
lawyer," Rebecca said, staring straight at
Edward. "I want to practice advocacy. For

women who have been abused by men like my father."

The court erupted in applause. Liam looked around as Marisa, Sam, Tara, Joe, Bay, Danny, Patrick, the reporters, and people sitting in the gallery joined in. His eyes met Lily's at the defense table, and he saw that she was clapping harder than anyone. The judge allowed the applause to go on for a few beats, and then she banged her gavel.

Edward and his lawyer were huddled, heads close together in conference. The judge stared at them with dispassion, waiting for a response.

"Your Honor," Lindsey said, "Mr. Hunter already has unfulfilled obligations to one daughter . . . and I submit that his reasons for maintaining to want to know Rose are a sham that go hand in hand with his proven history of abuse. Now, if he would like to pay child support to Rose Malone . . ."

"We withdraw our motion!" Edward's lawyer said hurriedly.

"The child, Rose Malone," the judge said, "has the right to know who her father is, as well as a right to parental support. Ms. Malone, if you would like me to enter an order compelling Mr. Hunter to take a paternity test . . ."

"No!" Lily said sharply. "I mean, thank you, Your Honor."

Edward spoke to his lawyer, stood up, and started down the aisle.

"Your Honor," the lawyer said, "Mr. Hunter asked to request a recess, so that he can—"

Joe Holmes stepped into the aisle, right in Edward's path. He spread his legs, flashed his badge. "FBI," he said. "And Mr. Hunter, you're under arrest, for violations of the Child Support Recovery Act."

"How's that for the wheels of justice?" Tara asked under her breath, catching Edward's eye as Joe snapped on the cuffs. "The local cops can get him for what he did to Maeve too." Across the aisle, reporters were scribbling madly in their pads, and courtroom artists were capturing the scene with sketch paper and charcoal for the afternoon news cycle.

The judge banged down her gavel, telling the marshals to clear the court. Lily was the first down the aisle, right into Liam's arms. Then he watched as she hugged everyone from Hubbard's Point, and everyone from

Cape Hawk. She saved her biggest hugs for Judy and Rebecca.

"Thank you," Lily said, holding Rebecca. "How can I ever tell you how much it means to me, that you'd be so brave and stand up this way?"

"I'm so, so proud of you, sweetheart," Judy said as tears ran from her eyes, down her cheeks and the edge of her scar.

"I did it for us, Mom," Rebecca said, her hazel eyes gleaming. "And I did it for Rose."

"Rose?" Lily asked.

"My half-sister," Rebecca said.

Chapter 28

Maeve knew that the time for farewell was upon them. She wanted to have everyone over to the house for a big party and celebration, and to meet Judy and Rebecca. Clara agreed, so between the two of them, they arranged for caterers and a big yellow-and-white-striped tent, to be erected in the side yard between the two houses.

"You realize that that's exactly where Edward and I got married," Lily said to her grandmother.

"Of course," Maeve said. "We have to purge the ground. Is he really in jail?"

"He is," Lily said. "They're holding him on

a federal warrant. Joe said that lots of dead-beat dads skate by every day, and that if they make even the simplest effort to set up a payment plan, they're allowed out. But Edward's arrogance was just so intense. Once they arrested him for the child support, they began investigating him for other things. Including hurting you."

"And there was that incident on the Internet," Maeve said. "That Marisa talked about."

"Edward was an equal opportunity predator," Lily said. "He never met a victim he didn't like. He's always been so arrogant about it all."

"Tara knew?"

"Everyone knew, I think," Lily said. "Tara was egging Joe on to get all the legal stuff in order, and Liam was pushing to make sure they brought Marisa and Judy back in time. And Patrick has never stopped trying to prove that he had something to do with poisoning you."

"Yes, that's a mystery," she said.

"When Judy told us that he used to work in a boatyard, Patrick decided to go talk to the owner. It turns out that Edward did lots of work on heating systems on boats. So he knows plenty about ducts and vents and fumes and all that."

"Well," Maeve said. "If he did it, I believe that Patrick will catch him. Life is long, and a person's character generally catches up to him."

"Is that another way of saying 'Right is might'?" Lily asked.

Her grandmother nodded. She sat on the loveseat, gazing out the window at the rippling blue bay. The light was reflected in her eyes, and a small smile played on her mouth. Outside, people's voices could be heard in the yard, on the rocks, everywhere. Workers preparing for the party were raising the tent, setting up the bar, tables, and dance floor. Liam and Patrick were down front with Rose, Jessica, Marisa, and Sam.

"Granny?" Lily asked. "You look lost in thought."

Maeve turned to gaze at her. Lily was struck, as she often was since returning to Hubbard's Point, by how much Maeve had aged. Nine years had passed since their last summer together, and the weight of every second hung heavy on Lily's heart.

"I'm thinking about you, my darling," Maeve said.

"What about me?"

"About how afraid I was, the day you went to court. Afraid that Edward would somehow pull off one of his magic tricks, by fooling the judge."

"Not Judge Porter," Lily said.

"She never heard the case, though," Maeve said. "I wonder how she would have decided, if Judy hadn't come forward."

"I know," Lily said.

"It's possible that she would have applied the law fairly," Maeve said. "But what does that even mean? I think that the judicial system in general, and men in particular, need to school themselves about the realities of emotional abuse."

"Rebecca will help see to that," Lily said.

"Oh, I can't wait to meet her at the party tonight," Maeve said. But her eyes were still so serious, Lily couldn't understand.

"What's wrong, Granny?"

Maeve sighed. She turned her head, but try as she might, she couldn't hide the tears in her eyes. "I want it to be enough," she whispered.

"What?" Lily asked. "What do you want to be enough?"

"This," Maeve said, waving her arm in a

sweeping arc. "Having you back here again. Spending time with my darling Rose—and Liam. Seeing justice served, and Edward incarcerated. It's so much. But . . ."

"It's not enough," Lily said.

Maeve shook her head. She picked up her glasses case—the one Lily had needle-pointed for her up in Cape Hawk, with the word NANOUK in big block letters, and a whale's tail curving in the background. "This was almost all I had of you for nine years," she said.

"The entire length of Rose's life," Lily said.

"You made it for me, sent it to me . . . I used to hold it against my heart," Maeve said, as she did now, clutching it tightly. "And pray for you and your little girl. I didn't even know her name!"

"I couldn't tell you," Lily said. "I was afraid he would somehow find out. And I think, also, I was afraid you'd want us as much as we wanted you. The more you knew about us, the more you'd miss us. It was the reason I couldn't let myself think about you, or home. Not consciously, anyway. But every night, my dreams . . ."

"Ah, dreams," Maeve said. "I had them of you too. Holding your hand."

"When I was a little girl, walking with you to the school bus," Lily said.

"We had the same dream," Maeve said.

"There were always roses in mine," Lily said. "Just like in your garden."

"Dublin Bays," Maeve said. "Scarlet Beauties, Garnet-and-Golds."

"And all the beach roses, between your yard and Clara's," Lily said.

"Do you suppose we'll dream the same dreams after you go again?" Maeve asked, reaching over to pull Lily closer.

"I don't think we'll have to," Lily said. "Because I'll never be gone long. And I want you to come up to Cape Hawk to visit—see our house and my shop, and walk Rose to school. We'll never miss another holiday together."

"Holidays were hard," Maeve whispered.

"For me too," Lily said, wiping her eyes as she remembered the terrible pain of missing home, especially the first few years.

The waves splashed up against the rocks, sending gentle music though the open windows. The reflection played upon the white ceiling, dancing with shadows and light. Seabirds called overhead. Rose's voice wafted up from the tidal pool, and Jessica's answered, both girls breaking into peals of laughter that couldn't help but make Lily and Maeve smile and dry their tears. Maeve handed Lily the glasses case.

"Your needlework is so beautiful," Maeve said.

"I can't wait for you to see my shop."

"What about those publishers? Do you think they'd like to know you're back and ready to create that magazine? *Lily's Home* has such a lovely ring to it."

Lily smiled sadly, shook her head. "I don't think so," she said.

"Another thing Edward stole from you?" Maeve said. "Don't you want to try to get it back?"

"I have a life I love, Granny," Lily said. "In a magical, amazing place. The only thing that was really missing in it was you. I sell my designs to women who really appreciate them. Rose . . . well, Rose takes up most of my creative time. Considering what she's been through, I'm not sure I'd ever have really been cut out for running a magazine. As flattering as it was."

"They loved the idea of your tapestries of life," Maeve said, smiling. "Creating them, designing them, and then selling them to all the women of America."

Lily hugged her grandmother. "When living them is really just about as much as I can handle."

Maeve hugged her back—hard, but not too hard, and tight, but not too tight. After all, Lily thought: her grandmother knew that Lily might be going away, but she also knew she'd be coming back. They broke apart and Maeve went to find Clara, and Lily went in search of Liam and Rose, to get ready for the party that night.

The band began to play just as the evening star came out. Venus glowing in the west, in the rose-violet twilight. The dark, rich colors shadowed the pine trees and rosebushes, and cast a mysterious net on the smooth bay. The air was balmy, without any hint of last week's chill. Just warm summer breezes for Lily's last night here in the south.

Friends from the beach and town arrived, greeted Maeve and Clara, standing at the wishing well. The two hostesses wore long dresses with shawls around their shoulders, and they directed everyone over to the tent for food and something to drink. When Lindsey Grant Winship arrived, Lily hurried over to meet her.

"Hi, Lily. How are you?" she asked.

"I'm fine, Lindsey," she said, giving her a hug, admiring her coral silk sheath dress.

"This is the first time I've really had the chance to tell you I'm sorry for dropping that bombshell on you in court. It's just that everything had happened so fast. Joe Holmes had just been filling me in on his plans to arrest Edward; he could have done that without my making that plea to the court, but I wanted the judge to see with her own eyes what kind of man Edward was."

"I was upset at the very moment you said you weren't my lawyer anymore," Lily said. "But after that, I couldn't have been happier."

Lindsey nodded. "I'd just met Judy and Rebecca, and I was interviewing them as our witnesses—when it occurred to me that the proceedings could be stopped before they even got started if I could get Rebecca on the record right away."

"Well, whatever you did, it worked," Lily said, smiling, and pointed her toward Tara and Joe.

And then Judy and Rebecca arrived. Scanning the crowd for Rose, Lily introduced them to Maeve and Clara.

"Our heroes," Maeve said, holding Rebecca's hands.

"We were happy to be there," Judy said. Her scar wasn't as apparent in the twilight, but just seeing a hint of it made Lily shiver. Leaving Rebecca with Maeve briefly, Lily pivoted Judy for a moment alone.

"I can't thank you enough," Lily said, gazing at Judy.

"There were so many times when I wanted to call you," Judy said. "Back when you first married him, and I saw the announcement in the paper. I remember looking at your picture, thinking you looked so happy. I thought, maybe he's different with her. Maybe it really was me—that I just made him so mad, we couldn't be together."

"It wasn't you," Lily said.

"No. But back then, I felt so terrible. Rebecca was nine then, and he'd never had one thing to do with her."

"Rose's age now . . ."

Judy nodded. "We had moved out of Hawthorne, up to Salisbury, where we live now. It's about as far from Edward as we could get in this state. At first, Rebecca used to wonder about her father, but then she stopped asking. It was as if he didn't really exist. But I would look in the mirror and know he did."

"I thought of calling you so many times," Judy continued. "I wanted you to find me. If you had, I would have said, 'I've been waiting for your call.' I knew, deep down, that Ed was doing the same kind of things to you. It's in him too deep to ever stop. I wanted you to know that you weren't alone."

"I know it now," Lily said, hugging Judy. Just then, Liam and Rose came over. They all stood there, and Lily's eyes roved back and forth between Rebecca and Rose.

Lily held out her hand to Rose.

"Honey," she said, "I want you to meet someone. Rose, this is Rebecca Houghton. Rebecca, my daughter Rose Malone. Rose," Lily said, "do you remember I told you about Rebecca? How you and she are related?"

Rose nodded. Rebecca crouched down, looking straight into her eyes.

"You're my sister," Rebecca said, holding Rose's hand. Their similarities were so great: they were both graceful, strong, beautiful brown-haired girls. Their eyes were hazel, green flecked with gold. Seeing them together, Rose's small hand in Rebecca's, brought a lump to Lily's throat.

"My mother told me," Rose said.

"Officially, we're half-sisters," Rebecca said. "But that doesn't sound right."

"Rebecca's not half anything," Judy said.

"Neither is Rose," Lily whispered, and Liam put his arm around her.

"We have the same father," Rebecca said. "So we can thank him for that—for each other. But other than that, we're fine without him. We have great mothers, and we have ourselves."

"Ourselves?" Rose asked.

"Yes," Rebecca said. "We're girls, and we're great. Don't ever forget that, Rose. When you get a little older . . ." She paused, and Lily had the sense of Rebecca remembering back to a younger version of herself, trying to figure out what she'd understood at nine. "You'll know what I mean. Girls who don't grow up with their fathers sometimes think they're not good enough. But you are, Rose."

"You are too, Rebecca."

"Rebecca is about to start law school," Judy said to Rose. "She graduated from college in May, and she took lots of pre-law classes. Now she's going to become a lawyer, and help women and kids. She's going to be their advocate."

"Advocate?" Rose asked.

"Someone who pleads a cause," Rebecca said. "I'm going to help everyone in the country understand that women and children have to be treated with respect. Especially judges and courts. Because so many people go there for help, and they don't get helped. I'm going to change that."

"That's good," Rose said. "I'll help you."

"She's going to end up on the Supreme Court," Judy said, her eyes shining as she faced Lily.

"I think you're right," Lily said as she stared down at Rose and Rebecca, the two bright and brilliant daughters of such a tarnished man.

After everyone had eaten, and the band got into full swing, Tara and Bay came dancing over to Lily and Liam. They tapped Liam on the shoulder, and he turned to look. At first

Lily thought they were cutting in to dance with him—but no. They wanted Lily. "May we have the pleasure of this dance, madame?" Tara asked.

"But of course," Lily said, smiling up at Liam, kissing him as they spun her away.

They had all kicked off their shoes the minute they'd arrived, so the three of them danced barefoot. Lily began to notice that her two friends were easing her through the crowd, to the edge of the dance floor, and then out from under the tent.

"Let me guess," she said. "You want us to dance under the stars."

"No," Tara said, grabbing her and Bay's hands, starting to run toward the rocks. "I want us to dance underwater."

Suddenly they were fourteen again. Tara didn't have to say another word for Lily and Bay to know what she meant. They had left many parties right in the middle to do this very thing. End-of-summer nights, with music soaring through the air, were made for this. They climbed down the seawall and walked across the rock ledges. Lily knew she could do this blindfolded. Her bare feet knew every inch of the rocks—every ridge, every crevice.

When they got to the edge, the black zone of shore, where the rocks were wet and slippery, they pulled their dresses over their heads, dropped them in a heap, and dove in. The water was silky and warm. Lily stroked through, tasting salt, her fingertips brushing her friends' hands as they all swam underwater.

She came up for air, to a night sky painted with stars. Brushing water from her eyes, she floated on her back, looking up. This was her element. Salt water surrounding her, holding her afloat, with constellations all around. Her best friends were floating beside her, and her daughter and true love were up at the house, and her grandmother was fine, and Lily had never been so happy—and sad—in her life.

"I can't believe I'm leaving tomorrow," she said.

"Sssh," Bay said. "Let's pretend that's not happening."

"We have to face facts," Tara said. "Or else we'll be really, really upset when we realize she's left."

Lily's heart swelled. To have come all the way here, and to have had so many wonderful things happen, and then to have to leave again. Was this what life was all about? Comings and goings, needing to let go again and again, never able to hold on to the things she loved most? Because how could she have it both ways: her love for everyone here at Hubbard's Point, and her life with Liam and Rose up in Cape Hawk? And what about Nanny? Lily glanced around the darkness, looking for that big, beautiful flash of white. But Nanny was gone. . . .

"You know," Tara said, swimming over to lift a handful of Lily's wet hair. "I almost hoped you wouldn't want to come swimming with us."

"Why?"

"Because I was hoping that tonight you were going to surprise us. Bay and I both secretly thought you'd stage a wedding. That we were all being invited here for a supposed farewell bash—when in fact, you and Liam were going to tie the knot."

Lily smiled, treading water.

"Liam's the one, isn't he?" Bay asked.

Lily nodded. "He always was. It just took me a long time to figure it out." So long, she thought now. Through all the years alone with Rose up in Cape Hawk. Liam had always been there, waiting and helping. He had loved them every step of the way, and Lily had finally felt brave enough to love him back. Trusting a man after what had happened with Edward was no small feat. But now, with Liam, it seemed as easy and lovely as swimming on a summer night.

"We're so happy for you, Lily," Bay said. "We thought we'd lost you forever. Now that we have you back, it's going to be so hard to let you go. . . ."

"I thought you were the one who didn't want to talk about it," Tara said.

"You were right," Bay said to Tara as she joined hands with both friends. "We'd better face the truth tonight, or we won't be ready when she leaves again tomorrow."

"This time you know I'll be back," Lily said.

"Promise?" Tara asked.

"I promise," Lily said, and she had never meant a promise more.

Patrick stood with Marisa, listening to the music. The party swirled around them, and Patrick realized that he was standing in the place where it had all begun—Maeve's garden.

"What are you thinking?" Marisa asked.

"Right there," he said, pointing toward the wishing well. "That's where I found her watering can and yellow boots. Lily walked out of her life nine years ago, and I walked in."

"Thank God you did," Marisa said.

Patrick felt himself redden. "For all the good I did," he said. "I never found her, in all that time."

"You found me," Marisa whispered, holding him.

"I didn't even know I was looking for you," he said, staring into her green eyes.

"I know," she said. "Out of something so terrible has come more than I've ever imagined."

Patrick followed her gaze across the rose garden, to Sam, Jessica, and Rose, playing with Flora. He thought of Tally, and held Marisa a little tighter.

He thought of the cases he had worked on, the crimes he had tried to solve. He thought of Edward Hunter's smug face, and he gazed into Marisa's luminous eyes.

"Sometimes you have to look at what's

really bad," he said, "to see what's really good."

She reached up, touched his cheek. Her smile was still sad, just a little, so much less so than when he'd first met her.

"I'm looking," she said, fixed on his eyes, "at what's really good, right now."

"So am I," he said.

"The best," she whispered, standing on tiptoes to kiss him as the music played on in Maeve's rose garden.

When she'd dried off and toweled her hair, and gotten dressed again, Lily went to find Liam. He was sitting out a dance with Rose, on the four-seasons bench. They moved over to make room for her, and they all sat very still for a few minutes, just listening to the music, and enjoying the party, and knowing that they had so much to celebrate tonight.

"I'm glad Jessica and Marisa and Patrick and Sam are here," Rose said. Marisa and Sam were talking to Maeve, and Jessica and Patrick sat not far away, with Flora at their feet.

"Me too," Lily said.

"It wouldn't seem right, having this party without them," Liam said.

"No, you're right," Lily said, smiling. "Not *this* party."

"It's pretty special, right?" Rose said.

"Oh, I'd say so," Liam said.

"Why is it so special?" Rose asked. "I think I know, but tell me."

"Well," Lily said, "lots of reasons. It's both a reunion, and a farewell. We're getting together with my oldest friends in the world—Tara and Bay, and their families—and you got to meet Rebecca and Judy."

"Rebecca says we're going to be real sisters. She's going to come visit me, and I'm going to go visit her at law school."

"I'm so glad about that," Lily said, hugging Rose. She had come so close to losing her several times in her life; but the surgeries had worked, and her heart seemed as good as could be.

"Why else is the party so special?"

"We're celebrating Maeve getting well and you being so healthy. And all the roses you planted, and the ones from long ago . . . that bloom year after year, always reminding us that summer comes again."

"No matter how long the winter seems," Liam said.

"All those things," Rose said. "And the surprise . . ."

"Ah, the surprise," Lily said. She looked across Rose's head at Liam. His blue eyes twinkled, as if he'd never been so happy.

"I'd say it's an all-around perfect night," Liam said.

"Except for Nanny," Lily said, looking out over the water. "When I went swimming, I hoped she'd show up. But she didn't . . ."

The music played on. Lily's stomach tumbled a little. It was almost time. She, Rose, and Liam sat on the old bench depicting the four seasons. Winter, spring, summer, fall. The months and years roll on, but some things endure forever. True love, she thought. For people, but also for places. Hubbard's Point was in her heart, in her very blood.

Across the yard, a cell phone rang. Patrick answered it, looked up, and called out, "Marisa!"

"Who can that be?" Sam asked.

"I don't know," Marisa said, and ran over to Patrick to answer the call.

"Hurry," Rose called. "We're about to start

the surprise." She smiled up at Lily and Liam, and went to get the basket she needed.

Alone with Liam, Lily leaned her head on his shoulder. If he minded her wet hair, he didn't complain. She felt his lips on her head, heard him chuckle.

"Salty," he said.

"I couldn't help myself," she said. "Swimming with the girls is a summer party tradition."

"All parties?" he asked.

"Yes."

"Even weddings?"

"Especially!" she said, and they laughed. He embraced her, pulling her close, and in the shadow of the cedars, they kissed. Lily melted into Liam, feeling liquid from her swim, and from the heady perfume of the rose garden. She was with him now, and she knew she'd be with him forever. Tonight was just one moment in their own private eternity. Their kiss was long and salty, and she tasted the sea on his lips.

Then Rose came walking back to them, holding a basket over one arm, filled with rose petals that she had gathered earlier—

from pink, red, yellow, and white roses blooming all through the garden.

"Guess who that was?" Marisa asked, joining them.

"Who?" Lily asked.

"Anne! And guess who's back in Cape Hawk?"

"Not Lafarge," Lily said.

"Definitely not. Nanny's there!"

The news was so happy and welcome, Lily's eyes filled with tears. Nanny had been their family angel this summer, guiding them from one place to the next. From Cape Hawk, to Boston for Rose's surgery, down here to Hubbard's Point to see about Maeve, and now back to the northern waters of the Gulf of St. Lawrence and Nova Scotia.

"Back in her home waters," Liam said. "And guiding us back to ours."

"Our home waters," Rose said, jumping up and down. "Cape Hawk!" In her exuberance, she jostled a few rose petals out of her basket. She started to pick them up, but instead looked up at Lily and Liam. "Is it time?" she asked.

"To surprise the party?" Lily asked, smiling. "I think so."

Lily's eyes met her grandmother's. Alone of everyone else there, Maeve knew what was about to happen. She smiled her radiant grandmotherly smile, and gave a nod to let Lily know she was ready and waiting.

Then Liam bent down, reached under the four-seasons bench. He pulled out a basket a little bigger than Rose's. It was covered with a needlepoint canvas made by Lily many years ago—when she was a young girl, not much older than Rose was now. It depicted Sea Garden, with all its magical, mysterious roses, shades of pink, peach, scarlet, crimson, and white. The white roses were the most beautiful, and showed the most detail. Lily had made this canvas with a dream of her wedding day.

She had always wanted to be married right here in this yard. She had envisioned all the roses being in bloom, especially the white ones, just right for a bride. When she was a young teenager, dreaming of her future, she had stitched this canvas. And she had vowed to celebrate a summer wedding, amid her grandmother's roses.

"What will they think of the ice?" Liam asked.

"It won't matter," Rose said. "We'll tell them to wear warm clothes!"

"The ice can be the most beautiful part," Lily said, holding Liam's hand and gazing into his blue eyes. She thought of that old photo, of the whaling ship covered in ice, its spars and rigging black and glistening under layers of silver, the fjord's cliffs rising majestically behind, faced with ice and snow.

That was Lily's landscape now. She had traveled north to find ice and snow, the aurora borealis, white whales, and more warmth than she had ever dreamed possible. She had had her daughter there, and she had met her true love—the great-great-grandson of that dark ship's captain; just when she thought her winters would last forever, she had met Liam Neill.

Seasons change, she thought. And roses bloom all year round, somewhere in the world. Her Christmas wedding would be full of roses, regardless of the fact that it would take place in Cape Hawk. She'd order them from somewhere warm, where the sun was always shining. Her friends and family would gather round, on the shortest day of the year, and they would celebrate Lily and Liam's wedding.

As they walked through the crowd, Lily and Rose reached into the basket and gave each person an invitation. Tara tore hers open right away.

"December twenty-first," she cried. "The winter solstice!"

"My new life with Rose began on the summer solstice, the longest day of the year," Lily said. "So we thought we would bring some light to the shortest day . . ."

"In Cape Hawk," Bay added.

"We want you all to be there," Lily said. "Please say you'll come. We'll rent a bus, a motorcoach, do whatever it takes to get you there . . ."

"We'll be there if we have to swim," Tara promised.

"Marisa and Sam, will you please play at the wedding?" Lily said, smiling at her friends.

"Fallen Angels?" Liam asked.

"The Flying Angels," Sam said, with her arm around her sister. "My niece gave us a new name."

"I like it better," Jessica said.

"Names are important," Rose said.

Liam nodded, and Lily leaned her head against his shoulder. Around them, the moonlight sparkled on mica, ledge, and sea.

The waves were gentle now. They beat in rhythm against the rocks, the force of life that bound everyone together, the salt of blood and hearts and sea. Ghost Hills were gone; time and tide swept north to Cape Hawk.

Lily felt Rose's hand slip into hers. She tugged, and Lily and Liam bent down to pick her up. A breeze whispered, and so did Rose.

Lily watched her press her lips to Liam's ear. Overhead, seagulls flew, their cries sounding for all the world like expressions of love, of joy. She couldn't hear her daughter's words, but from Liam's smile, she thought maybe Rose had just called him by the name she had dreamed of calling him for so long.

"Daddy . . ."

About the Author

LUANNE RICE is the author of twenty novels, most recently *Summer of Roses, Summer's Child, Silver Bells, Beach Girls, Dance With Me, The Perfect Summer,* and *The Secret Hour.* She lives in New York City and Old Lyme, Connecticut. *Beach Girls* has been made into a six-hour television series by the Lifetime network for release in summer 2005; and *Silver Bells* will be an upcoming Hallmark Hall of Fame feature presentation during the 2005 holiday season.

Visit the author's website at www.luanne rice.com.

1864

LINCOLN
at the
GATES OF
HISTORY

Charles Bracelen Flood

SIMON & SCHUSTER
New York   London   Toronto   Sydney

SIMON & SCHUSTER
1230 Avenue of the Americas
New York, NY 10020

First Simon & Schuster hardcover edition February 2009

SIMON & SCHUSTER and colophon are registered trademarks
of Simon & Schuster, Inc.

For information about special discounts for bulk purchases,
please contact Simon & Schuster Special Sales at
1-800-456-6798 or business@simonandschuster.com

Designed by Dana Sloan

Manufactured in the United States of America

1   3   5   7   9   10   8   6   4   2

Library of Congress Cataloging-in-Publication Data
Flood, Charles Bracelen.
1864 : Lincoln at the gates of history / Charles Bracelen Flood.
p.   cm.
1. Lincoln, Abraham, 1809–1865.   2. Presidents—United States—Biography.
3. United States—Politics and government—1861–1865.
4. Political leadership—United States—History—19th century.
5. Lincoln, Abraham, 1809–1865—Military leadership.
6. United States—History—Civil War, 1861–1865.
I. Title.   II. Title: Eighteen sixty-four.
E457.45.F58   2009
973.9092—dc22   2008034853
ISBN-13: 978-1-4165-5228-4
ISBN-10:   1-4165-5228-6

To my wife, Katherine Burnam Flood;
our daughter, Lucy; our son Caperton;
his wife, Jera; their son, Connor;
and to our son Curtis and his fiancée,
Christine Cotton.

CONTENTS

This next year will be the hardest of the war.

—General William Tecumseh Sherman, speaking of 1864

At the beginning of the year 1864 a large Democratic element began to clamor for peace . . . with an army terribly decimated and discouraged . . . with less apparent strength and less hope than when the first gun was fired, the North now knew what it is to suffer. . . .

—Republican political leader Thurlow Weed

This war is eating my life out.

—Abraham Lincoln, February 6, 1864

One of the most tender and compassionate of men, he was forced to give orders which cost hundreds and thousands of lives. . . . The cry of the widow and orphan was always in his ears. . . . Under this frightful ordeal . . . he aged with great rapidity.

—John Hay, At Lincoln's Side

Our husbandless daughters. No wonder. Here we are, and our possible husbands and lovers killed before we so much as knew them. Oh! The widows and old maids of this cruel war.

—Mary Boykin Chesnut,
wife of Jefferson Davis's aide James Chesnut,
writing in her diary in Richmond, Virginia,
January 1, 1864

And I saw askant the armies;
I saw as in noiseless dreams hundreds of battle-flags . . .
And the white skeletons of young men, I saw them,
I saw the debris and debris of all the slain soldiers of the war,
But I saw they were not as was thought;
They themselves were fully at rest, they suffer'd not,
The living remain'd and suffer'd, the mother suffer'd.
And the wife and child, and the musing comrade suffer'd,
And the armies that remain'd suffer'd.

—WALT WHITMAN

MN

L. Superior

CANADA

ONTARIO   QUEBEC

St. Lawrence R.

ME

MI

Georgian Bay

L. Huron

L. Champlain

VT

NH

WI

L. Michigan

MI

Connecticut R.

Detroit R.

L. Ontario

Niagara Falls

NY

Hudson R.

• Boston

MA

IA

Detroit •

L. Erie

Susquehanna R.

PA

New York •

NJ

CT

RI

Illinois R.

Chicago •

Cleveland •

Wabash R.

OH

Columbus •

Baltimore •

Wilmington •

IL

IN

Springfield •

Cincinnati •

Ohio R.

Potomac R.

Washington ☆

DE

MD

N

Missouri R.

St. Louis •

Louisville •

WV

VA

Richmond •

SHENANDOAH VALLEY

MO

KY

Ohio R.

Petersburg •

James R.

Hampton Roads

Cumberland R.

Norfolk •

AR

Memphis •

TN

Nashville •

Tennessee R.

Roanoke R.

NC

Arkansas R.

Chattanooga •

Mississippi R.

• Resaca

ATLANTIC

Kennesaw Mt. •

Savannah R.

SC

OCEAN

MS

Atlanta •

Wilmington •

LA

AL

Milledgeville •

Chattahoochee R.

Vicksburg •

Alabama R.

GA

Charleston •

Red R.

Mobile •

Savannah •

New Orleans •

FL

GULF OF MEXICO

**Locations of Selected
Significant Events, 1863–1864**

0   200   400 mi

0   200   400 km

PENNSYLVANIA

Chambersburg

Gettysburg

Susquehanna R.

MARYLAND

Potomac R.

Martinsburg

Frederick

Monocacy R.

Baltimore

Harpers
Ferry

Fishers Hill

Potomac R.

WEST
VIRGINIA

Winchester

FORT STEVENS

Cedar Creek

Washington,
D.C.

SHENANDOAH VALLEY

MASSANUTTEN MTS.

Shenandoah R.

New Market

Alexandria

Patuxent R.

VIRGINIA

The Wilderness

BLUE RIDGE MOUNTAINS

Rapidan R.

Chancellorsville

Potomac R.

Spotsylvania

Rappahannock R.

Yellow
Tavern

North Anna R.

Mattaponi R.

Lexington

Pamunkey R.

James R.

Cold Harbor

Richmond

Lynchburg

Appomattox R.

Drewry's Bluff

Bermuda Hundred

City Point

Petersburg

The Crater

Fort Monroe

C
H
E
S
A
P
E
A
K
E

B
A
Y

**Major Battles of 1863 and 1864 in
Virginia and Lower Pennsylvania**

0   20   40   60 mi

0   20   40   60 km

Potomac R.

WEST
VIRGINIA

Sharpsburg
(BATTLE OF
ANTIETAM
1862)

Monocacy R.

Frederick

to Baltimore

Shepherdstown

BATTLE OF THE
MONOCACY
JULY 9

Harpers Ferry

Potomac R.

MARYLAND

Winchester

SHENANDOAH
VALLEY

Shenandoah R.

Rockville

Silver Spring

FORT STEVENS

Washington,
D.C.

BLUE RIDGE MOUNTAINS

BULL RUN MTS.

LINE OF WASHINGTON'S
DEFENSES

Alexandria

Potomac R.

VIRGINIA

N

Jubal Early's Raid on Washington in July of 1864: Approaches and Defenses

0	20	40 mi
0	20	40 km

1864

── O N E ──

THE BELEAGUERED
GIANT

On the morning of January 1, 1864, 8,000 people waited in line on the frozen sunlit lawns of the White House, eager to greet President Abraham Lincoln at the traditional New Year's Day reception.

At noon, they poured into the mansion. Ushers pointed the way to the East Room, brightly lit by massive gas-burning crystal chandeliers. The Marine Band, splendid in scarlet tunics, played lively tunes. Official Washington had already passed through the receiving line: ambassadors and their wives, the justices of the Supreme Court, members of the cabinet, senators and congressmen with their families. Following them came officers of the Union Army and the United States Navy, veterans of the thirty-three months of fighting that had taken place thus far in the Civil War.

Abraham Lincoln towered above the crowd pressing around him, his rawboned body, just under 6 feet 4 and weighing 180 pounds, clad in an ill-fitting black suit. A man of great strength and stooped posture, he moved awkwardly and had a rumpled, untidy appearance. Despite his efforts to comb and brush what he called his "coarse black hair," he said it always looked like "a bird's nest." On formal occasions like this, he slipped his large hands into white kid gloves, giving them the appearance, Lincoln thought, of "canvassed hams." Beside him stood his wife, Mary Todd Lincoln, 5 feet 2 and plump, who came down from the family quarters late in the morning, ninety minutes after Lincoln began to shake hands with their guests. She wore what a newspaper account described as "a purple velvet dress, decorated with white satin flutings" that had "an immense train." A headdress with a large white plume topped off her costume. (In this era when most fashionable ladies wore hoopskirts, a heavyset short woman looked as if her top half had emerged from a dome.)

Aides kept trying to push the well-wishers past the president as soon as they shook his hand. One of the young men who served as his private secretary calculated that Lincoln could shake hands and say a word of greeting once every four or five seconds, but many of those who came to see the president stood rooted to the spot, as if they gained strength by staying near him.

Lincoln kept shaking hands, occasionally using his left hand while he rested his right, nodding encouragingly as he exchanged brief pleasantries. Sometimes his craggy, bearded face would break into a smile; answering a remark in his high-pitched voice, the man who had delivered the Gettysburg Address six weeks before occasionally slipped into the rustic terms "I reckon" or "By jings!" At other moments, he might greet a friend with a hearty "Howdy!" Lincoln pronounced "chair" as "cheer"—"Mister Cheerman"—and when he laughed, it reminded one listener of the neighing of a wild horse.

At times, his mind seemed elsewhere. During public receptions, he tried to greet everyone in a cheerful and confident manner, but few imagined not only the mental numbness but also the physical exertion and discomfort involved in shaking thousands of hands. As the crowd kept coming through, people jammed together so closely that one of them said "the crushing of bonnets and things was fearful." Some citizens acquired souvenirs by plucking buttons from embroidered furniture, and others surreptitiously used scissors to cut little squares from curtains. After these long sessions, when Lincoln took off his white gloves, his secretaries could see that his right hand was swollen, bruised, and sometimes bloody.

Occasionally, Lincoln saw something at these receptions that moved him to action. A friend observed this.

The President had been standing for some time, bowing his acknowledgments to the thronging multitude, when his eye fell upon a couple who had entered unobserved—a wounded soldier, and his plainly dressed mother. . . . He made his way to where they stood, and, taking each of them by the hand, with a delicacy and cordiality that brought tears to many eyes, he assured them of his interest and welcome. Governors, senators, diplomats, passed with merely a nod; but that pale young face he might never see again. To him, and to others like him, did the nation owe its life.

Before this reception on the first day of 1864 finished, something unique occurred. For the first time since 1785, when George Washington began the custom of having these New Year's gatherings when New York City was the nation's capital, blacks arrived as guests to be presented to the president. A California newspaper described them as being "four colored men of genteel exterior, and with the manners of gentlemen." Lincoln shook hands with each man, using his last name and calling him "Mister." The moment had its significance, but it was equally significant that only four black men, evidently without their wives, were at an occasion attended by 8,000 people.

II

The reception ended at midafternoon of this bitterly cold day. Lincoln escaped the White House and walked to the three-story brick building on the wooded White House grounds at the corner of 17th Street and Pennsylvania Avenue that housed a large part of the War Department. He walked in an odd way, moving the long legs of his lanky body in a full stride, covering the ground quickly, but he put the soles of his feet down so flat with each step that he seemed to be stamping along. Crossing the icy grass, a tall black top hat on his head and a grey plaid shawl flung across his shoulders, he was making one of his innumerable visits to the headquarters of the Union Army. A soldier there said that Lincoln would come over "morning, afternoon, and evening, to receive the latest news from the armies at the front. . . . He seldom failed to come over late in the evening before retiring, and sometimes he would stay all night." The White House was not connected to the telegraph system; all of the presidential telegrams came in or went out of the building to which he now headed. Lincoln did not have to go in person—military messengers could have carried telegrams back and forth swiftly—but he preferred doing this.

At the headquarters door, the blue-uniformed sentry raised his musket to "present arms," and Lincoln returned the salute with a bow and a touch of his hat. He climbed the stairs to the second floor and hung his shawl over the top of a high screen door that separated Secretary of War Edwin M. Stanton's office from the office that handled the most important telegrams, those in code.

Moving along one side of the room where young soldiers tapped out and received encoded messages at their marble-topped desks, Lincoln came to a chest against a wall. He opened the top drawer, into which these "cipher-clerks" placed the messages they had decoded, in order of receipt, each one in the form of a "yellow tissue-paper telegraphic dispatch." As one of the young operators described it, each time Lincoln entered, he would "read over the telegrams, beginning at the top, until he came to the one he had seen at his last previous visit." Today the most important of these indicated that Confederate Major General Jubal Early might have moved more than 6,000 men of his swift-striking forces into an area of Virginia and West Virginia only sixty miles northwest of Washington, and could begin attacks there within twenty-four hours.

Here was the war, staring Lincoln in the face. After three years of fighting, his massive army could not capture the Confederate capital of Richmond, ninety-five miles to the south, while Jubal Early, one of the Confederacy's better generals, could still threaten places northwest of Washington such as Harpers Ferry, West Virginia, or Sharpsburg, Maryland, scene of the Battle of Antietam, fought fifteen months before. Lincoln, whose constant involvement in military matters came from his mistrust of the Union Army's leadership, wrote a message to the officer in charge at Harpers Ferry—Brigadier General Jeremiah Sullivan, a prewar naval officer and civilian lawyer who earlier in the war served creditably in staff positions in the western theater. Sullivan was no match for Early, a West Point veteran of the Mexican War who since 1861 had gained much combat experience commanding large bodies of troops. Sent at three-thirty in the afternoon, Lincoln's message read:

HAVE YOU ANYTHING NEW FROM WINCHESTER, MARTINSBURG, OR THEREABOUTS?

A. LINCOLN

Once he dealt with his incoming telegrams, Lincoln would go over and sit at a wooden desk by the window. Starting early in the war, he found it a haven, an office without walls. No one bothered him there; the young operators kept working at their desks a few yards from him, and as one of them assessed the situation, "He would there relax from the strain and care ever present in the White House." Lincoln did more than that; he often worked there as he waited, sometimes for hours, for the answer to a message such as the one he had just sent; during a big battle he would walk into Stanton's office and "spend hour after hour with his War Secretary, where he could read the telegrams as fast as they were received and handed in from the adjoining room." In June and July of 1862, he sat at that desk beside the window in the telegraph office as he developed his ideas of how to begin to end slavery without losing the support of Maryland, Delaware, Kentucky, and Missouri—the Border States in which slavery was still entrenched. There he penned the first draft of his Emancipation Proclamation: issued in September of 1862 to take effect on January 1, 1863, the New Year's Day before this, Lincoln had signed the official document just after the New Year's White House reception identical to the one from which he had just come.

At today's reception, those eagerly crowding around him as the Marine Band played had seen what they wished to see: their president, their leader, the man with a strong, homely face to whom they looked for victory and the end of the national convulsion. If they saw him now, staring out the window into the cold darkening afternoon, a different image would confront them. The fifty-four-year-old president looked haggard, with what one man called "great black rings under his eyes." Thirty-three months of war had turned his leathery dark skin grey, and strands of grey ran through Lincoln's shaggy black hair. Another man who studied him closely observed: "Lines of care ploughed his face . . . the expression was remarkably pensive and tender, often sad, as if a reservoir of tears lay very near the surface." Since giving the Gettysburg Address in November, he had been ill of a fever, worse on some days and better on others; after it left him, it would later be thought he had contracted some form of smallpox.

As he sat at that window, waiting for an answer from General Sullivan at Harpers Ferry, Lincoln faced yet another year of crushing challenges. No American president had ever come under such pressure. When he left his home in Springfield, Illinois, for the White House three years before, he gave a brief speech from the steps of the train about to carry him away. Lincoln told the crowd of friends who came to see him off, "I now leave . . . with a task before me greater than that which rested upon Washington."

To work at that task, the nation had elected a leader who, in the editorial opinion of Connecticut's Republican-affiliated *Hartford Courant*, possessed "the intellectual power of a giant with the simple habits of a backwoods farmer." The ever-present Democratic opposition saw him as a terrible choice. In his own town, the *Springfield Register* called his election "a national calamity," while the *Atlas and Argus* of Albany, New York, described him as "a slang-whanging stump speaker . . . of which all parties are ashamed." The influential *New York Herald* characterized him as "a fourth-rate lecturer, who cannot speak good grammar," a man whose speeches consisted of "the most unmitigated trash, interlarded with coarse and clumsy jokes."

The war that started five weeks after Lincoln's inauguration on March 4, 1861, grew enormously; as 1864 began, close to a million Union troops confronted 700,000 Confederates, fighting in actions that ranged from major battles to guerrilla skirmishes in places as far from each other as the Virginia coast, Missouri, and Texas—a winding and often-shifting front of some 2,000 miles. To Lincoln's acute disappointment and frustration, as well as that of the Northern public, after three years of bloody campaigns, some of them bungled, the military struggle continued to hang in the balance. During 1863, Federal troops won at Gettysburg, Vicksburg, and Chattanooga, but the Confederate States Army still possessed the strength, the will, and much of the leadership that struck so hard at Chancellorsville and Chickamauga. (In addition to their skill and valor, during 1861 and 1862 the Confederates had captured immense amounts of Union Army equipment and supplies, much of it still in use; Robert E. Lee's office at his field headquarters was in a horse-drawn ambulance on whose canvas sides appeared the faded letters "U.S.," showing that it had belonged to Federal forces.)

Union casualties shocked the North. Twice as many soldiers died from disease as from enemy fire; from all causes, the Union had lost a total of 210,000 of its soldiers and sailors, and no one could predict how many scores of thousands might be sacrificed in the coming year. Wounded and dying men filled Washington: they lay not only in the twenty-one military hospitals created since the war began, but received care in converted warehouses, hotels, schools, and even private houses whose owners tended them. (At one time, wounded also lay in cots within the Capitol building.) In addition, more than 100,000 men had deserted. In late 1863, a patriotic youth who enlisted in the army at Albany found himself herded in among "eight hundred or one thousand ruffians, closely guarded by heavy lines of sentinels." These men, being sent to the front against their will, were "bounty jumpers" who accepted a bonus for enlisting and either failed to appear for service or deserted from the ranks at the first opportunity. This recruit found that some "had jumped the bounty in say half a dozen cities. . . . There was not a man of them who was not eager to run away. Not a man who did not quake when he thought of the front." During this contingent's shipment south to the fighting in Virginia, at different times guards shot eight men dead as they attempted to desert; one of those killed tried to escape by leaping off a steamer into the winter waters of the Hudson River.

Sitting there in the telegraph office, waiting to learn if Jubal Early might start the New Year by threatening Washington, Lincoln knew just how resolute an enemy he faced. Confederate president Jefferson Davis and the white South remained defiant and determined. In Davis's recent Annual Message to the Confederate Congress, he said, "At the commencement of this war we were far from anticipating the magnitude and duration of the struggle in which we were engaged"—the mirror image of the North's experience—but closed with, "We have been united as a people were never united under like circumstances before."

A succession of generals Lincoln chose to oppose Robert E. Lee in Virginia had failed him. The Confederate forces had themselves experienced significant numbers of desertions, but virtually all the regiments of Lee's formidable Army of Northern Virginia were about to reenlist to fight on as long as the war should last.

The passionately felt need to win the war, to stop the slaughter, agonized Lincoln as commander-in-chief. That distress extended into the civilian world; as this election year of 1864 began, the military situation dominated the North's increasingly painful political realities. The North was sick of this endless battle to determine whether the United States would be one nation or two. When the supply of Union volunteers ran out in 1863 and the Federal government introduced conscription, riots in New York City protesting the draft claimed more than a hundred lives and showed the weakening support for the war. The presidential election that lay ahead in November would in effect be a referendum on an unpopular war and on the war-weary Northern public's view of secession and slavery. One great question presented itself: whether to fight on after three harrowing years, losing more sons, brothers, husbands, and fathers, or cede to the South the issue for which the blood flowed—to let the Confederate States of America go its way, an independent nation practicing slavery.

Even if Lincoln could win the Republican Party's nomination to run for reelection—other prominent and popular Republicans wanted that nomination themselves—he faced a daunting task. No political consensus existed within his own Republican Party. The majority of Republicans, sometimes called "conservatives," supported Lincoln's moderate, conciliatory positions toward the states that had seceded. The fewer but far more vocal Radicals resolutely opposed Lincoln's more conciliatory plans. (Although not a separate party, this powerful Republican faction had such a distinct identity that people referring to it frequently used a capital *R*.)

Lincoln believed that the Constitution did not permit a state to secede and that the states now calling themselves the "Confederate States of America" were best dealt with by considering them as being "out of their proper practical relations" with the rest of the nation. (He avoided referring to Jefferson Davis as "President Davis," because that implied the existence of a validly constituted nation that Davis had the right to lead, and he used the term "rebels" rather than "Confederates.")

His moderate approach included the idea of starting the political reconstruction of any hostile Southern state as soon as the tide of war brought significant territory back into Union hands. Thus, even if in wartime 10 percent of a rebel state's prewar voters could be found who would swear an oath of loyalty to the Union and a willingness to obey presidential proclamations and federal laws regarding slavery, that state could begin the process of resuming its "proper practical relations" with the states that had not seceded. Based on that nucleus of 10 percent, if that state wrote a new constitution that included the abolition of slavery, it could be reabsorbed into the Union. Lincoln saw this plan as a way to undermine the Confederacy and fight a political war within the military one.

The Radicals, on the other hand, saw Lincoln's policies as being too slow in abolishing slavery and too lenient to those they regarded as being guilty of treason. They wanted immediate and complete equality for all slaves as soon as the land on which they lived came under the control of the Union Army. If the Union went on to win the war, they wanted severe restrictions on readmitting Southern state governments and Confederate soldiers to the nation's political process: a Confederate officer was not to be allowed to vote and hold office as if he had not taken up arms and led soldiers against the United States of America. The Radicals saw a postwar era in terms of states such as proud Virginia and incendiary South Carolina being on a strict and lengthy probation.

That was the scene in the Republican camp, but Lincoln's main opponents displayed even greater disarray. The "Peace Democrats," a significant faction sometimes referred to as "Copperheads" by characterizing them as poisonous snakes biting the Union in the back, eagerly explored every avenue that might lead to immediate peace negotiations and compromise. The larger body of Democrats, the "War Democrats," were willing to fight on, but their priorities placed the restoration of the Union far above the question of the present and future status of the 4 million slaves in the South.

The political turmoil might easily produce a third party. Confusion and inconsistency abounded. Indiana lived in political and fiscal limbo; when the state legislature's Democratic majority attempted to strip Republican governor Oliver P. Morton of his military powers, the minority Republicans walked out, leaving the assembly unable to form a quorum. After the legislature adjourned, deliberately leaving Morton without the power to enact taxes to finance the state's share of the war effort, the governor started to rule by executive order. Because Morton could not collect the revenue needed to run the state, Secretary of War Stanton sent him shipments of cash from Washington, and Morton also borrowed money from bankers and the county governments remaining loyal to the Union.

Facing all this—an increasingly unpopular war and a powerful, growing opposition—Lincoln intended to run for reelection. Exhausted and discouraged though he often was, his ability and ambition had brought him from being a penniless self-educated boy to the presidency. From youth to manhood he knew the uncertain harsh life of the Illinois prairie frontier, with its ice-locked winters and parched summers. In that unforgiving world, Lincoln survived, prevailed, went on to bigger towns and increasingly higher positions. Reporter Horace White of the *Chicago Press and Tribune*, who covered Lincoln during his debates with Senator Stephen A. Douglas in the 1858 Illinois senatorial contest that brought him to national attention, had six years before rendered this judgment: "There is no backdown in Old Abe." During his twenty-five years practicing law in Illinois, Lincoln won the reputation of making the best closing arguments of any lawyer in the state. Determined to be strong to the end in whatever he undertook, he wanted to see the nation through its greatest crisis.

Lincoln possessed a sense of the vastness of America, the possibilities of its people, and the challenges of its evolving society and economy. In August of 1856, fifty-five months before the war began to tear the country apart, the idea of a special American destiny and opportunity already firmly occupied his mind. He said this at a gathering of 10,000 Republicans at Kalamazoo, Michigan:

> *We are a great empire. We are eighty years old. We stand at once the wonder and admiration of the whole world, and we must enquire what it is that has given us so much prosperity. This cause is that every man can make himself.*

On this first day of 1864, Lincoln, the archetypal self-made man, now had a year in which to win the election and keep up the pressure to defeat the Confederacy. He had to win in political caucuses and on the battlefields, lead the Union on to victory, and finally exorcise slavery, the republic's original sin.

III

Two hours after he sent off his request for intelligence concerning Jubal Early's movements, Lincoln received General Sullivan's reply.

> *I HAVE ORDERED A FORCE TO WINCHESTER STRONG ENOUGH TO DEVELOP ANYTHING THAT MAY BE THERE. I BELIEVE THE REPORTS RECEIVED FROM MARTINSBURG THIS MORNING WERE PREMATURE. I AM NOW LEAVING FOR MARTINSBURG MYSELF.*

The telegram reduced Lincoln's fear that the unpredictable Robert E. Lee was launching a surprise New Year's offensive, an eruption from the Shenandoah Valley like the one the summer before in which Lee and his men advanced north into Pennsylvania before being decisively beaten at Gettysburg. (Because that valley became wider as it ran north, movements within it were referred to in counterintuitive terms: "Lee marched north down the valley.")

Later, Lincoln walked back to the White House in the dusk to have his usual simple supper with his wife and their ten-year-old son Tad. For Lincoln, the thirty-one-room mansion had become a place of shadows. In 1862, the second year he and Mary occupied the White House, their son Willie died of typhoid fever at the age of eleven. It was their second loss: in 1849, seven years after they married, their three-year-old son Eddie had died of tuberculosis at their home in Springfield. Though they had two surviving sons, Robert, nineteen in 1862 and a student at Harvard, and Tad, who was then not quite nine and continued to live with them at the White House, Willie had been the child on whom they particularly doted—a sensitive and graceful boy who loved riding his little pony on the White House lawns. Lincoln saw much of himself in Willie: on one occasion he said to a guest at breakfast, "I know every step of the process" (by which Willie solved problems), "as it is by just such slow methods I attain results." When Willie died, going from perfect health to death in two weeks, Mary was, as her seamstress confidante and freed slave Elizabeth Keckley wrote, "completely overwhelmed" by the tragedy. Elizabeth also recalled the moment when Lincoln first came into the second-floor White House bedroom in which his son had died, and saw him lying there.

> *He buried his face in his hands, and his tall frame was convulsed with emotion. . . . His grief unnerved him, and made him a weak, passive child. I did not dream that his rugged nature could be so moved. I shall never forget those moments—genius and greatness weeping over love's idol lost. There is a grandeur as well as a simplicity about the picture that will never fade. With me it is immortal—I really believe that I shall carry it with me across the dark, mysterious river of death.*

IV

Lincoln's suppers with Mary and Tad—sometimes a close friend or two joined them—were a bittersweet mixture of friendly conversation, wartime tension, and unhappy memories. Tad was a lively, mischievous boy—

during one White House reception he startled the presidential guests by driving through the gathering on a makeshift sled pulled by one of his pet goats. After Willie's death the Lincolns continued to spoil Tad as outrageously as they had always spoiled both those boys, but Mary was an unstable and demanding woman who had experienced grief and stress apart from the loss of her favorite child. The well-educated daughter of a prominent slaveholding family in Lexington, Kentucky, she and Lincoln came from different, warring cultures. Mary had a brother, three half-brothers, and three brothers-in-law in the Confederate Army. Her three half-brothers had died fighting for the Confederacy. Confederate general Ben Hardin Helm, the husband of her favorite half-sister Emilie, had died from wounds received at Chickamauga just thirteen weeks before this New Year's Day.

General Helm's death gave rise to an extraordinary situation. Lincoln, fond of Emilie himself, stepped in to help Mary's newly widowed half-sister and her seven-year-old daughter Katherine get back safely from Alabama, deep in the Confederacy, to her mother's house in Union-held Lexington, Kentucky. This involved her first entering Union territory by ship, landing at the Federal coastal bastion of Fort Monroe, Virginia. It appears that the Union officers there required her to take an oath of allegiance to the United States before allowing her to proceed to Washington. Emilie, an ardent Confederate sympathizer and the widow of a Confederate officer, evidently refused to do this. There are conflicting versions of what happened next—an undocumented story in Emilie's family had it that Lincoln broke the impasse by sending the authorities at Fort Monroe a four-word telegram: "Send her to me." In any event, Emilie did not sign the oath, and she and her little girl arrived in Washington about December 8 to stay for a time with Mary in the White House. Emilie recalled, "Mr. Lincoln and my sister met me with the warmest affection, we were all too grief-stricken at first for speech. . . . We could only embrace each other in silence and tears." The young widow also wrote, in her diary, "She and Brother Lincoln pet me as if I were a child, and, without words, try to comfort me."

News of a Confederate general's widow being a guest in the White House caused so much criticism, particularly of Mary Lincoln, that Emilie decided to cut short her visit. Aware of the adverse public reaction, Lincoln nevertheless urged Emilie to stay, saying that Mary's nerves had "gone to pieces" and Emilie's presence comforted her. Emilie agreed about Mary's mental condition, telling Lincoln, "She seems very nervous and once or twice when I have come into the room suddenly the look in her eyes has appalled me." Still, after less than a week at the White House, Emilie departed for Kentucky with her daughter on December 14, 1863.

In the hours before she left, Lincoln gave Emilie a pass signed by him that would get her through any Union checkpoints. He also handed her an oath of allegiance written in his own hand. Then Lincoln wrote out and gave her a letter granting her amnesty. Part of it read: "in regard to said restored rights of person and property, she is to be protected and afforded facilities as a loyal person." Perhaps because he knew that Emilie would never sign the oath herself, Lincoln went ahead and signed her name on that document.

Despite her family ties to the South, Mary firmly supported the Union cause and had always believed that an important destiny awaited her husband. She had thrown in her lot with him twenty-two years before in Illinois when he was, as her niece Katherine Helm later wrote, "a struggling young lawyer . . . the plainest looking man in Springfield." She, like he, experienced episodes of depression. (Lincoln, who sometimes called his states of depression "hypo," for hypochondria, a Victorian synonym for melancholy, once said, "I laugh because I must not weep—that's all," and also commented that "a good funny story . . . has the same effect on me that I suppose a good square drink of whiskey has on a toper; it puts new life in me.") Mary suffered from migraine headaches, as Lincoln occasionally did, and aspects of her behavior presented him with problems from the beginning of their marriage. This same niece recalled that, back in Springfield, "while Mary was courageous and daring about most things, a thunderstorm was terrifying to her. Mr. Lincoln, knowing this, at the first muttering of thunder would leave his law office and hurry home to quiet her fears until the storm was over."

Now, with long casualty lists appearing daily, Mary constantly feared that their oldest son Robert, a senior at Harvard, would enter the Union Army as he wished to do and be the third of her four sons to die. Just weeks before this New Year's she found herself in a sudden unexpected exchange on this subject that demonstrated the emotions that lay beneath Washington's polite talk. During a small White House gathering, Republican senator Ira Harris of New York, a man Mary considered to be a friend, abruptly asked her, "Why isn't Robert in the Army? He is old enough and strong enough to serve his country. He should have gone to the front some time ago." Mary's half-sister Emilie Helm was present, during her brief visit. She said that Mary's face "turned white" and she offered some explanation, but Harris rose to go, saying pointedly, "I have only one son and he is fighting for his country."

Another powerful set of fears haunted Mary, concerning her husband's safety. On their way east from Springfield in early 1861 for Lincoln's inauguration, a plot to assassinate Lincoln as he emerged from one railroad station in Baltimore to go to another was thwarted by putting him on an earlier train and spiriting him across that Confederate-sympathizing city at three in the morning. Traveling with her son Robert aboard the train on which Lincoln would have been, Mary was in one of its cars in Baltimore when a mob stormed onto their train looking for him.

Those fears never ceased. The White House could be entered by almost anybody, and on one occasion a man named Francis Xavier who proved to be harmless got in to see Lincoln and announced that he had been elected president in 1856 and that Lincoln should leave immediately so he could begin to govern.

Mary received a serious injury during an accident intended to harm her husband. On July 2, 1863, when she was the only passenger in a carriage that she and Lincoln usually shared whenever she could get him to take one of the late afternoon rides they both enjoyed, the driver's seat fell off and the driver fell to the ground. As the horses bolted, Mary was thrown out, cutting her head on a rock; infection set in, and she remained in bed for three weeks. (Mary had more of her severe headaches from this time on, and her son Robert felt that she never completely recovered from her injuries.) An inspection of the carriage revealed that the fastenings under the driver's seat had been unscrewed, ensuring that an accident would occur.

V

After supper, Lincoln usually went back to work. Family quarters occupied much of the second floor of the White House, but near one end was what those with whom he worked called the president's "business office" and Lincoln called "the shop." A journalist who saw this large room during the day described it as having "two large draperied windows looking out upon the broad Potomac and commanding the Virginia heights opposite on which [the tents of] numberless military camps are whitening in the sun." Down its center ran a long black walnut table used for the customary Tuesday afternoon meeting of Lincoln's cabinet. A visitor noted that "plain straw matting covered the floor." Two armchairs and a sofa upholstered in green worsted sat along one wall, under large maps of the different theaters of war; against the opposite wall stood an old mahogany upright desk with pigeonholes for filing papers. Between the two windows was a desk at which Lincoln wrote letters, read documents sent him for endorsement, and signed state papers.

When he came up to this room after supper to continue his labors, he might find senators and congressmen arriving uninvited to confer with him, but at other times, as his private secretary John Hay wrote, "he shut himself up & would see no one." Whether Lincoln worked alone or with others, intense activity always took place in his office during daylight hours. He rose at dawn or earlier, frequently after a night with little or no sleep, and often began the day working by himself at his desk between the "large draperied windows." Then he would go downstairs for a breakfast that consisted of a cup of coffee and an egg. (His lunch was similarly meager; Hay described it as "a biscuit, a glass of milk in winter, some fruit or grapes in summer.") By seven he was back at work, aided by two of his dedicated private secretaries, Hay and John Nicolay, who among other duties kept him connected with the government's administrative departments and his political constituencies.

Added to the official correspondence, letters poured in from citizens all over the Union. Twenty-eight-year-old William O. Stoddard was the secretary who sorted out this unofficial mail and decided which letters from the public should be discarded and which should be answered. He said of his job, "I doubt if there was any spot in the United States in those days, outside of a battlefield[,] that was more continually interesting than the correspondence desk of the Executive Mansion." Stoddard, who also served as Mary Lincoln's unofficial social secretary, had been a venturesome youth; a native of Syracuse, New York, he left the University of Rochester in his senior year and headed west for Chicago, where he was an itinerant book peddler and tried his hand at writing for that city's *Daily Ledger* before buying a farm in eastern Illinois. Disliking the realities of farming, he began to work for the *Central Illinois Gazette* and became involved in the editing and ownership of a small newspaper that backed Lincoln in his home state. When Lincoln became a candidate for president in 1860, Stoddard said that he "went into the political canvass, head over heels," and ran the Republican campaign in Champaign County "on my own hands." Brought into the White House not long after Lincoln was inaugurated, Stoddard had carved out for himself this daily task of sorting through Lincoln's voluminous nongovernmental mail and deciding what should be brought to the president's attention. (In addition to this, from 1861 to 1864 he submitted more than 120 weekly columns to the *New York Examiner*; writing under the pseudonym "Illinois," he provided a combination of inside-Washington gossip and admiring, sympathetic descriptions of Lincoln's activities.)

Stoddard's selection of the letters that Lincoln should see gave the president a bond with citizens who in some cases lived thousands of miles from the White House. On this first day of 1864, a man named Otho Hinton, of Santa Rosa, California, wrote Lincoln a letter that began, "I avail myself of the privilege exercised by the Humblest Citizen from the earliest ages of civil Government among Men to address the Executive upon great and important Measures of State policy and especially in times like these." This reflected a deep feeling among many citizens during the Civil War, something that one of the lesser secretaries described in these words: ". . . every patriot became intensely interested in the strife, and . . . felt that they must sit down and give their thoughts to the official head of the Republic." Even at a distance of a thousand miles, Abraham Lincoln seemed approachable, a man of the people who would listen to you.

And send him their thoughts they did. Stoddard reported of the incoming bundles of mail, "Some days there will be less than 200 separate lots, large and small. Some days there will be over 300." He opened every letter, but added: "Are they all read? Not exactly, with a big wicker wastebasket on either side of this chair. A good half of each mail belongs in them, as fast as you can find it out. The other half calls for more or less respectful treatment." That might mean forwarding a letter to the appropriate government bureau for a response, or Lincoln telling either John Nicolay or John Hay what reply should be written for him to sign, or Lincoln putting aside a letter that he wished to answer himself. Stoddard characterized some of those letters from the public that he threw out as being "stories of partisan bitterness and personal hatred; of the most venomous malice, seeking to shoot with poisoned arrows of abuse; of low, slanderous meannesses; of the coarsest foulest vulgarity to which beastly men can sink; of the wildest, the fiercest and the most obscene ravings of utter insanity."

In terms of meeting the public face-to-face, Lincoln tried to receive virtually anyone who wished to see him, and did this from ten in the morning until one in the afternoon. Wives and mothers of convicted deserters from the Union Army entered this room to plead with him, usually with success, to commute sentences of execution; men came asking for government jobs and promotions. (Others who did not need his help hard-heartedly referred to these sessions as "beggars' operas.") He listened to all requests, complaints, and comments, feeling that he owed that to the citizens he served, but he also found this useful; from many of these conversations he learned how people viewed him and his administration, and referred to these daily sessions as his "public opinion baths."

Lincoln usually treated his visitors patiently, but sometimes the constant strain under which he lived overcame him, and on one occasion this man of great mental power demonstrated the physical strength still possessed by the Illinois frontier woodsman who in his youth often swung an ax for hours as he felled trees. One of Lincoln's secretaries described the incident, unique in recorded presidential behavior. A man who had called on Lincoln almost every day for weeks was shown in, and proceeded to ask again for a government position that the president had repeatedly told him he was not going to be given. When Lincoln once more told him politely that the post he sought was not to be his, the man said, in what this eyewitness called "a very insolent tone," that the president was treating him unjustly.

> [*Lincoln*] *looked at the man steadily for a half-minute or more, then slowly began to lift his long figure from its slouching position in the chair. He rose without haste, went over to where the man was sitting, took him by the coat-collar, carried him bodily to the door, threw him in a heap outside, closed the door, and returned to his chair. . . . He said not a word then, or afterward, about the incident.*

(As for Lincoln's physical strength, during a visit to an army headquarters he picked up a heavy ax lying beside a log. Gripping the end of its handle in his right hand, he held the ax out horizontally for some time; after he lowered it, several young soldiers tried to duplicate the feat without success.)

• • •

On another occasion, Lincoln removed quite a different person from his office. An important conference with high officials had run past noon, and a servant appeared, telling him that his wife expected him to join her for what may have been a more formal lunch than he usually had. Intent on the discussion, Lincoln did not even nod, and the servant left his office. Some minutes later, the same thing happened, with no sign that Lincoln noticed this second summons. Soon after that, the door of the office was flung open, and Mary Todd Lincoln walked in, the picture of imperious indignation. Still listening carefully to what was being said in the conference, the 6-foot-4 president rose, put his exceptionally large hands on the sides of his 5-foot-2 wife's shoulders, lifted her off the carpet, wordlessly carried her through the door, and set her down in the hall. He came back into his office, closing the door behind him, and sat down with exactly the same intent expression on his face that he had had before she entered.

Shortly after the Battle of Gettysburg, this office had been the scene of two touching meetings, both witnessed by Lincoln's friend and Kentucky Unionist leader James Speed. At the end of several hours of receiving visitors of all sorts who had been waiting in the hall, Lincoln asked Edward McManus, the White House chief doorkeeper, "Is that all?"

"There is one poor woman there yet, Mister President," Edward replied. "She has been here for several days, crying and taking on—and hasn't got a chance to come in yet."

"Let her in."

The woman entered and explained her situation. Her husband and two sons were in the Union Army. At first, her husband had sent home part of his pay, but then had "yielded to the temptations of camp life"— presumably drinking, gambling, and possibly prostitutes—and had sent her nothing for months. She did not know where her two sons were. Penniless, she was hoping that Lincoln could help her find one of them and release him to come home to help her.

> While the pathetic recital was going on the President stood before the fire-place, his hands crossed behind his back, and his head bent in earnest thought. When the woman ended and waited a moment for his reply his lips opened and he spoke—not indeed as if he were replying to what she

had said, but rather as if he were in an abstracted and unconscious self-communion:

"I have two, and you have none."

With that, Lincoln went to his writing table and wrote out detailed instructions as to where she should go and what she should do to locate one of her sons and gain the discharge for him that he was authorizing. Some days later, again at the end of Lincoln's hours for receiving visitors, Edward said, "That woman, Mister President, is here again, and still crying."

"Let her in," Lincoln said. "What can the matter be now?"

The woman came in and said that the instructions he had given her had taken her right to the unit in which one of her sons served. When she got there, she found that he had been wounded at Gettysburg and had died in a hospital. Would the president please consider discharging her remaining son?

. . . he again walked to his little writing table and took up his pen for the second time to write an order which should give the pleading woman . . . [her son]. And the woman, as if moved by a filial impulse she could not restrain moved after him and stood by him at the table as he wrote, and with the fond familiarity of a mother placed her hand upon the President's head and smoothed down his wandering and tangled hair. . . . The order was written and signed, the President rose and thrust it into her hand with the choking ejaculation "There!" and hurried from the room.

At times, Lincoln displayed the occasionally dark side of the sense of humor that kept him going through all the stress. One night he mentioned to a friend who was in the office that he had in front of him a last-minute letter from a Catholic priest asking that he suspend an order to hang a man. "If I don't suspend it tonight," Lincoln said, "the man will surely be suspended tomorrow." He also enjoyed making up words, and characterized some people's conversational behavior as being "interruptious."

AFTER LINCOLN FINISHED working at night, he often prowled restlessly through this part of the White House. He could have gone to Mary in their living quarters, but often he would find one or more of his private secretaries—John G. Nicolay, John Hay, and William Stoddard—at work in their small offices down the hall. If it was really late in the evening, he might come upon the two of them who lived in the White House, John Nicolay and John Hay, talking and perhaps having something to eat in the bedroom they shared, and would join them for some conversation.

Nicolay and Hay played an immensely important part in Lincoln's daily life. The senior of them, thirty-one-year-old John Nicolay, was born in Bavaria and came to the United States with his family at the age of six. As had been the case with Lincoln—and this was a bond between them—Nicolay's was a story of hardship, managing to get only two years of education in log schoolhouses in which, he later said, "slates, pencils, paper and ink were unknown." Living on the frontier in Lincoln's state of Illinois, he knew a life that he described as "irregular and somewhat spasmodic, with quick fluctuations, vibrating between plenty and want,—from fullness to hunger, from dry to wet, from comfort to misery. Nothing was steady but ignorance and solitude." He became a typesetter for the small rural *Pike County Free Press*; in eight years the earnest, shy, hard-working Nicolay rose to become its editor and publisher, but still remained close to poverty. At the age of twenty-six, then working as the principal clerk in the office of the Illinois secretary of state in Springfield, he met Lincoln, who frequently visited those rooms in the state capital in connection with his law practice and his political interests; sometimes the two played chess there. When Lincoln won the Republican nomination in 1860, he hired Nicolay to handle his correspondence during the presidential campaign that took them both to the White House. As Lincoln's principal private secretary, Nicolay struck sophisticated Washingtonians as "sour and crusty" and he was characterized as "the bulldog in the anteroom," but no one worked harder than this loyal, driven, rail-thin man.

The second of these aides was another man from Illinois, John Hay, soon to be twenty-six, who grew up in far more comfortable circumstances and had all the charm that Nicolay lacked. Before going off to Brown University, Hay had become friends with Nicolay, who was five years older than he, and when Lincoln brought Nicolay with him to the White House, Hay came along. A young woman visiting Washington wrote in a letter describing her experiences in the capital, "The nicest looking man I have seen since I have been here is Mr[.] Hay the President's Secretary . . . he came into the Senate the other day to deliver a message from the President. He is very nice looking with the loveliest voice." Another young woman was struck by his "wonderful hazel eyes." Men called him "brilliant" and "an effervescent and fascinating fellow," characterizing him as one who "knew the social graces and amenities." It was not certain that Lincoln knew this, but, like Stoddard, sometimes in these midnight hours Hay would compose anonymous letters to the editors of newspapers around the country, hoping that they would print his praise of the president's accomplishments. (Nicolay occasionally did this as well.) Hay's career as a public servant had just begun: in the future, he would serve as assistant secretary of state under President Rutherford B. Hayes, who was a Union Army general in 1864, and as secretary of state under two presidents, William McKinley, a Union Army captain in 1864, and Theodore Roosevelt.

When Lincoln chatted with these young men after all of them had finished their long working day, he often entertained them with one of the folksy little stories he loved to tell and they loved to hear. When the talk turned serious, it had far less to do with ideals than with the tactics of political survival. Lincoln was a pragmatist; doing what he felt necessary to preserve the Union at all costs, and to bring his presidency and the Union's war effort this far, he had greatly expanded the executive powers of his office. He wanted broad public and congressional support; he never forgot that he won the White House in 1860 with only 40 percent of the popular vote. In the wartime midterm congressional elections of 1862, his Republican Party had kept its control by the narrowest of margins only because of the Union Army's intimidation of Democratic voters in Kentucky. Armed soldiers had stood at polling places throughout the state, discouraging Democrats from voting, and, without using the word "Democrats," there were threats of arrest for anyone running for office on a platform hostile to the Lincoln administration.

What he might not be able to accomplish through legislation in a Congress in which many opposed him, Lincoln tried to get by presidential decree. The Constitution does not include a clause on "war power." Nonetheless, using that term and acting under what he believed his wartime emergency powers to be, Lincoln had without congressional authority blockaded the Confederacy's ports, issued calls for massive numbers of volunteers, and authorized advances of Treasury funds to private citizens of the North for the purchase of armaments and ships.

In addition to taking what amounted to unilateral presidential action in issuing the Emancipation Proclamation, Lincoln had at times suspended the right of habeas corpus, a citizen's most fundamental defense against illegal imprisonment. Under Lincoln's authority, military commissions were bringing to trial protesters who opposed the war, many of them individuals who had done so only with words rather than deeds. More than 14,000 citizens had been jailed and tried using these highly unusual procedures.

One instance of the application of these methods was to have far-reaching consequences. When Democratic congressman Clement Vallandigham of Ohio was convicted in May 1863 of treason for urging a crowd to topple "King Lincoln" from his throne, there was a great outcry, even in the middle of a war, about suppression of free speech. Lincoln decided to change the sentence of imprisonment to one of banishment from the Union, and Federal troops under a flag of truce handed Vallandigham over to Confederate forces in Tennessee. The Confederate government assisted him in getting to Wilmington, North Carolina, and from that Confederate-held port he reached neutral British soil in Bermuda aboard a swift blockade runner, the *Lady Davis*, named for Jefferson Davis's wife, Varina. From there he sailed with impunity to Canada aboard a British vessel and was soon in comfortable exile. Eventually settling himself in a suite at the Hirons House hotel in Windsor, Ontario, across the Detroit River from Detroit, he was able to consult with any number of Democratic politicians who crossed the border to meet with him, as well as with Confederate agents who had entered Canada in a variety of ways.

In an astonishing example of what was and was not permitted in the states of the wartime Union, while in exile Vallandigham ran for governor of Ohio *in absentia* during the 1863 gubernatorial campaign. Even though he lost by a vote of 175,464 to 247,216 out of 422,680 ballots cast—a 60–40 percent defeat—the outcome nonetheless meant that close to 200,000 citizens of Ohio had voted for Lincoln's most virulent opponent. In his Canadian exile, Vallandigham stood as a symbol of potentially violent opposition to Lincoln in the states of the Old Northwest (the term Midwest had not yet come into being) and was making plans to reenter the United States illegally later in the year.

Talking of these and other problems with his secretaries Nicolay and Hay brought Lincoln into interesting combinations of broad policy and specific action. Tomorrow, on the second day of 1864, he was sending Hay down to Point Lookout, Maryland, with a book of forms to be signed by Confederate prisoners of war held there who wished to take an oath of allegiance to the Union. The men who did this had two choices. They could enlist in the Union Army, as some of them wished to do. Or, as Lincoln's letter of transmittal that Hay would carry said, the men "whose homes lie safely within our military lines" could return to their families and take no further part in the war. Here was Lincoln, waging both war and peace—girding for future battles by enlisting some former enemies in his ranks while allowing others to end their part in the fighting.

These evening discussions often touched on what was the seamy side of any presidency. During Lincoln's debates with Douglas in 1858, he had characterized his opponent as being the man committed to rewarding his followers with positions involving "postoffices, landoffices, marshalships, and cabinet appointments," but when Lincoln took office in March of 1861, the capital saw political patronage dispensed on an unprecedented scale. Even the Republican state chairman for New Hampshire lamented the "rush to reap . . . made by every slippery politician in the Republican party." Lincoln participated in the process wholeheartedly; half the communications that left his office during the first three weeks of May 1861, soon after his inauguration in March, involved using his influence on behalf of different individuals. Those at the top of Lincoln's incoming administration quickly feathered their nests: one of Secretary of State William H. Seward's sons was named assistant secretary of state, another was appointed an army paymaster, and a third was commissioned as a lieutenant colonel, while Seward's nephew received the post of consul in Shanghai. Of the 1,520 men who held presidential appointments under James Buchanan's outgoing Democratic administration, 1,195 lost their jobs. New postmasterships sprang into being; any man given a job by the incoming Lincoln administration understood that he would be donating up to 10 percent of his salary to one of the Republican Party's treasuries.

Everything was handed out, either for money or as a reward for past or prospective political support. Lincoln exceeded all previous presidents in what he did for the newspaper publishers, editors, and reporters who backed him. A simple form of this involved Lincoln's increasing the amount of required public notices and other government advertising in their papers, but he also appointed forty journalists to positions that included governor of Utah Territory, consul general at Paris, and commissioner to the Hawaiian Islands.

The great expansion of the Union Army required more leaders; it became common practice to distribute the ranks of brigadier general and colonel as political plums, often to men with no military experience. Every Union state was initially allotted a quota of four brigadier generals, but Lincoln stepped in and gave his state of Illinois six. (In Washington, so many of Lincoln's friends, advisers, and aides came from Illinois that the group could have been called "Illinois in Washington.")

A need existed to rally large constituencies such as the half-million military-age citizens of the North who were German-Americans, more than 200,000 of them born in Germany. Even before the war, Lincoln understood the German-speaking population's political importance: in 1860 he spent $400 to buy the *Illinois Staats-Anzeiger*, leasing that German-language newspaper back to its editor on the understanding that it would support the Republican Party. From the war's outset, Lincoln began placing some German-Americans into the army's command positions. Prominent among them was Major General Carl Schurz, a prewar leader of a German political action movement, the Turners, a name derived from the German word *Turner*, meaning "gymnast." The Turners had supported Lincoln in the 1860 election and provided his bodyguard at his inauguration. Schurz, a fiery bilingual antislavery orator who had campaigned enthusiastically for Lincoln, possessed minimal military experience, but when the war came, he wanted to be a general, and Lincoln made him one.

As the war had progressed, hundreds of thousands of German-speaking men entered the Union Army. Many regiments from Pennsylvania, Ohio, Wisconsin, and the St. Louis area of Missouri used German as the language for giving orders. On a day in 1862, Lincoln searched for a German name to add to those of Schurz and Franz Sigel, both born in Germany, and came across that of Prussian-born Colonel Alexander Schimmelfennig, commander of the German-speaking 74th Pennsylvania Volunteer Infantry. Lincoln said, "The very man!" Secretary of War Stanton quickly told him of men with better records who were eligible to become generals. Lincoln replied, "His name will make up for any difference there may be," and walked off, happily muttering "Schimmelfennig." Now, with Lincoln seeking reelection two years later, Schurz, who along with Schimmelfennig had proven to be a largely ineffectual general, wanted to campaign for Lincoln, and Lincoln intended to accept his help.

Connections coupled with payoffs determined the awarding of millions of dollars in contracts for military supplies. Lincoln made no money from it, but proved negligent in his oversight of the corrupt actions of Simon Cameron, his first secretary of war, who used the War Department to pay off old political debts he had incurred as a senator from Pennsylvania. Of 1,903,800 muskets and rifles Cameron ordered for the Union Army during the war's first months, 1,839,000 came from manufacturers who dealt with Cameron's cronies, and Cameron constantly steered other lucrative contracts through middlemen to manufacturers who produced shoddy goods for exorbitant sums. Among other examples, illustrative but not nearly the most egregious, the government paid $117,000 for a thousand cavalry horses, a third of them useless, that the suppliers had acquired for less than half that price.

More ways existed to gain advantages for one's political party and oneself; even before officially declaring his wish to run again, or receiving a single endorsement of any kind, Lincoln had an interesting plan in mind. He had long wanted to readmit Confederate states as the conquest of their territory made that possible. Part of Florida had come back under Federal military control, and Lincoln pushed to reconstruct a pro-Union state government there. If he could speed the process, it might result in Florida sending a pro-Lincoln delegation to the Republican convention later in the year.

VI

At about 11 P.M., Lincoln would stop working in his office. Sometimes his son Tad, ten years old as 1864 began, would be asleep in an armchair, having dozed off much earlier when they went through their ritual of Tad telling him everything he had done during the day. On nights when Tad was still there in the "shop," a friend of Lincoln's said, "shouldering the sleeping child, the man for whom millions of good men and women nightly prayed took his way through the silent corridors and passages to his boy's bedroom."

In the family quarters, Mary would be waiting up for him. As at supper, they would chat in friendly fashion, Lincoln often fondly calling her "Mother," but Mary resented having so little of his time in the evenings. Jealous of any woman who paid attention to her husband, she also saw the war as her rival.

That was only partly true. When Abraham Lincoln finally went to go to bed in his room next to Mary's on the first night of 1864, the many crises facing the nation weighed on him, but part of him cared very much for Mary and had continuing concerns about her. He saw her inconsistencies; she wanted the prominence that came with her position, yet she made no effort to attract notice of her frequent visits to the wounded soldiers in Washington's hospitals.

He worried about Mary's mental health. For months after Willie's death, the mention of his name provoked hysterical sobbing, and Lincoln employed a nurse to care for her. In her efforts to come to terms with her loss, Mary began attending séances conducted by spiritualists, then quite popular in Washington society. In a dimly lit room of the house of a spiritualist couple named Laurie who lived in the suburb of Georgetown, she came under the influence of clairvoyants who convinced Mary that during their sessions she was in communication with her sons Willie and Eddie. At times when these mediums seemed unable to conjure up Willie's spirit, they gave Mary what purported to be advance news of Confederate military movements, which she swiftly relayed to her husband. Mary also arranged to have eight séances conducted in the White House; Lincoln attended at least one of these, in an effort to protect Mary and to study the individuals manipulating her.

During the nearly two years after Willie's death, Mary seemed to emerge from her grief to some extent, but her half-sister, Emilie Todd Helm, had an extraordinary experience with her, during her visit to the Lincolns less than a month before this New Year's of 1864. Mary entered her room at the White House one night, her eyes "wide and shining." Emilie wrote in her diary what came next. Speaking of Willie, Mary said, "He lives, Emilie! He comes to me every night, and stands at the foot of my bed with the same sweet, adorable smile he always has had; he does not always come alone; little Eddie is sometimes with him. . . . You cannot dream of the comfort this gives me. When I thought of my little son in immensity, alone, without his mother to direct him, it nearly broke my heart." Emilie added that Mary was "so nervous and wrought up" and "is on a terrible strain." As for the whole episode, she wrote, "It *is* unnatural and abnormal, it frightens me."

Lincoln had learned to be careful about what he confided to Mary. As far back as 1847, when she accompanied him to Washington to start the one term he served in Congress, David Davis, an Illinois lawyer and circuit judge who later managed Lincoln's 1860 presidential campaign, remarked, "She wishes to loom largely." The first presidential wife to be called "The First Lady"—a title bestowed on her by William Howard Russell, the Washington correspondent of the *Times* of London—when Lincoln began his presidency in 1861, Mary acted as if she were a conduit of power herself, writing to newspaper editors and chatting with senators about her opinions on matters of state. She earned the enmity of Secretary of State Seward by referring to him as "that abolition sneak," and also alienated Secretary of War Stanton; both men remained on excellent terms with Lincoln.

Even worse for a woman married to a man known as "Honest Abe," her handling of money revealed serious character defects. She had a horror of becoming poor—something she had never been nor was likely to be—and at the same time spent money compulsively, once buying four hundred pairs of gloves in three months. Congress voted Lincoln, whose salary was $25,000, the customary appropriation of $20,000 given to incoming presidents to redecorate the White House; when he turned that over to Mary, she swiftly ran up bills for china, crystal, silver, rugs, curtains, and repainting that came to $6,700 more than that.

Lincoln found such expenditures in the middle of a war shocking, but Mary had just started, moving from spending money for public purposes to private gain. On a trip to New York, she ordered for the White House a set of china that bore the seal of the United States, and then ordered another set to be decorated with her initials, charging both to the government. Mary's favorite place to shop in New York was A. T. Stewart's elegant department store, built of marble and covering a square block. (Henry James later described the place as being "fatal to feminine nerves.") On one of her eleven wartime visits to this emporium, she bought with her own money several "black lace point shawls" for $650 each, "and the real camel's hair cashmere at $1,000."

Mary soon realized she would have to develop other sources of income to support her habits and find ways to avoid her husband's learning of these spending sprees. In collusion with John Watt, superintendent of the White House grounds, she began to present the Treasury with receipts for the purchase of every kind of seed, fruit tree, and bush, most of which were never ordered or planted. At a time when a Union Army private made $13 a month, they shared the governmental reimbursements for more than a $1,000 of these nonexistent purchases, and Mary showed a certain ingenuity in her additional fraudulent itemization. She billed the government for $700.75 for flowers that never grew and $107.50 for manure that never fertilized anything, and added a charge for a horse and cart that never carried the phantom manure. Mary and Watt expanded this practice to include the misrepresentation of the amount of food bought for the White House.

Slowly, rumors about the First Lady's financial maneuvers began to spread through various circles in Washington. One of the people who had a definite opinion about Mary was David Davis, the judge from Illinois whose masterful job of running Lincoln's 1860 presidential campaign had been rewarded when Lincoln named him to the Supreme Court. When former senator Orville Browning of Illinois, another of Lincoln's old friends from his prewar political career ("Illinois in Washington"), defended Mary's reputation in a conversation with him, Justice Davis replied that "she was a natural born thief . . . stealing was a sort of insanity with her."

Mary's record in financial matters would get worse, and better known, as her time in the White House went on. Her alleged behavior with men also caused gossip. On her shopping trips to New York in the first half of 1861 to refurbish the White House, she was accompanied by William S. Wood, whom Mary had asked a number of Lincoln's friends to support for the position of commissioner of public buildings, to which Lincoln then appointed him. An anonymous letter to Lincoln dated June 28, 1861 signed "Union" spoke of "the scandal of your wife and Wood. . . . If he continues as commissioner he will stab you in your most vital part." Lincoln King of Iowa, no relation of the president's, later said that Mary "used often to go from the White House to New York to pass the night with a man who held a high government office in Washington, given to him by her husband." Richard Yates, then governor of Illinois, indicated that Mary was not "true to her husband," while John Watt, the man with whom she conspired on fraudulent payments for White House expenses, claimed after falling out with her that "Mrs. Lincoln's relations with certain men were indecently improper."

Mary believed in her husband and wanted him to be nominated and win the coming campaign. But she also saw this election as a way to get out of debt and avoid Lincoln's learning more details of her compulsive extravagance. These included gifts to herself such as diamond earrings and gold-plated clocks. (Her seamstress, Elizabeth Keckley, alleged that Mary eventually owed "store bills" amounting to $70,000, but the figure came closer to $10,000.) She planned to use everything at her disposal, ranging from choice White House invitations for favored supporters, to none-too-subtle suggestions that she could secure important government appointments if Lincoln won a second term. Mary intended to link her implied influence with requests for gifts to her of money with which she would satisfy the merchants, the jewelers and clockmakers, the milliners and seamstresses, who still expected to be paid.

By 1864, this was an old game for Mary; there could be no doubt that she was already engaged in quid pro quo influence-peddling, even at the time when Lincoln had been elected for his first term and before they left Springfield for his inauguration. A shady character named Isaac Henderson, publisher of the *New York Evening Post*, had sent the soon-to-be First Lady some diamonds, and she knew that he wanted the lucrative position of naval agent in the New York Customs House. On the eve of the Lincolns' departure for Washington, a friend of Lincoln's named Herman Kreismann came to the hotel where they were staying to ask why he was late for a meeting. He found Mary in hysterics. Lincoln explained, "Kreismann, she will not let me go until I promise her an office for one of her friends." Mary's friend was Henderson; in April, Lincoln appointed him to the Customs House position, from which he was later dismissed on unproven charges that he had taken kickbacks from contractors doing business with the Brooklyn Navy Yard.

Lincoln seldom spoke of his feelings for Mary, but once, turning to a friend in the midst of a White House reception, he said impulsively, using the word "handsome" as the synonym for "beautiful" it then was, "My wife is as handsome as when she was a girl and I a poor nobody then, fell in love with her and . . . have never fallen out." On the other hand, he occasionally revealed a negative view of marriage, presumably based on his own experience. Pardoning an imprisoned soldier who had deserted and wanted to go home to marry, he commented that "probably in less than a year" the young man would wish that he had stayed in his prison cell.

VII

As the first day of 1864 ticked away, it seemed that the outcome of every major issue in the country depended on the man whom Mary called "Mister Lincoln." In his Gettysburg Address, he had laid out "the great task remaining before us . . . that this nation shall have a new birth of freedom; and that this government of the people, by the people, for the people, shall not perish from the earth." Lincoln spoke then of "the last full measure of devotion" given by the Union soldiers who died at Gettysburg. The coming year would test the limits of Lincoln's physical and mental strength, his political and military instincts, his idealism and character.

Thirty-three months into this ghastly war, Lincoln faced not only the obvious problems of his presidency, but also a question of personal integrity, clothed in what looked like an important but objective decision. He had been doing a lot of thinking about Major General Ulysses S. Grant, who had resigned from the prewar Regular Army as a captain in 1854 rather than face a court-martial for being drunk while on duty. Grant had begun this war by reentering the army as a colonel of Volunteers. (Far fewer officers held the prestigious Regular commissions, and even West Pointers like Grant who had resigned as Regulars received Volunteer commissions as they reentered the army.) First leading an infantry regiment of fewer than a thousand soldiers, Grant's meteoric rise in the western theater led to his becoming a major general of Volunteers; by the time of his great triumph at Vicksburg on July 4, 1863, he commanded 71,000 men. Five weeks before this New Year's Day, he had rescued the Union cause from disaster after the Confederate blow at Chickamauga by winning a critical victory at Chattanooga.

After Vicksburg, Lincoln had made Grant a major general in the Regular Army, and sent him a profoundly grateful letter of congratulations. Earlier, he had said that if Grant could win at Vicksburg, "Grant is my man and I am his [for] the rest of the war," but as 1864 began, Lincoln had not moved Grant above his position as commander of the western theater. Although George Gordon Meade had won the great victory at

Gettysburg, Grant's overall record—Fort Donelson, Shiloh, Vicksburg, Chattanooga—clearly established him as the man who should become general-in-chief of the entire Union Army.

The idea of this further promotion for Grant brought Lincoln into conflict between his responsibilities as the commander-in-chief and his ambition to be reelected as president. At this point, Grant's name resounded through the North as an eminently successful general. He had no clear party affiliation, and many in both the Republican and Democratic parties thought he could win the presidency if he ran in the coming election. By promoting Grant to lieutenant general, superseding the less able current general-in-chief, Major General Henry W. Halleck, in a move that would make Grant the Union's supreme military commander, Lincoln might shorten the war. That would save both Northern and Southern lives, but to promote Grant would also give a potential political rival even more credibility and fame.

Lincoln approached this conundrum by using an intermediary. He asked Republican congressman Elihu Washburne, who represented Grant's home district in Illinois and had used his influence on Grant's behalf throughout the war ("Illinois in Washington"), to ascertain whether Grant had his eye on the presidency. Washburne responded that Grant's friend J. Russell Jones of Chicago might know. As the New Year began, Lincoln hoped to hear from Jones.

Inescapably, this man in the White House at midnight of the first day of 1864 had everything bearing down on him: the war itself; the rapidly eroding public support for the war; the passionate political opposition he and his administration inspired; continuing grief for his beloved son Willie; the anguish of his erratic wife, Mary, at their loss. In addition to his other duties and responsibilities, he faced the struggle to win a second term. What Lincoln had said two years before, telling the people of the nation they could not dodge the decisions and sacrifices confronting them—"Fellow Citizens, *we* cannot escape history"—now applied to him with unique and enormous force. If in the coming year he lost his bid for reelection, if the objectives for which the Union entered the war were bargained away, if Robert E. Lee and his remarkable soldiers could bring off some victory that fatally weakened the faltering Northern support for the war, Lincoln's place in history would be that of a huge failure in a vast pointless tragedy.

The coming months would require a special personal philosophy. He had that, drawn from his days floating thirty-foot-long flatboats filled with cargo down the Mississippi River to New Orleans. Earlier, he had explained to Republican congressman James G. Blaine of Maine how he saw some of what lay ahead: "The pilots on our Western rivers steer from *point to point* as they call it—setting the course of the boat no farther than they can see; and that is all I propose to myself in this great problem."

That was Lincoln the tactician, the Lincoln who understood that in politics you took as much as you could get and seldom got everything you wanted. But in the White House, the citizens also had Lincoln the strategist, not only the leader determined to preserve the Union by fighting the war, but the man of the West who saw beyond the next bend in the river. Here the people had the visionary who sprang from the poorest among them, the awkward and eloquent frontiersman who could picture so much and then make it real, even in the midst of war and political crisis. As 1864 began, few understood how much else he was making happen, far from the battlefields, because of his policies—the legislation he initiated, the federal subsidies for the programs he supported and encouraged. Railroads were starting to cross the continent, with telegraph lines running beside them; hundreds of thousands of immigrants were arriving, to begin farming land given them by the government; unaffiliated banks were being consolidated into a stronger national system. The Union experienced growth in mines, in harvested timber, in the number of factories and the workers who labored in them.

There would always be mystery about Lincoln, the elusive questions attendant upon greatness, but this shambling, rumpled figure with the sad face and the sudden sweet smile was a man for all seasons, arriving in the nation's winter, its darkest hour, believing that God would yet grant America a rich harvest.

And so Abraham Lincoln, and the people of the Union, and the free and enslaved people of the Confederacy, headed into 1864.

STEERING INTO
A STORMY YEAR

O n January 11, Lincoln began his part in the year's maneuvering for his reelection by meeting quietly with Francis Preston Blair, the head of a powerful Republican political family. At the war's outset, Blair had been Lincoln's intermediary in offering Robert E. Lee the command of the Union Army. His younger son, Francis, Jr., who started the war as a congressman and went on to become a major general, had been instrumental in keeping both Missouri and Kentucky from joining the Confederacy; his older son, Montgomery, Lincoln's postmaster general, once summed up the clan's determination with, "When the Blairs go in for a fight they go in for a funeral."

The topic on this January morning was not how to beat the Democrats in November, but how to deal with Lincoln's secretary of the treasury, Salmon Portland Chase. A former United States senator from Ohio and later that state's governor, Chase was managing the Union's finances superbly in a time of crisis but wanted to become president himself.

To some degree, the political fates of Chase, Lincoln, and Secretary of State Seward were intertwined. During the 1860 election, both Chase and Seward, the latter a past senator from New York State as well as its former governor, had seen themselves as far better qualified to become president than Lincoln was. At that point, Lincoln's office-holding experience consisted of eight consecutive years in the Illinois legislature and one two-year term in Congress; what national reputation he had came only through his debates with Stephen Douglas in 1858, and an impressive speech he made in 1860 at New York's Cooper Institute, sometimes called Cooper Union. (James Russell Lowell of the Harvard faculty, who wrote acute wartime political articles, said that Lincoln slipped into the White House by default, a compromise candidate who was acceptable to a barely sufficient number of politicians and voters "because he had no history.")

When Lincoln won, he appointed both men to his cabinet. Seward, who had started 1860 as the Republican frontrunner, initially tried to expand his role into something of a copresident. At one point, when Seward said that it was he who should hold the first official reception of the newly elected Lincoln administration, Mary Lincoln shot back: "It is said that you are the power behind the throne—I'll show you that Mister Lincoln is President yet."

In December of 1862, nine Radical Republican senators tried to persuade Lincoln to remove Seward from his cabinet, basing their effort on the grounds that he and not Lincoln dominated Union policy, and that Seward displayed "lukewarmness in the conduct of the war" and gave Lincoln poor advice on military matters. The attempt produced offers to resign not only from Seward, but also, to make it easier for Lincoln to remove them as well if he wished to, from Chase, himself a Radical, and Secretary of War Stanton. Lincoln refused all three offers, the essence of the situation being his determination to stop the legislature's capture of the chief executive's right to appoint and remove the members of his cabinet. (He saw himself as the real target of the Radical senators' move: "They wish to get rid of me," he told his friend Orville Browning.)

Seward and Stanton had gone on to become the key figures in Lincoln's cabinet. At the outset of the war, Seward had in fact made some errors in judgment: he thought the struggle might blow over and also initially took such a hard line against England's guarded sympathy for the South that Lincoln had to lessen the force of words Seward intended to use. Thereafter, Seward conducted an effective, far-seeing foreign policy, and emerged as a friend to whom Lincoln turned for companionship, and advice in many situations. (Seward could move swiftly on domestic as well as foreign matters. At the end of September 1863, Lincoln sent over to Seward a letter he had just received from Sarah Josepha Hale, the editor of *Lady's Book*, the most influential American women's magazine. She asked the president to reinstate an annual proclamation of a Day of

Thanksgiving—an announcement that had been allowed to lapse since 1818—and "to appoint the last Thursday of November, annually, as Thanksgiving Day." Despite the daily demands on both Seward and Lincoln, on October 3, Lincoln issued the eloquently worded "Proclamation of Thanksgiving," written by Seward, that set the precedent for observing the "last Thursday of November . . . as a day of Thanksgiving and Praise to our beneficent Father who dwelleth in the Heavens.")

Chase presented a different picture. He performed exceedingly well in his Treasury post but remained convinced that the nomination of Lincoln at the 1860 Republican convention in Chicago had been some sort of error, a bad dream from which the nation would awaken by electing him in 1864. He had no doubt that he could do a better job of leading the Union. "There is no administration, properly speaking," he wrote, complaining of the lack of agendas and systematic reporting at Lincoln's often sparsely attended cabinet meetings. When it came to the cabinet's role in trying to save the country, he said: "We have as little to do with it as if we were heads of factories supplying shoes or clothing." According to Browning, it was Chase, supposedly Seward's cabinet ally although a Radical himself, who had told Radical senators "that Seward exercised a back-stairs and malign influence upon the President and thwarted all measures of the cabinet." Chase resented what he considered to be Seward's poaching in the appointment of New York and Boston Customs House positions that he felt were his to fill, and also lost out to Seward in other appointments such as postmasterships that fell in neither of their political spheres. Other members of Lincoln's cabinet saw Chase as being fully engaged in every kind of political infighting: on October 17, 1863, Attorney General Edward Bates wrote in his diary: "I'm afraid Mr. Chase's head is turned by his eagerness in pursuit of the presidency. For a long time back he has been filling all the offices in his own vast patronage, with extreme partizans, and contrives also to fill many vacancies, properly belonging to other departments."

As 1864 began, Chase disavowed any interest in becoming the Republican candidate, but this convinced no one: Colonel J. H. Puleston of the state of Pennsylvania's purchasing agency in Washington said of a recent conversation with Chase that he had "Presidency glaring out of both eyes." Lincoln saw it, commenting to his secretary John Hay that "No man knows what *that gnawing* is till he has had it." Ten thousand Treasury

Department employees around the nation felt unmistakable pressure from the top to work on Chase's behalf and to contribute money to his campaign when the time came.

In addition to Chase's national prominence, commanding presence, and many political connections, he had another asset in the person of his daughter, Kate Chase Sprague. Because Chase was a widower, she acted as his hostess in his Washington mansion. Beautiful, tall and slender, with creamy skin, thick chestnut hair, and a low musical voice, the charming and witty Kate was equally adept at chatting about Washington gossip or speaking knowledgeably about important legislative issues. She complimented women on their gowns, and had a nearly hypnotic effect on men. The newspapers loved her: Kate's wedding two months before to William Sprague, the wealthy young senator from Rhode Island, was the capital's most talked-of social event of the past decade. Lincoln's secretary John Hay, stubbornly loyal to the president, said, "Miss Chase is so busy making her father President that she is only a little lovelier than all other women." But, he admitted, "She is a great woman & with a great future."

Predictably, Kate was the incarnation of all that Mary Todd Lincoln disliked about Washington. Mary was better educated than most of the socialites, who she knew regarded her as an overdressed little provincial nobody. (The story about Mary's first meeting with Kate at the beginning of Lincoln's presidency may not have been true, but it was widely believed: when Mary said to her, "I shall be glad to see you any time, Miss Chase," she responded with, "Mrs. Lincoln, I shall be glad to have *you* call on *me* at any time.") When Lincoln made the fatal husbandly mistake of describing Kate as "young and handsome," Mary exploded with, "Young and handsome you call her! You should not judge beauty for me." The social rivalry between them was underscored when Mary stayed away from Kate's wedding, held at the Chase mansion, and the president went by himself.

In his confidential discussion with Lincoln, Blair suggested that the president should ask Chase to resign—something that Chase had offered to do in December of 1862, and again in May of 1863—but Lincoln decided to leave his treasury secretary in political limbo. To win the Republican nomination, Chase needed to become sufficiently attractive to Republicans of all persuasions, and he might find it hard to rally support for himself as the nation's future leader while still professing to be a loyal member of Lincoln's cabinet.

II

The night following Lincoln's talk with Blair, the members of the Democratic National Committee gathered in New York City at the Fifth Avenue mansion of their chairman, the financier August Belmont. Joined by the editors of several newspapers that supported the party, they agreed with the strategy their host put before them. The best man to name as the Democratic presidential candidate would be Major General George Brinton McClellan.

Just as Lincoln would have to cope with the division in his party between the Radicals and moderates like himself, Belmont had to deal with the fissures in the Democratic Party. He believed that McClellan would be embraced by the "War Democrats," and that the Peace Democrat-Copperhead wing of the party would have to come along with the majority.

George McClellan embodied the original Greek meaning of the word "tragedy": "What might have been." Brilliant at West Point, he was commissioned as a second lieutenant in the Army's elite Corps of Engineers and posted an excellent record in the Mexican War. Although marked as one of the Army's future generals, he became impatient with slow peacetime promotions and resigned to enter business; on the eve of the Civil War he was the highly paid president of the eastern division of the Ohio & Mississippi Railroad. With the country at war, he was back in the Army, first as a major general of Volunteers, and soon after that as a major general with a Regular Army commission. When Lincoln made him general-in-chief of the entire Union Army, "Little Mac" succeeded admirably in organizing and training its vast forces, but subsequently failed as a field commander. Despite having superiority in numbers and matériel, McClellan simply would not attack the Confederates.

From the outset, McClellan thought himself a better man than Lincoln. He told his wife that Lincoln was "an idiot" and began referring to him as the "original gorilla" and "nothing more than a well-meaning baboon." When after many months he realized that the patient Lincoln might relieve him for having squandered every military opportunity, he wrote his wife, "I can never regard him with other feelings than those of thorough contempt—for his mind, heart & morality." His self-serving vision was that Lincoln and others in Washington had conspired to weaken his immense Army of the Potomac so as "to render it inadequate to accomplish the end in view, & then to hold me responsible for the results."

When McClellan did not attack Robert E. Lee during the Confederate retreat after the Battle of Antietam in September of 1862, the exasperated president said of him, "He is an admirable engineer, but he seems to have a special talent for a stationary engine." Even then, Lincoln exercised more patience, but McClellan finally pushed him too far: in late October, six weeks after Antietam, he told Lincoln that he still could not go after Lee because his army's horses were "absolutely broken down from fatigue." Lincoln acidly inquired, "Will you pardon me for asking what the horses of your army have done since the battle of Antietam that fatigue anything?" Within a week, he relieved McClellan of all military commands. McClellan returned to his house in New Jersey, waiting for further orders that never came.

The extent of McClellan's failings never became known to the public. "Little Mac," short and dapper, had been popular with his soldiers. The picture of self-assurance, he spoke well. All in all, the Democratic leaders meeting at Belmont's house felt they had the right man; it would be hard to accuse a Union Army general of being a "Peace Democrat."

III

By mid-January, the political maneuvering had intensified. Lincoln remained wary of Chase's thus-far-undeclared candidacy and knew that other Republican contenders might enter the picture. He began to put out the word through Republican circles in every Northern state that he did in fact seek reelection and would welcome endorsements as soon as possible.

Lincoln did not have to wait long. On January 23 the New York State Republican Committee endorsed him. The record of the correspondence he dealt with in his "shop" on this same day reveals the range of other matters with which the president had to cope. The most important of these was a long letter Lincoln wrote in his own hand, replying to an inquiry as to "how the government would regard cases" in which the Southern owners of cotton plantations in areas back under Federal control would free their slaves and pay them wages to continue doing the work they had been doing before. Lincoln replied, "I should regard such cases with great favor, and . . . treat them [the former slaves] precisely as I would the same number of white people in the same relation and condition." He followed this by writing a permit for three Kentuckians, one a cousin of the late Henry Clay, to free their slaves and start paying them on plantations they owned in Mississippi and Arkansas. In a leap to another area of his responsibilities, Lincoln then signed a modification to the 1858 "Treaty between the United States and China" prepared for his signature by Secretary of State Seward. The next thing he wrote, after reviewing the record of good behavior of a prisoner in the District of Columbia jail, was a note to Attorney General Edward Bates that said in its entirety: "Hon. Attorney General please make out & send me a pardon in this case. A. Lincoln"

This was Lincoln at work, hour after hour. One of his secretaries was always at hand, ready to write whatever he dictated or directed to be written for his signature, but often, after receiving one of his endless streams of visitors, Lincoln simply jotted down his disposition of the matter, sometimes before the person who had come to him was out the door of his big office. He would then place it on the day's growing stack of communications to be mailed, or carried by messenger to other government offices in Washington. (Interestingly, an examination of the original letters shows that this master of the language frequently wrote "it's" where "its" would have been grammatically correct, and that he never capitalized the first letter of the day of the week. As for punctuation, Lincoln told a friend, "I have a great respect for the semi-colon; it's a very useful little chap.")

There were those who thought Lincoln's involvement with details wasted his time, but it served two purposes. He cut through red tape—a term already in use, referring to the ribbons used to tie up stacks of documents. A memo from the president received swift attention. Occasionally, he combined a valid interest with a touch of whimsy. Writing a memo to the ferociously hardworking Stanton, a man not noted for his sense of humor, he gave this instruction to his secretary of war: "Please have the adjutant general ascertain whether second Lieutenant of Company D, 2nd Infantry, Alexander E. Drake, is entitled to promotion. His wife thinks he is. Please have this looked into."

Apart from getting action on specific matters, all this fit into his "public opinion baths"—speaking with many ordinary citizens, as well as answering letters from all over the country. The people he met or corresponded with kept spreading the word that a real person lived in the White House, a man who listened and cared. He sometimes received fifty visitors a day. Few had an appointment; those who chose to walk into the White House on their own waited in the hall outside Lincoln's office until their turns came.

This occasionally spilled over into hours scheduled for other matters. One day, Navy Secretary Gideon Welles noted this in his diary: "As I went into the Cabinet-meeting a fair, plump lady pressed forward and insisted she must see the President—only for a moment, wanted nothing." Welles asked her a few questions, and then went in and told Lincoln that this lady from Dubuque, Iowa, was visiting in the East and said that she "came from Baltimore expressly to have a look at President Lincoln." Lincoln delayed the meeting and had her shown in; when he saw her, he laughed and said, "Well, in the matter of looking at each other, I have altogether the advantage." The lady left happily a few moments later, clutching a piece of paper with his autograph.

Lincoln was a compassionate man, but there was an additional aspect to his willingness to oblige those who waited to see him in his office. During his four successive two-year terms in the Illinois House of Representatives, he had learned about constituent service: If you helped individual voters who came to you with their problems, they were likely to vote for you the next time you ran for office. And if you were president, no matter what state the visitor in your office came from, he or she could probably help get you a few votes in a national election.

That was pragmatism, but at other moments Lincoln showed how much he cherished life, even in the midst of a war. On a warm but windy Tuesday morning when Lincoln's office windows were open, his friend Colonel John Eaton was with him when gunfire sounded from the northwest, soon followed by the smell of gunpowder. Lincoln turned from the window, tears running down his cheeks. It was the day of the week when deserters were shot by firing squads at the Execution Grounds some distance up Fourteenth Street. Lincoln suspended fully half the death sentences brought to his attention, sending them back for further review, making a recommendation for clemency, or sometimes issuing a pardon, but remained mindful of his generals' belief that those who deserted in the face of the enemy had to be severely punished to preserve discipline in the army as a whole. He had heard the Tuesday gunfire often, but could never get used to it.

IV

Mary Lincoln did not intend to wait for the political conventions scheduled for later in the year; she began accelerating her own campaign to get her husband reelected and, in the process, raise some funds to pay off her debts. She started inviting prominent men, who seldom brought their wives, to what was in effect a political salon over which she presided in the Blue Room of the White House. Of these evening gatherings, she told her black seamstress, Elizabeth Keckley, "These men have influence, and we require influence to re-elect Mr. Lincoln." She went on to say of her husband, "He glances at my rich dresses and is happy to believe that the few hundred dollars that I obtain from him supply all my wants. . . . If he is re-elected, I can keep him in ignorance of my affairs, but if he is defeated, then the bills will be sent in, and he will know all."

Among her guests was a man named Abram Wakeman, who was the postmaster of New York City and coveted the Customs House job of surveyor of the Port of New York, the administration's second-best patronage position after collector of the port. He had played an important part in getting New York's Central Republican Committee to give Lincoln the welcome endorsement he received late in January. Wakeman was also renegotiating Mary's bills with merchants in Manhattan; a letter from her told him, "Please say not a word to anyone . . . about the 5th Avenue business." Wakeman would be appointed to the post he wanted, surveyor of the Port of New York.

Mary did not confine her efforts to the White House, and visited officials in their offices and homes. "That lady," Commissioner of Agriculture Isaac Newton soon told John Hay, "has set here on this sofy and shed tears by the pint a begging me to pay her debts which was unbeknownst to the President." She began to get the idea that if Lincoln were defeated, it would be her fault, in good part because opposition politicians might "get hold of the particulars" of her debts and use them against her husband. This thought, Elizabeth Keckley said, made Mary "almost crazy with anxiety and fear."

As JANUARY ENDED, pressures on Lincoln existed that most citizens did not even connect with the White House. In the midst of war, settlers continued to push west. In some places, the Indians were fighting those taking their lands. They also had well-founded grievances about the breaking of treaties with their tribes, and about the corruption among Indian Office supervisors who among other things sold off entire warehouses filled with badly needed food the tribes had been promised. In 1862 and 1863, there were uprisings in Wisconsin, Minnesota, and the Dakota and Nebraska territories, attacks so bloody that Union Army units were sent back from fighting the Confederates to quell them.

Now, in the last week of January, a diplomatically delicate situation arose: Federal cavalry wanted to chase some bands of rebellious Sioux warriors into the Red River Country and Hudson's Bay Territories of Canada, as well as to stop others from using Canada as a safe haven from which to make further raids on American frontier settlements. This would involve armed American incursions across the Canadian border, and Lincoln had authorized Secretary of State Seward to ask what the president called "the authorities of Great Britain" for permission to do that. Canada's ties to England were strong, and British troops served there. The most important goal of the Union's foreign policy was to keep England neutral. This had not been easy to do, in part because the United States Navy's blockade of Confederate-held ports caused a critical shortage of Southern cotton for hundreds of British textile mills that had always depended on that supply. Within England, there were sporadic mercantile efforts to bring England into an alliance with the Confederacy. Early in the war, when a United States Navy warship stopped the British mail steamer *Trent* on the high seas and removed two Confederate envoys heading for England, hostilities might have occurred. In one of the first of many tests of his diplomatic skill, Secretary of State Seward managed to avert a situation in which the Union's fleet might have found itself fighting the far stronger Royal Navy.

This potential crisis with England in late January evaporated, with no record of a pursuit into Canada, but Lincoln's priorities placed the development of the western territories—the discovery of mineral wealth and the building of railroads that gave the economy needed stimulation in the middle of a war—ahead of any rights or needs of the Indian tribes. In his Annual Message to Congress given the past December he said, "Sound policy and our imperative duty to these wards of the government demand our anxious and constant attention to their well-being," but the same document spoke approvingly of additional treaties that "contain stipulations for extinguishing the possessor rights of the Indians to large and valuable tracts of land." As for factors that might influence Lincoln's feelings about them, his grandfather had been killed by Indians in Kentucky in 1786.

Not surprisingly, the blizzard of paperwork from all directions occasionally overwhelmed Lincoln. Near the end of the month, his secretaries found this in his office.

Memorandum
I find this bundle of somewhat old papers upon my table, & can not remember for what object they were left. Please file them.

A. Lincoln

Lincoln's state of mind at this point became apparent during a visit he made on February 6 to the house of his old Illinois political colleague Owen Lovejoy, whom he described as being his best friend in Congress. Lovejoy was dying from what was apparently cancer of both the liver and kidneys. As he spoke sympathetically to Lovejoy, Lincoln said of himself: "This war is eating my life out. I have a strong impression that I shall not live to see the end."

This was not a new thought for Lincoln. On the same day that he said this to Lovejoy, the Boston publication *Littell's Living Age* carried an article strongly praising him, written by Harriet Beecher Stowe. The author of *Uncle Tom's Cabin*, the powerful antislavery novel that had sold a million copies, met Lincoln at the White House earlier in the war. According to the story that came down in her family, at that meeting the 6-foot-4 president greeted the author, who stood less than 5 feet tall, with, "So you're the little woman who wrote the book that started this great [vast] war!" In this article, she wrote that as they discussed the war during their White House meeting, he told her, "Whichever way it ends, I have the impression that I shan't last long after it's over."

V

Despite the bloodshed and suffering that the war brought, the inexorable social activities of official Washington had a life of their own. In addition to her private political salons in the Blue Room, Mary Lincoln continued to hold large White House receptions, events the wives of presidents were expected to have; she was aware that many would criticize her for giving parties in a time of war and that there would be equal criticism if she appeared to be aloof, inviting few people to a house that belonged more to the nation than it did to her.

The man who had emerged as her social secretary and an important person in White House entertaining was William O. Stoddard, the young man Lincoln used for sorting out the incoming nongovernmental mail. Lincoln's secretaries Nicolay and Hay never saw his work as being on a par with theirs, but Stoddard had become an indispensable member of Lincoln's staff. In addition, unlike Nicolay and Hay, both of whom Mary Lincoln disliked as much as they disliked her—in private they referred to her as the "Hell-cat"—after arriving at the White House he became a favorite of the First Lady and was soon able to say, "I was . . . entirely in charge of the social side of the White House."

Stoddard not only possessed the knowledge and instincts necessary for placing the right people beside each other at dinner while keeping others yards apart, but in addition to his "Illinois" letters for the *New York Examiner* anonymously praising Lincoln, this former journalist had a gift for acute social reportage. When he later described a White House evening in his memoirs, he showed that he could see Mary Lincoln as dowagers from old-line eastern families saw her, but that his sympathies were with Mary—he resented these socialites' catty and condescending attitude.

Stoddard began by confessing that Mary's very low-cut red evening gown, "although made for her by one of the best dress artists in New York," did not look well in the Red Room, where Mary always held her large parties. He continued:

[The room] heightens the deep crimson shade of the silk . . . you cannot help disliking it. . . . You rebel more vigorously after this bevy of Boston, Concord, Lexington and Bunker Hill women come in, with one or two who are all the way from Plymouth Rock and the deck of the Mayflower. They, too, evidently agree with you. Not one of them but has deemed it her duty to dress as if the war-taxes had cut down her income but had not clipped the upper part of her wardrobe. The tall, gray-haired, severe-faced lady, in very plain black silk, has two sons in the army. She may own streets in Boston, for all you know, but her dark eyes search the crimson silk and every other item of Mrs. Lincoln's outfit remorselessly, in spite of the warm, hearty cordiality of her greeting. Every woman who has yet arrived has come as a critic, and not one of them will be capable of doing kindly justice; and they will be authorities, hereafter, swelling a miserable tide of misunderstanding. Somehow or other, the best of women make too much of dress. . . .

Stoddard was happy to see the arrival of a group of prominent New York women.

It is something of a relief to welcome a different bevy, now sweeping in; for the Knickerbockers are almost a distinct race from the Puritans. There are vivid colors now to help the situation, and you can be thankful to Manhattan Island, and to Staten Island, and to Long Island, and to Hell Gate, Spuyten Duyvil, the Dunderberg and Anthony's Nose. Red, blue, and other tints which you do not know the correct name of, and a fine glitter of diamonds. It is all right now, for the entire Bunker Hill party disapproves of the Hudson [River] party, and there is sincere reciprocity. . . . Nevertheless, the honors are largely with Bunker Hill; for the gray critic with the severe eyes comes out in all but fiercely enthusiastic approval of the Emancipation Proclamation, and it is not taken up very audibly by the echoes between Dunderberg and Anthony's Nose. Long Island and Staten Island do better.

On the whole, these women, queens of society in their own parishes, should have perceptive faculties capable of telling them, and others through them, that Mrs. Lincoln—a Kentucky girl whose years have been passed, for the greater part, in a growing village on Grand Prairie, among prairie villagers and settlers—is doing the honors of the White

House remarkably well. Not one woman in a hundred would do any bet-
ter; but then these women, the visitors of this evening, consider them-
selves, not as one in a hundred, but each as one in a thousand, with nine
hundred and ninety-nine ranged below her. So they will show no mercy.

VI

As February began, the year's military and political future started to evolve. J. Russell Jones of Chicago, the man most likely to know whether Ulysses S. Grant wanted to run for president, had arrived in Washington in January and handed Lincoln a letter in which Grant said, "Nothing would induce me to become a presidential candidate, particularly so long as there is a possibility of having Mr. Lincoln re-elected." A relieved Lincoln now set the stage for Grant's final military rise; he had a bill introduced in Congress that revived the rank of lieutenant general, last held by George Washington. Once the rank was enacted into law, Lincoln intended to nominate Grant for the position, which would also make Grant the Union Army's general-in-chief.

As this bill came forward, Major General William Tecumseh Sherman led 25,000 of his troops east from Vicksburg in what became known as his Meridian campaign. Sherman's wartime career had been as unusual as Grant's rise from obscurity to the prospective command of a million men. He recalled meeting with Lincoln early in the war as a newly promoted brigadier general: "I explained to him my extreme desire to serve in a subordinate capacity, and in no event to be left in a superior command. He promised this with promptness, making the jocular remark that his chief trouble was to find places for the too many generals who wanted to be at the head of affairs, to command armies, etc."

What Sherman feared came true, with consequences even greater than he feared. Succeeding to the command of the long, thinly manned Union front across Kentucky in September of 1861, he became convinced that overwhelmingly superior Confederate forces opposed him and could march into his headquarters at the Galt House in Louisville whenever they wished. There he could be found pacing the corridors of the hotel at all hours, smoking eight to ten cigars a night, and waiting for messages at the telegraph office at 3 A.M. He drank too much and ate virtually nothing; sometimes his hands shook. Sherman soon declined into a form of nervous breakdown; on December 11, a headline in the *Cincinnati Commercial* proclaimed:

GENERAL WILLIAM T. SHERMAN INSANE

Recovering, Sherman served with foresight and effectiveness as a supply officer supporting Grant's first big success at Fort Donelson in Tennessee on February 15, 1862. Seven weeks later, Sherman commanded the right wing of Grant's army with exceptional ability at the great victory of Shiloh. From then on, Grant and Sherman, who had known each other only by sight during the one year they overlapped at West Point, began the military and personal relationship that carried them through their western campaigns. By 1864, with Sherman acting as Grant's principal lieutenant, Union forces had opened the entire length of the Mississippi River and outflanked most of the Confederacy. Though the two generals were different in appearance and personality, Sherman a rangy red-headed man who talked incessantly, Grant shorter and dark-haired with a reserved manner, each saw in the other a soldier's soldier who put the Union cause ahead of personal advancement. Grant relaxed in Sherman's company as he did with no other officer; Sherman characterized the friendship that grew between them as being that of "brothers, I the older in years, he the higher in rank."

For nearly two years, Sherman learned from Grant and, as February of 1864 began, the man who had feared an independent command set off with 25,000 men on a 120-mile march from Vicksburg to Meridian, Mississippi, to inflict more casualties than he sustained and return a month later having outmaneuvered his Confederate opponents. What neither Lincoln nor Grant nor Sherman himself could then have understood was that this campaign completed Sherman's dress rehearsal for his conduct of far larger movements destined to have a tremendous impact on Lincoln's political destiny.

VII

Lincoln's life continued to swing between dealing with great issues and with personal matters. On February 10, a White House coachman named Patterson McGee was dismissed; the reason is uncertain, but McGee had previously refused to run such errands as going out to buy a newspaper that Lincoln wanted to see. At eight-thirty that night, a fire started in Lincoln's private stables, a brick building on the White House grounds between the mansion and the Treasury Department. A witness said that Lincoln "jumped over the boxwood hedge, threw open the doors to try to get the horses out," but it was too late. Lincoln's two horses and two belonging to his secretaries, Nicolay and Hay, perished screaming in the flames, as did Tad's pony and the one on which Willie had ridden around the White House grounds so often in the year before he died. Hours later, "Lincoln and others were standing in the East Room looking at the still burning stables. Lincoln was weeping." Nicolay wrote about this to Hay, who was in Florida as part of the effort to create a pro-Union government in recaptured territory. He said, "Tad was in bitter tears at the loss of his ponies, and his heaviest grief was his recollection that one of them belonged to Willie." It was as if Willie had died all over again. The next day, the coachman who had been fired was arrested on a charge of arson but released for lack of evidence.

Every day in the "shop" was busy, but on Monday, February 22, there was a remarkable buildup of matters requiring Lincoln's attention. He received the news that, although it was not a unanimous decision and would have to be ratified at the national convention later in the year, the Republican National Committee had endorsed him as the party's presidential candidate. That put him firmly in the running, but over the weekend two Washington newspapers, the *Constitutional Union* and the *Intelligencer*, had carried what became known as the "Pomeroy Circular." This was an open letter printed above the signature of Radical Republican Senator Samuel C. Pomeroy of Kansas. In it, Pomeroy, acting on behalf of an array of Radical senators, representatives, and other prominent Radical sympathizers, opposed Lincoln's nomination and urged the public to support Secretary of the Treasury Chase for president.

Lincoln knew all this before his working day began, but he soon received an astonishing letter from Chase. In it, Chase said, "I had no knowledge of the existence of this letter before I saw it in the *Union*." In fact, Chase had met a number of times with what he described in this letter to Lincoln as "a Committee of my political friends" and had approved both the idea of their starting an effort to have him nominated for president and to the publication of Pomeroy's letter. Nonetheless, Chase went on to assure Lincoln that his first loyalty was to him, adding, "For your-self I cherish sincere respect and esteem," and "I do not wish to adminis-ter the Treasury Department one [more] day without your entire confidence."

In some ways, Chase had been clever. At no point did he offer to re-sign; Chase characterized himself as feeling as a matter of duty that he should accept the judgment of these "political friends" particularly be-cause of his certainty that "the use of my name as proposed would not af-fect my usefulness in my present position."

As he had twice before, Lincoln decided not to remove Chase from his cabinet, leaving Chase in the awkward position of publicly competing with a man it was his duty to serve. Yet if he did resign, he would appear to be deserting Lincoln to run against him.

The Pomeroy Circular did more than place Chase in an awkward po-sition. Despite his disavowal of any disloyalty and his determination to continue to seek the presidency, it also disquieted much of the public and caused many of Chase's important supporters to lose faith in his judg-ment and political sense.

A few of those prominent figures brought trouble on themselves. General Sherman's older brother, Republican senator John Sherman (later known for his Sherman Antitrust Act), had been among those back-ing his fellow Ohio political colleague Chase. He had saved the Chase campaign the money they would have had to spend for postage by allow-ing the Circular to be mailed throughout Ohio under his congressional frank; when that became known, he heard from the public in no uncer-tain terms. (One angry letter to Sherman about his association with the "mean and dastardly" Circular told him, "it will brand with infamy your character as a statesman and your honor as a gentleman." Another said that if Sherman was trying to ruin Lincoln in the public's eyes, "You can[']t do it and . . . if you can[']t do better [as a senator] you had better quit.")

For Lincoln, this February day's agenda involved more than dealing with duplicitous actions by a member of his cabinet. On the purely mili-tary side, Congress created the rank of lieutenant general; he nominated Grant for that promotion immediately. Then, in a combination of the military and the political, he responded to a letter from General William S. Rosecrans, on duty in Kentucky, asking if United States Colored

Troops, now free men, should receive pay equal to that of white Union soldiers, and whether members of their families who were still slaves "will be made free?" Even at this stage in the war, with more than 100,000 badly needed black troops serving in the Union ranks, Lincoln remained wary of the political and constitutional problems involved in freeing some slaves and not others. Lincoln replied that "I am not prepared to answer" both the question of giving the black Union troops pay equal to those who were white and the matter of the civil status of their families who were still enslaved. Next, he sent an endorsement of a letter to the commissioner of Indian affairs that asked for further information on a report of "the extreme destitution to which the people of the Cherokee Nation have been reduced by the disasters of the present war."

The president had more appointments on his calendar. At seven-thirty that evening, accompanied by Mary and their son Robert, down from Harvard, he appeared at the Patent Office Building, part of which had been turned into one of the best military hospitals in Washington. Just that morning, a committee had arrived in his office asking him to attend the opening of a charitable event to be held at the Patent Office Building in support of the families of military volunteers from the District of Columbia.

Although Lincoln made such appearances on behalf of similar causes, he had an unusual tie to the Patent Office. Alone among American presidents, including the mechanically ingenious Thomas Jefferson, he held a patent for an invention. At the age of twenty-two, he had been one of two young men taking turns steering a 30-foot-long flatboat laden with tons of cargo as it floated down the Sangamon River at the beginning of a six-week trip that would continue down the Mississippi to New Orleans. At one point, their craft proved to lie too deep in the water to pass over a partially submerged milldam. When the unwieldy barge suddenly wedged against the bank at a turn in the river and water poured into the hull in a way that would soon swamp the boat and ruin its cargo, Lincoln went into action. He managed to cut a hole in the bow above water level and then used his great strength to heave some heavy barrels off the stern onto the shore, causing the stern to rise; when water then poured out of the hole he made in the bow, Lincoln and his companion got the lightened boat over the obstacle, repaired and reloaded it, and went on their way. Nothing about that was lost on him; some years later, living in Illinois, he invented a form of jack, a flotation device to be installed on the sides of a flatboat's hull, which could raise it if trapped in the same situation. He sent his drawings of the device to the Patent Office and received U.S. Patent No. 6469.

Now, at this evenings charitable event at the Patent Office thirty-three years after he ran aground on the Sangamon River, Lincoln listened to a scheduled speech and the recital of a poem, and found himself unexpectedly called on as the next speaker. Trying to make light of the situation, he told the audience this, as reported in the next day's *New York Tribune*:

> *He thought that the Committee had practiced a little fraud on him, for they did not intimate to him in the morning when they came to see him, that they had expected him to speak. . . . If he made any mistake it might do both himself and the nation harm.* [*Applause.*] *It was very difficult to say sensible things.* [*Laughter.*]
>
> *He therefore hoped that the audience would excuse him after expressing his desire that the charitable enterprise in which we were engaged might be abundantly successful.* [*Applause.*]

According to the following day's *Washington Star*, Mary described it as being "the worst speech I ever listened to in my life . . . I wanted the earth to sink and let me through."

CHASE AND LINCOLN were not finished with each other. Three days after Lincoln received the "Pomeroy Circular," a Republican caucus in Ohio voted to endorse Lincoln for president. This was a rejection of Chase by the Republican leaders of his home state; on March 5, Chase sent a letter intended for publication to state senator James C. Hall of Ohio saying that his quest for the presidency had ended.

There were those who felt, with reason, that the political arena had not seen the last of Salmon P. Chase. The *New York Herald* said, "The salmon is a queer fish . . . often it appears to avoid the bait before gulping it down." Supreme Court justice David Davis wrote: "Mr. Chase's declination is a mere sham. . . . The plan is to get up a great opposition to Lincoln [and] . . . present Chase again." Chase remained as Lincoln's secretary of the treasury, and their relationship grew shakier by the day.

LINCOLN JUGGLES IN THE "SHOP"; GRANT COMES EAST

As March began, Lincoln knew that Ulysses S. Grant was en route to Washington to take command of the Union Army; in his White House office he continued to work on a great variety of matters—political, military, economic—all of which he conscientiously believed required his attention and frequently his decision.

On March 7, Lincoln wrote a letter to a member of the Maryland legislature, urging him, after three years of war, to have that Border State enact legislation that would free all its blacks who were still slaves. Even now, Lincoln took a cautious approach to the subject of how and when to grant civil rights to blacks. Ever the lawyer, he had said that his Emancipation Proclamation was authorized only by what he thought his wartime emergency powers encompassed, and agreed that a postwar congress would in theory have the right to overturn his actions to free slaves. Lincoln believed that permanent freedom for slaves could come only by means of an amendment to the Constitution; in the meantime, if Maryland enacted legislation to free slaves, that would be the next-best thing, in that state. Soon after this, writing to the governor of Louisiana, head of a provisional regime installed by the Union after most of Louisiana was wrested from the Confederacy, he remarked on the state constitution about to be enacted there. As for who should be allowed to vote, Lincoln wrote, "I barely suggest for your private consideration whether some of the colored people may not be let in—as, for instance, the very intelligent, and especially those who have fought gallantly in our ranks."

His correspondence varied from hour to hour. On the same day as his communication to the Maryland legislator, among twelve other letters leaving his office was one to Queen Victoria, prepared for him by Secretary of State Seward. Starting with "Great and Good Friend," Lincoln expressed his "warm congratulations" on the birth of a grandson whose mother was "the Princess of Wales, the daughter of the King of Denmark," and whose father was "Your Majesty's well-beloved son His Royal Highness Albert Edward"—the future Edward VII.

Turning from the latest of these letters of congratulations or expressions of condolence to heads of state that required his signature, Lincoln signed as different a document as could be imagined: an "Order Designating Starting Point of Union Pacific Railroad." Much of Lincoln's law practice in Illinois had been as an attorney representing railroad companies. He had won important cases for them before the Illinois Supreme Court, including one that gained important tax exemptions for the Illinois Central, then the company that had more miles of track than any other in the world. In addition to tax breaks, he believed in governmental subsidies for the railroads, in the form of grants of Federal lands. With enthusiasm, he had seen railroad lines pushing back the frontier, opening up millions of acres for agriculture, mining, and manufacturing enterprises. He was providing leadership in this epic endeavor; he wanted to see railroad and telegraph lines moving side by side across the continent.

This permission by which the Union Pacific was now "authorized and required to construct a single line of Rail Road, and Telegraph" due west across the plains from a point on the border between the state of Iowa and the Nebraska Territory conformed with Lincoln's belief that westward expansion was vital to the Union's economy at this critical time. Beyond the needs of the moment, as far back as his early twenties Lincoln had been attracted by the Whig Party's program, which involved federal support of banks, encouragement of manufacturing, and subsidies for canals, turnpikes, and railroads. Lincoln shared the dream of building a railroad line that would run all the way to California. To make that happen, he had in effect lobbied Congress to pass the Pacific Railroad bill, enacted in June of 1862. That had enabled this newer entity, the Union Pacific, to begin planning to move westward, eventually to link up with the existing Central Pacific Railroad, which would lay track east from San Francisco. Both companies would receive Federal lands across which they could build, and Federal subsidies for construction costs. As for who would settle on those lands, Lincoln had pushed for the Homestead Act of 1862, giving land to farmers who would work the acres given them, and the Act to Encourage Immigration of 1864, which played its part in bringing hundreds of thousands of European immigrants to Northern ports despite the war.

In yet another area of responsibility, on this day Lincoln also signed an executive order designed to placate the French government, involving the release for shipment to France of "Seven thousand hogsheads" of tobacco that had been impounded in Union warehouses. France, which the Union wished to keep neutral, claimed that this approximately half-million pounds of tobacco had been bought from Southern sources before the war began. Even in this executive order, Lincoln pointed out that "it was subsequently ascertained that a part at least, of the said tobacco had been purchased subsequently to that date," but he added without going into detail that "a satisfactory understanding on the subject has now been reached" and that the tobacco could be shipped.

The decisions Lincoln reached in his office and the paperwork that poured out of his "shop" affected people throughout the country. But the physical man, towering and bony, so unpredictable in his awkward movements and gestures, affected people in a different way. He fascinated every kind of person. The harshest judgment on his appearance came from the Ohio newspaper editor and Republican politician Donn Piatt, who said, "His body seemed to me a huge skeleton in clothes." Nathaniel Hawthorne, after meeting with him in the White House as a member of a deputation from Massachusetts, had these impressions:

> . . . a tall, loose-jointed figure . . . about the homeliest man I ever saw, yet by no means repulsive or disagreeable. . . . He was dressed in a rusty black frock-coat and pantaloons . . . worn so faithfully that the suit had adapted itself to the curves and angularities of his figure, and had grown to be an outer skin of the man. He had shabby slippers on his feet.
>
> The whole physiognomy is as coarse a one as you would meet anywhere in the length and breadth of the States; but, withal, it is redeemed, illuminated, softened and brightened by a kindly though serious look out of

his eyes, and an expression of homely sagacity, that seems weighted with rich results of village experience.

(Lincoln had a sense of humor about his appearance. In one of their debates, when Senator Stephen Douglas characterized him as being "two-faced," Lincoln replied, "If I had another face, do you think I would wear this one?")

Lincoln's secretary John Nicolay noticed his effect on others. When former New York governor and United States senator Hamilton Fish came to call on the president, "Mr. Lincoln settled back in his chair, gradually sliding down into a half reclining posture with his feet on a chair before him, until Mr. Fish had serious apprehensions that they would go through the wall into the next room." The black leader Frederick Douglass, upon being ushered into "the shop" for his first meeting with the president in August of 1863, found Lincoln leaning back on a sofa while he read, and had the impression that his legs stretched into "different parts of the room." One could see that Lincoln's legs were longer than normal, even for a man of his height; his old Illinois law partner William Herndon remarked that "in sitting down on common chairs. . . . A marble placed on his knee thus sitting would roll hipward, down an inclined plane."

Lincoln acted spontaneously: discussing matters of the highest importance to the nation and its future, he would lift one of his large feet, clad in a wrinkled leather slipper, onto a corner of a desk or table. Sometimes he moved his long legs into an extraordinary position that his secretaries called "sitting on his shoulders." Continuing a conversation, he would slide down in his chair until he was nearly horizontal, raising both slippered feet so that they rested on the mantel of the office fireplace.

More than the movements of his body, it was the combination of that body with Lincoln's face and manner that fascinated those who came close to him. The Washington journalist Benjamin Perley Poore wrote this description:

His favorite attitude when listening—and he was a good listener—was to lean forward and clasp his left knee with both hands, and his face would then wear a sad, wearied look. But when the time came for him to give an opinion on what he had heard, or to tell a story, which something said

*"reminded him of," his face would lighten up with its homely, rugged
smile, and he would run his fingers through his bristly black hair, which
would stand out in every direction. . . .*

Congressman George W. Julian of Indiana, a Radical who liked and
admired him despite their political differences, commented, that "with
the exception of occasional seasons of deep depression, his nature was all
sunshine," and wrote this description of Lincoln as raconteur. "When he
told a particularly good story, and the time came to laugh, he would sometimes throw his left foot across his right knee, and clenching his foot with
both hands and bending forward, his whole frame seemed to be convulsed
with the effort to give expression to his sensations. His laugh was like that
of the hero of Sartor Resartus, 'a laugh of the whole man,' from head to
heel."

One of those who left a vivid account of an extraordinary encounter
with Lincoln was Cordelia Perrine Harvey, the widow of Governor Louis
Powell Harvey of Wisconsin, who had drowned in an accident on the
Tennessee River soon after delivering ninety boxes of medical supplies
for the Wisconsin soldiers wounded at the Battle of Shiloh. The Harveys
were of the indomitable breed that "built the frontier"—the supreme expression of praise the people of their region could bestow. As a childless
widow, Cordelia continued her husband's concern for the welfare of soldiers by getting herself appointed as an agent for the Sanitary Commission, a form of precursor to the Red Cross, visiting Union Army hospitals
along the Mississippi to determine their needs.

Working in disease-stricken parts of the South, she saw more and
more wounded men brought in who then died of malaria, typhoid, and
dysentery they contracted in the hospitals. She had wrenching experiences in what she called "these uncomfortable, illy-ventilated, hot, un-
clean, wretched rooms." Seeing what seemed to them an angel of mercy,
a man would clutch her skirt, another would touch her shawl and kiss it,
others would kiss her hand and press it to their fevered cheeks. She said
that one boy "in wild delirium cried, 'I want to go home! I want to go
home! Lady! Lady! Take me in your chariot, take me away!' "

Cordelia became convinced that many of these men dying of fevers
could survive if they were shipped to healthier surroundings in the North.
She tended to the needs of patients from every Union state, but had particular feelings for the men of Wisconsin. She saw them as did a journalist

who, having had the opportunity of seeing both the easterners of the Army of the Potomac and the men of what became known as "the Army of the West," said this.

> *The Seventeenth [Corps] is largely composed of Wisconsin men, splendid specimens of humanity—tall and well-made, with the long, free stride and regular, cadent step which no Army of the Potomac man ever got. It comes only from great practice, long legs, and long marches such as Sherman's men have had.*

Eventually, Cordelia became seriously ill herself, and friends brought her back to Wisconsin. When after several months she recovered, Cordelia decided that it was her mission to see that a hospital was built, in Wisconsin, for sick and wounded soldiers from Wisconsin. As the wife of the governor who had died trying to aid the young men of his state, she was able to mobilize considerable support for her idea. Cordelia came to Washington and was admitted one morning to see Lincoln, who had already received the advice of Stanton and others that her scheme was impractical.

> *The President took my hand, hoped I was well, but there was no smile of welcome on his face. It was rather the stern look of the judge who had decided against me. His face was peculiar; bone, nerve, vein, and muscle were all so plainly seen; deep lines of thought and care were around his mouth and eyes.*

Lincoln soon made it clear: "Madam, this matter of northern hospitals has been talked of a great deal, and I thought it was settled, but it seems not. What have you got to say about it?" Cordelia tried to make her case, one of her arguments being greeted with what she described as "a sort of a sneer," but at the end of what proved to be only their first talk, he sent her to Stanton with a note saying, "Admit Mrs. Harvey at once; listen to what she says; she is a lady of intelligence and talks sense." Cordelia was "kindly received" by the often-stern Stanton, who told her that the subject was still under consideration, but that to this point the Army medical authorities thought it better not to establish hospitals in places as far from the battlefields as Wisconsin.

Returning to Lincoln's office, Cordelia reported the standoff to Lincoln, who was still not at all persuaded by her argument that a hospital in Wisconsin would save lives of those wounded in the South. He did, however, say, "I will see the Secretary of War myself, and you come in the morning."

The following day, Cordelia returned, "full of hope." She did not know that the woman who had preceded her in Lincoln's office had been begging "for the life of a son who was sentenced to be shot for desertion under very aggravating circumstances."

When Cordelia was shown into his office, Lincoln waited for her to speak, and when she did not, "He said, 'well,' with a peculiar contortion of face I never saw in anybody else." When she asked Lincoln if he had made a decision, he replied impatiently, "No, but I believe this idea of northern hospitals is a great humbug, and I am tired of hearing about it."

To that, Cordelia answered, "I regret to add a feather's weight to your already overwhelming care and responsibility. I would rather have stayed at home."

As for what came next, "With a kind of half smile, he said: 'I wish you had.'"

Cordelia burst out with an impassioned unrehearsed speech. She told the president, "I come to plead for the lives of those who were the first to hasten to the support of this government, who helped to place you where you are, because they trusted you. Men who have done all they could, and now when flesh, and nerve, and muscle are gone, still pray for your life and the life of this republic. . . . I know that a majority of them would live and be strong men again if they could be sent north."

The atmosphere in the room became electric.

While I was speaking the expression of Mr. Lincoln's face had changed many times. He had never taken his eye from me. Now every muscle in his face seemed to contract, and then suddenly expand. As he opened his mouth you could almost hear them snap as he said; "You assume to know more than I do," and closed his mouth as if he never expected to open it again, sort of slammed it to.

I could scarcely reply. I was hurt, and thought the tears would come, but rallied in a moment and said: "You must pardon me, Mister President, I intend no disrespect, but it is because of this knowledge, because I do know what you do not know, that I come to you. . . ."

Lincoln remained adamant, to the point that his expression scared Cordelia. "I had noticed the veins in his face filling full within a few moments, and one vein in his forehead was as large as my little finger, and it gave him a frightful look." Still, Cordelia persisted, saying, "If you will grant my petition you will be glad as long as you live. The prayer of grateful hearts will give you strength in the hour of trial, and strong and willing arms will return to fight your battles."

The President bowed his head, and with a look of sadness I can never forget, said: "I shall never be glad any more." All severity had passed from his face.

Everything between this man and this woman changed. Cordelia said quietly, "Do not speak so, Mister President. Who will have so much reason to rejoice when the Government is restored, as it will be?"

"I know, I know," he said placing a hand on each side [of his head] and bowing forward, "but the springs of life are wearing away."

I asked if he had felt his great cares were injuring his health. "No," he replied, "not directly, perhaps."

I asked if he slept well, and he said he never was a good sleeper, and, of course, slept less now than ever before.

As she rose to go, Cordelia asked if he had made a decision; Lincoln asked her to come back at noon the next day. When she did, Cordelia was kept waiting for more than three hours because of an unexpectedly long conference Lincoln was having with his cabinet, but during that time he twice sent out word that he would meet with her as soon as the meeting ended. Cordelia finally heard "many footsteps" as the cabinet adjourned, and then Lincoln came toward her in the room where she sat alone, and pulled up a chair beside her. "Mrs. Harvey, I only wish to tell you that an order equivalent to granting a hospital in your State has been issued."

I could not speak, I was so entirely unprepared for it. I wept for joy; I could not help it. . . . I was so agitated I could not talk with him . . . he noticed it and began talking upon other subjects.

When they parted, Lincoln asked her to come back at nine the next morning so that he could hand her a copy of the order for a hospital to be built in Wisconsin. Cordelia never got to sleep, felt "very ill," and later said, "I suppose the excitement caused the intense suffering of that night." She arrived at the White House more than an hour late, but Lincoln received her immediately. Once again sitting in a chair next to her, he handed her a copy of the order. Taking the paper, Cordelia thanked him "not only for the order but for the manner and spirit in which it had been given, then said I must apologize for not having been there at nine o'clock as he desired me to be, but that I had been sick all night."

He looked up with: "Did joy make you sick?"
I said, "I don't know, very likely it was the relaxation of nerves after intense excitement."

After a minute, Abraham Lincoln said to Cordelia Harvey, "This hospital I shall name for you."

I said: "No, but if you would . . . I would like to have it named for Mister Harvey." . . . He took a card and wrote a few words on it, requesting the Secretary of War to name the hospital "Harvey Hospital" in memory of my husband. . . . I said, "You have been very kind to me and I am grateful for it."
He looked at me from under his eyebrows and said, "You almost think me handsome, don't you?" His face then beamed with such kind benevolence and was lighted by such a pleasant smile that I looked at him, and with my usual impulse, said, clasping my hands together, "You are perfectly lovely to me, now, Mister Lincoln." He colored a little and laughed most heartily.

All that was left was to say goodbye. Cordelia Harvey would never see Abraham Lincoln again.

As I arose to go, he reached out his hand, that hand in which there was so much power and so little beauty, and held mine clasped and covered in his own. I bowed my head and pressed my lips most reverently upon [his hand]. . . . I heard him say goodbye, and I was gone.

On Lincoln's order, three military hospitals were built in Wisconsin; the one in Madison, the Harvey United States General Hospital, treated

600 soldiers. It then became an orphanage for the children of soldiers from Wisconsin who had died. Cordelia Harvey continued to see to the needs of soldiers throughout the war.

II

One of the great moments of 1864, both in its understated drama and its future implications, came on March 8 when Ulysses S. Grant arrived in Washington. The newly promoted lieutenant general, then forty-two, arrived by train accompanied by his thirteen-year-old son Fred. A welcoming committee met the wrong train, so Grant, dressed in a nondescript linen duster that concealed the general's stars on his uniform, presented himself at the desk of the Willard Hotel, Washington's best. He was greeted condescendingly by a hotel clerk who assigned this rumpled-looking man and his boy to a room in the attic. When the clerk saw this unimpressive figure registering as "U.S. Grant and son, Galena, Illinois," he quickly took back the key to the attic room and led them to the hotel's best suite.

As it happened, the Lincolns had a reception under way at the White House that night, and harried aides found Grant and took him there. For once, Lincoln seemed not to exist: the hundreds of guests crowded around this simple but militarily gifted soldier, who "blushed like a school girl" as the East Room began to rock with cheers of, "Grant! Grant!" When he was persuaded to cross the room to stand on a sofa so more people could see him, Assistant Secretary of War Charles A. Dana noted the way Grant moved: he did not "march, nor quite walk, but pitches along, as if the next step would bring him to his nose." A reporter there wrote, "The little, scared-looking man who stood on the crimson-covered sofa was the idol of the hour."

The next day, after Lincoln handed Grant his commission as lieutenant general in the White House before an assemblage of dignitaries, the two of them went upstairs to talk. As Grant recalled it, Lincoln told him that he had been disappointed in his previous commanders, and that "all he wanted or had ever wanted was someone to take the responsibility and call on him for all of the assistance needed, pledging himself to use all of the power of the government in rendering such assistance. Assuring him that I would do the best I could with the means at hand,

and avoid annoying him or the War Department, our first interview ended."

Lincoln had found his man; indeed, in his office he would say jubilantly to his secretary Stoddard, "Grant is the first general I've had! He's a general!" Lincoln did not care about appearances: he told Stoddard, of Grant, "He's the quietest little fellow you ever saw. . . . I believe two or three times he's been in this room a minute or so before I knew he was here. . . . The only evidence you have that he's in any place is that he makes things *git!*"

Soon after receiving his commission, Grant went to Cincinnati, where he and Sherman, both cigar smokers, filled a room with fumes for two days as they pored over maps and lists of the units that were in Sherman's Army of the West, as well as those in the Army of the Potomac, which Grant would use to oppose Lee's Army of Northern Virginia. When they parted, Grant to be both general-in-chief and commander of the Virginia front, and Sherman to command the entire western theater, they had their strategy. Sherman put it concisely: "He was to go for Lee and I was to go for Joe Johnston"—Lee's West Point classmate General Joseph E. Johnston, the Confederacy's great master of defensive maneuver and evasion, then at Dalton, Georgia, commanding the 60,000 men of the South's Army of Tennessee.

III

During these weeks of early spring, Lincoln's office had an interesting new person quietly moving around in it. At the request of his dying congressman friend Owen Lovejoy, Lincoln granted permission to a young artist named Francis Carpenter to make sketches for and then paint a large canvas portraying Lincoln and his cabinet as they had assembled around the table in his office on the day he signed the Emancipation Proclamation. Carpenter not only had an eye for composition and color, but made a practice of writing down all that he saw and heard, everywhere in the White House. When he was first introduced to Lincoln at a Saturday White House reception given by Mary, he saw him this way:

Haggard-looking . . . standing, it seemed to me, solitary and alone, although surrounded by the crowd . . . responding half-abstractedly to the

well-meant greetings of the miscellaneous assemblage. . . . Never will I
forget the electric thrill that went through me at this instant. I seemed to
see lines radiating from every part of the globe, converging to a focus at
the point where that plain, awkward-looking man stood, and to hear in
spirit a million prayers . . . ascending in his behalf.

At the close of the reception, Carpenter presented himself in the president's office for a private meeting. "He received me pleasantly, giving me a seat near his own arm-chair . . . took off his spectacles, and said, "Well, Mr. Carpenter, we will turn you loose in here, and try to give you a good chance to work out your idea."

At that moment, the young painter had no thought that he would soon be on terms of intimacy with the president of the United States. On the Tuesday following their first meeting, at three in the afternoon, Francis Carpenter stood with Lincoln under the White House portico before they set out together on a mile-long walk. Their destination was the studio of the photographer Mathew Brady, where Brady would take a number of portrait photographs, including the one eventually chosen for the engraving used in printing the five-dollar bill.

The public had freedom to stroll through the White House grounds, and an incident occurred that Carpenter later described. "My attention was attracted to an approaching party, apparently a countryman, plainly dressed, with his wife and two little boys, who had evidently been straying about, looking at the places of public interest in the city." When the man realized that this was Lincoln, he "approached very diffidently, and asked if he might take the president by the hand." Lincoln shook hands, "after which, 'Would he extend the same privilege to his wife and little boys?'"

> *Mr. Lincoln good-naturedly approached the latter, who had remained*
> *where they were stopped, and reaching down, said a kind word to the*
> *bashful little fellows, who shrank close up to their mother, and did not*
> *reply. This simple act filled the father's cup full.*
>
> *"The Lord is with you, Mr. President," he said reverently; and then,*
> *hesitating for a moment, he added, with strong emphasis, "and the people*
> *too, sir; and the people too!"*

Some afternoons later, after what Carpenter called "an unusually long and interesting sitting" in the presidential office for the Emancipation

Proclamation painting, he saw a side of Lincoln that he had no idea existed. The great Shakespearean actor Edwin Booth would play *Hamlet* that night at Grover's Theatre, and Lincoln intended to go. He said to Carpenter: "There is one passage of the play . . . which is very apt to be slurred over by the actor, or omitted altogether, which seems to me to be the choicest part of the play. It is the soliloquy of the king, after the murder." Then, to Carpenter's added surprise and admiration, "throwing himself into the very spirit of the scene," Lincoln recited from memory the great passage that begins,

O my offense is rank, it smells to heaven,

going on through its next thirty-seven lines "with a feeling and appreciation unsurpassed by anything I ever witnessed on the stage." Carpenter would have great reason to remember the moment, and the reference to murder. Edwin Booth's younger brother, then in Virginia, was the somewhat less famous actor John Wilkes Booth; Lincoln, sitting in the presidential box at Grover's Theatre on April 11, 1863, had seen John Wilkes Booth make his Washington debut in Shakespeare's *Richard III*—a blood-drenched play in which Prince Edward, rightful heir to the throne, is murdered. Booth was an ardent Confederate sympathizer whose hatred for Lincoln had thus far progressed to the point that he wanted to organize a plot to kidnap the president. At this time his plan was to hold Lincoln as a hostage, to be exchanged for captured Confederate generals or large numbers of enlisted men.

—FOUR—

ON THE VERGE OF THE GREAT COLLISION

As May approached, the capital knew that the most massive campaigns of the war would soon begin. Along with everyone else Lincoln braced himself for the coming bloodshed. His forces needed constant replenishment; during the winter there had been significant numbers of deaths and desertions, and fewer volunteers were coming forward. On February 1, Lincoln had sent out a call for 500,000 more men, and on March 14 he signed orders calling for an additional 200,000.

The wording of these proclamations was ingenious; they appealed for volunteers, but the same document authorized the draft boards now in place throughout the Union to make up any shortage left by lack of volunteers. Some of the ranks were now being filled by scores of thousands of substitutes—men paid to serve in their place by more affluent citizens who did not wish to fight—and the number of men unwilling to fight who were simply rounded up and sent off to serve remained surprisingly low.

An emergency measure opened yet another source of men. On April 23, Lincoln accepted an offer made by the governors of Ohio, Indiana, Illinois, Iowa, and Wisconsin. These western states would attempt to provide a total of 85,000 more volunteers, to be known as "Hundred Days Men." They would serve for short lengths of time, acting as guards and in other rear-echelon duties, and then go home. The concept was that their service would release more experienced units to go forward into battle, in an effort to bring the South to its knees in one hundred days. In recommending that Lincoln accept the governors' offer, Grant wrote the president, "As a rule I would oppose accepting men for a short term, but if 100,000 men can be raised in the time proposed . . . they might come at such a time of crisis as to be of vast importance."

With the addition of all these men, Grant, who three years before had started as colonel of a regiment of less than a thousand soldiers, now commanded approximately a million. In terms of military history, he was proving to be a transitional figure; at Shiloh in April of 1862 he had been the general on horseback, cantering back and forth under fire to consult his division commanders as the battle progressed. Now he and his staff might ride near the head of a large column on the march, but in the coming campaign he would usually be at his headquarters well behind the lines, sending and receiving messages carried by mounted couriers, and using the telegraph to communicate with his subordinate generals' headquarters and with the War Department. Grant had devised his own structure of high command: rather than sit at a desk in Washington, he left an enormous amount of the Army's paperwork to its chief of staff, Major General Henry Halleck, whose office in the War Department was a few steps from that of Secretary of War Stanton. In the battles that lay ahead, the day-to-day commander of the Army of the Potomac would be George Gordon Meade, the victor at Gettysburg. Grant would direct the overall movements of that army as well as those of the Union forces down the Atlantic coast and in the Shenandoah Valley, and coordinate his campaign with Sherman's Army of the West.

No one doubted that Robert E. Lee would be ready for Grant in their first head-on clash. Southerners had long since given up the notion that one Confederate soldier was worth three or four Yankees, but they still displayed a resilience that confounded Northerners who had predicted that they could never endure more suffering. Concerning the campaign about to begin, the *Richmond Examiner* confidently told its readers, "So far, we feel sure of the issue. All else is mystery and uncertainty. Where the first blow will fall, where the two armies of northern Virginia will meet each other face to face; how Grant will try to hold his own against the master spirit of Lee, we cannot even surmise."

As for what comprised that "master spirit," Confederate colonel Joseph Ives, who had seen Lee in action from early in the war, had this to say: "If there is one man in either army, Confederate or Federal, head and shoulders above every other in *audacity*, it is General Lee! . . . He will take more desperate chances, and take them quicker than any other general in this country, North or South." Speaking of the fighting now ahead, Lee told his aide Walter Taylor, "Colonel, we have got to whip them; we must whip them, and it has already made me [feel] better to think of it." Lee analyzed the reports coming in from his spies, discerned Grant's overall strategy, and made plans to fight Grant in exactly the area of Virginia where Grant intended to make his first offensive movements.

II

The time for massing the Union's Army of the Potomac arrived. On April 25, with Secretary of War Stanton on one side of him and Major General Ambrose Burnside on the other, Lincoln stood on the balcony formed by the eastern portico of Willard's Hotel, watching the 30,000 men of Burnside's Ninth Corps march through the city. The troops were heading south into Virginia to reinforce Grant, and move on to where Lee and his formidable fighters awaited them.

The crowds saw a tremendous spectacle; at one time or another, units totaling hundreds of thousands of men had marched along Washington's unpaved streets during three years of war, but this was the largest single parade the city had seen. The day was cool and clear; the streets were muddy from recent rains, and men and horses slogged and splashed past Lincoln. The moment was doubly dramatic because these men, many of them veterans of the war's bloodiest battles, might be fighting any day; a woman spectator described their "old war worn clothing—with their torn flags—but such noble looking men." Throngs lined the sidewalks of Fourteenth Street for five hours: an observer described "banners flying, music swelling on the air, horses prancing, measured tramp of marching feet, the rolling of the drum, and the harsher music of thundering artillery." Interesting units appeared in the line of march: Company K of the 1st Michigan Sharpshooters was composed largely of Indian marksmen of the Ottawa, Ojibwa, and Chippewa tribes. Instead of a battle flag, at their head a warrior carried a six-foot-high pole atop which was "a little platform" on which there perched a "large live Eagle." (A Chippewa chief had praised the efforts of these braves, telling them, "If the South conquers you will be *slaves, dogs*.") Spectators also saw heading to the battle-front five large new regiments of United States Colored Troops, all commanded by white officers; as these 7,000 men passed Lincoln, "their marching being absolutely perfect," he raised his tall black hat to salute them.

In three of the Michigan regiments, many of the soldiers were college students who had enlisted instead of choosing to continue their education. As they passed President Lincoln, they broke into patriotic song, saluting him with:

> *We are coming, Father Abraham,*
> *Three Hundred Thousand more,*
> *Shouting the Battle Cry of Freedom!*
> *And we'll fill the shattered ranks,*
> *Of our brothers gone before,*
> *Shouting the Battle Cry of Freedom!*

Walt Whitman stood in the crowd; for the past fifteen months, the poet had dedicated himself to tending the wounded in Washington's hospitals. He often saw Lincoln passing through the center of the city in his carriage, usually accompanied by a mounted escort; being Walt Whitman, he saw not just a face, but its essence: "It is as if the Earth looked at me—dumb, yearning, relentless, immodest, inhuman." Today, Whitman stood there not to see Lincoln, but was hoping to catch a glimpse of his brother George, a captain in the 51st New York Volunteer Infantry; in the Union defeat at Fredericksburg in December of 1862, George had received a bullet wound to his cheek so severe, he told Walt, that you could put a stick through it. Beside Walt on the sidewalk stood his friend the twenty-eight-year-old naturalist John Burroughs, who profoundly admired his poetry; the future author of fourteen books, beginning with *Notes on Walt Whitman, as Poet and Person*, worked at the Treasury Department. After a time, Walt saw his brother coming past and fell into line with him, talking as they went along Fourteenth Street.

The appearance of the Ninth Corps was a good deal more impressive than the reputation of its commander, Ambrose Burnside, whose way of cutting his beard gave rise to the term "sideburns." He had some successes to his credit—an expedition against the North Carolina coast early in the war, and a successful defense of Knoxville against Longstreet in the autumn of 1863—but his fumbling delay at Antietam in September of 1862 enabled Lee to extricate his army from possible total destruction. Commanding the Army of the Potomac, the Union's main striking force, during the disastrous defeat at Fredericksburg in December of 1862, Burnside launched suicidal attacks that lost nearly 13,000 men in three hours. Lincoln replaced him as the Army of the Potomac's commander; since then Burnside had commanded smaller forces, but the fact that he was standing beside Lincoln at this critical time, taking the salutes of 30,000 men whom he was about to lead into battle, demonstrated the Union's lack of first-rate generals.

Burnside presented yet another problem. Because of the Army's system of seniority based on date of rank, he technically outranked George Gordon Meade, the victor of Gettysburg and the current commander of the Army of the Potomac, to which Burnside's Ninth Corps was attached. Grant solved the situation by giving parallel sets of orders to Meade, who acted under his direction as the Army of the Potomac's day-to-day commander, and to Burnside, whose Ninth Corps comprised 20 percent of Meade's overall force. In any realistic estimate of his generals, Lincoln's hopes lay with Grant, who had yet to face Lee.

DURING THESE LAST April days when Grant was assembling his army for the impending offensive, one of Lincoln's worst appointments was about to demonstrate his colossal ineptitude. The immense irony of the moment offered a perfect example of the way in which military and political considerations acted as an ionic bond during this war. Benjamin F. Butler, a man of little military experience who began the war as one of the most powerful Democratic politicians in Massachusetts, held the rank of major general in the Union Army. He gained that position only because, at the war's outset, Lincoln thought it wise, in appointing generals, to let the Democrats have a few generals of their own. Butler became known as "Beast Butler" in the South because of his infamous "Woman Order," issued when he was military governor of New Orleans—his General Orders No. 28, stating that any woman of that city who showed "contempt for any officer or soldier of the United States" would be treated as if she were a prostitute. He had eventually been relieved of command in New Orleans—among other matters, questions arose involving $800,000 in possibly mishandled funds—but what he had seen of the plight of blacks had turned him into an ardent "War Democrat" with views of punishing the Confederacy nearly identical to those of the Radical Republicans. This made him *persona grata* with the influential congressional Joint Committee on the Conduct of the War. Dominated by Radicals, many of these men were eagerly looking for a Republican nominee for president who was far more punitive-minded toward the South than Lincoln.

After leaving New Orleans in December of 1862, the War Department reassigned Butler to an area where it was thought he could do no harm—the then-quiet coastal command known as the Department of Virginia and North Carolina. Having few duties at his headquarters at Fort Monroe on the Virginia coast, he consented to speak at a number of patriotic rallies during 1863. Like McClellan, he performed well as an orator; despite his portly body, drooping eyelids, and occasionally irascible manner, the audiences found him attractive, another general in uniform who knew how to please a crowd.

Now, amid the political as well as the military turmoil of 1864, Lincoln saw Butler as a popular public figure who could possibly emerge as a presidential candidate, or might well add strength to any ticket by having his name put forward for vice president. When Grant let it be known before he came east that he wanted to sideline Butler from any significant command, Lincoln indicated that he wanted Butler to be handled gently, and in effect to be left alone.

During early February of 1864, Butler tried a raid in force in from the coast to Richmond, which failed. Soon after that, back in his headquarters at Fort Monroe, he became the object of backstage political maneuvering. Butler later claimed to have been approached about the vice presidency by a Treasury Department official acting on behalf of Secretary of the Treasury Chase. As for the propriety of a member of Lincoln's cabinet seeking the presidency for himself, Butler told the go-between that if Lincoln "doesn't object," Chase had the right to go on making "a very strenuous effort to be the candidate of the Republican Party, using, as well he might, all the great power of his office as Secretary of the Treasury for that purpose." He did, however, add of Lincoln's continuing to keep Chase in his cabinet, "I have for some time thought that Lincoln was more patient than I should have been."

Butler declined the offer. Lincoln received only vague reports of what Butler's political intentions might be, and in late March had Colonel Thomas H. Ford, a former lieutenant governor of Ohio, go and sound him out. Ford returned with the news that Butler had nothing to do with the rumors. (According to one of Butler's friends, this "greatly delighted" Lincoln.)

Then, in thinking of how to learn more of Butler's political views and ambitions, Lincoln turned to Simon Cameron, his first secretary of war, who had used his office to enrich his prewar political cronies. In January of 1862, Lincoln had brusquely dismissed him. The president's initial memorandum to Cameron, simply informing Cameron of his dismissal in favor of Stanton and telling him he was to hold the far less important post of minister to Russia, shocked him to tears, but he wisely disguised his hurt and anger. Lincoln later defended Cameron when he was censured by the House of Representatives; in November of 1862, after six months in Russia, Cameron returned to his native state of Pennsylvania, which he had served both as governor and as a four-time United States senator. He began working for Lincoln's reelection, often consulting with the president in the White House; by January 9, 1863, he was able to present Lincoln a petition from all of Pennsylvania's Republican state legislators that asked the president to run again. Now Lincoln quietly sent Cameron to make what Cameron described as being a direct offer to have Butler as his running mate. (Years later, Butler said that Cameron told him that Lincoln believed "your candidature would add strength to the ticket, especially with the war Democrats, and he hopes that you will allow your friends to co-operate with him to place you in that position.")

Thus, in the middle of a war, the emissary of Lincoln, who was both president and commander-in-chief, was exploring with a third-rate general from Massachusetts the possibility of becoming Lincoln's running mate on the Republican ticket if Lincoln dumped his present vice president, Hannibal Hamlin of Maine. Cameron returned with quite a report. Butler started his response by saying he appreciated the offer, but said "laughingly" that he found himself so eager to participate in the coming months' military campaigns that "I would not quit the field to be Vice-President, even with himself as President, unless he will give me . . . [assurances] that he will die or resign within three months after his inauguration." In his whimsical reply, Butler added this:

Ask him what he thinks I have done to deserve the punishment, at the age of forty-six, of being made to sit as presiding officer over the Senate, to listen for four years to debates more or less stupid, in which I can take

no part, nor even be allowed a vote . . . except when my enemies think my
[tie-breaking] vote would injure me in the estimation of the people. . . .

Out of all that, Lincoln learned enough about Butler, in addition to
what he already knew about Chase, to want both of these politically vola-
tile figures to stay just where they were: Butler in the army and Chase as a
frustrated but checkmated member of his cabinet. (It was worth noting
that Butler, sometimes mentioned during these months as a possible
presidential candidate, did not include the presidency in his statement
about offices that did not interest him.)

In terms of the impending military campaign, Butler's mission became
one that required far greater abilities than he possessed. From his former
position in charge of a static coastal front, he found himself commanding
the 35,000 men of the Army of the James. When Grant moved south
against Lee to begin the heaviest fighting inland, north of Richmond,
Butler was to advance toward Richmond along the James River from
Union positions on the Virginia coast. Butler appeared to be entirely
confident: a reporter from the *New York Herald* who saw him at this point
wrote that "his countenance is as serene as if he were on the point of attending a festive party instead of going to the scene of strife." A different
and painfully prophetic view appeared in a letter written to a friend
by one of Butler's two corps commanders, Major General William F.
"Baldy" Smith, himself a man with a wartime record that included a fine
performance at Chattanooga under the eyes of Grant. He described the
offensive to be launched by Butler as being one "which I dread as being
full of unnecessary risks & of the kind that may produce the most terrible
disaster."

III

During these last days of April, Robert E. Lee acted less like a commander
who possessed dramatic battlefield presence than a safecracker leaning
forward to listen to the tumblers in a lock while his sensitive fingers
moved the knob back and forth.

At the time Burnside's forces passed though Washington, Lee had ordered his generals to be ready to fight at any hour—to defend against any
attack, or to be ready to strike at Grant's strung-out columns and wagon

trains if that opportunity should occur. Now Lee decided that Grant was not quite ready to begin his offensive. This pleased Lee, because it gave him a few more days of spring weather that would cause more grass to grow, enabling many of his cavalry units and horse-drawn artillery and baggage trains to have enough fodder to keep the horses moving to a final and more advantageous set of defensive positions. Taking the opportunity to inspect several major units, on April 29 Lee went to Gordonsville, Virginia, to review the corps led by James Longstreet. This large part of his army, separated from him on detached service for seven months, had been badly battered on the slopes around Knoxville in the month before Christmas, and had still not received the replacements and supplies that it needed. Nonetheless, returning in time for the great campaign, they soon demonstrated their continuing devotion to Lee. A private among them said that, seeing him for the first time in half a year, "The men hung around him and seemed satisfied to lay their hands on his gray horse or to touch the bridle, or the stirrup, or the old general's leg—anything that Lee had was sacred to us fellows who had just come back. And the General—he could not help from breaking down . . . tears traced down his cheeks, and he felt that we were again to do his bidding." No number of seemingly realistic Northern military intelligence estimates of Confederate capabilities could ever give sufficient weight to the fighting spirit caused by the love that Lee's men had for him—an affection greater than that felt by any other soldiers for their leaders, North or South.

As for Longstreet, he had a unique perspective on the general whom Lee was about to face. Longstreet was a cousin of Grant's wife, Julia, and served as best man at their wedding. Having previously passed through West Point a year ahead of Grant and fought in some of the same battles near him during the Mexican War, he had noted during the last year how dramatically Grant turned the situation around at Chattanooga after the Confederate victory at Chickamauga. When some of Lee's officers who had never faced Grant made disparaging remarks about him, Longstreet told them, "We must make up our minds to get into line of battle and stay there, for that man will fight us every hour and every day till the end of this war."

THE MOMENT WAS upon the commanders. On April 30, Lincoln wrote to Grant: "Not expecting to see you again before the Spring campaign, I wish to express, in this way, my entire satisfaction with what you have done up to this time, as I understand it. The particulars of your plans I neither know, or seek to know. . . ."

Although he told Grant he did not need "the particulars of your plans," Lincoln always worried about Union casualties and battlefield reverses, and hopefully added: "While I am very anxious that any great disaster, or the capture of our men in great numbers, should be avoided, I know these points are less likely to escape your attention than they would be mine. If there is anything wanting which is within my power to give, do not fail to let me know it."

It remained only for Lincoln to send his new general-in-chief forward with an eloquent blessing:

> *And now with a brave Army, and a just cause, may God sustain you.*
> *Yours very truly*
> *A. Lincoln*

On the night of the same day whose immense impending drama prompted Lincoln to write these words, his secretary John Hay added this to a letter he was writing to a friend.

> *A little after midnight, as I was writing those last lines, the President came into the office laughing, with a copy of Hood's [Thomas Hood, the British humorist and poet who illustrated his own writings] Works in his hands, to show Nicolay and me the little caricature, "An Unfortunate Bee-ing," seemingly unconscious that he, with his short shirt hanging about his long legs, and setting out behind like the tail feathers of an enormous ostrich, was infinitely funnier than anything he was laughing at.*
>
> *What a man it is! Occupied all day with matters of great moment, deeply anxious about the fate of the greatest army of the world, with his own fame and future hanging on the events of the passing hour, he yet has such a wealth of simple* bonhommie *and goodfellowship, that he gets out of bed and perambulates the house in his shirt to find us that we may share with him the fun of poor Hood's queer little conceits. . . .*

While serving Lincoln devotedly in dramatic hours such as these on the eve of a military campaign that could decide the fate of the Union,

Hay made judgments of him that were far from sycophantic. He held a view of the president's reading quite different from that of Stoddard, who recorded that before attending a Shakespeare play in Washington, Lincoln would read over the play that afternoon, and through that and seeing the performance study Shakespeare "as intensely as he used to study him between cases and law-books and works upon mathematics in the old law-practice days." Hay said of Lincoln that, apart from the necessary presidential paperwork, "He read very little. Scarcely ever looked into a newspaper unless I called his attention to an article on some special subject. He frequently said 'I know more about that than any of them.' It is absurd to call him a modest man. No great man is ever modest.'" He added another comment that undercut the idea of Lincoln being a humble man: "It was his intellectual arrogance and unconscious assumption of superiority that men like Chase and [Massachusetts Senator Charles] Sumner could never forgive."

The next day, the first of May, Grant responded to Lincoln's momentous "may God sustain you" with: "Your very kind letter is just received. . . . It will be my earnest endeavor that you, and the country, shall not be disappointed. . . . Should my success be less than I desire, and expect, the least I can say is, the fault is not with you."

ON THE MORNING of Monday, May 2, Lee rode his grey horse Traveller to an observation post above the Rapidan River, where he had a view of Germanna Ford, the shallow part of the stream across which he expected Grant's forces to throw one or more pontoon bridges as they began their movements against him. Once over the water, they would be on a road leading south right into the Wilderness, a rectangular area of sixty-four square miles of marshes, tangled underbrush, and fallen trees.

Lee knew how to think as an opponent would: looking through his binoculars at that morass, he understood that Grant's objective would be to move his army through that area as swiftly as possible, trying to keep his columns on the four roads in there, and break out into the more open terrain sixty miles north of Richmond. He intended to thwart that. In a sense, Lee saw all those fallen tree trunks and muddy ponds as his friends, obstacles that could confuse, blunt, and disperse Grant's larger numbers, and render the superior Northern artillery ineffective. As Grant's foot soldiers struggled through vines and branches, unable to see their enemy even at close range, they would be vulnerable to the rifle fire of Lee's experienced country-boy fighters.

Lincoln, forty-five miles north of where Lee sat on Traveller studying the almost impenetrable broken land below him, would have been shaken if he had understood that in Lee's mind this was not to be just one vital battle, but might well be the decisive battle of the war. None of the Confederate generals had ever dreamt of marching into Northern cities such as New York or Boston. Their goal was to inflict on the Union Army one or more defeats so decisive and bloody that the North would lose heart and settle for the Confederacy's oft-stated terms: let us go our way, an independent nation with the future of slavery to be decided by us in our own time.

Lee knew his disadvantages in total strength but felt with reason that he still had the power to strike that one necessary mortal blow. He intended to meet Grant with a violent attack that would demolish the Army of the Potomac. If he could do that, it would enormously strengthen the "Peace Democrats" and their allies, quite possibly derail Lincoln's chances for reelection, and might well bring the North to the peace table.

Having come down from that hilltop observation post, Lee later in the day wrote a letter to his son, Confederate major general Custis Lee, who was serving as an aide to Jefferson Davis in Richmond. Speaking of the Confederacy, Lee said, "Our country demands all our strength, all our energies. If victorious we have everything to hope for in the future. If defeated, nothing will be left for us to live for. . . . My whole trust is in God, and I am ready for whatever He may ordain."

GRANT SAT BESIDE the campfire in front of his tent near Germanna Ford on the evening of May 4, smoking a cigar and talking with Meade as they prepared to cross the Rapidan the next morning. Lee was right. Unaware of Lee's preparation to strike first, they had no intention of fighting a battle in the Wilderness, and saw it as a place to pass through before attacking Lee.

As they spoke, Grant received a telegram from Halleck in the War Department telling him that Sherman had begun his march from Chattanooga into Georgia, heading south toward Atlanta. Riding with the advanced elements of his 98,000-man force, Sherman was starting the western side of the two-pronged 1864 Union campaign. Its strategy, worked out in his hotel-room conference with Grant in Cincinnati, was simple: Grant was to hammer Lee to death in Virginia, while Sherman cut in from the Confederacy's western flank to disembowel the South.

By the following afternoon, Grant and Lee were locked in battle, deep in the Wilderness. Lee's intention to strike first, in terrain favorable to him, had been aided by Grant's need to protect his long column of slow-moving supply wagons. That had delayed his infantry in passing through the Wilderness before they met the enemy. For two of the bloodiest days of the war, May 5 and 6, the armies of these two determined opponents fought each other. Before it was over, Grant had thrown into the battle 101,895 foot soldiers and artillerymen, while Lee committed an estimated 61,000. A combination of gunsmoke and the fires started by battlefield explosions created such thick clouds that some commanders, seeing only murky thickets and losing all sense of direction, had to move their units by looking at pocket compasses. Captain Horace Porter of Grant's staff portrayed the inferno:

> At times the wind howled through the tree-tops, mingling its moan with the groans of the dying, and heavy branches were cut off by the fire of artillery, and fell crashing upon the heads of the men, adding a new terror to battle. Forest fires raged; ammunition-trains exploded; the dead were roasted in the conflagration; the wounded, roused by its hot breath, dragged themselves along, with their torn and mangled limbs, in the mad energy of despair, to escape the ravages of the flames, and every bush seemed hung with shreds of blood-stained clothing.

In an almost perfect metaphor of war, correspondent Charles A. Page of the *New York Tribune* described how he would watch stretcher-bearers carry wounded men to the rear and then see those stretcher-bearers rush back to the front, using the same stretchers to carry forward boxes of cartridges to maintain the supply of ammunition.

At the end of his first day fighting Lee, Grant threw himself down in despair on the cot in his tent: one of his staff, Captain Charles Frances Adams, Jr., a member of the distinguished Massachusetts family that included two presidents, said, "I never saw a man so agitated in my life." Other accounts describe him as being composed. Whatever his condition that night, by dawn Grant was aggressively ordering his forces into the thick of battle. A Northern soldier described the kind of combat he experienced: "We fought them with bayonet as well as bullet. Up through the trees rolled dense clouds of battle smoke, circling about the pines and mingling with the flowering dogwoods. Each man fought on his own grimly and desperately." Many generals on both sides were right at the front. On the second day, Union general Alexander Hays of Pennsylvania was killed, as was Confederate general Micah Jenkins of South Carolina. Union general James S. Wadsworth of New York fell mortally wounded. In a nearly fatal repetition of what happened to Stonewall Jackson at nearby Chancellorsville twelve months before, Confederate soldiers mistakenly fired at their commander Longstreet, seriously wounding him in the throat and shoulder.

Reports abound of how Lee, fighting Union forces that outnumbered his men nearly two to one, could inspire the martial feats of the Army of Northern Virginia. Soon after sunrise on this same singularly bloody second day in the Wilderness, Lee found himself almost alone, mounted on Traveller, as veteran Confederate regiments streamed past him, retreating in the face of a powerful federal assault that was about to capture a Confederate artillery battalion. The advancing blue lines were only 200 yards away. Then, out of the drifting smoke through which Southern regiments were retreating, twenty men in ragged clothes ran forward with their muskets at the ready, entering the field at the end of a long forced march to reach that front.

"Who are you, my boys?" Lee shouted to these scarecrows as scores more dashed up to form a line of battle.

"Texas boys!" they yelled. In a few more seconds, there were hundreds of them.

"Hurrah for Texas!" Lee stood in his stirrups and waved his hat. "Hurrah for Texas!" He rode to the left of the line, and the Texans realized that he intended to lead the counterattack, right at the blue lines.

"Go back, General Lee!" they shouted. "Go back! We won't go on unless you go back!"

"Texans always move them!" Lee roared, about to spur Traveller right into the enemy. It was only when the combination of a sergeant, a colonel of his staff, and Brigadier General John Gregg of the Texans closed in on him, the sergeant grabbing Traveller's reins and Gregg maneuvering his horse to block Traveller from plunging forward, that Lee was led back from the front, still waving his hat and cheering on the Texans as they swept forward to save the Confederate artillery.

For the moment, the men of the Army of the Potomac were too busy surviving, each man on his own little battlefield, to form an opinion about their new leader Grant. In the confused aftermath of the two days of terrible carnage, many thought they might well have been beaten. Referring to the great Confederate victory that had taken place the previous year only a few miles to the east, a veteran soldier from Massachusetts recalled, "Most of us thought it was another Chancellorsville." Several war correspondents with the army also had that idea, which was reinforced when Grant refused to let them use his headquarters telegraph to send out their stories of the fighting.

Beyond the general uncertainty as to the situation, a resigned mood settled over these Union troops. They had seen nearly one in five of their comrades become casualties in just two days, and their past experience with the inadequate leadership of their Army of the Potomac made them feel certain that, whatever the outcome of a specific battle, their sacrifices would probably come to naught. They would either be held in place, handing the initiative back to Lee, or they would be pulled back toward Washington—in this instance that would involve marching back across the Rapidan—to recuperate and reorganize. That was what all their former commanders who had led them in this area had done. The frustrations of the long-suffering rank and file of the Army of the Potomac had begun in 1862: in one week of that summer, from June 25 through July 1, during the Seven Days' Battles of the Peninsular Campaign, Lee had beaten McClellan at Oak Grove, Mechanicsville, Gaine's Mill, White Oak Swamp, and Malvern Hill. Some of these same men had participated in the great victory at Gettysburg in Pennsylvania in July of 1863, but the ghosts of those earlier battles, and their defeat at Chancellorsville, still hung over this army.

Now, after the ghastly fighting in the Wilderness, on the afternoon of May 7 the orders came down to sling their packs and be ready to move out. The troops had no doubt that once again they had fought and bled on the soil of Virginia, only to march away from a battlefield and head back in the direction from which they had so often come. When the first column reached the crossroads where they would turn right to head back over the Rapidan, their officers on horseback turned to the left—south, toward the enemy, toward Lee, toward Richmond. Excited comments went up and down the line of march. Regiment after regiment turned left; there was no mistake. Grant was not giving up an inch; he was taking them south. "Our spirits rose," a soldier from Pennsylvania said. "We marched free, and men began to sing."

Dusk came; no one stopped. Everything was moving south: the artillery, the cavalry, the engineers who would build bridges, the ambulances, the wagons carrying food and supplies. Around nine in the evening, the word was passed down from the rear, "Give way to the right. Give way to the right." Something was coming down the road, heading south, heading to the very front, and must be let through.

Ulysses S. Grant came down the road on his big bay horse, Cincinnati, accompanied by Meade and their staffs. Horace Porter described what happened when the men saw Grant coming.

> *Wild cheers echoed through the forest. Men swung their hats, tossed up their arms [muskets], and pressed forward to within touch of their chief, clapping their hands, and speaking to him with the familiarity of comrades. Pine-knots and leaves were set on fire, and lighted the scene with their weird flickering glare. The night march had become a triumphal procession.*

Regimental bands, going along through the night carrying their instruments with them, brought them out and began to play spirited marches. Thousands of men sang. When Sherman later spoke of that night, he called Grant's decision to move on south the most important act of his life. Grant was going after Lee, whatever the cost, whatever lay ahead. Sherman was not there, but everything he learned confirmed what he knew about his friend's mind, heart, and methods: "Undismayed, with a full comprehension of the work in which he was engaged, feeling as keen a sympathy for his dead and wounded as anyone, and without stopping to count his numbers, he gave his orders calmly, specifically, and absolutely."

WHILE ALL THIS had been developing on the Virginia battlefront, no one in Washington or the rest of the nation knew the fate of Grant and his 100,000 men. No couriers arrived from the Army of the Potomac. The only communication attempted was this: near noon on the second day of attack and counterattack, Grant had sent Halleck a telegram that said, "We have been engaged with the enemy in full force since early yesterday. So far there is no decisive result, but I think all things are progressing favorably."

Why Lincoln was not told about this message is unknown. It was possible that the telegram never arrived at the War Department, because Confederate cavalry patrols and guerrillas were darting through the area south of Washington—one eyewitness reported, "as soon as our army had crossed the Rapidan, Lee's scouts and Moseby's [*sic*] men had begun to come in"—and the history of these wartime communications was replete with incidents of both sides cutting enemy telegraph wires when they found them. As of this second day of fighting, apparently the only telegram that had been received from Grant was sent before the battle began, telling Halleck that troops were crossing the Rapidan, and that contact with the enemy had not yet been made.

Thus, after two days of ferocious fighting and still twenty-four hours before Grant's enormously significant turn to the south to press on against Lee, Lincoln knew virtually nothing about the progress of the great opening battle of the campaign. Besieged by questions from his cabinet and every other person he encountered in the White House, Lincoln gave his frustrated answer: "Grant has gone into the Wilderness, crawled in, drawn up the ladder, and pulled in the hole after him."

Although he was nearly frantic for news, Lincoln carried on with his other duties, but went to the War Department telegraph office even more frequently than usual. When he walked in not long after nine that evening, one of the young operators told him about an incident that had just occurred at Union Mills, a Virginia village twenty miles south of Washington that had a Union Army telegraph office. "A man came into Union Mills a little while ago, claiming he had left the army early this morning . . . then he asked to send a telegram to the [*New York*] *Tribune*. Secretary Stanton refused to let us use the wire for a newspaper and demanded a message. The fellow said he would not give it unless we first sent a dispatch to his paper. The Secretary has said he was a spy and has ordered him shot in the morning."

"Ordered him shot?" Lincoln asked.

"Yes, Mister President."

Lincoln told the operator to ask this stranger at Union Mills if he would now communicate directly with the President, and received the word that he would.

The man at the other end of the line was Henry E. Wing of Litchfield, Connecticut, a cub reporter for the *New York Tribune*. Now twenty-five, he was a slightly built young man weighing a hundred and thirty pounds who started the war as a private in the 27th Connecticut Volunteer Infantry. Wounded in the leg and hand at Fredericksburg while trying to carry his regimental battle flag up Marye's Heights, he was invalided out of the army with a permanent limp, having learned the personal ravages of war firsthand. Just eight months after he had given what he called "an old-fashioned, rousing Fourth of July speech" while still a young civilian, an honored law student, Henry arrived home again in a condition he later described:

> . . . *a crippled and wasted caricature of humanity was assisted from a railroad train at Wolcottville. As I balanced myself unsteadily on my crutches, my father recognized me, and approached with a smile of welcome in which was a gleam of surprise and pity. I leaned forward and reached for his outstretched hand in greeting, but just then my strength gave way and I fell into his arms. With some assistance from bystanders he laid me in a corner of a low phaeton [carriage] standing at the curb; and thus, with his arm about me as a buffer against the slightest jar or jostle of the vehicle, we started on the trip up the rolling hills to the home of my boyhood.*

On the way home, he found himself telling his father this, "in broken sentences."

> . . . *the story of the crash and scream and roar of battle out of which I had come broken and bleeding; of the terror of the long, black night in which I lay half naked upon the battlefield, with the wintry rain turning to sleet and snow, listening to the groans and sobs of dying men, and of the weary days and nights of suffering while my strength was slowly recruited [restored] for this tiresome journey that had at last dropped me as a helpless child into my father's arms.*

As his health improved, Henry began working for the *Hartford Evening Press*, a strongly Republican paper founded by Gideon Welles, who became Lincoln's secretary of the navy. There he started writing editorials so good that Horace Greeley, the famous editor of the *New York Tribune*, offered him the job that led to his becoming the youngest of the *Tribune's* war correspondents. One of that paper's team of four reporters assigned to cover the Army of the Potomac, Henry had been with that force for some months. He survived the first day of fighting in the Wilderness, during which he was with Major General Winfield Scott Hancock's Second Corps, and managed to reach Grant's headquarters that night. There he found several high commanders as well as some older journalists, all arguing about what had happened that day and what should be done next. Three of these correspondents senior to him were from the *Tribune*; as the night went on, they told Henry that they intended to stay with Grant despite his ban on sending out stories, and Henry offered to head for Washington and try to get the story out to the *Tribune* by whatever means he could.

Through Meade's chief of scouts, Henry had previously procured for the *Tribune* a Kentucky-bred racehorse, a gelding named Jesse, sometimes called Jess, whom he had been riding for some time. In the darkness, Henry went to the headquarters corral and "instructed the 'boy' to give Jesse a hearty breakfast at three o'clock in the morning, and to have him groomed and saddled at four." Returning to the headquarters tents, he saw Grant sitting among some other men. Henry approached Grant, who may have known that this young reporter who limped had been wounded serving bravely earlier in the war.

> [I] *said that I was coming out early the next day, and asked him if he had any message to the people that I could insert in my dispatches to the Tribune.*
>
> *"Well yes," he replied, "you may tell the people that things are going swimmingly down here."*
>
> *The remark was so evasive, or purposely misleading, at the close of a day when every one of his plans had evidently gone wrong that I smiled as I entered the exact words in my note book, thanked him, and turned away. I had only taken a step or two when he got up and joined me. When we had walked out of hearing of his companions he laid his hand upon my shoulder and, quietly facing me, inquired, "You expect to get through to Washington?"*
>
> *I replied that was my purpose, and that I should start at daybreak.*

Then, in a low tone, he said: "Well, if you should see the President, tell him from me that, whatever happens, there will be no turning back." He silently gave me his hand in farewell greeting, and we parted.

With dawn, Henry mounted Jesse, and spent a harrowing day getting as far as Union Mills. Lincoln knew none of this as he stood in the War Department telegraph office and began this odd way of communicating with a young man of whom he knew nothing. He would talk to the operator in front of him, the operator would tap out his words to Union Mills, and the operator there would tell Henry Wing what the president of the United States was saying. The conversation went this way.

"The President wants to know if you will talk with him. He wants to know if it is true that you have come from the army."

"Tell him, yes."

"He wants to know if you will tell him what news you bring."

"Tell him if he will first send one hundred words to the *Tribune*, I will tell him."

"Write your hundred words and we will send it at once."

The message was simply a brief account of the initial movements, beginning with, "The Grand Army of the Potomac crossed the Rapidan on Wednesday." As the rest of the hundred words came into the War Department, it led Charles A. Tinker, a cipher-operator whom Lincoln had met in Illinois before the war, to conclude that although there was "no news direct from Grant," nonetheless "everything [is] pushing along favorably." It was more of a bulletin than a fully developed news story, but it was a scoop: the first news that Grant had crossed the Rapidan and was engaging Lee's army in a big battle that was the start of the crucial campaign. Apparently, Wing threw in some resentful remarks about Stanton and the order that a reporter should be shot for doing his job. Lincoln smiled as he read it, and ordered that the hundred-word message should be sent to the *Tribune* and that this reporter was not to be shot. (Wing later said that all he heard directly from Stanton that night "was a threat to arrest me as a spy unless I uncovered [told him all] the news from the army. This made me very anxious, but still I refused." Stanton had ordered that no correspondents be allowed to accompany the Army of the Potomac, but a number had.) Thus far, Lincoln knew nothing about a special message for him from Grant, but he wanted to see anyone who had actually been with Grant and his army these past days. The next exchange with Union Mills was this:

"If I send an engine for you, will you come to Washington?"

"Yes."

Thus, at between one and two o'clock on Saturday morning, May 7, a small military train arrived in Alexandria, across the river from Washington. A carriage was waiting for Wing, who was dressed in the rags of a field hand—a disguise he had adopted on his way north from the Rapidan—and was smeared with the red mud of the Virginia countryside through which he had been making his way. He was immediately driven to the White House. Limping into Lincoln's office, he found the entire cabinet waiting for him. Many odd-looking persons had entered Lincoln's office, but the cabinet was really taken aback by this slender youth who came among them in the middle of the night in muddy rags. One person recognized him: Secretary of the Navy Gideon Welles, who probably knew of his connection with the Connecticut newspaper he had founded and may have seen him doing his journalistic duties around the capital. Within a minute, while all the leading figures of the executive branch of the United States government gathered about him, Henry Wing took his place against a wall, pointing out on a big military map the movements of Grant's army during the time he had so recently been with it.

An atmosphere of disappointment settled on the room. These men did not want to know what had happened on Thursday when the battle began; they wanted to know what had happened between then and this early hour on Saturday morning. One after another they rose, said "Good night, Mister President," and left the room without speaking to Henry Wing.

After these leaders of the executive branch left, Lincoln remained standing in his office, apparently numb, confused, and spent. He finally looked at Wing as if he had no idea why he was there, and said, "You wanted to speak to me?"

"Yes, Mister President—a message from General Grant. He told me I was to give it to you when you were alone."

Suddenly alert, Lincoln asked, "Something from Grant to me?"

"Yes," the exhausted young reporter said. "He told me I was to tell you, Mister President, that there would be no turning back."

Lincoln swung one of his long arms around Henry, bent down, and impulsively kissed his cheek. "Come tell me about it." As they sat down, Henry began telling him of the horror of the first day's fighting, of Lee's unexpected counterattack, of the first night at headquarters, when generals had been arguing with each other, some suggesting that they fall back across the river, and of Grant's final statement: "No, we shall attack again in the morning." He explained that he had been all through the first day's fighting as a spectator and described the circumstances under which Grant had given him the message for Lincoln that he had now delivered.

By the time Lincoln and Wing finished talking, it was once again four in the morning. The president said, "It is time for you to go to bed, Henry, you look as if you needed rest, but come to see me tomorrow afternoon." Henry made his way out of the White House, down to the room in the National Hotel that the *Tribune* kept for him, and threw himself on the bed, still covered with Virginia mud. By the time he awoke, newsboys throughout Washington were shouting, "News from the army! Grant found!"

Henry crawled out of bed and went down to the *Tribune* office on Fourteenth Street near Pennsylvania Avenue. As soon as his journalistic colleagues saw him, they shouted, raised him up in their arms, and placed him so that he was standing on top of a table. Here he told the story again, including the fact that there was the possibility that Stanton might have had him shot; he could have been dead at this hour.

And how, one of the reporters asked, had he escaped that fate?

Henry looked around and said, "The President found it out and sent a train for me." Dimly, Henry was beginning to understand that, despite its gaps, his story was possibly the greatest scoop of the war. His colleagues were elated; brief though it was, the *Tribune*'s story of Grant's crossing the Rapidan and the battle's beginning was on the streets in Washington and in New York, and in the papers of many other cities, all of them giving credit to the *Tribune*. (It was now Saturday morning; the first *New York Times* dispatch from the Wilderness would not appear for two more days. Apparently, by that time Grant was again allowing journalists to file stories from his headquarters.)

That afternoon, cleaned up and wearing fresh clothes, Henry Wing sat down again in the White House with Abraham Lincoln, who wanted to know the details of Henry's journey from Grant's headquarters to Union Mills. Henry started by giving credit to Jess, the *Tribune*'s horse that he had so often ridden before this adventure. Speaking of the beginning of his ride north and their crossing of the Rapidan, he said, "I knew from the way Jess acted as soon as we were across the river that it was none too safe. Jess knows things, Mister Lincoln—knows danger, feels it. And he steals around like a cat when things are not safe. That's the way he acted . . ." When he reached the house of a friend in Culpeper, Virginia, who was a strong Union sympathizer, Henry told him he had to get through to Washington. The man said of the surrounding countryside, "Don't you know that the woods are full of Confederates? . . . The only chance of your getting there is to go as a Confederate carrying news to Confederate friends in Washington, news that Lee has defeated Grant, that in twenty-four hours he will be on his way to the city." With that, Henry's friend had fitted him out in the cast-off ragged clothing of a field hand.

Continuing to tell Lincoln his story, Henry said, "Well, I started out, but a few miles on . . . sure enough, I ran plumb into a troop of Moseby's [*sic*] men. I stopped to talk and told my story in dialect. "There was great hurrahing, and in no time they had an escort ready. There were Yankees still in the neighborhood, they said. I would not be safe. And so I started out with Moseby's men for escort."

This perilous arrangement lasted until, at a place named Kelly's Ford, he ran into Kelly, an ardent Confederate sympathizer who had seen him in the past, riding through on Jess, wearing handsome civilian clothes and accompanying Union columns. "He recognized me and as I rode up, jumped for Jess's bridle. Jess was too quick for him. He gave one great bound and rushed for the river—not the ford but the deep water. Jess knows more than I do every time. They fired on me but it was too late."

By that time, Henry told Lincoln, he was about thirty miles south of Washington, "but the road was not clear. You have no idea how the enemy has filled it up—cavalry, wagons, scouts." Stopped several more times, he avoided capture by "telling a story that set them hurrahing, [but] I knew that could not last, that I must leave Jess and take to the railroad ties."

As Lincoln listened intently, Henry explained what he did next, before walking the final ten miles to Union Mills along the railroad track in the dusk. "I led Jess into a thicket down around Warrentown [Warrenton]. I tied him loose [with a leather strap], poured out all the oats I had, put my arms around his neck and promised to come back. That is what I want to do now, Mister Lincoln."

Lincoln said, wonderingly, "And now you want to go for Jess!"

"Yes, I must go for Jess."

"Well, Henry, I think we owe you something. I will have to help you with that."

What that help was became evident the next morning. A train rolled out of Alexandria that had on it a unit of soldiers and a boxcar that was equipped with hay, water, and oats. At Manassas Junction, enemy scouts fired on the train, and the Union soldiers fired back. This went on, mile after mile, with exchanges of gunfire, until the train came to where Henry thought he had left his horse somewhere in the thickets and trees. At this place, no snipers fired at the halted train, and Henry jumped off and swiftly made his way down the embankment and through the underbrush. He found Jess just where he had left him. The horse still was attached to a tree by a leather strap; with his big teeth he could easily have cut through that strap and gone off through the woods, but it was clear that he was waiting for the man who had told him he would come back to get him. Now, seeing Henry, he took one bite through the strap and freed himself. Henry quickly led the horse back to the boxcar, where Jess was put aboard and began to eat some oats and drink some water.

That night Jess was installed in a comfortable stable in Washington, but the story did not end there. All the newspapermen of Washington had arranged that on Monday morning Henry, now riding Jess and using a fine saddle and bridle that they had chipped in to buy, would come to the White House lawn. When Henry rode up, he found the cabinet, with Lincoln in front of them, ready to greet him and take a look at the horse. At this point, the *Tribune* men told Henry that the newspaper was giving him the horse, to be his own.

An informal reception was held on the lawn; as the participants went their ways, Lincoln asked if he could mount and ride Jess. Lincoln was no mean horseman, although his feet dangled nearer the ground than those of a rider of average height, and so Lincoln and Jess moved back and forth across the White House lawn for a time, until Henry Wing mounted the horse that was now his, to start out of the grounds.

As they parted, Lincoln asked, "And now, you go back to Grant?"

"Yes, Mister Lincoln, I go back."

"Good," Abraham Lincoln said. "You will be coming to Washington sometimes and remember this, that when you do I want you always to come and see me. It is an order. You are to tell me all you hear and see."

That began a relationship that would last to the end of the war. When Henry Wing came in from being in the field with Grant's forces, he would clean up and go to the White House. Admitted to see the president, he would tell him of the harsh realities of life at the front, and of the troops' morale, as Lincoln heard those things from no one else. During one of their talks in the months before the election, Lincoln unburdened himself in a way he seems to have done with none of his associates. He said, "There's many a night, Henry, that I plan to resign. I wouldn't run again now if I didn't know these other fellows couldn't save the Union on their platforms, whatever they say." Lincoln paused and added sadly, "I can't quit, Henry. I have to stay." (After the war, Henry Wing became a Methodist minister; a noted preacher, he died near his home in Bethel, Connecticut, at the age of eighty-five.)

THE SAME MONDAY morning that Henry Wing rode out of the White House grounds on Jess, the *New York Times* finally carried its first, but by now updated, story of the Wilderness battle. The situation of the casualties made for grim reading. Written with a Washington dateline, underestimating the number of Grant's wounded, of which there were more than 12,000, and making no estimate of Confederate casualties, the story said in part:

> *The number of wounded is reported at about ten thousand; the killed at two thousand. . . . [The enemy] left his dead and disabled on the field, in our hands. The Ambulance Corps, with its admirable organization, is working up to its full capacity, carrying the wounded [in horse-drawn ambulances] to Rappahannock Station. Sixteen trains of cars, dispatched from Alexandria today, will receive them. It is expected that they will return, with their bruised and mangled freight, about daylight. Several car-loads of ice were also sent down for the comfort of the wounded. The Sanitary and Christian Commissions are on the field, with a full force of assistants, and with plentiful supplies of everything necessary for the wounded. The Government has hospital accommodations here for thirty thousand, which will probably meet all demands.*

On the same morning that readers of the *Times* had this story in front of them, Grant lost an important general. John Sedgwick, one of his corps commanders, was a West Pointer, and a veteran of the Mexican War and pre–Civil War Indian fighting. A disciplinarian who was nonetheless a much-loved figure in the Army, Sedgwick was a generous-spirited bachelor who loved to play solitaire and was known as "Uncle John" by his men. Thus far in the war, he had been wounded four times.

The Wilderness battle had ended on May 6; pushing south the next afternoon, near Spotsylvania, Grant's mounted forward elements began encountering the horsemen of units under the command of Lee's colorful and skilled cavalry leader "Jeb" Stuart. On this morning of May 9, two days into what evolved into the bitterly fought thirteen-day-long Spotsylvania Campaign, as Sedgwick moved about indicating where he wanted some cannon to be placed, his aides cautioned him about bullets being fired at them by snipers almost half a mile away. Assuring them that he and they were safe, he said of the Confederate marksmen, "They couldn't hit an elephant at this distance." An instant later a bullet hit him below his left eye and he fell dead. Meade wept when the news came to headquarters, and Grant, saddened and momentarily stunned, said quietly, "His loss to this army is greater than the loss of a whole division." A Union general said of Sedgwick's Sixth Corps that after their leader fell they "seemed like an orphaned household."

THE HORRIBLE STRUGGLE in the Wilderness had already taught Grant and his army that Lee and his men were ferocious fighters, but at Spotsylvania, Grant had an added lesson in how cleverly and effectively Lee could plan ahead. Just as Lee had calculated correctly how and where Grant would try to move his army through the Wilderness, he had also begun planning how to counter Grant's possible next moves. Lee ordered his artillery chief, William Nelson Pendleton, to cut a road through the woods to Spotsylvania, thus enabling Lee's First Corps under Major General Richard Anderson to reach that area ahead of Grant and thwart Grant's effort to turn Lee's right flank. By the morning that Sedgwick was killed, Lee had entrenchments prepared for his outnumbered men that enabled them to begin a stubborn defense.

Understandably, Grant thought of the fighting in the Wilderness and around Spotsylvania as being part of one continuous battle. In a letter that he wrote Halleck at eight-thirty in the morning on May 11, he said, "We have now ended the 6th day of very hard fighting." With an optimism he may not have felt, Grant added, "The result up to this time is much in our favor." In some ways it was favorable—Grant was moving into Lee's territory, slamming right into everything the great Southern leader threw at him from behind his well-prepared defenses, causing Confederate casualties Lee could ill afford—but he also had this to report to Halleck: "We have lost to this time twelve general officers killed, wounded, and missing, and probably twenty thousand men." (Lee had lost the severely wounded Longstreet for months to come, and on the day Grant sent Halleck this report, Lee's cavalry leader, "Jeb" Stuart, was killed at Yellow Tavern, six miles north of Richmond.)

In his way of combining the prosaic with the memorable, Grant finished that paragraph of his report with this: "I am now sending back to Belle Plaines [*sic*] all my wagons for a fresh supply of provisions and ammunition, and"—here they came, words destined to live in American history—"propose to fight it out on this line if it takes all Summer." Two days after Grant wrote that, the regimental surgeon of the 121st New York Infantry underscored the intensity of the continuing clash in a letter to his wife: "After eight days of the hardest fighting the world has witnessed . . . I am unhurt. . . . The rebels fight like very devils! We have to fairly club them out of their rifle pits. We have taken thousands of prisoners and killed an army; still they fight as hard as ever." On the same day, a Southerner wrote of Grant, "We have met a man this time who either does not know when he is whipped, or who cares not if he loses his whole Army."

As for what Lee thought of Grant during these first days of their fighting each other, on May 11, after six days of what had in effect become the Wilderness-Spotsylvania campaign, Lee had this to say when several of his officers criticized Grant's leadership: "I think General Grant has managed his affairs remarkably well up to the present time."

IV

Even with this enormously critical fighting underway, Lincoln still had to deal with the varied matters that required his day-to-day attention. Despite his anxiety about the fate of Grant's forces, during the first day of fighting in the Wilderness he wrote a letter to eighty-seven-year-old Mrs.

Abner Bartlett of Medford, Massachusetts, thanking her for sending him a pair of socks she knitted for him. To this lady who was born a year after the signing of the Declaration of Independence, he wrote:

My dear Madam.
I have received the very excellent pair of socks of your own knitting, which
you did me the honor to send. I accept them as a very comfortable article
to wear; but more gratefully as an evidence, of the patriotic devotion
which, at your advanced age, you bear to our great and just cause.
May God give you yet many happy days.

Yours truly
A. Lincoln

The following day, as the fighting roared on in the Wilderness, he held a cabinet meeting at which each member read his opinion, which Lincoln had requested, on the policy to be taken regarding the Confederate massacre of United States Colored Troops at Fort Pillow, Tennessee, three weeks before. Accounts differed, but the evidence indicated that more than 200 black Union troops, as well as 50 whites, were killed after they surrendered. Witnesses claimed that, as they slaughtered defenseless men, Confederate soldiers shouted, "Kill the damned niggers! Shoot them down!" There had been an outcry in the North demanding the retaliatory execution of an equal number of randomly chosen Confederate prisoners. The vague consensus reached at this cabinet meeting was that if Union forces should capture either of the Confederate commanders involved, Major General Nathan Bedford Forrest or Brigadier General James R. Chalmers, they would be tried for murder.

In other matters, during these days when Washington heard the beating of drums at all hours as reinforcements for Grant marched through the dusty streets on their way to the shifting Virginia front, Lincoln signed the bills that changed the Nevada and Colorado territories into states of the Union. His role in organizing the Territory of Montana showed once again the degree to which he and his administration dispensed patronage. Lincoln's "List of Applicants for Montana Appointments," written in his own hand, had on it eleven names to be considered for governor of the territory, twelve for "Secretary of Montana," thirteen for "Judgeships in Montana," three for District Attorney, two for "Marshall of Montana," and three for Surveyor General. Two other names were to be given "Something in Territories." Of the forty-six men whose names appeared on the list, only two lived in Montana; among the others, all presumably ready to move there if selected, were men from places as distant from Montana as Maine and Maryland.

Lincoln also concluded a treaty with the Delaware Indians of Kansas and one with the Shawnee tribes. Receiving a delegation of Chippewa chiefs in the White House, Lincoln treated them politely, conducting them on a tour through parts of the mansion and addressing them as he stood in the midst of a circle of chiefs who sat cross-legged on the East Room floor, but his tone was patronizing. He clearly believed they deserved less from the white man than did the blacks, who had lived in slavery.

In foreign relations, an astonishing and troubling situation continued to develop in Mexico. France's Emperor Napoleon III, the nephew of the late Napoleon Bonaparte, had for thirty-one months been trying to make Mexico a French colony. The pretext for this French action was to collect an unpaid loan of $82 million made to Mexico by France in conjunction with Great Britain and Spain. In early 1862, all three nations sent ships and troops to Mexico, but only France had kept its soldiers there.

The French deemed it important to march inland from the initial landings at Vera Cruz to Mexico City to demonstrate that they ruled in fact as well as by proclamation. Their initial attempt to take the city of Puebla on May 5, 1862, was repulsed by the army of the Republic of Mexico, and became the Mexican holiday known as Cinco de Mayo. Not until June 10, 1863, more than a year later, did the French forces succeed in entering and occupying the ancient capital of Mexico.

All of this had been a flagrant affront to the Monroe Doctrine, the policy that countries in the Western Hemisphere such as Mexico were "not to be considered as subjects for future colonization by European powers." On the other hand, the Confederacy welcomed the idea of an alliance with this quasi-colony to its south, although France was not ready to choose sides in the war.

Earlier in the spring, Lincoln had begun to push his generals to establish a strong Union military presence in Texas, partly to demonstrate that the French intervention south of the border was not being taken lightly even when great battles would soon begin far to the north. Organized and put into motion early in March, an expeditionary force that would grow to nearly 40,000 men had embarked on what became known as the Red River Campaign of 1864. Some sixty vessels were involved, including twenty Union warships. The object was to move northwest up the Red River from Louisiana, follow the stream as it looped through southwestern Arkansas, and then go west into Texas. The mission also included the potential destruction or capture of vast amounts of the South's supply of cotton.

The general commanding this major task force was another of Lincoln's political appointments: Nathaniel Banks, who had been both a prominent member of Congress before the war and the governor of Massachusetts at the time the war started. In 1862, he had lost 30 percent of his men at the hands of Stonewall Jackson during Jackson's victorious Shenandoah Valley campaign, and in 1863 his Nineteenth Corps made three large, failed assaults during the siege of Port Hudson, Louisiana, a Confederate stronghold that was finally compelled to surrender by Grant's victory farther up the Mississippi River at Vicksburg. As May of 1864 began, Banks and his men, repeatedly foiled by the Confederates for seven weeks and thrown back in several significant battles, were still hundreds of miles from the Texas border.

Now, with close to 30,000 French troops in Mexico, including two battalions of the Foreign Legion, trying to impose their order on a country as large as all of western Europe, came more news about the puppet dictator that Napoleon III was sending to rule there. He was thirty-two-year-old Archduke Maximilian of Austria, the younger brother of Austria's Emperor Franz Josef. At this moment in May of 1864, he and his wife, the beautiful Princess Charlotte of Belgium, now to be known as the Empress Carlota, were on the high seas in a ship called the *Novara*. They would soon go ashore at Vera Cruz to make their way to Mexico City, where Maximilian was to receive the "Crown of Mexico"—a crown hastily crafted to accompany his invented title of emperor of Mexico.

All of this added to Lincoln's load of problems. In spite of the "four score and seven years" of American independence of which he had spoken at Gettysburg, a major European power was claiming a large part of North America as a colony. The situation was not only intensely frustrating, but troubling because it made the Union look impotent at a time when it needed to appear powerful in European eyes to forestall any inclination to sign alliances with the Confederacy.

More than ever, Lincoln appreciated the skillful assistance of Secretary of State Seward, who was doing as good a job in handling the Union's relations with other nations as Salmon P. Chase was in handling the Treasury. Lincoln, who had never been out of the United States, fortunately had as secretary of state a man who had traveled to eleven foreign countries, speaking to influential men in all of them. Seward's delicate maneuvers concerning the French occupation, and now the impending arrival of Maximilian, equaled the seasoned diplomacy to be found in any European chancellery. Despite the increasing French military success and occupation of larger areas of Mexico, with Lincoln's approval Seward's State Department continued to recognize the representative of the Republic of Mexico, the government whose forces the French troops had driven from the capital and other major Mexican cities. The prewar Mexican ambassador remained *persona grata* in Washington as "the Minister plenipotentiary of the Mexican Republic residing at this capital." Seward had known for some time that Maximilian would be sent to Mexico. When Maximilian went first to Paris to receive his appointment from Napoleon III, Seward wrote to the American minister to France, telling him that, while the would-be emperor was there, he must "entirely refrain from intercourse with him." Along the way, Seward had managed to extract from the French an undoubtedly false statement that they had no intention of establishing a permanent presence in Mexico, but he used this to continue expressing friendly sentiments, while always repeating that the United States relied on the French promise to withdraw.

Seward danced the diplomatic minuet with great skill. He stayed in communication with the Mexican national hero Benito Juárez, believing with reason that Juarez, one of that nation's past leaders, could reappear in that role. Seward knew that Mexican nationalist guerrillas might well be receiving help from secret sources to fight the French. He may not have instigated it, but he also knew of plans to put a resounding affirmation of the Monroe Doctrine into the platform being prepared for the national election by the Republican Party, which was changing its name for the purpose of this election to the National Union Party. (The change in name was to invoke the concept of loyalty to the Union and make it easier for Peace Democrats to vote for Lincoln, but many organizations, newspapers, and individuals continued to use the term "Republican.") Again, regarding adherence to the Monroe Doctrine, it may not have been the fine hand of Seward at work, but some six weeks before this mid-May confluence of military, domestic, and foreign crises, on April 4 the House of Representatives unanimously passed a resolution stating that it opposed having "a Monarchical government, elected on the ruins of any republican government in America, under the auspices of any European power."

Not only did Seward's house provide a welcome place for Lincoln to spend some evenings (without Mary) while the secretary of state smoked cigars and they spoke of things having nothing to do with the war, but Seward also acted as an excellent host to the most important foreign envoys in Washington. At the moment, his crucial task was to keep the European powers in the position of favoring the Union over the Confederacy, and he brought to this a longstanding sophisticated view of the effect of international trade on national power. During this era when the British Empire was dominant in world affairs, Seward made a Senate speech in 1853, eight years before the war, putting forth his vision of the American future. Speaking to his senatorial colleagues as if he were addressing the nation itself, he said:

> *You are already the great continental power of America. But does this content you? I trust not. You want the commerce of the world. . . . Put your domain under cultivation, and your ten thousand wheels of manufacture in motion. Multiply your ships and send them forth. The nation that draws most from the earth, and fabricates the most, and sells the most to foreign nations, must be, and will be, the great power of the earth.*

Ten years later, in August of the wartime year of 1863, he had taken a number of ambassadors, among them the ministers from England, France, Spain, Germany, and Russia, on a tour through his native New York State, with stops in Albany, Schenectady and Cooperstown. While they enjoyed seeing Niagara Falls, the real point was to show them the might of the North. Seward's son Fred described what they saw: "Hundreds of factories with whirling wheels, thousands of acres of golden harvest fields, miles of railway trains, laden with freight, busy fleets on rivers, lakes and canals."

With all of these pressures on him, ranging from the situation in Mexico to the crucial military campaigns now bloodily underway, Lincoln did not for a moment forget his own political future. The Democratic convention, certain to nominate McClellan, was at that point scheduled for the Fourth of July in Chicago. The Republican convention was scheduled to be at Baltimore in early June. Lincoln was the presumptive Republican nominee, but at this point nothing was guaranteed; he had received many endorsements, but the official nomination could only come at Baltimore. Indeed, important figures were urging that the Republican/National Union convention be postponed until September. Despite endorsements for Lincoln from the National Republican Committee and the Republican organizations of almost every Union state, during the past weeks many Radicals had been taking the position that it would be better, as one of them put it, to "see whether we cannot close up the war" first, and then nominate the Republican candidate.

This policy was urged by William Cullen Bryant, the editor of the influential *New York Post*, acting in concert with a prominent group that included sixteen New York state senators, but the strongest voice was that of Horace Greeley, the powerful editor of New York's *Tribune*. A founder of the Republican Party and a man who had at different times supported and opposed Lincoln—in a famous 1862 open letter to Lincoln entitled "The Prayer of Twenty Millions" Greeley urged him to swifter action in freeing the slaves, calling him "strangely and disastrously remiss" in his policy to that time—he now wrote in an editorial, "Let us unite in the resolve to save the Nation first, if possible, and make the next President afterward." The translation of that was: maybe we can still find someone who's not a Democrat but can beat Lincoln.

It was not then the custom for a president seeking reelection to travel around the country making speeches, but occasionally Lincoln had the opportunity to make a speech in Washington that would combine the image of himself as both the commander-in-chief and as a man who appreciated the sacrifices made by civilians as well as soldiers. Women did not have the vote, but he always understood their influence. At a Sanitary Commission fair in the capital, held to support aid to military hospitals in which many women worked as volunteers caring for the wounded, Lincoln told the audience, "If all that has been said by orators and poets since the beginning of the world in praise of women were applied to the women of America, it would not do them justice for their conduct during this war. I will close by saying God bless the women of America!" (The *Washington Evening Star* reported that this produced "Great applause.")

FIVE

TROUBLED MILITARY AND POLITICAL CAMPAIGNS

As May ended, both the North and the South felt that cataclysmic forces had been released, with results no one could foresee. While Grant smashed at Lee relentlessly, piling up casualties on both sides, the news of Union efforts in other areas ranged from disappointing to catastrophic. The Red River Campaign commanded by Nathaniel Banks, involving territory in Mississippi, Louisiana, Arkansas, and Texas, had ended in a fiasco. By May 22, the badly handled Union troops who had started off on March 10 from Vicksburg, Mississippi, were back approximately where they began. The ill-fated expedition had lost a number of ships and several thousand men. This failure resulted in Banks being relieved of command; he received official censure for a disaster that Sherman characterized as being "one damn blunder from beginning to end."

If the news from the Southwest was bad, the reports from Grant's eastern flank were no better. There, on his left, Benjamin F. Butler had started carrying out his assignment to move from the coast up the James River toward Richmond. Grant, who seriously doubted Butler's military ability but understood that Lincoln wanted this potential political rival kept off the civilian scene, had some hope that Butler could accomplish this mission. With Grant's Army of the Potomac keeping Lee's forces fully engaged by constantly attacking them as they defended the approaches to Richmond north of Petersburg, Butler and the 39,000 men of his Army of the James might be able to drive in from the east all the way to Richmond, capturing Petersburg on the way.

Butler started off well enough: on May 5, the same day that Grant and Lee first clashed in the Wilderness, Butler marched unopposed into the small riverside settlements of City Point, on the south side of the Appomattox River where it flows into the James, and Bermuda Hundred, opposite City Point on the north shore of the Appomattox. This put him at a strategic place on the James River, less than twenty miles southeast of Richmond. In the following days, moving too cautiously, he gave his opponent P. G. T. Beauregard time to begin digging strong entrenchments to block his movements. By the time Butler reached Drewry's Bluff on the James River, seven miles south of the Confederate capital, the door to Richmond had been closed. Rather than try to slam through, as Grant was attempting to do to the northeast of him, after being repulsed at Drewry's Bluff, Butler withdrew on May 16 back down the James to Bermuda Hundred. This placed his 39,000 men in a defensive box on a peninsula, penned in there by 10,000 Confederates, and ended their usefulness to Grant. In a report of this failure, Grant wrote scathingly that Butler's entire Army of the James, "though in a position of great security, was as completely shut off from . . . Richmond as if it had been in a bottle strongly corked. It required but a . . . small portion of the enemy to hold it there." Some of the troops began to refer to Butler's campaign as a "stationary advance."

Thus, as May came to an end, Union efforts consisted of a significant but terribly costly advance for Grant, tapering off with inconclusive fighting along Virginia's North Anna River, most of it in an area eighteen miles northeast of Richmond. One Massachusetts politician, Benjamin F. Butler, had failed Grant, and Lincoln's other important Massachusetts political appointee, Nathaniel Banks, had presided over the major Red River defeat. Sherman was making some progress toward Atlanta, but the strong opposition he faced daily from General Joseph E. Johnston indicated that he had a long summer ahead of him, with no guarantee of success. Any hope of ending the war in the next hundred days, which had been part of the motivation for recruiting the "Hundred Days Men" regiments, vanished.

• • •

For more sophisticated observers of the war, there were concepts such as one that Sherman pointed out in a letter to Halleck: "One of my chief objects being to give full employment to Johnston, it makes but little difference where he is, so [long as] he is not on his way to Virginia." Sherman had that right: Lee and Johnston, both brilliant, good friends, and West Point classmates, were using their advantage of interior lines of communication and stayed attuned to the idea of using the South's railroads whenever possible. On the one hand, Sherman seemed unable to outflank Johnston and make a final drive into Atlanta, but if Sherman had not been pushing hard in that direction, Johnston could and would have released many thousands of troops to move north swiftly to reinforce Lee in Virginia.

Only four weeks into what Lincoln called "the Spring campaign," the horrendous Union casualties caused an increasing political problem for him and his administration. In terms of the North's manpower, these dead and maimed young men could be replaced, but the ever-lengthening casualty lists appeared at the beginning of what everyone knew to be only the start of months of fighting, with no sign of a Confederate collapse. After three years of bloodshed, the overriding question posed by the war's opponents remained more urgent than ever: is this suffering and death worth the cost? Lincoln saw public opinion as the lifeblood of politics. As far back as his first debate with Stephen A. Douglas in 1858, he had said: ". . . public sentiment is everything. With public sentiment, nothing can fail; without it nothing can succeed." The conclusion Lincoln might draw from this was clear enough; with the mounting casualties and frustration about a seemingly endless war, his administration could be doomed. In a sense, Lincoln had been through the dress rehearsal for this possibility just a year before. When he received the news of the defeat at Chancellorsville, two visitors in his office saw him start to pace back and forth, anxiously repeating to himself, "My God! My God! What will the country say? What will the country say?"

As June began, in twenty-six days Grant had lost 33,000 men, killed, wounded, or captured. Ships brought more than 1,000 casualties a day up the Potomac River to Washington. The scene of their arrival became ghastly, all the more so because, as one man who saw these grim disembarkations wrote:

It is inexpressibly sad to see so much pain and waste of life occurring right in the midst of this buoyant and springing season when nature seems her gayest and most vigorous. . . .

Every night, when the glowing hues of evening are gilding the waters of the Potomac and lending a softened splendor to the rich verdure which lines the picturesque banks, boatloads of wounded soldiers arrive.

Steamboats with names like *Lizzie Baker, Connecticut,* and *General Hooker,* their whistles blaring in harsh ghostly tones, landed at the Sixth Street wharves in downtown Washington, where long lines of horse-drawn ambulances waited to take the wounded to Washington's twenty-one overcrowded hospitals. The wounded who had died coming up the river lay under sheets in the bows of the vessels, and would be carried in hearses across the river on the Long Bridge to Arlington, the large farm overlooking the Potomac that had been Robert E. Lee's home and now began its time as a national cemetery. The badly wounded lay on the decks. When medical orderlies lifted them onto stretchers to be carried ashore, groans filled the air; sometimes a man screamed. Most of the men on stretchers went into the ambulances, but some who might not survive the jolting of these horse-drawn vehicles on the rough streets were carried on these same stretchers right to the hospitals. With the stretcher cases ashore, the walking wounded came lurching down the gangplanks. On one day, 3,000 sick and wounded arrived. A man who watched this noted "the solemn hush" of the waiting crowds.

There are anguished faces among the spectators who form the lanes down which the sad processions move from each boat; some are waiting for their own loved ones; others catch a glimpse of a maimed and battle-stained form, once so proud and manly, which they recognize as of their own flesh and blood.

A man wrote of Washington: "The whole city is more or less of a hospital." Church bells "are not allowed to actually ring nowadays, for . . . there is peril that waves of sound might carry too painful a vibration to the sensitive nerves of some sick or wounded soldier." A Washington resident also observed this:

The town is full of strangers from the North who have come in quest of friends and relatives who are in the hospitals or are lying dead on the battlefield. We recognize these bereaved and anxious people everywhere by their sad and thoughtful faces, their strangeness about the ways of Washington, and by their frequent inquiries for hospitals or the way to Fredericksburg [Virginia] where many thousands of the severely wounded still lie.

There were also the mentally wounded. The future Supreme Court justice Oliver Wendell Holmes, Jr., a twenty-three-year-old lieutenant colonel badly wounded three times earlier in the war and now serving on the staff of the Union Army's embattled Sixth Corps, would soon write home to his parents in Massachusetts: "I tell you many a man has gone crazy since the campaign began from the terrible pressure on mind & body. . . ." He added, in regard to the soldiers' opinions of the two presumptive presidential candidates, "Theres [*sic*] no use in disguising that the feeling for McClellan has grown this campaign. . . ."

One evening, Lincoln was in his carriage, moving near the gory scene at the waterfront. He had the coachman stop at a street corner so that he could have a word with a man he saw standing there, his trusted friend Congressman Isaac Arnold from Chicago. As they spoke, a line of wounded Union soldiers shuffled past silently in the dusk, some with their heads bound up in bandages, many with their arms in bloody slings, and others limping. Lincoln gazed at them and said, "I cannot bear it."

As his wife did, Lincoln visited the wounded in the hospitals. On one occasion, a man accompanying both of them through a ward of severely wounded men witnessed this:

Just beyond us, passed a well-dressed lady, evidently a stranger, who was distributing tracts. After she had gone, a patient picked up with languid hand the leaflet dropped upon his cot, and, glancing at the title, began to laugh. When we reached him, the President said: "My good fellow, that lady doubtless means you well, and it is hardly fair for you to laugh at her gift."

"Well, Mister President," said the soldier, who recognized Mr. Lincoln, "how can I help laughing a little? She has given me a tract on the 'Sin of Dancing,' and both of my legs are shot off."

During these weeks, the artist Francis Carpenter, free to come and go in the White House as he worked on his portrait of Lincoln and his cabinet at the signing of the Emancipation Proclamation, said of what he saw of the president:

It was the saddest face I ever knew. There were days when I could scarcely look into it without crying. . . . on one of these days I met him, clad in a long morning wrapper [another man called it a "a long-skirted, faded dressing-gown, belted at the waist"] pacing back and forth in a long narrow passage leading to one of the windows, his hands behind him, great black rings under his eyes, head bent forward upon his breast—such a picture of the effects of sorrow, care and anxiety as would have melted the hearts of the worst of his adversaries. . . .

(Carpenter spent many hours painting Lincoln, but apparently never noticed a particularly unusual thing about his striking face. Although all faces are slightly asymmetrical, the left side of Lincoln's face was significantly smaller than the right: the bony ridge above his left eye was rounder and thinner than the one on the right, and ran the other way than it does in normal skulls.)

DURING THESE DIFFICULT weeks, the principal Union civilian and military commanders—Lincoln, Stanton, Grant, and Halleck—could find signs of success in only one or two areas of their far-flung operations. In Georgia, Sherman continued to make progress, although Joseph E. Johnston kept opposing him vigorously and cleverly. What clearly demonstrated hope for the future was the emergence of Philip Sheridan. The short, red-faced, pugnacious West Pointer had come to Grant's attention at Chattanooga. For Sheridan, like Grant, the battle was never over: to them, the fact that after a day's fighting the Confederates had retreated from a certain place meant only that they were to be pursued until the Union troops chasing them literally fell to the ground, panting with exhaustion. At Chattanooga, where Sheridan commanded foot soldiers, he chased the enemies he faced on Missionary Ridge down its far side and pushed on after them through the night until two-thirty in the morning. Sheridan was soon promoted and assigned to command a combined force of 13,000 cavalrymen and horse artillery.

While Grant and Lee fought at Spotsylvania, Sheridan made a raid toward Richmond that indicated what he might be able to accomplish. Operating well behind Lee's lines, he swung near the Confederate capital, destroying irreplaceable railroad equipment as well as seizing badly needed Confederate food supplies and freeing Union prisoners. On May 11, at Yellow Tavern, six miles north of Richmond, a pitched battle developed between mounted forces of the North and South. Here the justly legendary Confederate cavalry leader "Jeb" Stuart met his end. In the close-quarters fighting, Stuart, a dandy who fought that day with a rose in a buttonhole of his grey uniform jacket, was on his horse in the middle of an attack by his 1st Virginia Cavalry. In a tumultuous tangle of men and horses, one of Sheridan's troopers fired a .44-caliber pistol at him from less than fifteen yards away. The bullet struck Stuart just below his rib cage, mortally wounding him. As an ambulance carried Stuart back to Richmond, Sheridan turned the tide of battle and went on to victory. Stuart died the next morning. After inflicting four defeats on the Confederates in fifteen days while he rode around Lee's entire army, Sheridan rejoined Grant and the Army of the Potomac.

During a month of dramatic struggle and heartbreaking stories, on May 15, the same day that Sherman took another slow step toward Atlanta by forcing Johnston to retreat from Resaca in northern Georgia, a remarkable battle erupted in Virginia's Shenandoah Valley. It exemplified what Lincoln constantly faced: the Southern military tradition and fighting spirit, and the frequent disparity between the experience and ability of Confederate and Union commanders. The leader of 4,000 Confederate soldiers was John Cabell Breckinridge, a veteran of the Mexican War who had become active in Democratic politics. After serving in the Kentucky legislature and then the United States Congress, he was James Buchanan's vice president immediately before the war. He had been one of several Democratic candidates for president running against Lincoln in the 1860 campaign. When Lincoln won, Breckinridge served briefly as a United States senator from Kentucky until he was expelled from the Senate in December of 1861 for having entered the Confederate States Army the month before. He fought as a brigadier general at Shiloh. Promoted to major general, he won distinction during the Stones River campaign, which involved operations in Kentucky, Tennessee, and Mississippi, and served with Joseph E. Johnston in the Vicksburg campaign. At Chicka-mauga and Chattanooga, Breckinridge commanded a division.

Facing him in the Shenandoah Valley stood Major General Franz Sigel, who owed his rank in the Union army to his being an important figure in the large German-American constituency that Lincoln wished to recognize by appointing men from among them. Grant ordered Sigel, who had 6,275 men, more than half again as many as Breckinridge com-manded, to move south into the Shenandoah Valley, a rich agricultural area and a strategically important north-south route for the opposing armies. The object was to put pressure on Lee from the west, as Butler had been supposed to do from the east in what became his bungled march inland toward Richmond from the coast.

When Breckinridge belatedly learned that Sigel was heading toward him, the Kentuckian hastily assembled all the men he could bring to his area. This included the 257 students of the Cadet Corps of the Virginia Military Institute in Lexington, Virginia. Most were between fifteen and seventeen years old; one was a boy of twelve, and another a man of twenty-three. The cadets marched eighty miles in four days to Breckinridge's headquarters at New Market, Virginia, in the Valley seventy miles south-east of Harpers Ferry. When the general first looked at these cadets as they arrived, marching in parade-ground order through a heavy rain, he was struck by their youth and called out: "Gentlemen from VMI, I trust I will not need your services today; but if I do I know you will do your duty!"

The moment that Breckinridge feared came swiftly. Soon after the battle began, he saw that Union fire had killed and wounded so many men that a gap more than a hundred yards wide had opened in the center of his line. Breckinridge had to fill it or retreat. One of his staff suggested sending in the boys from VMI.

"I will not do it," Breckinridge told him.

"General, you have no choice."

Breckinridge replied, "Send the cadets in, and may God forgive me." Coming in range of the Union cannon, Cadet John Howard saw a wounded Confederate officer lying on his side, lifting his sword in the air and waving it to urge his men of a regular unit to press forward in the at-tack. "Another shell exploded and he was cut down for a second time. . . . What effect that waving sword had on anyone else, I do not know but I

know there was no giving back as we passed forward through the storm."
Another cadet named Gideon Davenport said, "About this time we passed
a group of wounded soldiers who cheered us but a shell, intended for us,
burst in their midst, and they fell silent. Suddenly there was a crack in our
front[,] a gap appeared in our ranks[,] and First Sergeant Cabell, Privates
Wheelwright Crockett and Jones fell dead, and others were wounded . . .
the line went forward in the best of order."

Captain Henry A. Wise, an officer who had graduated from VMI only
two years before and was second-in-command of the Cadet Corps on this
day, came upon the scene of his comrades who had already been so badly
hit. "There lay poor Stannard, the worst shot up man I ever saw and poor
Cabell and my old room mate Crockett with the back part of his head
shot away and then little Randolph and the rest." Then he saw Color Sergeant Oliver L. Evans, the oldest of the cadets, moving ahead of him, carrying the institute banner. "I have read of the joy of battle," Wise wrote,
"but I never saw it so fully illustrated as in this case . . . he would glance
back over his shoulder occasionally and I would catch his eye . . . his
whole face was wreathed in smiles and seemed to radiate joy and happiness, his form seemed to swell in growing size, and as he carried that banner so gloriously and shook back his golden locks he appeared to me the
most inspiring figure on that gory field. Indeed, a very 'God of battle.'"

The Federal line broke and the Confederates, with the cadets in front,
led the charge through to victory, capturing a cannon and many men
from the 34th Massachusetts Infantry. Color Sergeant Evans climbed
atop the cannon that had so recently fired at him and his young comrades,
and stood there, waving the VMI flag. General Breckinridge rode by; lifting his hat in salute to Evans and the brave boys around him, he shouted,
"Well done!"

At the end of the day ten cadets lay dead, including Thomas Garland Jefferson, a collateral descendant of Thomas Jefferson. Another forty-five
cadets were wounded in the fight. Union general Franz Sigel was relieved
of his field command four days after his retreat from New Market and
reassigned to a rear area reserve division in West Virginia.

A JOURNALIST BASED in Washington at this time encountered a different
aspect of what young soldiers could do and be.

Today, while passing through the circular attached corridor leading from the rotunda of the Capitol to the Senate wing, I was attracted by the sound of vocal music and saw that two [sightseeing] soldiers, passing through, had discovered the echo there. They were singing a beautiful song called "Drifting Homeward," now very popular with the army. The voices of the singers were well trained, the words very beautiful, and every casual passerby stopped to hear the lovely strains as they rose and fell in perfect harmony through the vaulted chamber. More than one stout-hearted man was moved as the accordant voices of the singers breathed the words:

We dread not the storm that blows us on;
It blows us further home, further home.

It was but a little thing but it showed how much feeling, sentiment, and culture may be found in the ranks of the American army.

II

At the end of May, a movement that had named itself the Radical Democracy Party gathered in Cleveland to hold its own convention to nominate a president of the United States. The delegates formed an extraordinary group. They included Radical Republicans and War Democrats, as well as those who were in essence anarchists, opposed to virtually everything currently organized in the political spectrum. They would not vote for McClellan, the man certain to be nominated by the Democratic Party, and they did not like Lincoln. Many of them being largely ineffectual and inexperienced political novices or dilettantes, they hoped that the turmoil of 1864 might give their independent party the chance to put a new name before the public.

Extraordinary machinations lay behind the Cleveland convention, but it had one goal: to stop Lincoln, either by blocking his nomination at the upcoming Republican/National Union convention in Baltimore, or to bring forth a candidate who, on any ticket other than the Democratic one, could win the presidency in November.

The man in the minds of those converging on Cleveland was Major

General John Frémont. He had started his career in the prewar Regular Army in the elite Corps of Topographical Engineers. Sometimes using Kit Carson as a scout, he had made the first maps of the Oregon Trail, explored the Sierras, discovered Lake Tahoe, and later gave the name Golden Gate to the entrance to San Francisco Bay. Resigning from the Army, he was already known to the American public as "the Pathfinder," and became one of California's first two senators. In 1856, Frémont had been the newly organized Republican Party's first candidate for president, being badly defeated by the Democrats' Buchanan.

Early in the war, Lincoln made Frémont the commander of the Department of the West, with headquarters at St. Louis. It quickly became apparent that Frémont's lack of experience handling any large body of troops was working against him. Although he did not appear to profit from it personally, at St. Louis he willingly surrounded himself with a group of shady contractors who overcharged the government for everything ranging from supplies to building fortifications. Beyond this, his early public statements and proclamations in Missouri were so vindictive toward slaveholders and Confederate sympathizers in the Border States that Lincoln feared Kentucky would secede and join the Confederacy. (When Frémont's gifted and attractive wife, Jessie, the well-connected daughter of Senator Thomas Hart Benton of Missouri, traveled to Washington and asked Lincoln to support her husband's views and actions, she said that Lincoln received her rudely, soon dismissing her with the remark, "You are quite a female politician.")

As a result of Lincoln's displeasure with Frémont's attempt to issue an emancipation proclamation long before he felt the time was ripe to do that, in October of 1861 he relieved Frémont of command in the West. Put in charge of the Mountain Department, which consisted largely of the area that had just become the newly organized state of West Virginia, Frémont failed in his efforts to oppose Stonewall Jackson during his Shenandoah Valley campaign. Again relieved of command, he returned to New York, not officially out of the Army, but in the status, like the Democrats' standard-bearer McClellan, of "awaiting orders" that never came.

Frémont's abolitionist statements had made him the darling of the evolving Radical Republicans, who saw him as a true antislavery crusader and a man who, if the Union could prevail, would impose a suitably punitive peace upon the South. By this election year of 1864, Frémont was, while not officially separated from the Army, engaged in a business career of railroad promotion in New York City. His strongest supporters were German-Americans from St. Louis, where he started his war service as commander of the Department of the West, and Radical Republicans who believed that Frémont would carry through on a program to confiscate and redistribute the property of Confederate slaveholders, and work hard for an immediate grant of the vote to all freed slaves.

The call for a convention to nominate Frémont began in early May. Those wanting it condemned what they called Lincoln's use of "open, shameless, and unrestrained patronage," and also held that there must be a law enacted that a president could serve for only one term. These opponents of Lincoln saw this as their chance to strike at him before the Republican convention, and at the same time produce someone who would not be as conciliatory toward the South as the Democrats' McClellan would likely be.

The press was fascinated by the sudden appearance of an independent party that might change the political landscape. One of Lincoln's most vocal critics, Manton Marble, editor of the *New York World* and a man capable of holding two entirely different positions on the same issue, predicted that there would be a great turnout at Cleveland; he believed it would be "immense in numbers." The powerful James Gordon Bennett of the *New York Herald* was equally in favor of this Cleveland convention but wanted the delegates to nominate Grant and make Frémont his vice-presidential running mate. This, he thought, would be a "powerful ticket" that would attract many Radical Republicans as well as War Democrats. The firebrand Massachusetts abolitionist Wendell Phillips was drawn to the concept, as was the abolitionist Elizabeth Cady Stanton, no relation to the secretary of war and a crusader for women's right to vote; she informed the convention that she would be there and would expect to be a delegate with full voting rights. Stanton, the president of the Women's National Loyal League, an organization devoted to bringing women into political affairs, had such a low opinion of Lincoln and his administration that earlier in the war she expressed the hope that "the rebels will sack Washington, take Lincoln, Seward and McClellan[,] and keep them safe in some Southern fort until we man the ship of state with those who know whither they are steering and for what purpose."

Some of Lincoln's political allies believed that the scheme at Cleveland was to put Frémont forward only to use his candidacy to negotiate with those Republican delegates, soon to meet in Baltimore, who would otherwise nominate Lincoln. The plot, Lincoln's supporter Major General Francis Blair thought, would give the coy and capricious Secretary of the Treasury Chase what he wanted. Blair said sarcastically, "It is expected . . . [that] Chase who has so *magnanimously* declined to be a candidate, will be taken up as a compromise candidate."

As the day neared, the Cleveland platform included the following planks: unrelenting continuation of the war to the end; a constitutional amendment permanently abolishing slavery; prohibition of a president from holding office for more than one term; the reconstruction of the South to be conducted by Congress with no role for any Confederate state governments; the confiscation of rebel property and its division among Union Army veterans. At the same time, some heading for Cleveland subscribed to the views of the Peace Democrats, who wanted far softer positions to be taken on all these issues.

There were those who also wanted another candidate than Lincoln but were skeptical about this amateurishly organized convention. Horace Greeley, still preaching postponement of a nomination until September, could only bring himself to tell a group of Frémont supporters that he did not find them to be "a factious"—he may have been sparing them the word "seditious"—"movement." Many felt that the men who wished to fashion the nation's political future in Cleveland were overly intellectual theorists: in what were code words in a day when most men's hair was cut no longer than to the backs of their collars, the *New York World*'s description of the early arrivals suggested that they were effete: "gentlemen whose hair is brown, long, and parted in the middle." A dispatch from the pro-Lincoln *New York Times* referred to them as a "motley set" of "witless fellows," and a subsequent story called them "a conglomeration of malcontents . . . representing no constituencies, and controlling no votes." Many Radical Republican politicians who still hoped to stop Lincoln stayed away, feeling that this would not be the time and place to start.

On the morning of May 31, delegates began gathering in Cleveland's Chapin Hall. They discovered that this nationally publicized meeting was an ad hoc proceeding. No one had to present credentials. No slate of delegates was placed before the meeting. Literally anyone could walk in and sit down anywhere. During the course of the day, anyone could raise his hand and make a speech, and when the voting came, anyone there could cast a ballot, and almost everyone did. The reporter present in

Cleveland for the *New York Times* claimed that only 156 people attended, and described them as "gentlemen who came here ostensibly as friends of General Grant." No one estimated an attendance of more than 400.

Ill organized though they were, the delegates managed to nominate Frémont by acclamation; Salmon P. Chase's name was never mentioned, burying what then seemed to be possibly his last chance to slip back into the presidential race. Warning the forthcoming Republican/National Union Party convention of what might occur, Frémont said, "But if Mr. Lincoln should be nominated—as I believe it would be fatal to the country to endorse a policy and renew a power which has cost us the lives of thousands of men . . . there will remain no other alternative but to organize against him all elements of conscientious opposition with a view to prevent the misfortune of his reelection."

The epitaphs for the Cleveland meeting came swiftly. Lincoln's appointee Postmaster Edwin Cowles of Cleveland wired Postmaster General Montgomery Blair: "Convention tremendous fizzle." The same word was used by Solomon Newton Pettis, the Pennsylvania lawyer who had swung that state's delegation for Lincoln at the 1860 Republican convention and been rewarded for his efforts with a judgeship in the Colorado Territory. Back practicing law in Pennsylvania, he was apparently at the meeting as an observer for the president. Before leaving Cleveland, he telegraphed Lincoln that he had witnessed "the most perfect failure, the most magnificent fizzle I have ever been upon."

The message from Cleveland might be weak, but its meaning was clear: there were those who wanted neither Lincoln nor McClellan, and the election was still five months away.

III

On the evening the Cleveland convention ended, Ulysses S. Grant began a military operation that would make the word "fizzle" seem like high praise. He began a march toward the important crossroads at Cold Harbor, Virginia (not on a body of water, despite its name), eight miles northeast of Richmond. Lee also moved in the same direction. After two days of maneuvering, skirmishing, and a general increase in the fighting, all conducted in the most intense heat, heavy rain started on the afternoon of June 2 and continued through the night. As the rain and the fighting continued, a reporter for the *New York Times* wrote of the unit he had been with.

> *At one point we were losing at the rate of a man a minute. I am writing this in the hospital of the Eighteenth Corps. Around me are hundreds of wounded in every stage of mutilation. Some are protected from the rain by shelter-tents, others have nothing over them except green boughs. The rain is not unpleasant to these poor sufferers. On the contrary, it refreshes them in their fevered condition.*

But this was not yet the main battle; that would take place the next day. Private Frank Wilkeson, who served in the 11th New York Battery in the Army of the Potomac's Second Corps, had been through the fighting in the Wilderness and Spotsylvania. Moving toward the battle he knew would take place at Cold Harbor, he had passed Grant, who was standing under a tree near a bridge across the Pamunkey River.

> *Grant looked tired. He was sallow. He held a dead cigar firmly between his teeth. His face was as expressionless as a pine board. He gazed steadily at the enlisted men as they marched by, as though trying to read their thoughts. He had the power to send us to our deaths, and we were curious to see him. Grant stood silently looking at his troops. . . .*

Now, on what everyone knew was the night before the main battle, Private Wilkeson sensed that tomorrow would be a bad day. "There was considerable confusion as the infantry marched in the darkness." His unit of horse-drawn artillery with their 3-inch guns was positioned in a relatively safe place "just back of the crest of a hill," but near them were the men of the 7th New York Heavy Artillery, whose cumbersome cannons, more suitable for sieges, had been left behind. These men, converted into foot soldiers, had little experience with that kind of fighting. Talking with them, Wilkeson found "they were sad of heart. They knew that they were going to go into the fight early the next morning, and they dreaded the work. The whole army seemed depressed the night before Cold Harbor."

On the following morning, June 3, Grant had his Army of the Potomac ready to make an enormous attack that he hoped would wipe out Lee. The Army of the Potomac had 108,000 men facing Lee's 59,000.

The main Federal assault was ordered to begin at four-thirty in the morning. After the terrible casualties of May, the troops of the Union army were, one officer noted, "calmly writing their names and home addresses on slips of paper, and pinning them on to their coats, so that their dead bodies might be recognized and their fate made known to their families." (One soldier wrote this in his diary. "June 3. Cold Harbor. I was killed." The diary was found on his body.)

The terrain favored Lee: The land the Union troops had to cross was flat, with some of the ground swampy. The Confederate defensive line, six miles in length, was interspersed with hills big enough for some men to call them "heights"; Lee's men dug a network of shallow trenches called rifle-pits into these slopes, along with deeper emplacements for artillery that could sweep the area through which Grant's men must come.

Somewhat after four-thirty, 60,000 of Grant's troops rushed forward, cheering. From the moment these three divisions started toward the Confederate positions, hundreds of men began falling, struck by bullets, shells, and canister fired by Lee's well-entrenched troops. One Union survivor said, "It seemed more like a volcanic blast than a battle." Brigadier General Edward Porter Alexander, commander of the Confederates' First Corps artillery, said, "We turned loose on them, everything, infantry & artillery, canister, shot, & shell."

Grant's men advanced into the greatest concentration of firepower in the history of warfare to that time. To make things worse, the three main attacking forces began to diverge, opening up into three huge wedges of attacking men instead of presenting the enemy with right-to-left advancing lines. This gave the Confederates the chance to fire not only at the men advancing directly at them, but also to fire at an angle into the sides of the other two massive moving triangles of Union troops.

Minute after minute, hundreds of men fell under the Confederate barrage, spinning, pitching forward, being torn to bloody shreds by cannonballs. In General Winfield Scott Hancock's Second Corps, eight colonels died in the first eight minutes while leading their regiments; a ninth, Colonel James P. McMahon of New York, reached the Confederate lines, picked up his regiment's battle flag when the color bearer fell, waved it once, and was killed. Private Wilkeson said that, trying to support the Union advance, he and the other gunners of his battery working their cannon "sprung in and out from the three-inch guns and replied angrily," but the enemy fire "was as the fury of hell." He described more of the slaughter.

> *Twenty minutes had not passed since the infantry had sprung to their feet, and ten-thousand of our men lay dead and wounded on the ground. The men of the Seventh New York Heavy Artillery came back without their colonel. The regiment lost heavily in enlisted men and line officers. Men from many commands sought shelter behind the crest of the hill we were behind. They seemed to be dazed and utterly discouraged.*

How he knew this was the case, Confederate general Alexander did not say, but in writing of that morning he stated, "About 7 A.M. Gen. Grant authorized Gen. Meade to suspend the attack whenever he felt that it would fail. But Meade continued to press his corps commanders to renew their assaults." Confederate Lieutenant General Richard H. Anderson, commander of Lee's First Corps, reported that by 8 A.M. his positions had fought off fourteen successive attacks. Henry Wing, the young reporter who had brought Grant's message from the Wilderness to Lincoln, was there watching.

> *[The Union soldiers] went against those heights without a waver. There wasn't a chance of success. They knew it, but they went on just the same, dropping in their tracks as they came; and those behind rushed over the dead and wounded and fell. You could not believe so many men could die in twenty minutes; and that is all the time it took.*

As the morning went on, the Union advances became sporadic. The Confederates, continuing the murderous fire from their earthworks, could hear the enemy officers exhorting their men to rush on again, but the Federal troops, while not retreating, simply lay on the battlefield amid their dead and wounded comrades, using the strewn corpses as sandbags to protect themselves as they continued to fire. Grant was to say that his men were "at some places fifty yards" from the enemy rifle-pits; other accounts made the distance twenty. By eleven in the morning, while both sides continued firing at each other with everything they had, it was clear that the Federal attack had failed, with Grant's men badly exposed on open ground still short of the Confederate positions.

Grant's headquarters papers do not show him ordering Meade to call off the attacks until 12:30, eight hours after they began. There had been enormous losses in the first hour of fighting; Wilkeson may well have overestimated when he said that "ten thousand of our men lay dead and wounded" after twenty minutes, but other estimates ran as high as 7,000 casualties in that hour. In regard to Alexander's undocumented claim that Grant gave permission to Meade to call off the attacks as early as 7 A.M., it seems possible that by then, two and a half hours after those cheering 60,000 men started forward, the immensely aggressive but intuitive Grant sensed that a terrible repulse was taking place all along his front and gave Meade that authority, which Meade declined to use.

As for what went on that morning in the minds of the Union rank and file, Confederate general Alexander said this of the Army of the Potomac's morale: "There can be no doubt that the temper, as it were, of Grant's army had been impaired by the fighting & losses of the last 30 days." Private Wilkeson saw this, as the battle went on, among some troops who had been thrown back, had regrouped near his artillery position, and now received the order to attack again.

> *. . . I heard the charging commands given. With many an oath at the military stupidity that would again send good troops to useless slaughter, I sprang to my feet and watched the doomed infantry. Men, who I knew well, stood rifle in hand not more than thirty feet from me, and I am happy to state that they continued to so stand. Not a man moved . . . I heard the order given, and I saw it disobeyed.*

Eight miles away in Richmond, Jefferson Davis's postmaster general, John Reagan, a Texan who was one of Davis's most trusted advisers, heard the roar of battle and set out for Lee's headquarters, accompanied by two judges. Joining Lee, Reagan found that at the front the constant exchange of gunfire from thousands of weapons of all sizes sounded like the continuous tearing of a sheet. Speaking of Grant, he asked Lee, "If he breaks your line, what reserve have you?"

"Not a regiment," Lee answered; then, in the midst of the immense slaughter his troops were inflicting on Grant's men, he explained to Reagan that his men were starting to get scurvy because of a lack of vegetables in their diet. Knowing that to speak with Reagan was like talking to Davis himself, Lee asked him to have supplies of onions and potatoes sent swiftly to his troops.

Reagan assured Lee that he would do that as soon as he rode back into the city, and added that in the Confederate capital people worried that Lee constantly commanded from so far forward that he might be killed or wounded. Lee acknowledged the risks. "I have as good generals as any commander ever had," he told Reagan, but he often needed to see the terrain himself: "It is well for me to know the position of our lines." He illustrated the point by speaking of losing "a good many men" the day before in retaking a position on a line that had been badly placed because he had not been there to see it done correctly.

While Lee spoke calmly with a member of the Confederate cabinet, his men continued to pin down the advancing Union soldiers. In one area of five acres of ground in front of Lee's trenches, the blue-jacketed Union dead lay so thick that it would have been possible to walk across their corpses for a hundred yards without having one's feet touch the blood-soaked grass.

Grant understood the magnitude of his failure. That evening, he told his shaken staff: "I regret this assault more than any I have ever ordered. I regarded it as a stern necessity and believed it would bring compensating results; but no advantages have been gained sufficient to justify the heavy losses suffered." Confederate Major General Evander McIvor Law put it plainly: "It was not war, it was murder."

With Grant's losses at Cold Harbor, the Army of the Potomac had lost more than 40,000 men in thirty days. Throughout, Lee had been fighting with something like 50 to 60 percent of the men available to Grant. His losses at Cold Harbor had only been a fifth of those suffered by Grant, but in the overall campaign, Lee's losses were comparable to Grant's in percentage terms.

For the North, however, it was not a matter of percentages. It was the Union casualty lists, bearing the names of sons and brothers and fathers, that meant heartbreak for families from Maine to Iowa. What remained to be seen was the effect on the Republicans' national convention in Baltimore, scheduled to begin on June 7, four days after the fighting ended at Cold Harbor.

IT HAS NEVER been clear how much the delegates heading to Baltimore knew about the magnitude of Grant's losses at Cold Harbor. At two in the afternoon on that bloody day, an hour and a half after he called off his failed attacks, Grant wired Halleck that "our loss was not severe nor do I suppose the Enemy to have lost heavily." It is possible that it seemed so then to Grant, but by nightfall when he spoke to his staff, he knew he had suffered an enormous repulse. Although in the days after the battle Grant and Lee communicated with each other concerning methods for bringing in the wounded and dead lying between their lines, there is no record of Grant sending to Halleck in Washington any indication of the size of his losses during that time. What the Confederates may have known about this is uncertain, but the *Richmond Dispatch* told its readers, "[Grant] had the hardihood to telegraph the Yankee Secretary of War of continued successes, with the object of securing the nomination of Lincoln at the Baltimore Convention." A similar story appeared on the same day in the *Augusta* (Georgia) *Constitutionalist*.

Whatever the Northern public knew or sensed right after Cold Harbor, Grant's popularity began to decline. According to Mary Lincoln's seamstress and maid, Elizabeth Keckley, the First Lady had already begun referring to Grant as a "butcher." When Lincoln remonstrated with her, Mary replied, "He loses two men to the enemy's one. . . . According to his tactics, there is nothing under the heavens to do but to march a new line of men up in front of the rebel breastworks to be shot down as fast as they take their position. . . . Grant, I repeat, is an obstinate fool and a butcher."

Despite Lincoln's earlier admonition to Grant—"I am very anxious that any disaster, or the capture of our men in great numbers, should be avoided"—he continued to support him.

TRIMMING THE POLITICAL TREE

Some thought of Lincoln as being essentially passive, but when it came to the political convention in Baltimore, he left little to chance. He understood that Union military reverses would work against his reelection in November, but his first order of business was to become the Republican/National Union Party nominee. Despite a last-minute statement he made, declaring himself as standing aside from the decisions about to be reached in Baltimore, work had been going on for months to lay the groundwork for the results he wanted.

Although Grant's losses had affected the general's popularity, the Republican politicians remained committed to Lincoln. Starting with his first official endorsement from the New York State Republican Committee on January 23, an array of powerful figures began working for him, and some had made their moves even earlier.

Among those helping Lincoln was his first secretary of war, Simon Cameron once discredited but now rehabilitating himself through his political usefulness, including his role earlier in the spring in sounding out Benjamin F. Butler concerning the vice presidency. Cameron had organized for the Baltimore convention a delegation that ranked as a political work of art. Pennsylvania was entitled to cast 52 votes; the delegation, committed to vote unanimously for Lincoln, was filled with federal employees whose jobs came to them as patronage appointments made by Lincoln himself.

At a time when there were many party-affiliated newspapers whose publishers and editors often became de facto political bosses, Lincoln had two exceptionally influential allies in the key state of New York, which had 66 votes. The first was Thurlow Weed, an influential editor and powerbroker in Albany, the state capital; Weed had at times been critical of Lincoln, recently expressing doubts about his ability, but now he threw himself into engineering the New York delegation's unanimous preconvention endorsement of the president. In New York City, Lincoln had the invaluable support of Henry J. Raymond, the founder and editor of the *New York Times*, the one paper in the city that backed almost every move made by the Republican administration. Raymond would be in Baltimore as chairman of the platform committee.

Lincoln had a less-known but effective operative in Leonard Swett, one more of his cronies from his years of practicing law in Illinois. At the Republican convention of 1860, Swett did some clever footwork to help secure the nomination for Lincoln. Swett began loyally working for Lincoln again in 1864, but he offered some hard-eyed appraisals of "Honest Abe." He saw Lincoln, in political matters, as always keeping his cards close to his chest, with a few extra up his sleeve: "[He] always told only enough of his plans and purposes to induce the belief that he had communicated all, yet he reserved enough to have communicated nothing." Using the word "trimmer" in its meaning of a person who will let each of two people think he is the one he favors, Swett said that Lincoln "was a trimmer, and such a trimmer as the world has never seen." He did, however, observe that while Lincoln manipulated men, he "never trimmed his principles," first among them being his policy of doing whatever he thought it would take to preserve the Union.

Lesser politicians had also been hard at work. On April 29, shortly before Grant's offensive in the Wilderness, John Van Valkenburg of the Republican National Committee wrote Lincoln from Fort Madison, Iowa, concerning the Baltimore convention, then nearly six weeks away. He informed the president that the Iowa delegation "will be unanimous— for your Excellency's re-nomination." Sempronius H. Boyd, a congressman from the politically yeasty border state of Missouri, reported that the caucuses conducted in his district had "without an exception" instructed their delegates to vote for Lincoln. On the same day, Cuthbert Bullitt, a leader in the effort to create a new pro-Union government in Louisiana, wrote Lincoln that his state's delegates "are to a man in your favor" and asked that he and the Louisiana delegation have the opportunity to meet with him in the White House on their way to Baltimore. As similar expressions of preconvention support continued to arrive from the Republican organizations throughout the Union, Lincoln's colleagues had no doubt that he would become the nominee.

The vice presidency was a different matter. The man who had been Lincoln's vice president during his first term, Hannibal Hamlin of Maine, was a former Democrat who became a Republican at the time the party was founded. He went on to become governor of Maine, and then one of its United States senators. During the 1860 presidential campaign, Hamlin's candidacy for the office of vice president put before the voters a ticket that combined this former Democrat from the East with Republican Lincoln's support from the West and successfully brought Lincoln to the White House. Once elected, Hamlin was a typically powerless vice president, although he moved to a stronger antislavery position than Lincoln held at the beginning of their term; when Lincoln issued his Emancipation Proclamation, Hamlin hailed it as "the great act of the age."

There would always be controversy concerning Lincoln's position as to the desirability of Hamlin continuing in a second term as his vice president. It seemed a perfect example of Lincoln as "trimmer"; of the two private secretaries who worked most closely with him, John Nicolay thought the president was entirely open to the prospect of having Hamlin as his running mate, while John Hay felt certain that Lincoln did not favor him. (It was never clear that either Nicolay or Hay, who spent hours in the "shop" with Lincoln every day, knew that he had sent Cameron to explore Benjamin Butler's interest in the vice presidency.)

Among those convinced that Hamlin was on the way out without knowing it was Ward Hill Lamon, whom Lincoln described as being "my particular friend." A big, burly man, he was yet another Lincoln loyalist from Illinois, a lawyer who rode the judicial circuit with him in the 1850s. A man not averse to rough-and-tumble politics, Lamon engaged in a special kind of forgery at the 1860 Republican convention in Chicago that eventually nominated Lincoln. Seeing after the first day that men who supported Seward's candidacy were filling the hall and creating an impression of greater support than Lincoln had, he had additional tickets printed and distributed to Lincoln backers who were told to come early on the second day and pack the place.

Lamon came east to Washington on the same train with Lincoln after he was elected, and Lincoln appointed him as marshal of the District of

Columbia. He ran the District prison and had among other ceremonial duties served as marshal-in-chief at the dedication of the military cemetery at Gettysburg, introducing the president before he gave his famous address. Lamon acted as Lincoln's unofficial bodyguard, occasionally carrying combinations of two revolvers, a knife, brass knuckles, and a slingshot. He was to say unequivocally that while Lincoln had no personal animus toward Hamlin, he did not want him as his running mate in 1864 and preferred Andrew Johnson.

Johnson represented a different kind of balance on the ticket for the second term. A Democrat from Tennessee, he had served in Congress and been twice elected governor of Tennessee; as the war began, he was a United States senator. The only senator from the states that seceded who remained loyal to the Union, Johnson retained his seat and became one of Lincoln's strong supporters. When Grant's initial victories in the West at Fort Henry and Fort Donelson in February of 1862 drove the Confederate forces out of the western side of Tennessee, Lincoln appointed Johnson military governor of the state, holding the rank of brigadier general of Volunteers.

One could not find a stronger War Democrat than Andrew Johnson. The story of Johnson's early life may not have influenced Lincoln, but he, too, struggled up from poverty. His father died when he was four, and his mother raised him in difficult circumstances. Without a single year of formal education, he was apprenticed to a tailor and moved from that occupation to politics, being elected to the Tennessee legislature at the age of twenty-seven and becoming a congressman when he was thirty-five. A Lincoln-Johnson ticket would pair two eminently self-made men. (Ward Lamon later claimed that Lincoln sent him to the Baltimore convention carrying a letter that set forth Lincoln's preference for Johnson but gave him instructions to use it only as a last resort.)

While Lincoln's secretary Nicolay always remained convinced that Lincoln was truly neutral on the subject of Hamlin, there were a number of individuals who testified to the contrary. Andrew Johnson's own private secretary, Benjamin C. Truman, later wrote: "I saw and handled all his correspondence during that time, and I know it to be a fact that Mr. Lincoln desired the nomination of Johnson for vice-president." Senator Jim Lane of Kansas, a tobacco-chewing roué who in the uncertain first days of the war organized a group of armed Kansans who camped out in the East Room as they guarded the White House, had the same view.

Earlier in this spring of 1864, he had interrupted a conversation among several men of his state as they were agreeing that Lincoln would want Hamlin to continue as vice president. "No," Lane told them firmly. "Andrew Johnson. Mister Lincoln does not want to interfere; but he feels that we must recognize the South in kindness. The nominee will be Andy Johnson."

Yet another voice, and one that had interesting things to say, was that of Alexander Kelly McClure, a powerful Republican politician from Pennsylvania and a man who had worked hard at the 1860 convention to bring the Pennsylvania delegation to support Lincoln instead of Seward. According to McClure, who had again been chosen as a delegate, when he met with Lincoln, the president set forth a reason for supporting Johnson that no other individual recorded. In addition to Johnson's being a candidate who represented both a concession to the South and a way of creating something of a political offensive into the South to parallel the military advances, Lincoln said that to nominate a true Southerner who was nonetheless a supporter of the Union would diminish the chances of England and France recognizing the Confederacy. As he explained it to McClure, this presidential ticket of a Northerner and a Southerner would persuade these foreign powers, who had to be kept neutral, that the fractured United States could be put back together again and that they could not profit from recognizing two separate American nations.

McClure did not use Swett's term "trimmer," but he said this of Lincoln's handling of those whom he wanted to act on his behalf at the convention:

> *He moved with masterly sagacity at every step in his efforts to nominate Johnson . . . in this as in all Lincoln's movements his confidence was limited with each of his trusted supporters. . . . Neither Swett nor Lamon had any knowledge of Lincoln's positive movement for the nomination of Johnson until within a day or two of the meeting of the convention. . . .*
>
> *How shrewdly Lincoln moved, and with what extreme caution he guarded his confidence, is illustrated by the fact that while he consulted Cameron confidentially about the nomination of Johnson some months before the convention, and consulted with me on the same subject the day before the convention met, neither of us supposed that the other was acting [specifically on Lincoln's behalf]. . . . Had he been willing to tell me the whole truth, he would have informed me that Cameron was also en-*

*listed in the Johnson movement, and that he specially desired [us] . . . to
be active supporters of Johnson's nomination.*

Apart from the maneuvers concerning the choice of vice president,
Lincoln worked to ensure that the Republican Party would present to its
delegates at Baltimore a powerful, unequivocal pledge to adopt an amendment to the Constitution that abolished slavery. Lincoln continued to
think that his Emancipation Proclamation had legal standing only
through what he believed his wartime emergency powers to be, and that a
future peacetime congress could nullify his effort to end slavery. A constitutional amendment was the only sure way to make slavery a thing of the
past.

That was proving to be hard to accomplish. The Constitution had last
been amended in 1804, when the Twelfth Amendment was enacted to
prevent a repetition of the situation that occurred when Thomas Jefferson and Aaron Burr received an equal number of electoral votes in the
election of 1800. Over the next half century, the Supreme Court increasingly became the interpreter of the Constitution, and there had been an
obvious legislative reluctance to solve national problems by further revision of that document. An effort begun in late 1863 by congressional Republicans to enact a thirteenth amendment, permanently outlawing
slavery, had passed the Senate in April of this year of 1864 by a vote of 38
to 6 but was headed for defeat at the hands of the Democrats in the
House.

To make whatever could be made out of this in the coming presidential campaign—the difference between a clear antislavery Republican
position and a Democratic platform that might say nothing on the
issue—Lincoln turned to the Republican national chairman, Senator
Edwin D. Morgan of New York, who had previously been that state's
governor. (As a measure of the youth of the Republican Party, Morgan
had been its only national chairman since it was organized eight years
before.) Morgan intended to have a last-minute conference with Lincoln
before heading for Baltimore, where he would be the man calling the
convention to order. Lincoln already knew that his ally Henry J. Raymond would deliver the antislavery plank he wanted in the platform.
Now, in this eleventh-hour meeting, Lincoln intended to prime Morgan
to set the stage for that by having him say to the delegates, within a minute of bringing down the gavel to start the first session, that he felt certain

that the convention would call for an amendment to the Constitution that would turn that antislavery plank into law.

ON THE EVE of the convention, all these letters and conversations began turning into action. Writing to his brother Charles Edward Hay from the White House on June 5, John Hay used the word "patriots" sarcastically as he spoke of the delegates passing through to Baltimore who hoped that Lincoln would reward them for their support. Hay and Nicolay had taken to referring to Lincoln privately as "the Tycoon," a title synonymous with Shogun, the autocratic military ruler of Japan, and Hay used it now.

> *For a day or two the house has been full of patriots on the way to Baltimore who wish to pay their respects & engrave on the expectant mind of the Tycoon, their images, in view of future contingencies. . . . Among the genuine delegations have come some of the bogus & the irregular ones . . . the South Carolina delegation came in yesterday. The Prest. says, "Let them in." "They are a swindle," I said. "They won't swindle me," quoth the Tycoon. They filed in; a few sutlers, cotton-dealers and negroes, presented a petition & retired.*
>
> *Florida sends two delegations; neither will get in. Each attacks the others as unprincipled tricksters.*

Hay added that Lamon, scheduled to go to Baltimore the next day, "Says he thinks Lincoln rather prefers Johnson or some other War Democrat as calculated to give more strength to the ticket."

All this was happening on June 5, two days after Grant's disastrous attack at Cold Harbor. At Baltimore, it was all about politics. John Nicolay, sent by Lincoln on this same day to observe the convention and to report as events developed, went there with Simon Cameron, evidently unaware of Cameron's mission to work for Andrew Johnson's nomination for vice president. Nicolay checked into the Eutaw House, where many delegates, including the entire New York delegation, were staying, and began talking to the influential men he found walking the hallways and gathering in caucus rooms. Within hours, Nicolay wrote Hay an initial report, addressing his friend and White House roommate as "My dear Major," because Hay had recently been made an assistant adjutant general to facilitate his reporting of political conditions in recently captured areas.

He told Hay, "One of the first men I met was B. C. Cook, who stands at the head of our Illinois delegation, and had quite a long and confidential talk with him. . . . He says the delegation will in good faith do everything they can for Lincoln that is in arranging the Vice-P., the Committees, platform &c. taking his own nomination of course as beyond question."

Nicolay added, "I told Cook that I thought Lincoln would not wish even to indicate a preference for V.P. as the rival candidates were all friendly to him." He continued, commenting on the fact that there were two delegations claiming to represent Missouri: "There will be some little trouble in arranging the matter of the contestants [contested] seats from Missouri. The Radicals seem to have the technical right to be admitted. Cook says that they intimated to him that they would even promise to vote for Lincoln in the convention, for the promise of an admission to seats." Referring to the Washington correspondent for the *Cincinnati Gazette* who was an ally of Salmon P. Chase, Nicolay added, "Whitelaw Reid is here and told me this evening that the Radicals conceded Lincoln's re-nomination, but their present game would be to make a very radical platform."

Showing his ignorance of what had gone on behind the scenes, Nicolay inquired whether, on the subject of the vice presidency, "the President has any preference . . . or whether he wishes not even to interfere by a confidential indication." He closed by urging Hay to get that information back to him "by express so that it will reach me by the earliest practicable hour on tomorrow (Monday)."

Nicolay's letter reached the White House the next morning, the day before the convention was to begin. It was now that Lincoln took the position of being above the fray. In effect telling Hay how to answer Nicolay, Lincoln wrote on Nicolay's letter, "Wish not to interfere about V.P." He added, concerning the platform, which was already set to include the strong antislavery statement he wanted, "Can not interfere about platform." He followed this with the brief summation, "Convention must judge for itself." Hay fleshed this out, to be sent back swiftly to Baltimore. Disposing of the lesser questions of whether Leonard Swett, or Joseph Holt of Kentucky, had any appeal for Lincoln as vice-presidential possibilities, Hay wrote Nicolay:

The President wishes not to interfere in the nomination even by a confidential suggestion. He also declines suggesting anything in regard to

*platform or the organization of the Convention. The Convention must be
guided in these matters by their own views of justice and propriety.*

IN THE MIDST of all these political maneuvers, Lincoln continued with his
many other duties. Just before the clash at Cold Harbor, Secretary of the
Navy Welles wrote in his diary, referring to applicants for Annapolis:
"Called on the President relative to the appointment of midshipmen.
After looking over the list with some care, he finally designated two sons
of officers [and] one apprentice, and desired me to complete the nominations." This matter of appointing the sons of regular naval officers was in
itself a form of patronage in the sense of rewarding service, but as Welles
was in the White House on his errand, he came across something more
intensely political. "When I called on the President, Major-General
[Robert C.] Schenck was with him, and as I went in, was giving the President a list of names of persons to be selected to fill the board about to be
appointed on the question of retired officers, his brother, Commodore
[James F.] Schenck being one." Schenck, a man from Ohio who served
four terms in Congress before the war, had campaigned strenuously for
Abraham Lincoln and was yet one more military political appointee
named by Lincoln to be a brigadier general of Volunteers in the spring of
1861. Wounded at Second Manassas and transferred to the Middle Department and the Eighth Corps at Baltimore as a major general in 1862,
he had resigned from the Army at the end of 1863 and was once again in
Congress, holding the key chairmanship of the Committee on Military
Affairs. Speaking of Schenck putting forward his brother to be a member
of an important board, Welles commented, "It was a cool [brazen] proposition, but characteristic of General Schenck, and I think of the Schencks
generally."

The day after Welles recorded this, Lincoln received an urgent message. It served as a reminder that even if his seemingly certain nomination came through, many hurdles lay between that victory and his winning
a second term. Problems away from the battlefields might cause convulsions that could lose the war for the Union. The chilling telegram came
from General William Rosecrans, who, after his disastrous defeat at
Chickamauga in Tennessee during September of 1863, had been given
command of the less active Department of Missouri, headquartered at St.

Louis. In his telegram, Rosecrans spoke guardedly of being unable for reasons of security to transmit the details of "information of high national importance, of a plot to overthrow the government, which you should know." Because of a previous incident in which Rosecrans had sent a courier to Washington who was put under military arrest for traveling with the wrong kind of orders, he asked special permission to send a courier to Washington now, carrying a description of what he had learned.

The story behind the telegram from Rosecrans added an electrifying dimension to rumors that a "Northwest Conspiracy" was afoot in the states of the Old Northwest, as well as in the border state of Missouri. There had been stories of a secret organization of Northerners, some of them Southern sympathizers and others who simply felt that Lincoln was a tyrant whose rule must be ended. Known for a time as the Order of American Knights, formerly the Knights of the Golden Circle, they had now become a shadowy action group called the Order of the Sons of Liberty. Part of what Rosecrans wanted to report was that he and other Federal authorities in Missouri had, according to Lincoln's secretary Hay, "carefully investigated the matter by means of secret service men who had taken the oaths" and penetrated the groups. The conspiracy's strategy, in which many Southerners placed their hopes, was that an armed insurrection would succeed in taking Ohio, Indiana, Illinois, and Missouri out of the Union in a second secession. These newly aligned state governments would then create a "Northwestern Confederacy" that would expand to embrace Michigan, Wisconsin, Minnesota, Iowa, and Kansas. The goal: these nine states would withdraw from the war, separate themselves from the Northeast, and form a new nation. This Northwestern American nation might then enter a full partnership with the South in what would be a confederation of agrarian states.

Some of what Lincoln already knew of this involved Clement Vallandigham, the Democratic congressman now exiled in Canada as a result of exhorting a crowd to hurl "King Lincoln" from his throne. Looking further into this, Hay discovered that "a convocation of the Order [Sons of Liberty] was held at Windsor, Canada, in the month of April under his personal supervision; to this came delegates from every part of the country. It is not definitely known what was done there. . . ." As could happen with intelligence matters, different sources knew different parts of the puzzle; it was soon learned that at this meeting Vallandigham accepted the title of "Supreme Grand Commander" of the Sons of Liberty. Thus linked to a secret organization that might foment an uprising, he was planning to return to Ohio.

It was assumed that the more moderate McClellan would emerge as the Democratic Party's presidential candidate at its Chicago convention, then scheduled for the Fourth of July, but many of Vallandigham's views resonated with even rank-and-file Democrats. As far back as March 23 of this election year, when Ohio Democrats gathered in Columbus to adopt resolutions and to name at-large delegates to the convention, they adopted a plank that termed Lincoln's administration "an abject failure." That could be viewed as standard campaign rhetoric, but another resolution demanded "the immediate inauguration of peaceful means" to end the war—a euphemism for negotiations that could result in the Confederacy becoming a separate slave-owning nation. There seemed little doubt that Vallandigham would be named as a delegate to the Democratic convention in Chicago; if he succeeded in getting there, he would be one of the prominent speakers.

Nevertheless, Lincoln had decided that Vallandigham should not be stopped from reentering the United States; once across the border, he was to be watched as carefully as he was being watched while in Canada. Every morning, Vallandigham could look out the windows of his hotel suite in Windsor, on the Canadian side of the narrow Detroit River, and see the USS *Michigan*, a United States Navy gunboat, anchored so near that a man with a spyglass could observe his every move. (One reporter said that the warship had its guns trained on the hotel.) Lincoln did not send it, but drafted a letter to Governor John Brough of Ohio and General Samuel Heintzelman of the Northern Department that revealed the kind of surveillance he wanted. He told them to "watch Vallandigham and others closely, and upon discovering any palpable injury or imminent danger to the military proceeding from him, them, or any of them, arrest all implicated; otherwise do not arrest without further order. Meanwhile report the signs to me from time to time." It was one more of Lincoln's calculations; unless Vallandigham was unmistakably shown to be inciting a revolt, he was not to be treated in any way that would give the Democrats a political martyr.

Lincoln's words also conjured up the murky side of the potential crisis. It would be one thing to have any number of antiwar and anti-Lincoln speeches being given around the country, but the threat of rioting and what that might lead to was another matter. Everyone remembered the bloody Draft Riots in New York City the summer before, and now in 1864, Grant's losses might similarly inflame a population that was increasingly turning against the war. All this was particularly worrisome at a time when Grant's and Sherman's armies were fully engaged on their own fronts and unable to spare any of their regiments to be sent to the Northwest to guard against local violence or an attempted widespread uprising.

And here was Rosecrans, in his telegram to Lincoln, warning of naked treason, a specific "plot to overthrow the government." The facts were these: Colonel Benjamin Sweet of Wisconsin, badly wounded in the battle at Perryville, Kentucky, had taken command of the Military Post of Chicago, which had its headquarters at Camp Douglas, three miles south of the center of the city and 200 yards west of Lake Michigan. This installation started as a Union Army training center and later became a prison camp, which now held 10,000 Confederate soldiers. Sweet had recently learned of a frightening plan and transmitted the intelligence to Rosecrans: on the Fourth of July—the day the Democratic convention was then scheduled to begin in Chicago—there was to be an outbreak within the prison. This would be coordinated with an outside incursion of conspirators who would free the prisoners and arm them to burn Chicago and take over the city.

Sweet knew only the sketch of the plan, which was still being developed by the Sons of Liberty. As it evolved, the attack on the camp to free the prisoners was to be made by 100 well-armed Confederate agents coming down from Canada. To support this, an attempt would be made to capture the USS *Michigan*, bring her to a point a few hundred yards out in the lake, and have her guns fire on the Union Army guards at Camp Douglas. The commander of the many Sons of Liberty who lived in Chicago was mobilizing 2,000 men, who would be reinforced by members of the secret order coming up from southern Illinois. (The conspirators hoped that the large crowds in town for the convention would make the initial influx of rioters and arsonists less noticeable.) A simultaneous attack was to be made on the large Confederate prisoner-of-war camp at Rock Island, Illinois, by a second group of Confederates coming in from Canada. All of this was to be coordinated with efforts by militant Copperhead groups to seize the offices and armories of the state governments of Illinois, Indiana, and Ohio.

The chance that militant Copperheads might succeed in this bold strike at Camp Douglas was greater than might have been thought. The 10,000 Confederate prisoners were in a rebellious condition, having spent a winter in unheated barracks that were in such bad condition that the wind cut through open spaces between their planks; as one report put it, the men were "restive and inventive in an uncommon degree." Among these prisoners were a good number of troopers who had served under Kentucky's famous John Hunt Morgan, cavalrymen who in a combination of conventional and guerrilla warfare made daring and usually successful raids. In addition to bold strikes against Union forces in Tennessee and Kentucky, they had ventured into Indiana and Ohio. Many of Morgan's men had succeeded in escaping from Camp Douglas, and those who remained as prisoners were certainly willing to try an armed insurrection if given the weapons.

Once alerted, Colonel Sweet had been able to strengthen his contingent of guards and forestall this particular attempt, but to Lincoln and Stanton it served as a warning that the fight for the Union could now involve significant bloodshed within states far from Grant's battle lines in northern Virginia or Sherman's struggle to reach Atlanta. Thus, with Grant's Army of the Potomac deeply wounded and discouraged after Cold Harbor, and a threat of rebellion in the Northwest that was hard to assess and had to be prepared for, the delegates to the Baltimore convention assembled.

II

The convention was scheduled to begin on Tuesday, June 7, with the resolutions composing the party platform and the nominations for president to be made the following day. The afternoon before the convention began, Lincoln's secretary William Stoddard decided to take a train and travel to Baltimore, not in an official capacity, but to see this making of history for himself. Once there, he strolled around to the various hotels, listening, as he put it, "to what these throngs of our over-excited fellow-citizens are saying." Stoddard was recognized and greeted by one political operative after another. By evening, he found himself at a meeting of the Grand Council of the Union League.

Starting with a group founded in Illinois thirteen months into the war, these Union League organizations, devoted to solidifying Northern support for the war and opposing Copperhead antiwar sentiment and activities, had grown greatly in number and political power. Many of their members sympathized with the Radical wing of the Republican Party; as Stoddard remarked of what he was seeing that evening, this meeting was "where all the anti-Lincoln steam is to be let off," and it attracted all the "hot-headed and free-tongued representatives of every faction of the Republican party inimical to Mr. Lincoln." These citizens ardently desired the South's defeat, but wanted it to be achieved by men other than Lincoln and his cabinet, and to be followed by a far harsher peace than what they believed Lincoln intended to impose. Stoddard saw them as political opponents, but his view of all the delegates differed from that of his colleague Hay, who had sarcastically referred to many of the Republicans heading for Baltimore as "patriots" who were simply hunting for patronage positions and payoffs. Writing of this historic evening in the present tense, Stoddard said, "let us . . . look out over the long rows of keenly intelligent faces. No other nation can call together more intellect and capacity in such a gathering . . . these men are worthy of their trust."

As the meeting continued, Stoddard became increasingly worried about the attacks on Lincoln being made on the eve of what was assumed to be his certain nomination. Without identifying the man, he described one Republican senator's speech:

> [An] eloquent, powerful arraignment of Abraham Lincoln's administration . . . his story of malfeasance, of tyranny, of corruption, of illegal acts, of abused power, of misused advantages, of favoritism, fraud, timidity, sluggish inertness, local wrong and repression . . . Mark the keenness of the personal thrusts, and the subtlety with which he keeps in the foreground the President's alleged frivolity and unfeeling jocoseness, in close companionship with a suggestion of selfish ambition instead of devotion and duty.

Stoddard remarked next on "this Congressman who follows him in the same path, repeating, adding to and enforcing the counts of a long and shameful indictment. Another and another, all on the same side! Has Lincoln no friends left?"

Lincoln did. Tobacco-chewing Senator Jim Lane of Kansas rose. Unkempt, ill-mannered, a rangy man nearly as tall as Lincoln and one who had sometimes opposed the president, this womanizer seemed an unlikely man to seize the moral high ground for Abraham Lincoln. Thirty-six days before this, he had been involved in a sensational episode on a street in downtown Washington, which one reporter wrote up this way:

A UNITED STATES SENATOR WHIPPED

Considerable excitement was occasioned yesterday afternoon by an encounter in front of the Washington House between a well-known senator and a woman of the town. There appears to have been some former quarrel between the parties, as the woman gave a note to the senator who tore it up insultingly, whereupon the woman knocked off his hat, then grabbed it, and with it beat for several minutes the head and ears of James H. Lane, United States Senator for Kansas.

There were other aspects to Jim Lane, who earlier in the day had conferred with Lincoln in Washington before coming to Baltimore. Here stood an undoubted patriot, a veteran of the Mexican War, a major general of militia in the prewar struggle in "Bloody Kansas" during which he fought to keep it from becoming a slave state. Some called this controversial and contentious legislator "the Liberator of Kansas." He glared at these members of the Union League as he began by addressing them as "Gentlemen of the Grand Council." With a voice that Stoddard said "would go through a wall," Lane started in on these Radicals who considered themselves to be the keepers of the Union's political flame; looking them in the eye, he poured invective on them "with so brutal a harshness that a hundred faces blaze with wrath." Nonetheless, within minutes the atmosphere in the hall began to change. Stoddard said, "He is doing it, sentence after sentence, as he pulls to pieces the indictment, and paints in many-colored fire the truth of Lincoln's work and that of his assailants." Stoddard studied this audience of politicians.

Men lean forward and listen, while they more or less rapidly are swept into the tide of conviction and are made to believe, with him, that any other nomination than that of Lincoln to-morrow is equivalent to the nomination of McClellan by the Republican Convention and his election by the Republican party; that it would sunder the Union, make permanent the Confederacy, reshackle the slaves, dishonor the dead, and disgrace the living.

This Kansan with a well-deserved reputation for loose living and bad behavior in the nation's capital had done what he came to do: tear the fangs out of those present who still opposed Lincoln. Almost as soon as Lane finished his counterattack, Lincoln received a last-minute endorsement from the Union League. Stoddard said of the moment, "There is no need for another speech on our side of the question, and in the tempest which follows Jim Lane's closing shout, the resolution is adopted, with a mere handful of dissenting voices."

BY LATE THE next morning, some six hundred delegates and many additional spectators stood impatiently in the ferocious heat outside the Front Street Theatre, waiting for its doors to open. The Republican organizers of "The National Union Convention" had wanted to hold all their meetings in Baltimore's far more suitable convention hall but found it unavailable because of a singularly spiteful act. Maryland congressman Henry Winter Davis, an ardent Radical implacably opposed to Lincoln's reelection, had earlier rented that better place for these days, so it stood empty and unused.

At eleven, the doors swung open and the crowd poured in. The official delegates came through the side doors to find places on the main floor, and alternate delegates seated themselves in the theater's first balcony. Ladies settled down in the second balcony, the Dress Circle, which was reserved for them. Other spectators jammed into an even higher balcony, or stood wherever they could; a reporter from the *New York Times* said the building was "densely packed, from the lower floor to the ceiling." Flags and red-white-and-blue bunting hung from the balconies, and "a canopy of flags" decorated the stage. A running newspaper account noted, "There is a considerable number of telegraph messengers in attendance, whose duty it is to convey dispatches direct from the reporters' tables to the telegraphic instruments in the lobbies." At noon the army band stationed at Baltimore's Fort McHenry began to play patriotic tunes; considered to be the best band in the army, they had played at the Gettysburg ceremonies during which Lincoln made his address.

Shortly after noon, Senator Edwin D. Morgan of New York called the convention's opening session to order. This first gathering, scheduled to last only until three, was to set the stage, in terms of purpose and agenda. Speaker after speaker stressed that this was not an assemblage of Republicans; everyone was coming together, as Ohio's former governor William Dennison told the crowd, not as "representatives of either of the old political parties"—Republicans or Democrats—but as a party committed to "an unreserved, unconditional loyalty to the Government and the Union." There was room inside this new tent for any who wished to enter—Radicals, War Democrats—but it had to be understood that, as Morgan said to the delegates, certain principles must be agreed upon. Of these, "the first and most distinct is that we do not intend this nation to be destroyed." Applause greeted this; there could be no compromise with the Confederacy, in the manner contemplated by many Democrats. The formal resolutions, the planks of the party platform, would be voted on tomorrow, but Morgan gave the crowd a taste of what they had come to hear: there would be a declaration "for such an amendment to the Constitution as will positively prohibit African slavery in the United States."

This brought the crowd to its feet. Men shouted and women waved their handkerchiefs as they cried out their enthusiastic approval. Lincoln was forty miles away, but the exact words Morgan used might well have been recently said to him by Lincoln when Morgan met with him in the White House on his way to Baltimore. Not only were Lincoln's ideas, whether orders or suggestions, being followed, but he was keeping in touch with events at the convention through direct reports from Baltimore: at about the time Morgan was speaking, the convention's chairman pro tem, Frederick C. Meyer, sent Lincoln a telegram saying, "The Convention has just been called to order everything progressing."

During these first three hours, the crowd heard from a man whose family embodied the brother-against-brother discord that led to this war in which so many people were dying even as the delegates sat in this theater. Reverend Robert Jefferson Breckinridge of Kentucky, a nationally prominent member of the Presbyterian General Assembly, was an ardent supporter of Lincoln and the Union. His nephew was Confederate general John C. Breckinridge, the former vice president of the United States under Buchanan, who in the prewar election of 1860 had been the Democratic presidential candidate defeated by Lincoln. It was General John Breckinridge who had committed the Virginia Military Institute cadets to battle at New Market just three weeks before. Reverend Breckinridge's two sons had also thrown themselves into the Southern cause: his son William P. C. Breckinridge was a colonel in the Confederate Army, and his son Robert Jr. was also a colonel, and a member of the Confederate

Congress. In the pivotal period when Southern states were seceding but Fort Sumter had not yet been fired upon, Reverend Breckinridge had thrown all his influence behind Lincoln's efforts to keep the Border States from seceding. (Lincoln said in that crucial hour, "I think to lose Kentucky is nearly the same as to lose the whole game.") He made a vital contribution to keeping Kentucky in the Union, and Lincoln continued to consult with him frequently, but Breckinridge had failed to deter his sons from serving the Confederacy. Writing his son William on November 18, 1860, twelve days after Lincoln was elected, he asked him to "Show this letter to Robert," and said, "Let me earnestly beseech you both not to take a single step . . . into the direction of disunion. The whole thing is utter madness."

And here was this tall, thin, sixty-four-year-old man, the only nationally known member of the distinguished Virginia and Kentucky clan of Breckinridges who did not throw in his lot with the South. This learned and famous preacher's voice had become weak and reedy, but the delegates heard him well enough as he echoed Governor Dennison's appeal for "unreserved, unconditional loyalty" to the Union. Every faction represented in the hall must come together: "As a Union Party, I will follow you to the ends of the earth, and to the gates of death! But as an Abolition party—as a Republican party—as a Whig party—as a Democratic party . . . I will not follow you one foot." The crowd was ready for this call for unity: a reporter said, "The venerable speaker was cheered to the echo . . . drowned in a whirlwind of most boisterous applause."

Even with the convention under way, Burton C. Cook, chairman of the delegation from Lincoln's state of Illinois, rushed over to Washington to try to clarify who Lincoln really wanted for vice president. When they met, Lincoln evidently disclosed nothing to Cook of what he had said to others who were already at the convention; after talking with him, Cook returned to Baltimore, and later recalled, "I was satisfied that he would be content with the nomination of Hamlin; in fact, I feel that he really desired it."

At three in the stifling hot afternoon the convention adjourned; it would reconvene that night. When it met again, different factions began wrangling about which delegations had the right to be seated. The powerful Radical leader Congressman Thaddeus Stevens of Pennsylvania, inveighed against allowing delegates from the "damned secessionist provinces" to be seated, but interim recommendations were made to seat pro-

Union delegations from Tennessee, Arkansas, and Louisiana, states now largely under Federal control. This led to the appointment of a number of committees to examine credentials and to report the next morning on their findings as to which delegations were entitled to vote.

To close the evening, the Republicans put more of their old heroes in front of the crowd. One of these was the Reverend William Brownlow of Tennessee. In 1838, after ten years as an itinerant Methodist preacher, he had become the editor of the *Knoxville Whig*, staunchly supporting the Whig Party that the Republican Party replaced when it came into being in 1856. His antislavery views, expressed eloquently and vigorously at some risk to himself in a slaveholding state, led him to be called the "Fighting Parson." A supporter of Lincoln, when the Civil War began, Brownlow refused to take an oath of allegiance to the Confederacy and kept flying the Stars and Stripes from his house in Knoxville.

Retribution came swiftly. His newspaper was shut down. Brownlow was falsely charged with burning railroad bridges, and Confederate soldiers were ordered to shoot him on sight. Arrested and jailed, he became a martyr to the many Union sympathizers in Tennessee. In the reverse of the treatment Lincoln meted out to United States Congressman Clement Vallandigham, Brownlow was handed over to Union forces in Tennessee under a flag of truce in March of 1862. Lincoln and others urged Brownlow to make what proved to be an enthusiastically received lecture tour through the North, which made him enough money so that by September of 1863 he could return to Knoxville, by then in Union hands. Resuming publication of his newspaper, Brownlow became both a journalistic and a political power in eastern Tennessee.

Arriving at Baltimore after a difficult trip from Tennessee, Brownlow intended to proclaim his faith in Lincoln and ask the convention to support for vice president his fellow Tennessean Andrew Johnson, a Democrat with whom he had often differed in prewar days. He also wanted this predominantly Northern crowd to understand that scores of thousands of Tennesseans had remained loyal to the Union, risking their lives and losing their livelihoods by doing that.

Brownlow knew how to gain the sympathy of an audience, and the crowd he faced wanted to honor him. He began with this:

Gentlemen of the Convention: I assure you [that] you have tonight waked up the wrong passenger. I am a very sick man and ought to be in my bed, and not here. I have journeyed on, however, through great tribulation, to meet you. The last regular meal I took was on Saturday [three days before], upon a boat on the Ohio River. I am sick, sick, and I come forward now because so enthusiastically called for, to make my bow and apologizing for not attempting to speak.

In fact, Brownlow was just getting started, and the transcript of his remarks in the *New York Times* indicated the response to his words.

But before I take my seat, I know you will take of me kindly any suggestion I may make, or any rebuke I may administer to you. I am one of the elder brethren, the old apostles; [laughter] and I heard when I came to town that you had some doubts in your mind about the propriety of admitting the delegation from Tennessee—a State in rebellion.

I hope you will pause, gentlemen, before you commit such a rash act as that, and thereby recognize secession. We don't recognize it in Tennessee. [Applause.] We deny that we are out. [Applause.] We deny that we have been out. [Applause.]

Next he lashed out at the Copperheads. "I have fought the venomous reptiles for two years . . . they are beginning to organize in Tennessee, and I confidently look for them to be represented at the forth-coming [Democratic] Chicago convention. . . ." But Brownlow's Tennesseans were different; they "instructed us before we left home to advocate and vote for *Abraham Lincoln*, first, last, and all the time. [Applause.] He has got his hand in; he has learnt the hang of the ropes, and we want to try him for a second term."

And now for the vice presidency. "We have a man down there whom it was my good luck and bad fortune to fight untiringly for the last twenty-five years—*Andrew Johnson*. [Applause.] For the first time in the providence of God, three years ago, we got on the same platform, and we are now fighting the devil, . . . *Jeff Davis*, side by side. [Applause.]"

Like Jim Lane of Kansas, the "Fighting Parson" had done what he came to Baltimore to do. Lincoln's friend and sometime bodyguard Ward Hill Lamon, one of his many operatives at the convention, sent the president a telegram at nine o'clock that night that read: "Enthusiastic unanimity beyond even my expectations. Preliminaries not yet settled. Nomination to be made tomorrow."

• • •

At ten the next morning, the convention reassembled. The questionable status of certain delegations was settled. Arkansas, Louisiana, and Tennessee, the three partly reconquered states in which Lincoln was reinstating governments acceptable to Federal policy, were to have full voting rights. Other places that were territories and not yet states were similarly accepted: Colorado, Nebraska, and Nevada. The District of Columbia, Florida, Virginia, and the Territory of New Mexico could participate in discussion but not vote. The South Carolina delegation was rejected. The behind-the-scenes maneuvering that concerned which of two Missouri delegations to seat was settled when the delegation composed of Radicals, who had promised to vote for Lincoln in the end, received official approval.

Then came the adoption of the party platform. The man who came forward to announce the party planks, one by one, was the platform committee chairman, Henry J. Raymond, of the *New York Times*. The first resolution affirmed the unity of all factions present and pledged all possible support "to aid the Government in quelling by force of arms the rebellion now raging against its authority, and in bringing to the punishment due to their crimes the rebels and traitors arrayed against it." The *Times* noted that this brought forth "prolonged applause." Cheers also greeted the second resolution, which stated that there would be no compromise with the Confederacy; quoting the terms stated by Grant at the surrender of Fort Donelson, there must be "unconditional surrender."

The audience had been waiting for the third resolution, on slavery. Early in the resolution there was this: "justice and the national safety demand its utter and complete extirpation from the soil of the Republic"; it went on to call for an amendment to the Constitution "as shall terminate and forever prohibit the existence of slavery within the limits of the jurisdiction of the United States."

With that, the crowd exploded; delegates leapt to their feet as they cheered; the *Times* called it one of the assemblage's "wildest bursts of enthusiasm." Those looking ahead to the presidential campaign, of which this convention was only a first step, realized that their party had just taken the moral high ground.

A fourth resolution expressed thanks to the Union's soldiers and sailors, and promised "ample and permanent provision" for those wounded. When the fifth resolution, which in effect endorsed Lincoln, spoke of "the practical wisdom, the unselfish patriotism and the unswerving fidelity" with which he had discharged the duties of his office, the *Times* said of the reaction to that, "The mention of the name of ABRAHAM LINCOLN was received with tremendous cheering, the whole house rising and waving hats and handkerchiefs."

The sixth resolution, for those who understood it, was a red flag warning of trouble to come. The language seemed innocuous: it called for harmony in the national councils and said that only high officials should serve who could "cordially endorse the principles proclaimed in these resolutions."

This was aimed straight at Lincoln's postmaster general, Montgomery Blair, of the clan of Missouri Blairs who had helped Lincoln in so many ways. Montgomery was indeed a controversial figure, both publicly and within Lincoln's cabinet. He had a puzzling record. In 1857, Montgomery had been the lawyer who represented the slave Dred Scott before the Supreme Court in the historic case of *Dred Scott v. Sandford*, arguing that Scott, whose master took him to live on "free soil" in the Louisiana Territory, thereby became a free man. (The court's majority decision held, among other things, that Scott remained a slave and that slaves were not citizens and had no standing to bring a suit in a Federal court.) Then in 1860, Montgomery Blair assisted the Kansas abolitionist John Brown to find lawyers to defend him in his trial for treason and murder resulting from his raid on the Federal arsenal at Harpers Ferry. While clearly opposed to slavery, Blair believed along with Lincoln that, in the event of a Union victory, there should be a conciliatory attitude toward Southern whites. As for the freed blacks, he differed from Lincoln, feeling that they should not be entitled to vote and should be strictly segregated. He also suggested that for their own and the nation's sake they should be deported to Latin America and be assisted in starting their own colonies there—an idea in which Lincoln remained quietly interested.

The very idea—that the man who had stepped forward to represent Dred Scott would oppose the vote for blacks—drove the Radicals into a frenzy, and had brought calls for Blair's removal from the cabinet. It left Lincoln trying to work out one more calculation; he was politically indebted to the Blairs, and, overall, Montgomery Blair stood ready to back his plans for Reconstruction, however they might evolve. Within the cabinet, Blair mistrusted Seward and disliked Stanton and Chase. In what was now coming to a head in Baltimore, it appeared that the backstage deal to seat the Radical Missouri delegation involved something more than just their promise to come around to supporting Lincoln; they would do that, but their price included this resolution intended to put the skids under Blair.

Most of the other planks of the platform that Raymond put before the delegates had to do with different aspects of the Union's progress and needs. Foreign immigration "should be encouraged by a liberal and just policy." Reflecting Lincoln's vision of the future, westward expansion should be spurred by "a speedy construction of the railroad to the Pacific coast." Other language concerned sound fiscal policies.

The final resolution, which produced "long-continued applause," was about Mexico, without naming that country or mentioning the French effort to establish it as a colony in defiance of the Monroe Doctrine: ". . . the people of the United States can never regard with indifference the attempt of any European power to overthrow by force or to supplant by fraud the institutions of any republican [democratic] government on the western continent."

The platform was adopted; the moment had arrived for which delegates had traveled from as far as Louisiana and Nevada and California. A delegate from Ohio said, "I move that this convention now proceed to the nomination of candidate for President and Vice President of the United States."

This was followed by the convention's most surprising act. Simon Cameron, who had been specifically enlisted by Lincoln to work quietly for the nomination of Andrew Johnson for vice president, rose and offered this resolution: "That Abraham Lincoln of Illinois be declared the choice of the Union Party for president, and Hannibal Hamlin, of Maine, be the candidate for Vice President of the same party."

The words barely left Cameron's mouth before there were, as seen on the record, "Cries of 'No, no.'" What Cameron intended to be the result of this would never be fully understood; with all the discussion and deliberation that had led to this moment, it may have been yet one more calculation, and probably one that he and Lincoln previously discussed. Certainly, it brought to a head, as it may well have been intended to do, the difference in reaction to the names of Lincoln and Hamlin; even in mid-sentence, there had been applause at the mention of Lincoln, whereas Hamlin's name elicited the shouts of, "No, no."

This threw the nominating procedure back into the frantically waving hands of a melee of delegates, all clamoring to be recognized. A man from Maryland got Platform Committee Chairman Raymond's attention first, and said, "I call for a division of the question"—consider Lincoln first, and then open up the nomination for vice president. After some wrangling, this was agreed upon in principle, but even then delegates differed on how to proceed. Cameron, who probably wanted it all to come to just this, said, "I will modify my resolution to make it 'nominate Abraham Lincoln by acclamation.'"

Raymond, handsome, trim, elegantly dressed, forty-four years old, remained cool in the midst of the storm. He wanted to make sure that this could not be seen as railroading Lincoln's nomination through, as some critics had said would happen. "I suggest," he told the delegates as they began to calm down, "that the wisest course would be to allow the roll of the States in this convention to be called, and let every delegation declare its vote."

That was agreed upon and led to yet another difficult situation. As the states cast their ballots, each in turn voting unanimously for Lincoln, they came to Missouri. The chairman of these Radicals, whose right to be there had been the subject of so much discussion and dispute, rose and said that he was sorry, but they had been instructed to vote for someone else, at least on the first ballot.

This brought howls of disbelief and frustration. Missouri cast its twenty-two votes for Ulysses S. Grant, who had specifically disavowed any interest in running for president. Things became quiet again; the roll call continued. When the first ballot finished, with Nevada voting last, the votes were 484 for Abraham Lincoln and 22 for Grant. The chairman of the Missouri delegation rose again, switched his state's votes to Lincoln, and made it unanimous.

"The enthusiasm was perfectly indescribable," said the *Times*, "the whole convention being on their feet, shouting, and the band playing 'Hail Columbia.'" A reporter from California described "a scene of the wildest confusion. Men hurrahed, embraced one another, threw up their hats, danced in the aisles or on the platform, jumped up on the benches, waved flags, yelled . . . the racket was so intolerable that I involuntarily looked up to see if the roof of the theater were not lifted by the volume of sound."

The nomination process for vice president brought several contenders into play. It became obvious that Hamlin was not getting any official support from Lincoln, who could have had him on the ticket simply by saying so; Lincoln's eloquent silence was a political kiss of death. The Indiana delegation put forward Andrew Johnson's name, which was seconded by a delegate from Iowa. After the first ballot, Johnson had 200 votes, Hamlin had 150, and Daniel S. Dickinson of New York had 120. Seven other candidates had 61 votes among them.

The moment of truth had arrived. Delegations began getting behind the men who seemed to have a chance. Cameron, who had started off by nominating Hamlin, switched Pennsylvania's 55 votes to Johnson. In the midst of this, arch-Radical Thaddeus Stevens of Pennsylvania, who had argued unsuccessfully against seating delegates from the "damned secessionist provinces," prowled around the hall unhappily. He turned to McClure, who along with Cameron had been enlisted by Lincoln to work for Andrew Johnson, and said of the Tennessean who was now well ahead in the votes, "Can't you find a candidate for Vice-President in the United States without going down to one of those damned rebel provinces to pick one up?"

Now everyone began switching to Johnson. Finally, even the Maine delegation moved away from Hamlin, the man from their state who had been Lincoln's vice president since they were sworn in together in March of 1861. And there it was, greeted by more cheers: unanimous for Abraham Lincoln and Andrew Johnson.

In Washington, Lincoln had been in the War Department telegraph office for several hours, communicating with Grant in the aftermath of Cold Harbor. A message from Baltimore came through at four-thirty that afternoon; it referred to Andrew Johnson's nomination for vice president, and it was only then that Lincoln learned that for some reason he had not seen a telegram received two hours earlier that gave news of his own nomination. Lincoln said to the young soldier cipher-operators surrounding him, "What! Am I renominated?" Speaking of Mary, he said, "Send it right over to the Madam," and added, perhaps a bit disingenuously, "She will be more interested in it than I am." Later in the day, Richard Wallach, Washington's mayor, called on him to offer his congratulations. Lincoln showed no sign of jubilation. That night he relaxed, going by himself to Grover's Theatre, where he saw a play that was sometimes called an "equestrian drama," *Mazeppa, or the Wild Horse of Tartary.*

(In Washington's theaters, when Lincoln wished to be alone and unobserved, the manager would meet him at the stage door and slip him into one of the dimly lit side boxes.)

The next day, a group composed of a Baltimore convention delegate from each state came to the White House to pay its respects as the delegates passed though Washington before going home. Governor Dennison of Ohio spoke for them when he said that the convention had given "utterance to the almost universal voice of the loyal people of the country." Lincoln replied, "I will neither conceal my gratification, nor restrain the expression of my gratitude." Later in the day, Lincoln used the East Room to receive some of the group from the Union League that had been at Baltimore. Stoddard had attended the Union League meeting the night before the convention at which were men who criticized Lincoln vociferously. Now everyone smiled and added to the expressions of hopeful good wishes pouring in to the White House. In a cheerful mood, Lincoln said to them, "I have not permitted myself, gentlemen, to conclude that I am the best man in the country; but I am reminded . . . of a story of an old Dutch farmer, who remarked to a companion once that 'it was best not to swap horses when crossing streams.'"

So Lincoln was nominated, unanimously and enthusiastically. (There is no record of his communicating with Hannibal Hamlin in any way about his not being nominated for vice president.) Despite the bad battlefield news, many of Lincoln's supporters took heart at having him settled on as their candidate and thought the road ahead to the November election could be smooth. Lincoln's opponents had their chance to voice their reactions: "The politicians," James Gordon Bennett of the *New York Herald* said in an editorial the morning after the Baltimore convention adjourned, "have again chosen this Presidential pigmy as their nominee." Manton Marble of the *New York World* chimed in with this appraisal of the Union's situation, and of Lincoln and Andrew Johnson: "In a crisis of the most appalling magnitude, requiring statesmanship of the highest order, the country is asked to consider the claims of two ignorant, boorish, third-rate backwoods lawyers, for the highest stations in the government . . . God save the Republic!" (There is no record of Andrew Johnson's ever practicing law.)

This kind of criticism had often been heard before, to be shrugged off by those who believed in Lincoln, but even the most ardent among them would have shuddered if they could have seen what his most prominent supporters would be saying in two months, with the November election then still another three months away. By that time, a combination of events, some entirely unexpected, had brought Lincoln's fortunes to the point that Henry Raymond of the *New York Times*, who had now become chairman of the Republican/National Union Party's National Committee and in that capacity was running Lincoln's campaign, felt compelled to write him some bad news. Raymond told him, "I am in active correspondence with your staunchest friends in every state and from them all I have but one report. The tide is setting strongly against us." The powerful New York political figure Thurlow Weed, who supported Lincoln strongly during the convention and worked hard for him thereafter, would pronounce Lincoln politically dead; in this coming August he would write Seward, "I told Mr. Lincoln that his re-election is an impossibility." He was also quoted as saying, "Lincoln is gone." The discouragement, close to despair, went right down the line. Writing his wife at that time from New York City, Lincoln's loyal and trusted political worker Leonard Swett told her: "Unless material changes can be made Lincoln's election is beyond any possible hope. It is probably clean gone now." In a later letter, he added, "We are in conspiracies equal to the French Revolution."

By far the most telling estimates came from Lincoln himself. Talking with a Radical who told him that he might be "beaten overwhelmingly," Lincoln replied, "You think I don't know I am going to be beaten, *but I do* and unless some great change takes place *badly beaten*." In a meeting in his White House office on August 23, he would ask all the members of his cabinet to sign the blank side of a sheet of paper, pledging themselves to support a statement by him, the words of which were on its other side, which he did not show them. In an act of faith and duty, all of them signed. The words they did not then see read:

> *This morning, as for some days past, it seems exceedingly probable that this Administration will not be re-elected. Then it will be my duty to so co-operate with the President elect, as to save the Union between the election and the inauguration; as he will have secured his election on such ground that he cannot possibly save it afterwards.*

SEVEN

"I BEGIN TO SEE IT" — THE ELUSIVE "IT"

Within days after the slaughter of his troops at Cold Harbor on June 3, Grant began one of the most remarkable movements of the war. While his wounded army remained in place opposite Lee, with some of his positions only 40 yards from the Confederate lines, Grant worked in secrecy, letting none of his officers know his overall plan. He gave orders that put into motion "Chess wagons," used to carry the planks for pontoon bridges; under additional orders, ferryboats gathered far down the James River, forty miles southeast of Cold Harbor, and engineer companies known as "pioneers" laid down log-surfaced roads through nearly impassable swamps. At the same time, Grant sent gunboats up the James River toward Richmond, to which all previous offensive efforts had been directed, and had Philip Sheridan move 10,000 of his cavalrymen to the west and north of Richmond in a massive raid against the Confederate railroad lines in that area.

Everything that Lee and his generals and frontline pickets could see indicated that Grant was resting and reequipping his battered Army of the Potomac in place, right in front of them. All they knew of Grant, including his relentless advances since starting this campaign in the Wilderness, led them to believe that he would soon resume his attacks on their fortified positions, making yet another bloody effort to break through their lines and finally capture the Confederate capital that lay only eight miles away. Lee, a shrewd and imaginative general, his skilled and experienced intelligence officers, and his combat commanders, all braced themselves for the attack to come.

During these early June days, Northern public attention fixed itself on the Baltimore convention and the events leading to Lincoln's nomination. The little war news concerned itself mainly with the area around Marietta, Georgia, where Sherman continued his often-thwarted efforts to push Joseph E. Johnston back toward Atlanta. In the Shenandoah Valley, Union general Andrew Hunter won a minor victory that enabled him to take Staunton, Virginia; on the day the Baltimore convention nominated Lincoln, in Kentucky the Confederate raider John Hunt Morgan captured Mount Sterling and its small Federal garrison, only to be decisively defeated at Cynthiana a few days later. No one expected a dramatic movement in northern Virginia.

At dawn on Monday, June 13, the Confederate pickets in their holes in front of Lee's lines at Cold Harbor looked over at the Union campfires that had been burning through the night and did not hear the usual sounds of men talking and cooking breakfast as they kept their heads down in their trenches. Patrols went out, moving cautiously as they approached the Union lines. They found the trenches empty. The patrols moved on through areas where they would have been killed instantly the day before. Everything had vanished—artillery, cook wagons, hundreds of tents. Because Lee had sent his own cavalry off to the north to act as a screen against Sheridan's two divisions, watching them and being ready to block a sweep behind Richmond, he had few mounted scouts available to range out farther and bring back more information.

Virtually overnight, Grant had slipped 115,000 men off to the east, away from the approaches to Richmond. All the different parts of his scheme were coming together. While Lee remained confused, continuing to assume that the presence of Union gunboats and cavalry near Richmond meant that Grant still intended to attack the Confederate capital, the fleet of ferryboats Grant had assembled down the James River came up to the landing at White House, on the Pamunkey River, and to Wilcox Landing on the James itself. The following day, these vessels began to transport the 18,000 men of "Baldy" Smith's Eighteenth Corps and the 28,000 men of Hancock's Second Corps across to the south side of the James. This put the first of Grant's infantry units on the same side of the river as Petersburg, Virginia.

Smith's corps at first met no resistance in the flat terrain east of that important city, which was Grant's real objective. Richmond, twenty-two miles north of Petersburg, could wait; the Union gunboats he had sent up there, and Sheridan's two divisions of cavalry, had all been a massive and successful deceptive move, a feint that kept Lee anchored exactly where Grant wanted to keep him as long as possible. At the same time that Union ferryboats continued taking men from the north side of the James to the south, Grant's engineers began throwing across the river the longest pontoon bridge ever built, 2,100 feet in length and 13 feet wide. They finished the bridge at eleven at night on June 14. Thousands of troops began pouring across it, along with horses pulling cannons, supply wagons, and ambulances.

On the morning of Wednesday, June 15, Grant, his hands linked behind his back and with no cigar in his mouth, watched from a bluff on the north side of the James as his long blue columns kept crossing the river on the pontoon bridge. Thus far, he had wired Halleck at the War Department only twice about the details of his massive secret move. At five-thirty on the afternoon of June 13, he had sent a terse telegram from Wilcox Landing, which began, "The advance of our troops has just reached this place. We will commence crossing the James tomorrow." Then at one-thirty on the afternoon of the fourteenth, he had sent this to Halleck:

> *Our forces will commence crossing the James today. The enemy show no signs yet of having brought troops to the south side of Richmond. I will have Petersburg secured, if possible, before they get there in much force. Our movement from Cold Harbor to the James River has been made with the greatest celerity and so far without loss or accident.*

Halleck showed this to Lincoln early on this morning when Grant now stood watching his army cross the James; at seven, Lincoln wired Grant:

> *HAVE JUST READ YOUR DISPATCH OF 1 P.M. YESTERDAY. I BEGIN TO SEE IT. GOD BLESS YOU ALL.*
>
> *A. LINCOLN.*

Grant had a full appreciation for what he had done. By afternoon, having established his headquarters on a bluff at City Point, where the

Appomattox River flowed into the James, he sent out several orders, the last at eight-fifteen that night, and then wrote his wife. "Dear Julia," he began:

> *Since Sunday, we have been engaged in one of the most perilous move-*
> *ments ever executed by a large army, that of withdrawing from the front*
> *of an enemy and moving past his flank crossing two rivers over which the*
> *enemy had bridges and rail-roads whilst we have bridges to improvise.*
>   *Thus far it has been eminently successful and I hope will prove so to*
> *the end.*

Speaking of the pressure he continued to put on Lee and what he thought the Confederates' reaction must be, he told Julia, "They are now on a strain that no people ever endured for any great length of time." Grant did not specify what that "length of time" before the Confederacy's collapse would be, but Lincoln, the night before sending Grant his "I begin to see it" telegram, had expressed a far more cautious assessment of the war's progress. Chatting with his friend the journalist Noah Brooks at this moment when his nomination, combined with the Union Army's coming within eight miles of Richmond, had momentarily raised the morale of many Northerners, he told him this: "I wish, when you write or speak to people, you would do all you can to correct the impression that the war in Virginia will end right off and victoriously . . . there are plenty of people who believe that the war is about to be substantially closed. As God is my judge, I shall be satisfied if we are over with the fight in Virginia within a year."

Grant's optimism that he could exploit his brilliant surprise and "have Petersburg secured"—captured—began to diminish within a day. On that morning of June 15, when Grant stood watching an endless column of his army continue to pour across the James River on the pontoon bridge, he had already issued orders that should by dawn have produced the first attack on the defenses of Petersburg.

The man supposed to throw his force at the city and possibly take it with the first rush was Major General "Baldy" Smith, commander of the 18,000 men of the Eighteenth Corps, whose units had been put ashore by ferryboats before the engineers completed the pontoon bridge. It was Smith who had written of Lincoln's political appointee Major General Benjamin F. Butler, tasked with the mission to advance toward Richmond from the coast at the same time Grant started into the Wilderness toward Richmond, that he feared Butler's offensive would be "full of unnecessary risks & of the kind that may produce the most terrible disaster."

Butler had failed to take Richmond, not producing a "terrible disaster" but losing an enormous strategic opportunity. On May 16, after being repulsed at Drewry's Bluff on the James River at a time when Smith and his corps served under him, he retreated back to Bermuda Hundred, becoming useless to Grant. Then Butler bungled another opportunity. On June 9, with a good chance to capture lightly defended Petersburg, he sent 4,500 men to seize the city, held at the time by roughly half that number of Confederates. Due to a miscommunication between Butler's infantry and cavalry, the attack failed, and Butler remained with his Army of the James in the same useless static position, near where Grant was now trying to mount his own larger offensive against Petersburg.

After the defeat at Drewry's Bluff and before Butler's added failure to take Petersburg, Grant brought "Baldy" Smith and his corps back to the Army of the Potomac, in time to take their share of the heavy casualties at Cold Harbor. At the moment Grant selected Smith to make the first strike on Petersburg, Smith had his entire confidence; Grant was thinking of the general he had seen render conspicuous service under his command at Chattanooga, and Smith performed neither better nor worse than any of Grant's other major commanders in the debacle at Cold Harbor. As for Smith, he may have been unnerved by the 3,000 casualties his Eighteenth Corps sustained in that bloodbath, and there could be no doubt that he now commanded men who were, as one of them said, "exhausted and discouraged troops." It was Smith's turn to produce a "most terrible disaster"—one produced by hesitation.

The defense of Petersburg rested on the Confederates' skilled and versatile Beauregard, who had scraped together 2,200 assorted troops overnight. Among them he had soldiers convalescing from wounds, and a combination of militiamen and home guards ranging from old men of seventy-two to boys of twelve. Far from attacking Beauregard at dawn as ordered, Smith did not get his units placed until noon, and then spent hours going down his lines, checking the positions and trying to see if he could learn more about the enemy numbers and defenses. Even then, Smith's chances for an immensely important victory remained good; when he launched his attack at sunset, his 18,000 men swiftly captured more than two miles of the Confederate defensive earthworks outside of the city, and fifteen cannon. Beauregard, still having only his 2,200 gallant defenders of all ages and states of health, later wrote of the moment, "Petersburg was at that time clearly at the mercy of the Federal commander, who had all but captured it."

The following day, despite the arrival of an additional 17,000 men from Hancock's Second Corps, bringing the available Union force to 35,000, the advance went no farther. Beauregard swiftly rounded up another 7,000 men to add to the 2,200 he had the day before, and started pulling men out of the area where he had the inert B. F. Butler bottled up. Grant, seeing the opportunity to take Petersburg slip away by the hour, ordered Burnside to rush his 25,000 men into place around the city, thus raising the Federal strength to 60,000, and told Meade, his day-to-day commander of the Army of the Potomac, to throw everything he had into an attack to be made at six that evening.

Nothing went right. Beauregard's men fought off the evening attack; the Union reinforcements brought in swiftly by Hancock and Burnside attacked as ordered, but Smith remained tentative. This produced a series of sporadic Union movements, to which Beauregard swiftly adapted by shortening his lines, falling back to the very edge of Petersburg so that the units of his growing force of defenders could better support each other. Grant sent forward another corps that had by now crossed the James; the Fifth Corps under Major General Gouverneur Kemble Warren arrived during the night with 20,000 or more men. Beauregard later wrote of how things then stood; speaking of the addition of Warren's corps, he said, "Its presence before our lines swelled the enemy's aggregate to about 90,000, against which stood a barrier of not even 10,000 exhausted, half-starved men, who had gone through two days of constant hard fighting and many sleepless nights in the trenches."

Meade ordered another attack to be made at dawn, now two mornings after the time that Smith was supposed to make the first rush that might well have captured the city. Things went wrong again; Burnside attacked on schedule, Hancock did not move until two hours later, Warren never started, and, two days after delaying his first attack from dawn to dusk, Smith did not move. Once more, Beauregard recorded the magnitude of the Federal failure in coordinating the attacks against him, writing that if Warren had come at him any time on June 17, "I would have been compelled to evacuate Petersburg without much resistance." He also said with some bitterness, "The Army of Northern Virginia was yet distant, and I had failed to convince its distinguished commander [Lee] of the fact that I was then fighting Grant's whole army with less than eleven thousand men."

The Army of the Potomac had squandered a seventy-two-hour-long opportunity to capture Petersburg. Smith was to have made his original attack at dawn on Wednesday, June 15; the sun now stood high in the sky on Saturday morning, June 18. Meade ordered yet another effort to take the city, the attack to begin at noon. Again, the Union forces attacked sporadically, hesitantly. In the next hours, strong Confederate reinforcements began to arrive. Sent by Lee, who reached Beauregard's headquarters himself at eleven-thirty that morning, brigade after brigade of his best veterans rushed down from Richmond; by dusk they filled the trenches around Petersburg. Grant and Meade stopped ordering attacks.

The siege of Petersburg had begun. Lee was almost fatally slow to understand and react to Grant's brilliant initial movement away from Cold Harbor, and on his side Grant would see his forces pay a terrible price for the failure to take Petersburg during these mid-June days. Had Petersburg been captured then, Grant could have concentrated a far greater number of his forces in a narrow arc around Richmond. Instead, he and his men now faced a line of Confederate defenses that ran approximately twenty-two miles from north to south, anchored on the north by Richmond, the Confederate capital, and on the south by Petersburg, Virginia's strategically placed second-most-important city. Lee knew how to turn those twenty-two miles into a vast Union graveyard.

All this had gone badly for the Union's battered and exhausted Army of the Potomac, but Grant's change of front, his abandoning the effort to break through to capture Richmond and having to settle reluctantly for what would be a siege of both Petersburg and Richmond, opened a strategic vista not lost on Lee. He saw that Grant, with his superior numbers, could keep extending his lines around the east side of Petersburg and then west into Virginia to the city's south. To avoid being outflanked, Lee would have to spread his fewer defenders thinner and thinner, with what he believed would be an inevitable result: Grant would break through somewhere, Lee told General Jubal Early, and after that the loss of Petersburg and Richmond would be "a mere question of time."

Lee's estimate of the military balance in Northern Virginia could not be faulted, but the war's future depended on more than those numbers. In Georgia, Sherman and his opponent Joseph E. Johnston continued to fight an entirely different campaign, a war of movement that in any week could produce dramatic victories or reverses. Northern public support for continuing the war might easily collapse: long before this, the patriotic wife of a Union naval captain gave voice to the feelings of millions when she spoke of herself as "panting for peace." Not only women longed for peace: in the Union Army, men hardened by horrible fighting sometimes found themselves in situations that might still crack their will. Writing twenty-three years later, a Union veteran remembered this from the hours after a battle during the failed effort to take Petersburg. "That night, while searching for fresh, clean water, I found several dead [Confederate] cavalrymen in the woods, where they had probably crawled after being wounded. I struck a match to see one of these men plainly, and was greatly shocked to see large black beetles eating the corpse." Two days later, the same soldier had this encounter as he and his unit moved swiftly to the front.

> *Sitting at the base of a pine tree I saw a line sergeant. His face was stained with blood, which had oozed from under a bandage made of an old shirt sleeve, tightly bound around his eyes. By his side sat a little drummer boy, with unstrung drum and the sticks put up standing on the ground in front of him. The muscular form of the sergeant was bent forward, his chin resting on his hands, his elbows on his knees. His figure conveyed to me the impression of utter hopelessness. The small drummer looked up the road, and then down the road, with anxious gaze.*
>
> *I stopped for an instant, and asked, "What is the matter?" The drummer looked up at me, his blue eyes filled with tears, and answered: "He's my father. Both his eyes were blinded on the picket line this morning. I am waiting for an ambulance to come along. I don't know where the field hospitals are."*
>
> *I hurriedly pointed in the direction of some field hospitals we had passed a few hundred yards back. The two rose up and slowly walked off, the son leading his blinded father by the hand, leading him to the operating-table, and I hastened on, swallowing my tears. . . .*

These were all Lincoln's people, suffering for ideas, some for the preservation of the Union, some for the end of slavery, some for a combination of both. In addition to the shock the Northern public felt as the casualty lists from the recent Virginia battles appeared, the reports from the Union front at Petersburg started a general mistrust of newspaper accounts about the campaign. On June 17, the day before Grant and Meade called off the attacks on Petersburg, Secretary of War Stanton mistakenly announced the city's capture—news flashed by wire from Washington that appeared the following morning in the *New York Tribune* and other leading papers. The next accounts said that Union troops were not in the city but had taken some of its outer defenses, suffering heavy losses as they did; the stories implied that the city would soon fall. Then came the real picture: after being thrown back repeatedly, Grant's troops were digging in to besiege Petersburg. From the moment the fighting had begun in the Wilderness on May 4 until the siege of Petersburg began on June 18, Grant had lost nearly 60,000 men in what became known as his Overland Campaign—60,000 men to advance sixty miles. In the same period, Lee lost 35,000—casualties increasingly hard for the South to replace—but the recent surge in the slaughter shook the morale of the North more than that of the South.

As for "Baldy" Smith, whose military career began when he entered West Point as a plebe in 1842, he was on the way out of high command. Smith did not go quietly. He criticized the still-influential B. F. Butler, calling him "as helpless as a child on the field of battle and as visionary as an opium eater in council," and also voiced strong criticisms of Meade. Four weeks after Smith's lamentable performance at Petersburg, which by itself may have well ended any chance for Union victory in 1864, he was relieved of command of his Eighteenth Corps and ended the war in relative obscurity.

THE DAY AFTER the final failed attacks on Petersburg, Lincoln started from Washington on a trip to Grant's headquarters. Writing in his diary about Lincoln's departure from Washington at five in the afternoon aboard the USS *Baltimore*, Secretary of the Navy Gideon Welles said, "The President in his intense anxiety has made up his mind to visit General Grant. . . ." That suggested a serious review of the military situation, but with Mary visiting friends in New York, Lincoln was accompanied by his eleven-year-old son, Tad, as well as Assistant Secretary of the Navy Gustavus Fox.

From the moment the *Baltimore* arrived at the wharf below Grant's City Point headquarters at noon on June 21, it became clear that Lincoln intended to emphasize his appreciation for all that this army had suffered and the amount of enemy territory it had taken since starting its advance through the Wilderness seven weeks before, and save any questions he might have for Grant until later. As Grant and several of his officers went up the *Baltimore's* after-gangway and stepped onto the main deck, Lieutenant Colonel Horace Porter of Grant's staff witnessed this:

> *The President came down from the upper-deck . . . reaching out his long, angular arm, he wrung General Grant's hand vigorously, and held it in his for some time, while he uttered in rapid words his congratulations and expressions of appreciation of the great task which had been accomplished since he and the general had parted in Washington.*
>
> *The group then went into the after-cabin. General Grant said: "I hope you are very well, Mister President."*
>
> *"Yes, I am in very good health," Mr. Lincoln replied, "but I don't feel very comfortable after my trip last night on the bay. It was rough, and I was considerably shaken up. My stomach has not yet entirely recovered from the effects."*
>
> *An officer of the party now saw that an opportunity had arisen to make this scene the supreme moment of his life, in giving him the chance to soothe the digestive organs of the Chief Magistrate of the nation. He said: "Try a glass of champagne, Mister President. That is always a certain cure for seasickness."*
>
> *Mr. Lincoln looked at him for a moment, his face lighting up with a smile, and then remarked: "No, my friend; I have seen too many fellows seasick ashore from drinking that very stuff."*
>
> *This was a knockdown for the officer, and in the laugh at his expense Mr. Lincoln and the general both joined heartily.*

Grant then suggested that Lincoln might want to see some of the units of the army, and added, "I am sure that your presence among them would have a very gratifying effect. I can furnish you a very good horse, and will be most happy to accompany you to points of interest along the line."

Lincoln replied, "I am ready to start at any time," and soon mounted Cincinnati, Grant's favorite, a bay horse seventeen and a half hands high, given him by an admirer after his victory at Chattanooga the previous November. Grant, who along with Lee was one of the great horsemen of the prewar United States Army, rode beside Lincoln on Jeff Davis, a big black pony captured during the Shiloh campaign on the plantation of the Confederate president's brother. Colonel Porter rode along with Lincoln and Grant, and described Lincoln on horseback.

Mr. Lincoln wore a very high black silk hat and black trousers and frock coat. Like most men who had been brought up in the West, he had good command of a horse, but it must be acknowledged that in appearance he was not a very dashing rider. On this occasion, by the time he had reached the troops he was completely covered with dust, and the black color of his clothes had changed to Confederate grey. As he had no straps [for riding, running from one side of the bottom of a trouser leg to the other, under the sole of the rider's shoe], his trousers gradually worked up above his ankles, and gave him the appearance of a country farmer riding into town wearing his Sunday clothes . . . the picture presented by the President bordered on the grotesque.

The troops, however, greeted him with "enthusiastic shouts" wherever he appeared. After a time, Grant said, "Mister President, let us ride on and see some of the colored troops," mentioning a recent battle in which they "behaved so handsomely." Lincoln agreed, saying that he had "read with the greatest delight" of "how gallantly they behaved" in that fighting.

The action of which Grant and Lincoln spoke had taken place six days before, during the first day's fighting at Petersburg on June 15, when a division composed of black soldiers made a successful attack as part of the overall assault that "Baldy" Smith failed to exploit. The morning after that, a Union soldier from a white unit saw this as he moved up to the enemy positions that the United States Colored Troops captured some fourteen hours before.

. . . I came on the line of rifle-pits which had been used by the Confederate pickets, and saw two dead men lying close together. I walked over to them. One was a burly negro sergeant, as black as coal, in blue; the other was a Confederate line sergeant, in gray. Their bayoneted rifles lay beside them. Curious at the nearness of the bodies, I turned them over and looked carefully at them. They had met with unloaded rifles and had fought a duel with their bayonets, each stabbing the other to death.

Porter told what happened when Lincoln reached the encampment of these regiments of black troops who had fought so well a week before and they poured out to see him.

A scene now occurred that defies description. They beheld for the first time the liberator of their race—the man who by a stroke of his pen had struck the shackles from the limbs of their fellow-bondmen and proclaimed liberty to the enslaved. . . . They cheered, laughed, cried, sang hymns of praise, and shouted in their negro dialect, "God bress Massa Linkum!" "De Lord save Fader Abraham!" "De day ob jubilee am come, shuah."

They crowded around him and fondled his horse; some of them kissed his hands, while others ran off crying in triumph to their comrades that they had touched his clothes. The President rode with bared head; the tears had started to his eyes, and his voice was so broken with emotion that he could scarcely articulate the words of thanks and congratulation with which he tried to speak to the humble and devoted men through whose ranks he rode.

II

The day after his visit to the United States Colored Troops, Lincoln set out on a voyage up the James River to see the Union positions nearer Richmond. Accompanied by Grant and his aide Porter, they picked up Acting Admiral Samuel Phillips Lee, commander of the United States Navy's gunboats on the James, who came aboard from his flagship at Bermuda Hundred; also boarding there was the hesitating political general B. F. Butler. (No one mentioned Lincoln's young son, Tad, as being on this part of the inspection trip; it involved going closer to enemy artillery positions, so he may have remained at Grant's headquarters at City Point.)

As they steamed on up the river—Grant had a section of a pontoon bridge on which his men had crossed the James opened, so their vessel could go nearer to Richmond—this trip gave Lincoln a close look at an area of the front and proved interesting in terms of what the principal figures did and did not say. Here was Grant, who had not wanted to have this political figure Butler serve under him as a general and felt that Butler had repeatedly failed him. (Nine days after this, he would write Halleck a letter exploring ways of "sending Gen. Butler to another [and less demanding] field of duty," something that proved to be politically impossible to do at the time. Seven months in the future, after more of Butler's incompetence and blundering, Grant would finally receive Lincoln's permission to relieve him of command.) As for Butler, who Lincoln's intermediary Cameron approached to run for vice president, he had congratulated Lincoln on his renomination, but at the same time wrote his wife, "This country has more vitality than any on earth if it can stand this kind of administration for another four years."

Porter, a twenty-seven-year-old West Pointer, had never seen Lincoln before the president's arrival at City Point for this three-day visit. He wrote that Lincoln's features showed "the deep lines which had been graven on him by the mental strain to which he had been subjected for nearly four years." Lincoln and Grant enjoyed each other's company, and as the vessel went upstream, Porter noted an example of the president's unique way of characterizing people. "When his attention was called to some particularly strong positions that had been seized and fortified, he remarked to Butler: 'When Grant once gets possession of a place, he holds on to it as if he had inherited it.'"

Lincoln mixed his appreciation for Grant's tenacity with his feelings about the human costs of this campaign. According to Porter, "Several times, when contemplated battles were spoken of, he said: 'I cannot pretend to advise, but I do sincerely hope that all may be accomplished with as little bloodshed as possible.'" Just as Grant had sent Lincoln the message from the Wilderness, "There will be no turning back," he now displayed the same determination. The Richmond newspapers defiantly said of Grant's efforts to take the Confederate capital that it would be "a long summer's day before he does his work," but Lincoln later told his secretary John Hay that during this visit Grant expressed certainty he would prevail: "He is as sure of doing it as he is of anything in the world."

Porter also described Lincoln sitting in front of Grant's headquarters tent at City Point in the evening, surrounded by officers of Grant's staff as he "told some of the stories for which he had become celebrated." He wrote:

He did not tell a story merely for the sake of the anecdote, but to point a moral or clench a fact. . . . He seemed to recollect every incident in his experience and weave it into material for his stories. One evening a sentinel whose post was near enough to catch most of the President's remarks was heard to say, "Well, that man's got a powerful memory and a mighty poor forgettery."

He seldom indulged even in a smile until he reached the climax of a humorous narration; then he joined heartily with the listeners in the laugh which followed. He usually sat in a low camp-chair, and wound his legs around each other as if in an effort to get them out of the way, and with his long arms he accompanied what he said with all sorts of odd gestures.

III

"The President arrived today from the front," John Hay wrote in his diary on June 23, "sunburnt and fagged, but still refreshed and cheered." Despite the casualties and the failure to take Petersburg, Hay said that Lincoln "found the Army in fine health, good position, and good spirits." (As for public opinion at this point, while Lincoln was on that visit a reporter in Washington sent a story to California saying, "Just now the public feeling about military matters is one of depression and anxiety.")

In the next days, after sending Attorney General Edward Bates a query that helped resolve the question of whether black troops should receive pay equal to whites'—a question finally resolved in their favor—Lincoln had the opportunity to act on a constitutional issue that went to the core of past and present attitudes, including his own, about slavery. The issue—some regarded it as being a purely legal matter that did not require an interpretation of the Constitution—was remarkable in that it still existed. Thirty-eight months into a war that had the extinction of slavery as one of its principal objectives, the Fugitive Slave Act remained on the books.

Of all the damning aspects of slavery, the fact that slaves continually attempted to gain their freedom by running away provided its most dramatic indictment. This legislation, first enacted in 1793 and strengthened in 1850 as part of the long-settled legal precedent that treated a slave as an object, personal property like a carriage or a clock, mandated that an escaped slave must be returned to his or her owner. In 1864, at a time when Sherman's slow advance toward Atlanta freed more slaves every day, it remained a law, although one that was increasingly ignored. That paradox found its equal in the fact that the Emancipation Proclamation purported to free the slaves in states that were "in rebellion." The Northern states had already passed their own individual state laws that declared slavery illegal, but the Proclamation left the slaves in the Border States, which had not seceded and were thus not "in rebellion," in a legal limbo, awaiting a comprehensive overriding action that permanently ended slavery everywhere. This could only be accomplished by the proposed constitutional amendment that Lincoln wanted and that the Democrats in Congress had recently rejected.

The status of runaway slaves had been the subject of the 1857 Supreme Court decision in the case of *Dred Scott v. Sandford*, which held that slaves were not United States citizens and that Dred Scott, a slave who lived for a time on "free soil" in the Louisiana Territory, had not thereby gained the status of being a free person and still belonged to his owner. The man who wrote that opinion was Chief Justice Roger Brooke Taney, who in 1864 still presided over the Court as an invalid at the age of eighty-seven. The son of a Maryland planter, Taney had freed his own slaves in 1818 but felt that the institution of slavery was protected under the Constitution, citing the Constitution's words that fugitive slaves "shall be delivered up."

During his years as a lawyer and rising politician, Lincoln had walked a tightrope on this subject. Convinced that the Constitution as it stood did in fact favor slaveholders in these cases, he was more interested in trying to bring slavery itself to an end, and thus start a new page in American history. As a practicing attorney, in his years at the Illinois bar he took cases representing clients on both sides of the issue. In 1849, during his term as a congressman, he developed a bill intended to abolish slavery in the District of Columbia. Lincoln had hoped that by including language to "deliver up to their owners, all fugitive slaves escaping into said district," he might placate Southern congressmen, but they saw it as the antislavery document it was, while Northern abolitionists rejected the idea of returning any escaped slave. Finding little support for his proposed legislation, he never introduced it.

On the eve of war twelve years later, as a newly elected president, Lincoln continued to hope for peace. In his inaugural address on March 4, 1861, he said to the South, "We must not be enemies," and indicated that as part of his conciliatory stance he stood ready to enforce the act. In the event of secession, he needed to keep the slaveholding Border States on the side of the Union, and to do that he could not then call for the repeal of the Fugitive Slave Act. When the war came and Union forces began advancing into the South, thousands of slaves escaped behind Union lines, creating a situation in which many noncombatant slave owners appeared at Union camps demanding their return. For a time, some United States Army officers handed them over.

Lincoln saw that this must stop, but moved into the overall problem tentatively. His friend Orville Browning of Illinois, then a senator, wrote in his diary that Lincoln had this to say in a conversation on July 7, 1861, eleven weeks after the surrender of Fort Sumter. "We also discussed the negro question, and agreed upon this as upon other things that the government . . . should [not] send back to bondage such as came to our armies, but that we could not have them in camp, and that they must care for themselves until the war is over . . ."

A long road still lay ahead for American slaves: a year later, Congress passed the Second Confiscation Act, freeing the slaves of "persons engaged in or assisting the rebellion," and on September 22, 1862, Lincoln issued the Preliminary Emancipation Proclamation, to become operative on January 1, 1863. (This produced the final irony: slaves in the Confederacy—"states in rebellion"—were considered to be free, while slaves in the Border States of Delaware, Maryland, Kentucky, and Missouri were not.) While Lincoln wanted slaves to be free, wherever they were, in his conversation with Browning he was still thinking, just as his postmaster general Montgomery Blair had, about colonization as being at least a partial solution to the nation's racial problem.

The idea of freeing slaves and sending them back to Africa had a long history. The African nation of Liberia was created by sending freed American slaves there: the concept, originated during the Monroe administration, gave that country's capital its name of Monrovia. Central America had replaced Africa in the minds of those interested in giving freed slaves a new life in what Lincoln called "a climate congenial to them." On August 14, 1862, Lincoln received a delegation of five leaders of the black community at the White House. On the one hand, he was the first president ever to meet with a group of black men to discuss their status in American society; on the other, he came close to telling them that their presence on the North American continent had caused the war, and that therefore the war was their fault. He also conveyed his belief that they had no real future as citizens of the United States. While he told them that blacks suffered "the greatest wrong inflicted on any people," he saw no solution to this on American soil. "We are different races," he told them. "We should be separated . . . but for your race among us there could not be war, although many men engaged on either side do not care for you one way or another." He urged them to support efforts to expatriate themselves, and promised to work for a society of their own in a new place where they would all be equal to each other and subordinate to no one.

The abolitionist editor Fredrick Douglass, the nation's foremost black leader and not one of the five freedmen with whom Lincoln spoke, found Lincoln's remarks to be infuriating. As a freedman, Douglass had voted for Lincoln in 1860 and written articles in his support; hearing of what Lincoln said at this meeting in the White House, Douglass felt betrayed. He dashed off a statement that Lincoln's words revealed "all his inconsistencies, his pride of race and blood, his contempt for Negroes and his canting hypocrisy," and called him "a genuine representative of American prejudice and Negro hatred."

Still wishing to try colonization, in 1862 Lincoln signed a contract on behalf of the government in which a shady figure named Bernard Kock was paid $50 a head to settle blacks in Haiti. The venture ended in disaster: Kock was expelled by the 500 settlers he was supposed to protect and nurture, and the government later repatriated them to the United States. Another plan had remained under consideration; now at the end of June 1864, Lincoln finally dropped a scheme to send 500 able-bodied black men to the Chiriqui Lagoon in what would later become Panama, to start a colony of American freedmen in a location that had the potential to be an outpost of American empire. A man owning several hundred thousand acres of land there, millionaire shipbuilder Ambrose W. Thompson of Philadelphia, pointed out that it had climate and soil ideal for growing cotton, and that the lagoon itself would make a fine naval base. He believed that the area contained many veins of coal, which he would sell to the United States Navy at half the price it could be bought anywhere else. (Whatever might have happened to this arrangement, governmental interest in it ceased because of opposition to the idea expressed by the neighboring states of Honduras, Nicaragua, and Costa Rica.)

Finally, on June 28 of 1864, out of the welter of so many problems and attitudes regarding slavery, Lincoln had before him a bill he had long wished to see. The Congress, while not as a whole ready to vote slavery out of existence, had repealed the Fugitive Slave Act of 1850 and all other legislation for "rendition" [return] of fugitive slaves. He signed the bill into law.

As for Chief Justice Taney, much as many in the North disdained him for his *Dred Scott* decision and other views sympathetic to the white South, an accurate view of his relationship with Lincoln would not display the president as a knight in shining armor. Taney continued to have considerable support for his decision in *Ex parte Merryman*, his holding that even in wartime Lincoln had no right to suspend habeas corpus by executive order. From the outset of this dispute, Lincoln in effect defied Taney and continued these often arbitrary jailings. In his Fourth of July message to Congress in 1861, Lincoln stated that he would not let "the government itself go to pieces" over what he considered to be a narrow interpretation of the law on which Taney based his *Merryman* holding. Supporting Lincoln, on March 3, 1863, the Congress passed a Habeas Corpus Indemnity Act. It said in part, "during the present rebellion, the President . . . is authorized to suspend the privilege of the writ of *habeas corpus* in any case throughout the United States or any part thereof." Taney's saddened response to this, and to other actions that he believed unconstitutionally suspended civil liberties, came in a letter to an old friend: "The supremacy of the military power over the civil seems to be established, & the public mind has acquiesced in it & sanctioned it."

IV

On the same day that Lincoln signed the bill repealing the Fugitive Slave Act, he wrote a letter to Secretary of the Treasury Chase concerning an opening for the position of assistant treasurer in New York City. The job was the second-most-important in the Treasury Department after that held by Chase himself. Like Lincoln, Chase felt great daily pressure, in his case caused by the difficulties in providing the immense sums needed to finance the war. Chase now attended few cabinet meetings; he and the president had often been at odds, and his transparent failed backstage efforts to get the Republican nomination for himself had soured things between them.

To fill the key position in New York created by a resignation, Chase wanted to appoint Maunsell B. Field, who for some months had been acting as an assistant secretary of the treasury in Washington. Lincoln's friend Noah Brooks thought that Field's biggest contribution in that job had been "to superintend the fitting up of Chase's private offices with Axminster carpets, gilded ceilings, velvet furniture, and other luxurious surroundings." The Register of the treasury, a former Vermont state senator named Lucius E. Chittenden, admired Chase but described Field as a nonentity with "no financial or political standing." Apparently expecting Lincoln to sign on the dotted line, Chase sent his request for approval of Field's appointment accompanied by a blank nomination form "for your signature if approved." He had followed this with a note suggesting a private conversation about the matter. Lincoln replied, "I do not think Mr. Field a very proper man for the place, but I would trust your judgment, and forego this, were the greater difficulty out of the way."

Lincoln explained "the greater difficulty." He had supported Chase in two situations that brought the New York Republican establishment to what Lincoln described as "the verge of open revolt": one was the retention of an unpopular official, Hiram Barney, as collector of customs at New York and the other was the appointment of Judge John T. Hogeboom "as general Appraiser." This had caused Lincoln so much trouble that he sent John Nicolay to New York in a poorly received attempt to mollify the feelings of the Republican leader Thurlow Weed. If Lincoln now appointed Field, he would also be going squarely against the expressed wishes of two of his strongest supporters, the influential senators from New York, Ira Harris and Edwin D. Morgan. The latter, who had served as governor of the state, was the recently retired chairman of the Republican National Committee and the man who presided over the Baltimore convention that nominated Lincoln just three weeks before. "Strained as I already am, at this point," Lincoln now wrote Chase, "I do not think I can make this appointment in the direction of still greater strain."

As a former governor of Ohio, Chase should have been able to read Lincoln's words for what they were: one politician telling another that he had done a lot for him, and could not give him this next thing he wanted. Lincoln continued to think well of Chase's performance in handling the Union's finances, and intended to do a lot for Chase, in a different area of government. Although Chase had not yet received the message, a few days before this Lincoln had asked Congressman Samuel Hooper of Massachusetts to pass the word to Chase that he intended to name him to the Supreme Court, to replace Chief Justice Taney, now gravely ill and expected to die soon. Within that lay the implied suggestion that Chase could resign from the cabinet, relieving the tension between them, and be confident that he would accede to an even more important position that was both prestigious and permanent.

At this moment, even without knowing what Lincoln was prepared to give him, Chase remained one of the most powerful men in the government, an influential figure running a department that had 10,000 or more employees. As events would prove, he did not understand that Lincoln's renomination had for the moment strengthened the president's position. Chase thought he held cards stronger than they were. Lincoln had refused to accept three previous resignations, and Chase felt that when he sent a fourth, the president would back down and give him the appointment he wanted for Field.

Acting on that assumption, on June 29, Chase wrote Lincoln a short letter that began by referring to the specific "difficulty" about Field's appointment, and went on to say:

> . . . *I cannot help feeling that my position here is not altogether agreeable to you; and it is certainly too full of embarrassment and difficulty and painful responsibility to allow in me the least desire to retain it.*
>
> *I think it my duty therefore to enclose to you my resignation. I shall regard it as a real relief if you think it proper to accept it; and I will most cheerfully tender to my successor any aid he may find useful in entering upon his duties.*

The next day Chase was at the Capitol, having a conversation with Senator William Fessenden of Maine, the chairman of the Senate Finance Committee, and Congressman Justin Smith Morrill of Vermont. As they discussed a proposal he had made to raise taxes, Chase said this occurred.

> *While we were talking a Messenger came in to summon Mr. Fessenden to the Senate. The Messenger said something privately and then [Fessenden] came back to me saying, "Have you resigned[?] I am called to the Senate and told that the President has sent in the nomination of your successor." I told him I had tendered my resignation but had not been informed till now of its acceptance. He expressed his surprise and disap-*

pointment and we parted—He to the Senate and I to the [Treasury] Department.

At his office, Chase found this, from Lincoln:

Your resignation of the office of Secretary of the Treasury, sent me yesterday, is accepted. Of all I have said in commendation of your ability and fidelity, I have nothing to unsay; and yet you and I have reached a point of mutual embarrassment in our official relation which it seems can not be overcome, or longer sustained, consistently with the public service.

Your Obt. Svt.
A. Lincoln

Shocked, Chase wrote in his diary, "I had found a great deal of embarrassment from him, but what he had from me I could not imagine. . . ." The things Chase "could not imagine" included his lying to the president about his knowledge of the Pomeroy Circular that promoted his own presidential ambitions and his nearly constant battles to have his way in everything touching his department, as well as in regard to appointments outside his preserve.

Lincoln left no doubt that Chase had at last gone too far. John Brough, governor of Chase's state of Ohio, was in Washington and came swiftly to Lincoln. Referring to the situation as "another Treasury imbroglio," he asked, "Is it beyond mediation?" Lincoln let Brough get as far as saying, "I think it can be arranged," and then told him, speaking of Chase's past resignations and forgetting one of them, "But this is the third time he has thrown this at me, and I do not think I am called on to beg him to take it back." Lincoln put it more bluntly when he told his secretary John Hay why he finally came to this: "I thought I could not stand it any longer." He also gave a graphic description of the moments before he started writing his acceptance of Chase's resignation. "I put my pen into my mouth, and *grit my teeth* upon it. I did not long reflect."

Events moved swiftly. Lincoln sent a telegram to David Tod of Youngstown, Ohio, a War Democrat who was a former governor of that state and a lawyer and businessman who made a fortune in railroads and mining. It read: "I have nominated you to be Secretary of the Treasury in place of Gov. Chase who has resigned. Please come without a moment's delay."

At about the same time Tod received this in Ohio, the five members of the Senate Finance Committee arrived in Lincoln's office, led by their chairman William Fessenden. According to John Hay, who was present, "They not only objected to any change, but specifically protested against the nomination of Tod as too little known and too inexperienced for the place." Lincoln met them head-on, telling them that he "had little personal acquaintance with Tod, that he had nominated him on account of the high opinion he had formed of him as Governor of Ohio . . . he could not, in justice to himself or Tod, withdraw the nomination." He also pulled Chase's previous resignations out of a drawer and read them to the committee, along with the conciliatory replies he had made to what had been the Secretary's threats to leave.

That evening, Lincoln received Tod's answer: "The condition of my health forbids the acceptance of the distinguished position you offer me." Lincoln immediately sent Hay to the Capitol, "to communicate this information to the Senators," as Hay wrote, "so that no vote might be taken on the nomination." By early the next morning, Lincoln had decided to replace Chase with Fessenden, who as chairman of the Senate Finance Committee had copious knowledge of Treasury affairs. By naming Fessenden, a Radical, he might also soothe the anger of the Radicals, who had numbered Chase among them. When he gave this written nomination to Hay to carry to the Senate chamber, Hay told him that Fessenden "was then waiting in the ante-room to see him."

From what happened at that moment and what Lincoln later told him, Hay reconstructed what came next. Lincoln began by telling Hay, "Start at once for the Senate, and then let Fessenden come in."

> The Senator . . . began immediately to discuss the question of the vacant place in the Treasury, suggesting the name of [Comptroller of the Currency] Hugh McCulloch. The President listened for a while with a smile of amusement, and then told him that he had already sent his nomination to the Senate. Fessenden leaped to his feet, exclaiming, "You must withdraw it. I cannot accept." "If you decline," said the President, "you must do it in open day, for I shall not recall the nomination." "We talked about it for some time," said the President, "and he went away less decided in his refusal."

As for what happened at the Senate when Hay handed in the nomination of one of their own senior committee chairmen, he reported that "the nomination was instantly confirmed, the executive session lasting no more than a minute." In poor health and not wanting the job in any case, Fessenden still intended to decline the post. He told Secretary of War Stanton that he thought taking on the Treasury might kill him. Stanton, who had been working night and day at the War Department for twenty-seven months, replied, "Very well. You cannot die better than in trying to save your country." When Fessenden said the same thing to Lincoln the following morning, the president told him that "the crisis was such as demanded any sacrifice, even life itself."

Fessenden agreed to serve, but did not do so meekly. He had watched the cabinet members' infighting and some of their strained relations with the president. He was an old political horse trader; soon after accepting, he extracted from Lincoln a document written in Lincoln's hand that he filed among his papers. Referring to Fessenden, Lincoln wrote in part:

It is, and will be, my sincere desire, not only to advance the public interest, by giving him complete control of the department, but also to make his position agreeable to him.

In Cabinet my view is that in questions affecting the whole country there should be full and frequent consultations, and that nothing should be done particularly affecting any department without consultation with the head of that department.

The news of Chase's departure from office produced varied reactions. The *Chicago Tribune* called him "the greatest financier of the century." Even Lincoln's loyal secretaries Nicolay and Hay, when they later collaborated in writing about these times of crisis, spoke of Chase as "the greatest financial secretary the country had known since Alexander Hamilton." Others were ready to see Chase go. The painter Francis Carpenter, still in the White House and working on his portrait of Lincoln's cabinet watching him sign the Emancipation Proclamation, wrote of the arrival in Lincoln's office of "a delegation of New York bankers who, in the name of the banking community, expressed their satisfaction at the nomination [of Fessenden]." According to Hay, Mary Lincoln's New York friend Postmaster Abram Wakeman appeared to be "in high glee" and hailed Lincoln's action, saying that "he thought it a great thing to do: that henceforward the fifty [actually nearer ten] thousand Treasury agents would be friends of the President instead of enemies." The political Blair clan, always opposed to Chase, expressed delight: their patriarch Francis Preston Blair, Sr., wrote his son Francis, a major general, that Chase had "dropped off like a rotten pear."

On the evening of the day that the news of Lincoln's acceptance of Chase's resignation surged through Washington, the senior Blair's son Postmaster General Montgomery Blair and Attorney General Edward Bates came to the house of Secretary of the Navy Gideon Welles to discuss the matter. In his diary, Welles noted that "they gave me to understand that they were as much taken by surprise as myself" and went on to say of Chase's departure, "I look upon it as a blessing. The country could not go on a great while longer under his management, which has been one of expedients and no fixed principles, or profound or correct financial knowledge." Welles, whose Navy Department had constant dealings with Chase's Treasury Department, added this from his personal experience in a later entry: "Honest contracts are not fairly treated by the Treasury. Men are kept out of their money, after due, wrongfully. I had the material, and began the preparation, for a pretty strong statement to Mr. Chase at the time he resigned."

A different and urgently expressed view came from Register of the Treasury Lucius Chittenden. Within hours of hearing the news about Chase, he came to see Lincoln and told him that if Chase left, the financial impact on the nation would be "worse than another Bull Run defeat."

Lincoln often dealt with critical situations by telling folksy stories that served as political parables, but in reaffirming this decision he offered Chittenden a straightforward analysis of Chase's character and behavior.

> *I will tell you how it is with Chase. It is the easiest thing in the world for a man to fall into a bad habit. Chase has fallen into two bad habits. . . . He thinks he has become indispensable to the country. . . . He also thinks he ought to be President; he has no doubt whatever about that . . . [and all this makes him] irritable, uncomfortable, so that he is never perfectly happy unless he is thoroughly miserable.*

As for Chase, on the evening of the day he learned that Lincoln had let him go, he wrote in his diary, "So my official life closes." Chase followed this with an appreciation of his own accomplishments, including this: "I have laid broad foundations. Nothing but wise legislation—and especially bold yet judicious provision of taxes."

As many who knew him thought might prove to be the case, despite his "So my official life closes," even now Chase did not slam the door on his presidential ambitions. Lincoln was the Republican/National Union Party nominee for the election in November, but the Democrats had yet to hold their convention. Chase described himself as being able to become a Democrat "if the Democrats could only cut loose from slavery and go for freedom and the protection of labor by a national currency." Seven days after being dropped from the cabinet, before leaving to travel through New England he wrote an ambiguous diary entry in which he described himself as "not willing now to decide what duty may demand next fall." In one sense, Chase was dreaming; in another, he saw Lincoln as sailing into heavy seas, with the war becoming increasingly unpopular, a heavy Democratic vote mobilizing against him, and many Republicans, Radicals as well as those from the mainstream of the Party, opposed to his reelection. The incomplete record of the visits in New England that he now began to make showed him at many purely social gatherings, but he did more than attend dinner parties. Chase also had discussions with leading Republicans who could still be brought into a third-party movement, and such an effort would have to produce a candidate other than Lincoln or the presumptive Democratic candidate McClellan. "No man knows what *that gnawing* is till he has had it," Lincoln had said of Chase's hunger to be president. Chase continued to yearn for power.

JUNE OF 1864 had been an epic month, giving hope to the Union cause at the same time it demonstrated unresolved problems and the military and political pitfalls that could lie ahead. Lincoln needed good news, something better than his being nominated and that Grant was besieging Petersburg and Richmond while continuing to lose so many Northern lives.

Six hundred miles south of Washington, General Sherman fought a major battle during the same days that saw Lincoln deal with the Fugitive Slave Act and Chase's resignation. Having moved southeast from Chattanooga with 90,000 men at the same time Grant began his march into the Wilderness in early May, by late June he had come ninety miles through Georgia, fighting his way toward Atlanta. On June 27, Sherman threw 16,000 men at the Confederate defenses on Kennesaw Mountain, eighteen miles northwest of Atlanta. What happened across the next two days showed him to be, as in his failure at Missionary Ridge during the overall Union victory at Chattanooga, far better at the war of maneuver than in a head-on fight. Until Sherman's decision to fight at Kennesaw Mountain, on his march from Chattanooga he had managed to keep turning and outflanking the redoubtable Joseph E. Johnston, slowly pushing him back toward Atlanta. Avoiding as many pitched battles as he could, Sherman had nonetheless sustained 9,300 casualties—nothing compared to Grant's frightful losses, but still nearly 10 percent of the massive force with which he began his campaign. Unlike Grant's situation, replacements for Sherman's army took longer to reach him, and he also had to detach significant numbers from his main striking force to guard the one railway supply line running back to Chattanooga. Conversely, Joseph E. Johnston had been pushed back nearer his sources of replacements and supplies in Atlanta. As Johnston slowly yielded territory—thus far a total of ninety miles in fifty days—Sherman wrote of the situation, "Our enemy has gained strength by picking up his detachments." This meant that, as he retreated, Johnston had added to his main force the detachments that had guarded his now shortened supply lines.

Just why Sherman decided to change the nature of his campaign and try to defeat Johnston decisively in the big hills eighteen miles north of Atlanta never became clear. Intense heat and two weeks of rain had slowed down his moving columns, he thought that Johnston had chosen weak defensive positions, and he sensed that his troops wanted one big fight rather than to keep marching through red mud, occasionally skirmishing as they had been doing for seven weeks. He may also have wanted to cut down the enemy's numbers before marching even farther into hard-core Confederate territory, where he knew that able guerrillas and raiders such as the men under Nathan Bedford Forrest were operating. Finally, he could have felt, with reason, that tough as Johnston's men were, there in the hills, they might be just that much more formidable if they were in trenches surrounding Atlanta with their backs to the wall.

Whatever led to his decision, on the morning of June 27, Sherman sent a major portion of his 16,000 men in an assault up the steep 700-foot-high slope of Kennesaw Mountain. For once, the Confederates had a superiority in numbers, some thousand more than Sherman had. As the

Union troops neared the enemy trenches and other earthworks at the top of the massive hill, the defenders slaughtered them as they came. Sherman ordered a second attack, which was repulsed, and a third. A Confederate defender wrote of what he saw.

> *A solid line of blue came up the hill. My pen is unable to describe the scene of carnage that ensued in the next two hours. Column after column of Federal soldiers were crowded upon that line. No sooner would a regiment mount our works than they were shot down or surrendered. Yet still they came. . . . All that was necessary was to load and to shoot. In fact, I will ever think that the only reason that they did not capture our works was the impossibility of their living men to pass over the bodies of their dead men.*

Sherman reported the event unsparingly: "At all points the enemy met us with determined courage and in great force. . . . By 11:30 the assault was in fact over, and had failed." His Army of the West had lost 1,999 men killed and wounded, while the defenders lost only 270. Although Sherman's casualties in one morning were less than a third of those suffered by Grant's men in their first hour at Cold Harbor, Kennesaw Mountain was a Union disaster, and seen as such by friend and foe. Many in the North, resigned to a drawn-out bloody contest between Grant and Lee in Northern Virginia, had hoped that Sherman could provide a significant victory deep in the South that would raise Union morale and strengthen the faltering resolve to continue the war. The decisiveness with which Joseph E. Johnston had thrown back Sherman shocked them and gave Southerners new heart. After all, Grant's forces were virtually at the gates of Petersburg and Richmond, and being held right there by an iron defense; why should Sherman's men do any better, from eighteen miles outside of Atlanta? Even from where they now stood, day after day Sherman's frustrated men could see the smoke of Atlanta's factories in the distance. A soldier of the 104th Illinois shouted to an enemy outpost, "Hello, Johnny, how far is it to Atlanta?" and received the answer, "So far you'll never get there!"

As the news of Sherman's failure and its implications sank into the Northern public's mind, another potential disaster, literally and figuratively invisible, came into being. On June 25, the day before Lincoln signed the repeal of the Fugitive Slave Act, some Union soldiers from

Pennsylvania, coal miners by occupation, began digging a narrow tunnel at a point under the Union trenches besieging Petersburg. It would run for approximately 500 feet, 20 feet beneath the surface of the ground separating the Union and Confederate lines, and end under a redoubt on a knoll, a Confederate artillery position placed at a key corner of the enemy defenses known as Elliott's Salient. Eight thousand pounds of gunpowder would be brought through the tunnel and placed directly under the enemy fortification; when this "mine" was detonated, the explosion would destroy the men and cannons above. The calculation was that it would create a hole 30 feet deep, nearly 200 feet long and 60 or more feet wide. To exploit this sudden breach in the enemy lines, thousands of men from Burnside's Ninth Corps would dash across from their trenches, pour into and through the crater, climb up its sides, and fan out behind the Confederate defenses. From there, they would have a chance to capture Petersburg itself.

This project received endorsement at the highest level, largely by default. The 48th Pennsylvania Infantry had originally been composed almost entirely of some 800 miners from Schuylkill County. During the unsuccessful efforts to seize Petersburg, the regiment had fought as hard as any other unit of foot soldiers and had lost 75 of its men killed and wounded. (By this time, only 80 of the original 800 miners were still in the ranks.) When this unit took up its assigned positions for what promised to be a long and bloody siege, its commander, Lieutenant Colonel Henry Pleasants, who had been a prewar mining engineer, looked across at Elliott's Salient. Tired of seeing his men cut down by enemy musket balls as they rushed at hostile emplacements, it suddenly came to him that this was an enemy position that could be attacked from underground, with his men safe right where he stood while a mass of gunpowder did the work. He ran a quarter of a mile to the headquarters of his superior, Brigadier General Robert Potter. As quickly as he could get the general's attention, he told him, "We could blow that damned fort out of existence if we could put a mine shaft under it." Potter, a New Yorker who had been a lawyer in peacetime and knew nothing about engineering, nonetheless had been looking over at Elliott's Salient and been struck by the same idea. Now here he had an engineer who thought it could be done, and Potter wanted very much to try it.

The enthusiasm for the idea reached its high point right there. What followed demonstrated how bureaucracies can fail to promote good ideas and let bad ones slip through. Potter's superior, Burnside, met with Pleasants and Potter, and later wrote, "I authorized General Potter to commence the work, making the remark, if I remember right, that it could certainly do no harm to commence it, and it was probably better to have the men occupied in that way." Burnside agreed to "lay the matter before General Meade." In his turn, Meade told Burnside that siege operations of this sort lay outside the scope of his authority; the proposal should go to General Grant. When it reached the desk of the general-in-chief, Grant gave the scheme the same kind of tepid assent that Burnside had: this harmless digging would keep the troops busy. Planning ahead, Burnside made a decision. If all this materialized, he would use his division of black soldiers, his largest and currently most rested unit and the men Lincoln had recently visited with Grant, to lead the attack into the explosion's aftermath.

EIGHT

A PRETTY PLACE FROM WHICH TO DROP INTO A DARK, DRAMATIC SUMMER

As July began, the Lincolns moved out of the White House for the third summer to take up residence until autumn at a comfortable big Gothic Revival house with a stucco-covered brick exterior and a large porch on the grounds of the Soldiers' Home, a Federal establishment three miles northwest of the White House. Acquired in the 1850s, this peaceful wooded tract of 270 acres provided accommodation for two hundred pensioners, veterans of the old Regular Army, some of whom had served as far back as the War of 1812, and many who had been wounded in the Mexican War or in fighting the Indians. In these cooler surroundings, Lincoln would rise early as usual and eat his Spartan breakfast. Occasionally, he would spend the day working in the wood-paneled library of this house, but on most days he stepped out the door at some time after seven and climbed into a carriage. Surrounded by a cavalry escort riding with drawn sabers, he would be driven to the White House, arriving at his office half an hour later. His working days in the White House remained the same, but in the evenings his time of return varied. Despite the admonitions of Secretary of War Stanton and his friend Ward Lamon, the Federal marshal of the District of Columbia, Lincoln sometimes dispensed with his armed bodyguard, mounted a horse, and rode back to the Soldiers' Home through the dusk by himself.

The Lincolns' summer retreat had an atmosphere far less formal than that of the White House. Dinner guests or officials who came there on government business (Stanton and his family spent the summers in the big cottage next door, and Seward frequently visited in the evenings) found the president more relaxed. Lincoln enjoyed walking around the grounds near the house after supper, watching his energetic son Tad climb one of the many trees and often chatting with the young members of his mounted escort and the sentries guarding the grounds.

This fraternizing with the soldiers led to the president's forming a close friendship with forty-four-year-old Captain David V. Derickson, a prewar businessman from Meadville, Pennsylvania, now commander of Company K of the 150th Pennsylvania Infantry, one of that regiment's two companies camped there to provide security. During the summer of 1862, with Mary away much of the time, Derickson and the other company commander frequently dined with Lincoln. Some nights, Derickson would stay at the house, sleeping with Lincoln in his bed. At that time, this was not unusual—during his days traveling the circuit of Illinois county courthouses, Lincoln often shared a bed with other lawyers in rural taverns—but the closeness of this sudden friendship between the president and an army captain caused talk. When Lincoln was driven to the White House in the mornings, more often than not Derickson—one of his superior officers said he had "most pleasing manners"—sat beside him in the carriage, the two of them talking, and soon after the Battle of Antietam, Lincoln took him along on a four-day trip to visit McClellan's headquarters in western Maryland.

The reasons for this intimacy probably did not involve sexuality, but seemed more likely to spring from Lincoln's need for good company and moral support while he was still at the Soldiers' Home, staying there into the fall of 1862. Only a few months after Willie's death, Mary was away for the time, having taken Tad with her. Some of his Illinois friends had returned to Springfield after spending the first year of the war in Washington, while others still in Washington went on about their lives without him. On a daily basis, he faced the enormous problem of whether, or just when, to issue his Emancipation Proclamation. He felt the pressures of the tidal wave of demands that he relieve McClellan from command. Also—always somewhere in most of Lincoln's friendships—Derickson was a man of politics, albeit a minor one. Before the war, he had been a community leader, one of the founders of the Republican Party in Pennsylvania's Crawford County, and had organized a patriotic rally when the Confederates fired on Fort Sumter. As they talked on the first day they met, Lincoln invited Derickson to accompany him into town; on the way, as Derickson put it, Lincoln "made numerous inquiries" about who he was and what he had done to this point in his life. From his prodigious memory for names Lincoln decided that he had heard favorably of Derickson, either in relation to some appointment for which he had recently been considered, or from a letter Derickson did in fact write him three months before the war began, urging him to appoint Pennsylvanian Simon Cameron as secretary of war. Derickson also told Lincoln that one of his associates from Meadville had become a member of General Halleck's staff. This led to a situation in which on this same day he found Lincoln introducing him to Halleck—clearly, Lincoln saw him as being something more than just another junior officer. As they rode into the city together on many following mornings, Derickson recalled, Lincoln "discussed points that seemed to trouble him."

Now, in the summer of 1864, Derickson remained on duty at the Soldiers' Home, but during the summer of 1863, Mary Lincoln had been there almost constantly and would be there frequently in the coming months. There is no record of any continuing particular closeness between the captain and the president.

Pleasant though life at the Soldiers' Home could be, when Lincoln came in to his White House office during the first days of July, he found himself inundated with matters that once again demonstrated the scope of his responsibilities. On Saturday, July 2, he signed legislation amending the Pacific Railroad Act. Four months before this, he had signed the "Order Designating Starting Point of Union Pacific Railroad." Now this legislation to enable the building of a transcontinental railway expanded the subsidies Congress gave to the Union Pacific and Central Pacific railroads in 1862. That line was to run from Omaha to San Francisco, a distance of close to 2,000 miles. As if it were not enough to put that titanic project into its first stages in the middle of a war, the amended act granted public lands in the Pacific Northwest to be used for railroad and telegraph lines. As part of what he signed, Lincoln chartered a new company, the Northern Pacific. This corporation had as its enormously ambitious

objective the construction of a line 1,450 miles long that would run west
from Lake Superior, possibly starting at Duluth, Minnesota, to the Pacific Ocean. Whatever its exact route, it would open many millions of
acres of western lands for settlement. Those lands were already becoming available under the Homestead Act, which Lincoln had signed on
May 20, 1862, five days after he created the Agriculture Department.
Under that law, designed to encourage farming, a citizen could gain title
to 160 acres of land if he paid a fee of $10 and lived there for five years.

To complete his vision of productively settled western lands, Lincoln
had on his desk a bill titled "An Act to Encourage Immigration," to be
enacted into law in two more days. He had given his views on this subject
in his Annual Message to Congress the previous December, stating:

> . . . *there is still a great deficiency of laborers in every field of industry,*
> *especially in agriculture and in our mines, as well of iron and coal as of*
> *the precious metals. While the demand for labor is thus increased here,*
> *tens of thousands of persons, destitute of remunerative occupation, are*
> *thronging our foreign consulates, and offering to emigrate to the United*
> *States if essential, but very cheap, assistance can be afforded them. It is*
> *easy to see that, under the sharp discipline of civil war, the nation is be-*
> *ginning a new life. This noble effort demands the aid, and ought to re-*
> *ceive the attention and support of the government.*

How well the parts of Lincoln's plan for the western lands fit together
was demonstrated by the fact that European immigrants, eager to start
working the land under the terms of the Homestead Act, marveled at a
government that would give them "free farms." By this point in Lincoln's
administration, at least half a million immigrants had come from Europe,
and many thousands of them were settling west of the Mississippi River.

Later on this Saturday, Lincoln received in his office Congressman
George W. Julian of Indiana. Julian was a strong and influential Radical, a
member of the congressional Joint Committee on the Conduct of the
War, and an enthusiastic proponent of punitive measures to be taken
against Confederates if the Union forces gained victory. Thirty-two
months before this meeting with Lincoln, whom he continued to respect
despite the increasing differences between their political positions, Julian
set forth his views on any postwar settlement in a speech to the House of
Representatives:

The rebels have demanded a "reconstruction" on the basis of slavery; let us give them a "reconstruction" on the basis of freedom. Let us convert the rebel States into conquered provinces, remanding them to the status of mere Territories, and governing them as such in our discretion. Under no circumstances should we consent to end this struggle on terms that would leave us where we began it. . . .

Although Julian was strongly committed to the Radicals' vindictive approach to the Confederacy, he tended to play a lone hand. Neither he nor Lincoln left a record of what they discussed. In light of what he knew would soon land on Lincoln's desk, he may have been emphasizing his ardent feeling that, being rebels, Confederates should have their lands officially confiscated as they fell into Union hands. He may also have been acting as a scout for his fellow Radicals, trying to sound out the president concerning positions on which they and Lincoln varied only in degree. More problems would confront Lincoln soon, thrown at him by Radicals who did not get along with him as Julian did.

As Julian left the White House, an entirely different situation was developing. Unknown to anyone in the nearby War Department, Confederate general Jubal Early was leading a force of 20,000 men down Virginia's Shenandoah Valley, passing through the town of Winchester, sixty miles west of Washington, which had changed hands dozens of times during the war. Several thousand of Early's men belonged to Richard Ewell's formidable Second Corps that had been commanded by the late "Stonewall" Jackson, and under him had a record of moving so swiftly that they became known as Jackson's "foot cavalry."

Two weeks before this, Early had repulsed Union general David Hunter at Lynchburg, much farther away from Washington. Hunter then began an astonishingly roundabout retreat through the West Virginia mountains under harsh conditions that badly depleted his strength. Harassed first by Confederate cavalrymen and thereafter by guerrilla raiding parties, he managed to get his forces as far from Washington as Parkersburg, West Virginia, on the Ohio River 250 miles from the capital. Hunter and his ragged men marched themselves completely out of the theater of operations; one Union general after another expected Hunter to reappear and play an important role in stopping Early somewhere, but his force ceased to be a factor in the rapidly evolving situation in the

Shenandoah Valley. (After the war, when Hunter wrote to Robert E. Lee, in effect asking Lee to speak well of how he had handled his retreat, Lee replied, "I certainly expected you to retreat by way of the Shenandoah Valley, and was gratified at the time that you preferred the route through the mountains to Ohio—leaving the Valley open for General Early's advance into Maryland.")

Early's ability to move quickly created an eerie echo of the question that had existed on New Year's Day, when Lincoln sent a wire to Union headquarters at Harpers Ferry anxiously asking for "anything new" about a rumor that Early might be within striking distance of the capital. This time Early's forces were in fact making a march that would, unless they were stopped, put them into the area northwest of Washington within days. They were coming closer every hour, and no one in authority saw the growing threat.

For hours the next day, a Sunday, no one in Washington knew of Early's movements, although Lincoln came in to the White House from the Soldiers' Home and worked in his office, and both Stanton and Halleck were at work in the War Department at the corner of the White House grounds. At two-thirty in the afternoon Halleck received a telegram from Major General Franz Sigel, who had been relieved of field command after his defeat at New Market, and was now at Martinsburg in administrative charge of assorted units of the West Virginia reserve division. Sigel had learned that Early was coming his way. He did not know where to find Hunter's worn-out retreating force to try to get their help, but enumerated the units available in the immediate area that he could use to oppose this impending attack. They totaled some 6,000 men, few of them equal to Early's advancing veterans. "I have taken command of all these troops," Sigel wired Halleck, "and will concentrate them at a proper point in case of emergency."

Alerted to the danger, Halleck tried several times to telegraph Hunter but could not reach him. At 4 P.M., Halleck wired Grant at City Point, reporting that he had heard nothing from or about Hunter. Making the assumption that Early was indeed marching down the Shenandoah Valley toward Washington, he said of the currently available defenders, "The three principal officers on the line of the road are Sigel, [Major General Julius] Stah[e]l, and [Brigadier General] Max Weber. You can therefore judge what probability there is of a good defence, if the enemy should attack the line in force."

An hour later, Grant replied to Halleck that Early could not be threatening Sigel. "Early's corps is now here," Grant said, referring to Lee's forces defending Petersburg and Richmond. He based that statement on information from Confederate deserters, but soon discovered that those deserters had no firsthand knowledge of what they said, and merely had heard that Early's men had moved back to the east from Lynchburg, rather than going to the northeast down the Valley. At 8 P.M., Grant sent Halleck this correction to his earlier communication but heard nothing further from Washington.

On the following day, Monday the Fourth of July, Grant sent Halleck a telegram at 4 P.M. that sounded as if he still considered the capital to be safe from a serious threat. On the one hand, he told his chief of staff of a new report: "A deserter who came in this morning reports that Ewell[']s Corps [of which Early's division was a part] has not returned but is off in the valley with the intention of going into Maryland and Washington City. . . . I think it is advisable to hold all of the forces you can about Washington[,] Baltimore, Cumberland and Harpers Ferry ready to concentrate against any advance of the enemy." On the other hand, he added that if Hunter's men could be located and ordered into place, "there ought to be veteran force to meet anything the enemy have and if once put to flight he ought to be followed as long as possible." Grant closed by repeating that there might not be an impending attack. "This report of Ewell[']s Corps . . . is only the report of a deserter and we have similar authority for it being here and on the right of Lee[']s army. We know however that it does not occupy this position."

Although these exchanges among generals had been going on since the day before, the White House still heard nothing about 20,000 Confederates under an able general approaching Washington from the northwest. On the morning of the Fourth of July, Lincoln knew nothing of this. The principal matter before him, one that foreshadowed a great political struggle, arose in a visit made to the office he sometimes used at the Capitol building. Even in the middle of a war, Congress was about to take its summer recess, adjourning at noon; all morning, messengers from the Senate and House had been bringing him bills, passed by both houses.

To become law, these documents needed to be signed before the clock struck twelve. Lincoln signed most of them as soon as an aide placed them before him, but he put a particularly important one aside, and, as Nicolay and Hay said in their joint memories of that day, "went on with the other work of the moment."

The proposed law that Lincoln put aside became known as the Wade-Davis bill. He knew what the bill contained—it had been debated in the House and Senate, and extensively discussed and in one aspect changed in conference between the two houses—but Lincoln probably had not seen its final version and could have felt with good reason that bringing it to him at the last minute was an all-out effort to push it through. The legislation went beyond Lincoln's plans for what should be required of the Confederate states and their white population to make themselves eligible to reenter the nation's political process. The most significant difference was a requirement that 50 percent of prewar voters, rather than 10 percent, must take an oath of future loyalty to the United States. It also specified that no high-ranking Confederate civilian officials or military officers could take part in any postwar reorganization, and further specified that if the bill passed and such prominent Confederates continued to play their roles in the war, they were forever barred from having United States citizenship.

This bill had been eloquently introduced and resolutely moved through the House by Representative Henry Winter Davis of Maryland, a Radical whose relationship with Lincoln was described in these terms by Nicolay and Hay:

> *In spite of all the efforts which the President made to be on friendly terms with Mr. Davis, the difference between them constantly widened. Mr. Davis grew continually more confirmed in his attitude of hostility to every proposition of the President. He became one of the most severe and least generous critics of the Administration. He came at last to consider the President as unworthy of even respectful treatment; and Mr. Seward . . . was continually attacked by him as . . . little less than a traitor to his country.*

Davis's colleague in writing this bill was Senator Benjamin Franklin Wade of Ohio, known as "Bluff Ben." Chairman of the Joint Committee on the Conduct of the War from its creation in December of 1861, he believed that every Confederate should be considered a traitor and held that "mercy to traitors is cruelty to loyal men."

On some parts of the controversial proposed law, Lincoln and the Radicals could agree. His views coincided with the bill's provision that with the end of the war, all slaves must be free, but he and the Radicals differed on what needed to be done. Lincoln remained of the opinion that an amendment to the Constitution must be enacted to supersede his Emancipation Proclamation, which held force only because of his assumption of wartime emergency powers. The Radicals believed that the bill they now wanted to enact could by itself abolish slavery forever. They felt that Lincoln's plan of letting states reenter the political process if one could find 10 percent of their prewar voters ready to take an oath of loyalty was not enough. Lincoln thought that requiring 50 percent was asking an impossibility and would kill any chance of starting the reconstruction of Confederate states as their territory fell into the hands of Federal troops. The Radicals saw the seceded Confederate states as being out of the Union and requiring readmission; Lincoln thought that to regard them in that light would set a precedent that a state could in fact leave the Union, rather to hold as he did that a state might be rebellious—he sometimes used the word "insurrectionary"—but remained one of the United States whether it liked it or not.

All this came to a head as Lincoln continued signing bills into law late on the morning of the Fourth of July. At some point, the members of his cabinet had entered and taken seats. In came a small but politically powerful group of Radicals. As Nicolay and Hay put it, "Several prominent members entered in a state of anxiety over the fate of the bill." Wade and Davis were not among them, presumably to avoid waving a red flag at a bull. Their spokesman was Senator Zachariah Chandler of Michigan, who forthrightly asked Lincoln if he intended to sign the Wade-Davis Bill.

Lincoln looked at him and said, "This bill has been placed before me a few moments before Congress adjourns. It is a matter of too much importance to be swallowed in that way."

Raising his voice, Chandler suddenly appealed for a unified Republican position. Referring to the coming November election and the area of his own state, he told Lincoln, "If it is vetoed, it will damage us fearfully in the Northwest. The important point is that one prohibiting slavery in the reconstructed states."

As the clock ticked, Lincoln replied, "That is the point on which I doubt the authority of the Congress to act."

Speaking of the Emancipation Proclamation, Chandler shot back, "It is no more than you have done yourself."

Lincoln answered him, "I conceive that I may in an emergency do things on military grounds which cannot be done constitutionally by Congress."

Realizing that Lincoln did not intend to sign the bill, Chandler walked out, "expressing his deep chagrin," with the other Radicals behind him. After they left, the members of the cabinet began assuring Lincoln that he had done the right thing. Although he did not tell them this at the time, he felt that the Wade-Davis bill had within it an acceptable plan for reconstruction to be adopted by any Confederate state wishing to use it, but he did not want to be committed to any one specific plan, which signing this bill would have done. He pointed out to them once again that he had "earnestly favored the movement for an amendment to the Constitution abolishing slavery, which passed the Senate and failed in the House." The clock struck noon; he had neither signed the bill nor vetoed it, and it died for that congressional session by default, in what was known as a "pocket veto."

When his action became known as the Senate and House adjourned, it caused an uproar, many siding with Lincoln and many attacking what he had done. In his diary entry for that evening, the recently resigned Salmon Chase wrote bitterly that he believed they had seen a stratagem "of possible *reconstruction with slavery*, which neither the President nor his advisers have, in my opinion, abandoned." One thing remained certain: Lincoln had handed the Radicals a cudgel they intended to use.

While Lincoln still remained unaware of the threat to Washington, Early's forces seized the strategically important Union position at Harpers Ferry, fifty miles northwest of Washington; the troops stopped for hours while they consumed all the food and drink that the Union garrison had set out for their hastily-abandoned Fourth of July celebration. An infantryman from Louisiana wrote home that "our boys got the Fourth of July dinner" and listed such delicacies as oysters, wines, hard liquor, and all kinds of fruit, jams, and meat. Ironically, at Charlestown, West Virginia, Confederate sympathizers hurt their cause by plying the 43rd North Carolina with so much food and drink that the regiment became "half demoralized" and halted its march to join Early for more than a day.

Finally, on July 5, Lincoln gave evidence of being aware of the gathering threat. Possibly because he mistrusted the way the military was gathering and handling its intelligence, he sent off a telegram to J. W. Garrett, president of the Baltimore & Ohio Railroad, asking him what he might be learning from his railway men and telegraph operators. No immediate reply came, but Lincoln directed Stanton to ask the governors of Pennsylvania and New York each to send 12,000 men, militia or volunteers, to serve as "Hundred Days Men" to defend Washington. No one could say when they might arrive. By now, Grant had started to organize some forces to send to both Baltimore and Washington, but the transport ships to take the reinforcements for Washington down the James and around to the Potomac would not be ready for another day.

People in Washington gradually became aware that large numbers of Confederates were probably marching toward them, but the newspapers kept that in doubt. They would put out an edition with a headline that the rebels had crossed the line from Virginia into Maryland, and a few hours later print editions saying the first reports had been only an "idle scare." The citizens went on about their business, but Halleck knew that everything must be done to strengthen what he had available. He had rifles distributed to the clerks who worked in government offices, and to wounded soldiers in the hospitals who were well enough to walk and raise the weapons to their shoulders. As of the Fourth of July, orders were given to units of the Veterans Reserve Corps, originally known as the Invalid Corps, to stand on alert. These men, officers and men unfit for field duty, served around the city as guards, or worked as nurses and cooks in the hospitals. Their weapons were twenty-year-old "buck and ball" muskets. Residents of Washington started seeing government clerks of all ages in civilian clothes awkwardly drilling in parks and empty lots. The city's defenses needed far more foot soldiers and artillerymen of good quality; it had many cannons, although some of the earthwork forts had fewer guns than might be needed against a determined attack on their particular front.

In response to further questions and warnings about a Confederate invasion, Lincoln, now as exhausted as before his visit to Grant's headquarters, replied, "We are doing as well as we can," and devoted his time to other matters. He pondered what to do about the effects of his "pocket veto" of the Wade-Davis Bill. The Radicals were saying that, once again, Lincoln was acting as a dictator—a claim underscored by his "Proclamation Suspending Writ of Habeas Corpus" issued on July 5 and specifically aimed at secessionists in Kentucky who he said were "inciting rebel forces to renew the . . . operations of civil war within the said State." The Radicals saw all this as proof of Lincoln's determination to rule by executive fiat, blocking the constitutional right of Congress to enact the nation's laws. Lincoln decided to take his case concerning the Wade-Davis veto directly to the people and began working with Attorney General Bates on a "Proclamation Concerning Reconstruction," to be published as soon as they had it drafted to his satisfaction.

In the midst of all this, he heard from Horace Greeley, the brilliant, often ambivalent, immensely influential editor of the *New York Tribune*. Greeley had been among those Republicans who spent the past spring trying to find a candidate other than Lincoln; now he wrote the president an extraordinary letter, one with a viewpoint far from that of the Radicals with whom Lincoln had been dealing. He enclosed a letter and telegram from an acquaintance of his, William Cornell Jewett, who went by the nickname of "Colorado" Jewett. The son of a rich family in Portland, Maine, Jewett had always had enough money to live a life of leisure, but had gone west and become involved in the promotion of gold mines in Colorado. A man whom Henry J. Raymond of the *New York Times* described as having a head "with so many screws loose," he had at times tried to pass himself off as being the son-in-law of the capitalist and railroad magnate Cornelius Vanderbilt. During the course of the war, Jewett had made three trips to Europe, acting in a private capacity as he tried to interest different governments in mediating a peace settlement—an interference in foreign affairs prohibited under Federal law. In the early months of 1863, Jewett had succeeded in getting Napoleon III to propose that Union and Confederate representatives should meet at a neutral site to discuss solutions ranging from possible reunification to recognition of the Confederacy as a separate nation. Lincoln and Secretary of State Seward had rejected the offer, partly on the grounds that to enter into such open-ended negotiations conferred upon the Confederacy a sovereign status they were not prepared to acknowledge. On August 29, 1863, Jewett wrote Lincoln a Southern-sympathizing letter about what he called Lincoln's "despotic policy," which he said was keeping him in power against "the will of the people." If only, Jewett lamented in that letter, Lincoln had after his inauguration implemented Jewett's recommendation that a Southerner should be made "Secretary of State, that would have prevented the War." (This was only one of a number of letters Jewett had sent Lincoln during the course of the war: John Hay eventually wrote Jewett that "in the choice of letters to be submitted to the personal attention of the President . . . I have to inform you that your letters are never so submitted.")

In the covering letter that Greeley sent Lincoln, forwarding the communications from Jewett, Greeley began with "I venture to inclose you a letter and a telegraphic dispatch received yesterday from our irrepressible friend, Colorado Jewett"—"friend" being an unusual way to refer to Jewett, whose hero was Lincoln's archcritic, the leading Copperhead figure Clement L. Vallandigham. In his messages to Greeley, Jewett said that he was on the Canadian side of Niagara Falls, with two Confederate emissaries he described as possessing "full & complete powers [to negotiate] for a peace." Jewett asked Greeley to come to Cataract House at Niagara Falls, or if Lincoln would permit them to cross the border, "they will come on & meet you." Jewett told Greeley that "the whole matter can be consummated by me you—them & President Lincoln."

Greeley did not vouch for the veracity of any of this but plunged into an eloquent plea, asking Lincoln to seize any effort to end the war. He referred to his certainty about "the anxiety of Confederates everywhere for peace," and added:

> *I venture to remind you that our bleeding, bankrupt, almost dying country also longs for peace—shudders at the prospect of fresh conscriptions, of further wholesale devastations and new rivers of human blood . . . a widespread conviction that the Government and its prominent supporters are not anxious for peace, and do not improve proffered opportunities to achieve it, is doing great harm now, and is morally certain, unless removed, to do far greater in the coming election. It is not enough that we desire a true and lasting peace; we ought to demonstrate and establish the truth beyond cavil.*

Wrong and naïve as he could sometimes be, the fifty-three-year-old Greeley had for twenty-three years been the editor of not only the *New York Tribune,* but also the *Weekly Tribune,* the latter with a circulation of 200,000, many of its readers in such politically pivotal states as Illinois and Ohio. Lincoln had to listen to him. Greeley was passionate in his desire for peace, but he also reiterated the point that, whatever might come of any negotiation, it was important for Lincoln to convince both the Democrats and the South that his administration would listen to reasonable peace proposals. He listed what some of those should be, including the idea that the Union should pay the Confederacy $400,000,000 "in compensation for the losses . . . by the abolition of slavery." Using the word "ultimatum" in its sense of being a final offer, Greeley ended by saying to Lincoln that, in any case, "I beg you to invite those now at Niagara to exhibit their credentials and submit their ultimatum."

Lincoln sensed trouble in all this. He knew that if he refused to talk with these Southerners, whoever they were, Greeley could accuse him of being determined to continue the bloodshed, no matter what. He also saw that if these emissaries could return to the South saying they had made any kind of offer and been rejected, it would strengthen the hardline Confederates and weaken his own position with the millions in the North who longed for an end to the fighting.

He decided to checkmate Greeley. In a further exchange of letters, Lincoln agreed to hear what these men had to say but would do so by sending his secretary Hay up to Canada, and he insisted that Greeley, who had probably not expected Lincoln to acquiesce in any of this, be present with Hay during whatever talks might ensue. There the matter rested, with consequences that would make news everywhere.

Throughout these days of rising military and political tension, Lincoln continued to receive ordinary citizens at the White House. A man identified as "Reverend Mr. Henderson," of Louisville, Kentucky, was in Lincoln's office and witnessed an example of that. In came "a small, pale, delicate-looking boy about thirteen years old. The President saw him standing, looking feeble and faint, and said, "Come here, my boy, and tell me what you want."

The boy advanced, placed his hand on the arm of the President's chair, and with bowed head and timid accents said: "Mister President, I have been a drummer in a regiment for two years, and my colonel got angry at me and turned me off; I was taken sick, and have been a long time in hospital. This is the first time I have been out, and I came to see if you could not do something for me."

The President looked at him kindly and tenderly, and asked him where he lived. "I have no home," answered the boy. "Where is your father?" "He died in the army," was the reply. "Where is your mother?"

continued the President. "My mother is dead also. I have no mother, no father, brothers, no sisters, and," bursting into tears, "no friends — nobody cares for me."

Mr. Lincoln's eyes filled with tears, and he said to him, "Can't you sell newspapers?" "No," said the boy, "I am too weak, and the surgeon at the hospital told me I must leave, and I have no money, and no place to go to."

... The President drew forth a card, and addressing it to certain officials to whom his request was law, gave special directions "to care for this poor boy." The wan face of the little drummer lit up with a happy smile as he received the paper, and he went away convinced that he had one good friend, at least, in the person of the President.

II

On July 8, Lincoln issued his "Proclamation Concerning Reconstruction." As with all the important official presidential statements, it quickly appeared in newspapers throughout the Union. In it, Lincoln tackled the subject of his veto of the Wade-Davis bill, declaring himself to be "unprepared, by a formal approval of this Bill, to be inflexibly committed to any single plan of restoration." He agreed that the bill contained "one very proper plan for the loyal people of any State choosing to adopt it," and pledged himself "to give the Executive aid and assistance to any such people, so soon as the military resistance to the United States shall have been suppressed in any such State, and the people thereof have sufficiently returned to their obedience and the laws of the United States,—in which cases, military Governors will be appointed, with directions to proceed according to the Bill."

This seemingly reasonable, statesmanlike language infuriated the Radicals. Lincoln had killed their bill and now told the nation that if a conquered Southern state wanted to do what the Radicals had provided for in their vetoed legislation, it would be done, but by the White House and not by direction of the Congress. Davis, the bill's coauthor with Senator Wade, had this reaction: "Pale with wrath, his bushy hair tousled, and wildly brandishing his arms, [he] denounced the President in good set terms." He saw this as "dictatorial usurpation" of the role of Congress in writing the nation's laws; Davis and Wade set to work writing an inflammatory counterproclamation.

DESPITE THE INTEREST in the legislative battles and the lack of news about military movements, the city of Washington began to realize that nothing had thus far stopped a large and determined Confederate advance toward the capital—in a letter to her husband, the wife of Admiral Samuel Phillips Lee told him, "Cannon was heard here all day by some of the family[.] Others say it was thunder."

As darkness fell on the evening of July 8, Union Major General Lew Wallace, the man who would later write the enormously popular romantic novel *Ben-Hur*, retreated through Frederick, Maryland, forty miles northwest of Washington. Commanding the only force in a position to try to stop or delay the Confederate advance, he noted what he observed of Early's oncoming army before sunset: "There could no longer be room for doubt; what I saw were columns of infantry, with trains of artillery. Good strong columns they were too, of thousands and thousands." At dawn on July 9, with Frederick now in his possession, Early stood even closer to Baltimore than to Washington. From there, he could attack either city, and possibly both. The Union defenders northwest of Washington might have to divide their forces to oppose two separate offensives. Union general David Hunter, who Grant had been sure would arrive on the scene and reverse the military balance, had still not appeared, and the transports filled with the reinforcements sent by Grant to Washington had yet to be seen coming up the Potomac. However, the reinforcements sent by Grant to Baltimore had arrived there by ship, been sent west by train, and came under the command of Lew Wallace at what proved to be virtually the last minute.

Now, early on this fateful Saturday morning, strengthened by these veteran troops Grant had detached from his forces besieging Petersburg, Wallace decided to stake everything he had. He still expected Hunter to appear, but felt he could not wait; from all sources available to him, Wallace had received only 6,000 men to oppose the 14,000 men coming toward him, but resolved to fight it out along the Monocacy River, southeast of Frederick.

The battle began at eight in the morning and went on all day. Some of

Wallace's soldiers proved fully equal to Early's veterans: perhaps remembering the Revolutionary War exhortation, "Don't fire until you see the whites of their eyes," Colonel William Henry told his men of the 10th Vermont, "Wait, boys, don't fire until you see the C.S.A. on their waist belts and then give it to 'em." During the spread-out fighting, a cavalryman from Illinois suddenly found himself alone on his horse at the edge of a cornfield, facing several Confederate foot soldiers on the other side of a fence, one shouting at him, "Surrender, you son of a bitch!" The trooper pulled out his revolver and fired at his would-be captors, crying out that these shots were in honor of his mother. When he emptied his revolver, the surviving Confederates surrounded him, one of them grabbing his reins as his comrades fired at other Union soldiers until they ran out of ammunition. When the soldier from Illinois, still on his horse, saw that his captors now had only empty muskets and their bayonets, he twisted the reins out of the hands of the Confederate who thought he had him under control and galloped off while his enemies shook their fists at him.

The Confederates fought with the same determination: every officer of the 26th Georgia was killed or wounded, and an enlisted man remembered that "private soldiers of our brigade without leadership" carried on the battle for the rest of the day. The legendary general John Gordon of Georgia, whose brigade had fought at Chancellorsville, Gettysburg, the Wilderness, and Spotsylvania, said that his men's savage spirit as they attacked along the riverbank, shouting the high-pitched "Yip! Yip! Yip!" of the rebel yell, "amounted almost to a martial delirium."

Wallace's men, even those of whom he could expect little, fought bravely, but that proved not enough to throw back Early's advance toward Washington. Numbers told: the battle ended in the late afternoon, with a loss of close to 2,000 Union soldiers, a third of Wallace's men, many of them missing and unable to be accounted for. Seven hundred who had been taken prisoner were marched off to Frederick. (Among those wounded was one of Secretary of State Seward's sons, William Henry, Jr., a colonel who lay on the battlefield pretending to be dead; he later found a mule and made his way back to his command.) For Wallace, his only effective line of retreat now was to fall back toward Baltimore, rather than Washington, leaving the defense of the capital to those who could man the earthworks surrounding it.

As for the victor at Monocacy, Early lost fewer than 700 men, but he lost something else: a day during which the defenses of Washington were strengthened. His exhausted men lay down where they had fought, to sleep there for the night, thirty miles from their goal.

All day, Washington had heard the sound of cannons firing to the northwest, but not a single official military report reached the capital. Trying to find out something from someone, Lincoln once again turned to J. W. Garrett, president of the Baltimore and Ohio, telegraphing him, "What have you heard about a battle at Monocacy? We have nothing about it here except what you say." At 7:15 P.M., Garrett replied, quoting an aide of General Wallace as stating, "Our troops at Monocacy have given way, and that General Wallace has been badly defeated." After Lincoln went out to the Soldiers' Home to spend the night, Stanton sent him a note that said, "A fact that has just been reported by the watchman of the [War] Department, viz. that your carriage was followed by a horseman not one of your escort and dressed in uniform unlike that used by our troops induces me to advise you that your guard be on the *alert* tonight." Two hours later, Stanton followed this with another note saying that the Lincolns should move back into the White House "tonight."

Lincoln decided not to move back to the city that night, but came in to the War Department, where he was displeased to learn that a gunboat was standing by on the Potomac to evacuate him from the city if that became necessary. He settled in at the War Department telegraph office, as he so often did, particularly in times of crisis. At three minutes before midnight, Halleck sent Lew Wallace a telegram that read, "I am directed by the President to say that you will rally your forces and make every possible effort to retard the enemy's march on Baltimore." During these hours, Lincoln received a message from a group of prominent citizens of Baltimore that began: "Baltimore is in great peril. We have been appointed by the mayor a committee to confer with you [regarding] the absolute necessity of sending large re-enforcements." He responded to this at 9:20 A.M. the next morning, Sunday, July 10, in these words: "I have not a single soldier but whom [*sic*] is being disposed by the Military for the best protection of all. By latest account the enemy is moving on Washington. They can not fly to either place. Let us be vigilant but keep cool." Using a word that would help no one "keep cool," he closed with, "I hope neither Baltimore nor Washington will be sacked."

• • •

From the time it became light on this Sunday morning, Early's leading contingents could see the Capitol dome, and some individual soldiers and squads were much closer than that. As the hours passed in the city, rumors abounded; no one had solid information. Attorney General Bates wrote in his diary about Early's advance, "How an army so great could traverse the country, without being discovered, is a mystery. There must have been the most supine negligence—or worse. . . . I fear that our generals, Wallace, Segel [*sic*] &c. are helpless imbiciles [*sic*]."

Bate's cabinet colleague Secretary of the Navy Gideon Welles had a startling experience. He was going through his mail on this Sunday morning, sitting in his office in the rooms allotted to the Navy Department within the War Department building, when a clerk told him that Confederate scouts were "on the outskirts of Georgetown, within the District lines." He added:

> *There had been no information to warn us of this near approach of the enemy, but my informant was so positive—and soon confirmed by another—that I sent to the War Department to ascertain the facts. They were ignorant—had heard street rumors, but they were unworthy of notice. Ridiculed my inquiry.*
>
> *Later I learned that young King, son of my neighbor Z. P. K. [King], was captured by the Rebel pickets within the District lines and is a prisoner.*

With Welles, the fact of young men having their lives at risk was no abstraction: his son, eighteen-year-old Thomas G. Welles, had just joined the army and was about to be assigned to the staff of Major General Alexander McCook, in charge of the northern defenses of Washington. A father's love and concern for his son permeated the diary entries he made at this time, entries that alternated with his observations about official matters. "I regret his passion for the service and his recklessness and youth," Welles wrote, later adding, "I have tried to dissuade him so far as I could go with propriety, but there was a point beyond which I could not well go. With the condition of the country and when others were periling their lives and the lives of their children, how could I refrain, and resist the earnest appeals of my son, whose heart was set upon going?"

As for the threat to the capital, Welles summed up his view of the situation on this Sunday morning when rumors were flying.

The truth is the forts around Washington have been vacated and the troops sent [earlier] to General Grant who was promised reinforcements to take Richmond. But he has been in its vicinity for more than a month, resting, apparently, after his bloody march, but has effected nothing since his arrival on the James, not displayed any strategy, while Lee has sent a force threatening the National Capital, and we are without force for its defense.

Welles added an understatement, and a judgment. "I am sorry to see so little reliable information . . . Stanton, Halleck and Grant are asleep or dumb."

At noon on this Sunday, Private John C. Cannon, a member of the 150th Ohio National Guard posted at Fort Stevens, the northernmost in the ring of fortifications surrounding the city, saw a carriage surrounded by horsemen with drawn sabers swiftly approaching the gate of the fort that faced inward toward the city.

. . . the Black Horse Cavalry escort of the President . . . dashed up to our postern. Lincoln hastily left the barouche, entered the fort, and passing from gun to gun, looked out upon the field it covered. In his long, yellow-ish linen coat and unbrushed high hat, he looked like a careworn farmer in time of peril from drouth [drought] and famine.

At this moment, Fort Stevens, on the rustic Seventh Street Road (later Georgia Avenue) and the place most directly in the line of a probable Confederate attack, was garrisoned by only 209 soldiers, some of them convalescent men unfit for field duty and others from an artillery unit, the 13th Michigan Battery. More cannon and men were arriving, and there would soon be eighteen guns of varying sizes facing north. The fort, named for Isaac Ingalls Stevens, a general fatally wounded in 1862, was a big structure, much of it constructed with concrete and stone. When Lincoln looked out from the U-shaped openings in the top of the wall through which the cannon could fire, he saw before him an area of pastures, cornfields, groves, and orchards, sloping away from the fort and then rising on its other side to a low ridge somewhat more than half a mile away. Within a mile of him lay five houses, now abandoned by their owners, some being used by Confederate snipers. One of them, a thousand yards in front of Lincoln just west of the Seventh Street Road, was a big structure with a cupola atop it, which belonged to a Post Office employee named Carberry.

After his inspection of the fort, Lincoln left, going straight back to the War Department. At one o'clock, Halleck showed him a wire from Grant at City Point, sent at six the previous evening, but just received and deciphered. It revealed that Grant thought the units normally guarding Washington could not only defend the city, but strike back with a strong counteroffensive that might destroy all of Early's columns. Grant said in part, "Force enough to defeat all that Early has with him should get in his rear, South of him, and follow him up sharply, leaving [cutting him off and forcing] him to go North." He had, however, begun to understand the confusion at the capital, and added, "If the President thinks it advisabl[e] that I should go to Washington in person I can start in an hour after receiving notice leaving everything here on the defensive." Lincoln discussed this with Halleck, Stanton probably being present, and fifty-five minutes later sent this message in cipher to Grant.

> Your despatch to Gen. Halleck, referring to what I may think in the present emergency, is shown to me. Gen. Halleck says we have absolutely no force here fit to go to the field [and undertake offensive operations]. He thinks that with the hundred-day men, and invalids we have here, we can [here Lincoln had first written, "may possibly but not certainly," which he scratched out before writing "can"] defend Washington, and scarcely Baltimore.
>
> Wallace ... was so badly beaten yesterday at Monocacy that what is left can attempt no more than to defend Baltimore. . . . Now what I think is that you should provide to retain your hold where you are certainly, and bring the rest [of the reinforcements] with you personally, and make a vigorous effort to destroy the enemie's [sic] force in this vicinity.

Halleck followed this ninety minutes later, telegraphing Grant that he must not continue to consider Hunter's force, last heard from as being somewhere on the west side of the Shenandoah Valley, as being available to do anything. ". . . where the remainder of Hunter's army is, I cannot ascertain. Rumor says that it has lost almost everything, & is badly cut up." Grant decided to stay where he was on the Petersburg-Richmond front, saying, "I think on reflection that it would have a bad effect for me to leave here."

Things got no better as this Sunday wore on. Noah Brooks wrote: "The news of the approach of Early was brought into the city . . . by the panic-stricken people from Rockville, Silver Spring, Tenallytown, and other Maryland villages. These people came flocking into Washington by the Seventh Street road, flying in wild disorder, and bringing their household goods with them. . . . Washington stood agape as we listened to the sound of the rebel cannon less than ten miles away."

Everyone knew there were Southern sympathizers in the city; Brooks reported that over the weekend, "In Georgetown one nest of secession-ists was rudely broken in upon by the provost guard [military police] who discovered a half-finished Confederate flag in the house. The men were marched over to the guardhouse, and the unfinished colors, probably in-tended to be presented to Early, were promptly confiscated. This was not the only flag made to be presented to the rebels when they should effect their triumphal entry into Washington." The provost marshal himself, Brigadier General William E. Doster, wrote in his diary, "It seems funny to hear the rumbling of street cars mixed with the rumbling of hostile cannon." That night the Lincolns left the Soldiers' Home and moved back into the White House.

The next morning, at the dawn of a day when temperatures rose to the mid-nineties, the transports carrying the reinforcements sent by Grant began arriving at the Sixth Street wharves. The ships tied up, and large crowds cheered wildly as the veterans of Major General Horatio G. Wright's famous Sixth Corps, wearing their distinctive Greek cross insig-nia on their caps, filed down the gangplanks with their packs on their backs and their rifles in their hands. Lincoln was waiting to greet them, and stood among them chatting and eating army biscuits as they began to form up on the dock. Being among these vigorous, experienced young soldiers lifted Lincoln's spirits; as the troops clustered about him, he cheerfully told them that they had better hurry if they expected to cap-ture Jubal Early.

The regiments of the Sixth Corps began moving off, marching through the city toward Fort Stevens. Among the officers was General Wright's aide-de-camp, the young, three-times-wounded Lieutenant Colonel Oliver Wendell Holmes, Jr., one day to be a prominent justice of the Supreme Court. Enthusiastic crowds moved alongside each unit. Ser-geant Hiram P. Thompson of the 49th New York Volunteers, one of the men marching to battle, described being followed by "an immense throng," some of them shouting, "It is the old Sixth Corps, the danger is over now!"

After a time Lincoln left the docks and headed for Fort Stevens himself, riding in a carriage. Ahead of him, his cavalry escort was shouting to soldiers and civilians alike, "Give the road for the President!" It became a remarkable scene: the commander-in-chief at the head of his marching soldiers and a great crowd of civilians, all headed out of the city along a wooded road toward the thunderclaps of cannon fire from an artillery duel already underway.

Impressive as the ranks of the Sixth Corps were, something even more impressive revealed itself in the spirit of resolve shown by two other columns that headed out of the city to the city's perimeter defense. One was composed of 2,800 wounded soldiers who left their hospital wards to go to the front. Many limped and most had bandages somewhere on their bodies, but they all carried muskets. Some made their way by themselves: Major J. W. Causby of the 61st Pennsylvania, a regiment defending the city, was confined to a hospital bed with a head wound from an earlier battle. Hearing the cannon fire, he said, "I must go to my boys." Causby managed to get out of bed: he put on his uniform, hired a horse, found his unit, and reported for duty.

The other column heading out to join the defenders was made up of 1,500 armed civilian employees of governmental departments, many of them men far past military age, led by Major General Montgomery Meigs, the Union Army's quartermaster general. They were going into the rifle-pits along the defensive perimeter, and would be followed into the trenches by sailors and Navy Yard civilian workers, commanded by Rear Admiral Louis Goldsborough.

As time went on, Federal soldiers atop two of the highest forts along the defensive perimeter saw an immense cloud of dust rising into the blazing sky above the hard dirt pike that, once it passed through the little settlement of Silver Spring and entered the city limits, became known as Seventh Street Road. Out there, Early's men were trudging through 94-degree heat; men of even an elite division such as Gordon's Georgians struggled just to keep coming. When Union general McCook learned that Early was moving some of his units off the Seventh Street Road, trying to approach the city through the less-exposed valley in the part of the Rock Creek area northwest of the fort, he took immediate action. Sending men into those woods to cut down trees and make obstacles out of fallen brush, he succeeded in thwarting Early, who put all his units back into this strung-out advance straight toward Fort Stevens. On the way, going through Silver Spring the Confederates passed two large and handsome houses, empty even before this. One belonged to Lincoln's friend and political adviser, Francis Preston Blair, Sr., and the other to Blair's son, Lincoln's controversial postmaster general Montgomery Blair.

At some point after noon, Lincoln arrived at Fort Stevens. Precisely what happened to him then and the next day became the subject of varying accounts from persons in the fort, but for the first time in American history, a president while in office came under enemy fire. The artillery duel, first heard in the city early in the morning, continued. The defenses of Washington had a total of many more cannon than Early's attackers did, but all the Union guns stood in fixed positions around the city, while the Confederate field artillery batteries could all be concentrated to support an attack made at a specific point. Both sides blazed away, with different kinds of cannonballs throwing up geysers of reddish earth, and some munitions exploding with a brilliant white-gold flash that turned to red, rimmed with black smoke.

More enemy snipers had taken up positions in the houses in what became a no-man's-land; one account spoke of Confederate sharpshooters hidden high in a tulip tree. Both sides had sent skirmishers into this area of pastures and cornfields; at one in the afternoon, the signalman stationed atop the fort had sent out an urgent message saying, "The enemy is within twenty rods [110 yards] of Fort Stevens." Those watching from the fort saw not a classic battle, with waves of men charging enemy positions, but a landscape with many little puffs of grey smoke popping up here and there. One officer present estimated that the fort was then "within range of five hundred rebel rifles." Bullets snapped over the heads of the defenders in the earthworks; occasionally a Union soldier somewhere on the walls of the fort who became visible to the enemy fell, wounded or dead.

The tops of the walls of Fort Stevens consisted of masonry terraces, running around the fort to form a parapet several feet wide. One could hide behind it, or rise up to shoulder height to see the action, or even expose all of oneself on the flat unprotected surface of this parapet-terrace. After a cannon fired out through its U-shaped opening in the parapet, it was walked backward down a flagstone ramp behind its position to a place several feet lower, reloaded, and pushed back into place to fire again.

In the midst of this, Abraham Lincoln climbed up on the parapet to get a better look at the scene. He stood there completely exposed, six feet four inches tall. With his black stovepipe hat on his head, he made a target more than seven feet high. Bullets began snapping past him. Anyone out there in the open—others were at least partially exposed—would have drawn fire, but Sergeant James H. Laird of the 150th Ohio later wrote, referring to the Carberry house, "Some of our boys who brought in prisoners said the captured men told them that Lincoln was seen from the cupola of a house, recognized and fired at." (There could be no doubt that many Confederate snipers were capable of seeing and killing Lincoln from farther away than the Carberry house, a thousand yards up the Seventh Street Road: their English-made Whitworth rifles had a 14½-inch telescopic sight and an effective range of a mile. This was the weapon that had killed Union General John Sedgwick two months before with a shot under his left eye from nearly half a mile away, just after he told his aides that the Confederate marksmen "couldn't hit an elephant at this distance.")

What happened next was predictable, although several accounts differed about who, other than Lincoln, became involved. Everyone near him was appalled to see the president of the United States standing there with bullets cracking past him, and immediate and strenuous efforts were made to get him down from the parapet and behind the thick wall. In one version of what happened, as plausible as any other, a young officer standing with his head below the parapet shouted up at this tall civilian, "Get down, you fool!" Lincoln climbed down. The officer was Oliver Wendell Holmes, Jr.

Soon after this, Lincoln left Fort Stevens to go to the White House. One account, which if accurate proves Lincoln knew who had ordered him off the wall, includes this: ". . . just as Mr. Lincoln was quitting the fort, he took the trouble to walk back. 'Good-bye, Colonel Holmes,' he said. 'I'm glad you know how to talk to a Civilian.'"

Lincoln's day was far from over. In his diary entry for July 11, Hay made this entry.

At three o'clock P.M. the President came in bringing the news that the enemy's advance was at Ft[.] Stevens on the 7th Street road. He was in the Fort when it was first attacked, standing upon the parapet.

*A soldier roughly ordered him to get down or he would get his head
knocked off. I can see a couple of columns of smoke just north of the White
House.*

(One of the "columns of smoke" Hay saw was rising above the settlement of Silver Spring on the Seventh Street Road, where the Confederates had set fire to Falkland, Postmaster General Blair's handsome country
house.)

An hour later, Provost Marshal Doster made the first of his two diary entries for the day.

*"Hextry Staar. [Extra, Star!] Second Edition. Great Battle at Seventh
Street" is the newsboys' cry. The paper says our troops have been attacked
at Fort Massachusetts [sic], with what truth it is impossible to say. . . .
The only sign of excitement, except the newspaper boys, is the rapid gait at
which men gallop through the streets. This is an affectation of business
which I noticed many officers assume after the second battle of Bull Run.
It is not exactly hypocrisy but a feeling that in an emergency one ought to
be seen doing great things, even if accomplishing nothing whatever. News
is scarce, rumors abundant.*

In his second entry, Doster added this.

*. . . The signal officers of our army state that the troops of the rebels stretch
as far as the eye and the glass can reach. . . . I saw about twenty Rebel
prisoners taken down the avenue. . . . All railroad and telegraph communication is cut off. . . . An attack in force is expected during the night.
They would be fools if they waited.*

In fact, Early had decided to wait, but no one in the city knew that.
After Lincoln left Fort Stevens, he picked up his son Tad and went back
to the Sixth Street wharves, where from time to time ships were still arriving with reinforcements. After they watched this for a time, father and
son went back to the White House; observing Lincoln at the end of a
memorable day, Hay recorded this in his diary: "The President is in very
good feather this evening. He seems not in the least concerned about the

safety of Washington. With him the concern seems to be whether we can bag or destroy this force in our front."

The next day, Tuesday, July 12, the cannon were still thundering from the direction of Fort Stevens, but Lincoln spent the morning at the White House and in the telegraph office. Reports that proved to be true indicated that Confederate cavalry had cut the railroad lines and telegraph lines running north of Baltimore to Philadelphia and New York. Now the only safe way of traveling or sending documents or valuables from Washington to New York was by ship, going down the Potomac and then up the Atlantic Coast; with telegraph communication stopped, Washington was cut off from the rest of the North. In an indication of how little Lincoln or anyone else knew of the overall situation, at eleven-thirty he sent off a cipher message to Grant at City Point that read: "Vague rumors have been reaching us for two or three days that Longstreet's corps is also on its way [to] this vicinity. Look out for it's [*sic*] absence from your front." The Washington newspapers reflected the informational miasma by saying that news of Confederate movements "are confusingly conflicting."

At noon, Lincoln held his usual Tuesday cabinet meeting. As Secretary of the Navy Welles entered the president's office, Postmaster General Montgomery Blair quietly told him that, when he arrived early, Lincoln had told him that the usual agenda was not "to be brought forward." With the sound of the cannon fire to the north in their ears as they sat around the long table in the "shop," Lincoln and the cabinet members discussed what was happening. Welles, who was surprised and displeased to find Stanton and two or three other cabinet members absent, asked Lincoln "where the Rebels were in force. He said he did not know with certainty, but he thought the main body at Silver Spring." Welles also recorded this:

> *I am sorry there should be so little accurate information of the Rebels, sorry that at such a time there is not a full Cabinet, and especially sorry that the Secretary of War is not present. In the interviews I have had with him, I can obtain no facts, no opinions. He seems dull and stupefied. Others tell me the same.*

After the cabinet meeting, Lincoln and Mary got into a carriage to drive to Fort Stevens. Evidently, their coachman drove them faster than the pace being set by the cavalry escort assigned to surround Lincoln's carriage; they decided to stop at a barracks, just to the rear of the fort, that had been converted to a military hospital where the surgeons of the Second Division of the recently arrived Sixth Corps were preparing to receive wounded men. A surgeon who talked with them gave this description of their visit.

> *President Lincoln and his wife drove up to the barracks unattended, except by their coachman, the superbly mounted squadron, whose duty it was to attend his excellency being left far behind. The carriage stopped at the door of the hospital, and the President and his affable lady entered into familiar conversation with the surgeons in charge, praising the deeds of the Old Sixth Corps, complimenting the appearance of the veterans and declaring that they, as well as the people of the country, appreciated the achievements of the wearers of the Greek Cross.*

At four in the afternoon, Lincoln and Mary entered Fort Stevens itself. On this second day of artillery duels and the skirmishing in the contested fields in front of the fort, many prominent figures came out to see the fighting, like moths drawn to the flame. Among those recorded as being there, some probably arriving in the same file of carriages, were Stanton, Seward, Welles, Montgomery Blair, Radical senators Benjamin Wade and Zachariah Chandler, and Register of the Treasury Lucius Chittenden. (One account also placed recently resigned Treasury Secretary Chase as being there.) The wife of General Wright, the Sixth Corps commander, a lady who lived in Washington, drove out to the fort with a group of her women friends. Other fashionably dressed ladies and gentlemen appeared, awakening memories of the First Battle of Bull Run, when many Washingtonians drove out to see the fighting as if to see a sporting event and ended up fleeing back to Washington, their carriages mixed in with the routed Federal troops.

By the time Lincoln and Mary arrived, despite the nearby explosions and sounds of small-arms fire, crowds including every kind of Washington resident had gathered at a short distance from the gate to the fort, wanting to enter and find a place from which to see the fighting. A line of soldiers acting as policemen held them back, and a procedure had been set up allowing only those civilians carrying a pass signed by Secretary of War Stanton to enter. Several of these guards called out to a sergeant who described his assignment that day as being "stationed with about one hundred and twenty men to the rear of the line of battle, with orders to permit no citizen to go to the front nor soldiers to the rear." Coming toward his men who had hailed him, he became involved in a difficult situation.

> ... *I noticed several carriages. In the front I saw President Lincoln and Secretary of War Stanton, neither of whom I knew personally, but I had noticed Mr. Lincoln and his little son, Tad, the evening before when we landed at Sixth Street, from City Point, Virginia. And there could be no mistaking that face.*
>
> *As I approached him with a military salute he inquired what my orders were? I informed him that my instructions were to let no citizens to the front without a pass from the Secretary of War. He informed me that he was President Lincoln and that the Secretary of War was his companion. I told him that I did not question that, but that I must have written authority to protect myself, or I could not permit him to pass. Mr. Stanton, while this conversation was going on, was writing, and calling me to him, handed me a piece of paper on which was written: "Guards and patrols, Pass President Lincoln, Secretary of War, and suite, to the front. E. M. Stanton, Secretary of War."*

Once inside Fort Stevens, Lincoln proceeded to the area near the parapet where he had stood the previous day. Again, accounts of what happened next varied, but it appears that many important individuals, including Mary Lincoln, stood or moved around nearby, trying to see something of the spectacle. The day was as hot as the one before. Two and three miles to the left of the nearer orchards and groves there had been actions considerably more like a conventional battle: attacking along the River Road, the 2nd Massachusetts Cavalry, which had in its ranks many volunteers from California, pushed some of Early's units back one and a half miles. One of the houses that Lincoln had seen in the distance the day before lay burnt, destroyed in some way by Union soldiers. Describing the action in the brushy area on either side of the Seventh Street Road, where both Union and Confederate soldiers were moving around and firing at each other, Lucius Chittenden said, "Not a man was visible, but from every square rod of it as it seemed to me we could see the smoke and hear the report of musketry." He described the sound as being "a constant popping."

Lincoln probably surmised that Jubal Early was watching all this through binoculars, as indeed he was, from a point a mile away up the far ridge. The president may not have realized that one of Early's division commanders, also somewhere across the way, was Major General John C. Breckinridge. The victor in the mid-May battle of New Market in the Shenandoah Valley during which the Virginia Military Institute cadets played a gallant and important part, Breckinridge embodied the painful split between North and South. The former vice president of the United States under President Buchanan now faced Lincoln across an increasingly bloody battlefield.

Lincoln knew that by now there were thousands of Grant's soldiers manning the capital's perimeter, with more arriving as the day went on, and he felt ever more aggressive. The president even had the opportunity to issue, or at least endorse, a military order on the battlefield. One of the senior Union officers near Lincoln, possibly Sixth Corps commander General Wright, in effect asked him to approve of shelling some of the abandoned civilian houses sheltering Confederate riflemen in the no-man's-land in front of the fort. Lincoln later said of his response, "I certainly gave my approbation to its being done."

In contrast to Lincoln's increasing confidence, Early had given up any thought of advancing far into the city, if at all. At dawn, he realized that, despite all his efforts, he had arrived in front of Washington a day or two after the time when he might have been able to get all the way in to the White House. He came to the conclusion, as he later told Lee, that even if he had now been able to break into the city, it would have been "with such great sacrifice as would insure the destruction of my whole force." Before the time Lincoln arrived at four in the afternoon, Early had made up his mind to keep up a brisk fire until dark, exploiting any possibilities that arose, and then retreat to the Potomac River, ten miles due west of where he faced Fort Stevens.

Lincoln now gave Early's men their second chance in two days to kill him, which would have created a crisis that might well have caused a Northern political collapse leading to a peace on terms conceding much to the Confederacy. He may not have exposed himself to enemy riflemen quite as completely as he did before, but as events proved, Lincoln certainly came into their line of fire. Of those describing what happened, a vivid account came from Private Edgar H. Hinman of the 150th Ohio, a youth who had planned to enter Oberlin College but enlisted instead. According to Hinman, Lincoln was at that moment "accompanied by Senator Zack Chandler of Michigan"—the man who had stalked out of Lincoln's office angrily when Lincoln used the pocket veto to kill the Wade-Davis Bill. "The enemy was firing lively from the bushes in front of the fort," Hinman said in his account, "and it was dangerous for any person to look over the parapet. Chandler hugged close to the parapet, but the President was bound he would look over and see what was going on." Lincoln may well have stood up on the parapet again: a number of accounts portray him as doing that, and Captain Aldace F. Walker of the 1st Vermont Heavy Artillery wrote home the next day that he saw "Lincoln with a hole in his coat sleeve," while Private Thomas Hyde of the Sixth Corps said of the moment, "I saw the President standing on the wall a little way off." According to Hinman, as Lincoln remained visible to the enemy, evidently now sitting on a crate on the parapet, this happened:

> Soon a sharpshooter fired at him, and he dodged, in doing so tipped over the . . . box on which he was sitting and tumbled down. The ball fired at him struck one of the large guns, glanced back, and went through a soldier's leg. . . . Lincoln gathered himself up and laughing said: "That was quite a carom."
>
> I was standing back of him at the time and was curious to know what a carom meant, and so I asked one of the boys versed in billiards, and he told me. . . . Some of those standing by thought that the President was given to a little too much levity and that the remark was a little too jocose for the occasion, but he did not realize what had happened [the soldier being hit by a ricocheting bullet] until after he said it.

The wounded soldier was the assistant surgeon of the 102nd Pennsylvania, Captain C. V. A. Crawford. One account specified that the bullet struck him in the ankle; another mentioned a "severe" wound that kept him in the hospital for a long time. During these minutes, before or after Captain Crawford was hit, different individuals urged Lincoln to seek shelter. The person most mentioned in that regard was General Wright, who may well have known or been in the midst of the incident the previous day; one account said that Mary "entreated" her husband "to leave the fort." Welles, who with Senator Ben Wade of Ohio had been watching the action from "the summit of the road to the right of the fort," now accompanied the senator "into the fort, where we found the President, who was sitting in the shade, his back against the parapet [that faced] towards the enemy."

In contrast to the day before, when he had left Fort Stevens soon after being fired upon, today Lincoln stayed near the parapet, occasionally raising his head just above the level of the sandbag wall to see what was happening. Other notables stayed, too, including Mary, all finding places from which they could scan the valley in front of the fort.

Soon a tremendous scene unfolded. At five on this ferociously hot afternoon, an hour after the Lincolns had arrived, Sixth Corps commander Wright decided to drive the Confederates out of the valley in front of the fort. The leading element of that advance would be a brigade of 1,000 men, composed of soldiers from New York, Maine, and Pennsylvania, under the command of Colonel Daniel D. Bidwell. Other units assembled to follow in successive waves.

These soldiers filed out of the fort and lay down in the grass with their muskets as the artillery began the barrage to prepare the way for their attack. Enemy fire immediately began killing and wounding them. When the artillery of Fort Stevens replied, twenty-five cannonballs struck the Carberry house, the structure with a cupola on top and the place from which captured Confederate snipers later claimed that they had seen Lincoln. At the moment, thirty marksmen occupied the house; as it caught fire, five men escaped from upper windows, and the other twenty-five perished in the flames. Then, as the Union artillery ceased firing, Bidwell's men rushed forward to the attack in what one soldier called "as fine a bayonet charge as could be." Welles described what he saw from the fort: ". . . our men ran to the charge and the Rebels fled. We could see them running across the fields, seeking the woods on the brow of the opposite hills." At this moment, the civilians watching from Fort Stevens apparently shouted and clapped their hands; there is no eyewitness account that Mary joined in the applause, but in light of something she later said to Stanton, she may well have cheered enthusiastically.

As far as those at Fort Stevens could see, the Union troops had routed the rebels, but out of their sight a bigger and bloodier battle developed. Three Union brigades were now committed to action, and the able Confederate artillery general Robert Rodes supported Early's foot soldiers as they gradually withdrew, occasionally making minor counterattacks or simply stopping the Sixth Corps troops where they were. One infantryman of the 122nd New York recounted that at one point he and his comrades "fell back, rallied again, charged them without ammunition, and drove them back again," soon thereafter being resupplied with bullets and powder. Among the Confederate units who a Confederate colonel said "went up beautifully" but "could not succeed in getting quite as far as their original line" was the 43rd North Carolina, the regiment that had been given so much liquor and food by Confederate sympathizers at Charlestown, West Virginia, that they had become "half demoralized" and lost more than a day on their march to join Early.

By nightfall, all the guns had fallen silent. Union soldiers occupied the battlefield but had no orders to press on and keep contact with Early's retreating troops. In Bidwell's brigade of a thousand men, all his regimental commanders had been killed or wounded, and the brigade suffered between 250 and 375 casualties. Lincoln and Mary entered a carriage and toured some of the city's other defensive positions, with the troops cheering them as they came by.

As the long bloody day closed and the threat to Washington vanished in the night, two officials of Lincoln's administration had experiences and thoughts they recorded. Treasury Register Louis Chittenden went into the area in front of Fort Stevens where Confederate casualties lay, including those who had been burnt to death at the Carberry house and other still-smoking ruined dwellings, and described this: "On all the floors, on the roofs, in the yards, within reach of the heat, were many bodies of the dead or dying, who could not move, and had been left behind by their comrades . . . the odor of burning flesh filled the air; it was a sickening spectacle!"

Welles, whose newly enlisted son Private Thomas Welles was not hurt during the day and would spend the next day in charge of 50 black men burying the Confederate dead, closed these strained hours by seeing and thinking this:

As we came out of the fort, four or five wounded men were being carried by on stretchers. It was nearly dark as we left. Driving in . . . we passed fields as well as roads full of soldiers, horses, teams, mules. Camp-fires lighted up the woods . . . the stragglers by the wayside were many. Some were doubtless sick, some were drunk, some weary and exhausted. Then men on horseback, on mules, in wagons as well as on foot, batteries of artillery, caissons, an innumerable throng. It was exciting and wild. Much of life and much of sadness.

Strange that in this country there is this strife and struggle, under one of the most beneficent governments which ever blessed mankind[,] and all in sight of the Capitol.

NINE

TRYING TO PICK UP
THE MILITARY AND
POLITICAL PIECES

When it became light the next morning, Lincoln rode out to the scene of the previous day's battle, accompanied by his son Robert, who had finished his year's studies at Harvard, and John Hay. What Lincoln hoped to see was the rear elements of Wright's Sixth Corps, preparing to follow the combat units that were already pursuing and harassing Early's retreating force, but Hay described what they actually saw. At one place, this:

> . . . we proceeded through the encampment, which was stretched in a loafer-like, gipsy style among the trees—the Artillery ready to move, the Infantry diffused through the brush—dirty, careless, soldierly in all else—every variety of style among the officers. We went to Ft Stevens & had a good view from the parapet of the battlefield of yesterday. Then we went to McCook's headquarters and drank lager beer. The room was full of regulars from the bureaus at Washington.
>
> We took a ride over to the Qr Mrs Hdqs [Headquarters of Quarter Master General Montgomery Meigs] and lunched under the trees with General Rucker.

Moving around among these men who seemed to be in a self-congratulatory mood after repelling the Confederate attack on the capital, Lincoln became frustrated and angry. Hay noted his reaction.

*The President thinks we should push our whole column right up the River
Road & cut off as many as possible of the retreating raiders.*

*There seems to be no head about this whole affair. Halleck hates re-
sponsibility: hates to give orders. Wright, Gillmore and McCook must of
course report to somebody & await somebody's orders which they don't get.*

That was indeed the state of affairs. Although some of Wright's men
were in fact following and sometimes skirmishing with Early's rearguard,
it was not until two-thirty in the afternoon that Grant sent this, not to
Halleck, not to Stanton, but to Assistant Secretary of War Charles A.
Dana, who had evidently stepped in to send Grant the best information
available. Grant told Dana, concerning Early's forces still operating near
Baltimore, "Boldness is all that is wanted to [drive the] enemy out of
Maryland in confusion. . . . I hope and believe Wright is the man to as-
sume that."

The next twenty-four hours consisted of confusion, but on the part of the
Union Army, not the Confederates; with Union forces unable to cut off
any part of Early's overall withdrawal, some of Early's men, instead of retreating south after they crossed the Potomac, moved to the northwest of
Washington, into Maryland and Pennsylvania. The next evening, when
Lincoln left the White House to go out to the Soldiers' Home where he
and Mary had resumed their summer residence, Hay asked him what the
news was from the telegraph office and noted that Lincoln gave him this
sarcastic appraisal of the situation: "Wright telegraphs that he thinks the
enemy are all across the Potomac but that he has halted & sent out an infantry reconnoissance [*sic*], for fear he might come across the rebels &
catch some of them."

Hay added, in his own words, "The Chief is evidently disgusted."
Mary Lincoln felt the same way. When Stanton said to her in what he
meant as a compliment, "Mrs. Lincoln, I intend to have a full-length portrait of you painted, standing on the ramparts at Fort Stevens overlooking the fight," Mary answered coldly, "I can assure you of one thing, Mr.
Secretary, if I had had a few *ladies* with me the Rebels would not have
been permitted to get away as they did."

There was of course the public perception of what had happened.
Two days after the end of what Welles called "the Rebel Invasion," he
noted in his diary, "the *National Intelligencer* comments with a good deal

of truth and ability on our national humiliation, as exemplified in this late affair. There is no getting away from the statement and facts presented." The Democrat-supporting *New York Herald* spoke of "the great noodles who mismanage our military and all other matters at Washington." In the Confederate capital, the *Richmond Examiner* saw Early's marches, including those that continued northwest of Washington, as demonstrating Northern impotence and helping the "Peace Democrats" win the November election and begin peace talks on terms acceptable to the South. Early, the paper said, was "stumping the States of Maryland and Pennsylvania for the peace party." As for Confederate morale, one of Early's foot soldiers left this note in the flyleaf of a book found at Silver Spring.

Near Washington
July 23, 1864

Now Uncle Abe, you had better be quiet the balance of your Administration, as we came near your town this time to show you what we could do. But if you go on in your mad career, we will come again soon. . . .

Yours Respectfully, the worst
rebel you ever saw,
Fifty-eighth Virginia Infantry

The aftershock of Early's raid reached into Lincoln's cabinet. On the evening of the day it became clear "the Rebel Invasion" had receded from Washington, former senator Orville Browning of Lincoln's state of Illinois, accompanied by his wife, paid a call on Attorney General Bates at his house. When Browning recorded his talk with Bates in his diary, he said, "In conversation with him upon the State of the Country he expressed the opinion that our great want was a competent man at the head of affairs, or as he expressed it a competent leader . . . but still did not know how we were to do better than Lincoln. . . . Company came in and conversation was broken off." As for Bates, he wrote this of what happened when the cabinet met two days later and the conversation turned to Early's raid. "—To day, I spoke my mind, very plainly, to the Pres[iden]t. (in presence of Seward, Welles and [Secretary of the Interior] Usher) ab[ou]t the ignorant imbecility of the late military operations, and my contempt for Genl. Halleck." Probably soon after this, Browning encountered Lincoln: "Met the President between the War Department & White House—Said he was in the dumps—that the rebels who had besieged us were all escaped."

A new dimension of frustration and anger was reached when Postmaster General Montgomery Blair went out soon after the battle to see what had happened to Falkland, his showplace summer home. In contrast to the fate of Silver Spring, his father's neighboring mansion, spared by Breckinridge and other Confederate officers because of various prewar acts of hospitality and friendship on the senior Blair's part, Montgomery Blair's house was burnt to the ground. The day after the battle, an unspecified high-ranking Union officer brought to Halleck's attention that in a conversation Blair burst out with comments to this effect: ". . . the officers in command about Washington are poltroons . . . that it was a disgrace; that General Wallace [defeated by Early at Monocacy] was in comparison with them far better as he would at least fight." Halleck, who had once again demonstrated that his skills and instincts were those of an administrator and not a warrior, immediately took it upon himself to defend the Army's honor. In a letter to Stanton that the secretary of war swiftly and "respectfully" referred to Lincoln, Halleck demanded that "it should be known whether such wholesale denouncement & accusation by a member of the cabinet receives the sanction and approbation of the President. . . . if so the names of the officers accused should be stricken from the rolls of the Army. . . . if not, it is due to the honor of the accused that the slanderer should be dismissed from the cabinet."

Lincoln replied to this in a judicious letter, not to Halleck but to Stanton. Speaking of what he pointed out were alleged remarks by Blair heard by an unnamed officer, he said, "If they were made, I do *not* approve them; and yet, under the circumstances, I would not dismiss a member of the Cabinet therefor. I do not consider what may have been hastily said in a moment of vexation at so grave a loss, is sufficient ground for so grave a step. . . . I propose continuing to be myself the judge of when a member of the Cabinet shall be dismissed." Knowing that any number of Radicals, and members of his cabinet such as Stanton, Seward, and the now-departed Chase, had for some time wanted him to "dismiss" Montgomery Blair, he prepared this memorandum to be read to the cabinet. Whether he actually read it at a meeting is not certain, but he intended for all his advisers to understand exactly how he felt.

I must be the judge, how long to retain in, and when to remove any of you from, his position. It would greatly pain me to discover any of you endeavoring to procure anothers [sic] *removal, or, in any way to prejudice him before the public. Such endeavor would be wrong to me; and much worse, a wrong to the country. My wish is that on this subject, no remark be made, nor question asked, by any of you, here or elsewhere, now or hereafter.*

II

At this moment in mid-July of 1864, Lincoln was more than ever the linchpin holding together the Union's military and political structure. On May 9, a few days after the Wilderness battle began, the *New York Times* had carried a story saying of Washington, which had a prewar population of 75,000, "The Government has hospital accommodations here for thirty thousand, which will probably meet all demands." Now, nine weeks later, Orville Browning noted in his diary that he had just seen the Army's surgeon general, who told him "that 30,000 [beds] had not been sufficient to supply the wounded sent from Grant's army."

Lincoln was seeing the overall picture of the manpower needs of the Union forces faster than anyone, and responding to them quickly: when Grant wired Lincoln on July 19, saying, "In my opinion there ought to be an immediate call for 300,000 men," Lincoln answered, with some satisfaction:

Yours of yesterday about a call for 300,000 is received. I suppose you had not seen the call made for 500,000 the day before, which I suppose covers the case. Always glad to have your suggestions.

Grant was swiftly reorganizing his command structure to prevent, as he put it, "a recurrence of what has just taken place," merging five geographical military departments, including the Washington District, "into one Department under one head who shall absolutely controll [sic] the whole." From City Point, Grant sent repeated specific instructions to Halleck and other generals concerning the next movements to be made in the summer campaign. When Lincoln saw a telegram from Grant to Sherman saying, "I shall make a desperate effort here which will hold the enemy without the necessity of so many men"—possibly enabling him to send reinforcements to aid Sherman in his campaign to take Atlanta—he intervened in one more of his efforts to strike a balance. "Pressed as we are," Lincoln telegraphed Grant, ". . . I am glad to hear you say this; and yet I do hope that you may find a way that the effort may not be desperate in the sense of great loss of life." Lincoln even soothed the feelings of General David Hunter, whose forces had been so conspicuously unavailable during Early's advance toward Washington. When Hunter went out of the chain of command, sending directly to Lincoln from Harpers Ferry a request to be relieved of command because he thought he was being "selected as the scapegoat to cover up the blunders of others," Lincoln replied, "You misconceive . . . Gen. Grant wished you to remain in command . . . and I do not wish to order otherwise."

There was, however, a strongly implied criticism of Halleck and possibly Stanton in one of Lincoln's communications. Grant had wired Halleck that he wanted Sheridan to go into the Shenandoah Valley and "put himself south of the enemy and follow him to the death. Wherever the enemy goes, let our troops go also." Reviewing this message from Grant to Halleck, Lincoln sent Grant words of strong approval, and an admonition:

> *This, I think, is exactly right, as to how our forces should move. But please look over the dispatches you may have received from over here [in the War Department] even since you made that order, and discover, if you can, that there is any idea in the head of any one here, of "putting our army South of the enemy" or of following him "to the death" in any direction. I repeat to you it will neither be done nor attempted unless you watch it every day, and hour, and force it.*

The Union Army was for the moment pulling itself together, but on the intricate and explosive subject of Greeley's dealings with the Confederate agents at Niagara Falls, Lincoln was left to play a lone hand. Even from Greeley's optimistic point of view, things were ill defined. The Confederates with whom he was talking had admitted that they currently had no credentials or powers to negotiate terms for peace on behalf of Jefferson Davis, but assured Greeley that, as he had in turn told Lincoln, if Lincoln agreed to see them in Washington, they would immediately be "clothed with full power . . . with the view of hastening a consummation so much to be desired & terminating at the earliest possible moment the calamities of war."

Lincoln had already sent Greeley a wire saying, "I was not expecting you to *send* me a letter, but to *bring* me a man, or men." His emissary Hay arrived at Niagara on July 20, carrying with him a letter written in Lincoln's hand, addressed "To Whom It May Concern." It set forth Lincoln's terms for continuing this shadowy effort.

> *Any proposition which embraces the restoration of peace, the integrity of the whole Union, and the abandonment of slavery, and which comes by and with an authority that can control the armies now at war with the United States will be received and considered by the Executive government of the United States, and will be met by liberal terms on other substantial and collateral points, and the bearer, or bearers thereof shall have safe-conduct both ways.*
>
> *Abraham Lincoln*

Lincoln wrote this on July 18. It is doubtful whether at that moment he already knew the results of another effort at a peace feeler, made with his permission but not on his initiative by James R. Gilmore, a businessman with extensive prewar experience and connections in the South, accompanied by a Union Army colonel, James F. Jaquess, a prominent prewar Methodist clergyman who had a strong relationship with the Methodist Church, South. Some of the facts concerning the extraordinary odyssey of these two men never became clear, but documents showed that Lincoln asked Grant to have them passed through the Union lines, and that Grant arranged this.

According to the accounts of both Gilmore and the Confederate secretary of state Judah Benjamin, on the evening of July 17, Jefferson Davis walked into Benjamin's office in the old United States Customs House in Richmond to confer with these two men who had come there with Lincoln's permission. Davis put the two men from the North at ease with his courtesy and charm, but any possibility of meaningful negotiations vanished within minutes. After expressing his desire for peace, Davis explained that the Confederacy would never rejoin the Union. He stated as a fact that he and the white South were less interested in the preservation of slavery than in being an independent nation. Davis told them:

We will go on [fighting] unless you acknowledge our right to self-government. We are not fighting for slavery. We are fighting for independence, and that, or extermination, we will have. . . . You may emancipate the rest, you may emancipate every negro in the Confederacy . . . but we will be free! We will govern ourselves! We will do it, if we have to see every Southern plantation sacked, and every Southern city in flames.

Davis presented his view of the South's prospects: the military situation was strategically sound; his armies and people had ample food and supplies; according to him, the Confederate dollar was solidly backed by the cotton crop. Gilmore and Jaquess soon left the meeting; four days later, back in Washington, Gilmore read to Lincoln his written report of the talk with Davis. There would be various interpretations of both Gilmore's motivation in undertaking this mission and Lincoln's reason for letting the two men go. Gilmore later said that his intention was to undercut the repeated assertions of the Peace Democrats and Copperheads that peace could be had without letting the Confederacy become an independent nation.

While still giving Greeley time to produce whatever he could from the murky situation at Niagara, Lincoln wrote this to New York City postmaster Abram Wakeman, his political supporter who, evidently still unknown to him, was helping Mary conceal the size of the bills she was running up in that city's fashionable stores. Clearly now knowing the results of the Gilmore-Jaquess meeting with Jefferson Davis, he said:

The men of the South, recently (and perhaps still) at Niagara Falls, tell us distinctly that they are in the confidential employment of the rebellion; and they tell us as distinctly that they are not empowered to offer terms of peace. Does any one doubt that what they are empowered to do, is to assist in selecting and arranging a candidate for the [forthcoming Democratic] Chicago convention? Who could have given them this confidential employment but he who only a week since declared to Jaquess and Gilmore that he had no terms of peace but the independence of the South — the dissolution of the Union?

Thus the present presidential contest will almost certainly be no other than a contest between a Union and a Disunion candidate, disunion cer-

tainly following the success of the latter. The issue is a mighty one for all people and all time. . . .

A never-solved mystery surrounds an astonishing memorandum Lincoln then had in his office. Written in his hand, with the information possibly supplied by Wakeman (or even Greeley, although the contents varied greatly from what the would-be Southern envoys at Niagara were telling Greeley their mission was), it sets forth Lincoln's understanding of what one of the Confederates at Niagara was doing.

Greeley had said he was engaged in talks with two Southerners; it appeared that there were in fact three. One of them, Clement Claiborne Clay, Jr., a former United States senator from Alabama, is represented in Lincoln's memorandum as having "prepared a Platform and an Address to be adopted by the Democracy [Democratic Party] at the Chicago Convention."

The first of the three planks enumerated called simply for the restoration of the "*Union as it was*"—Lincoln marked this in italics—specifically barring any further action to free slaves. The second called for "no additional negroes . . . to be taken from their masters," and set forth that all blacks in the Union Army and the Navy "be at once disarmed and degraded to menial service." The third required "all negroes not having enjoyed actual freedom during the war to be held permanently as slaves" and reopened the status of those who had thus far been freed.

Other than holding out the possibility of the Confederate States rejoining the Union on these terms and not insisting on the status of a sovereign state, this was as complete a pro-Confederate platform as could be imagined. Its suggested keynote address included these words referring to Lincoln.

The stupid tyrant who now disgraces the Chair of Washington and Jackson could, any day, have peace and restoration of the Union; and would have them, only that he persists in war merely to free the slaves.

There is more, all still in Lincoln's handwriting, with nothing in or attached to the memorandum that explains where he got this. (The only clue is that in a letter to Wakeman he referred to a conversation that they had during the latter part of July.)

Mr. Clay confesses to his Democratic friends that he is for peace and dis-union, but, he says, "You cannot elect [a Democrat to replace Lincoln] without a cry of [continuing the] war . . . but, once elected, we are friends, and can adjust matters somehow." He also says, "You will have some difficulty in proving that Lincoln could, if he would, have peace and re-union, because Davis has not said so, and will not say so; but you must assert it, and re-assert it, and stick to it, and it will pass as at least half proved.

All of this was political dynamite, and had to be handled as carefully as if it were the explosive itself. It revealed a predictable effort by Confederate secret agents to influence and control the Democratic Party's presidential campaign during the coming autumn, but also demonstrated freelancing duplicity by a Southern operative. Here was a former United States senator from Alabama deliberately misrepresenting the policies and convictions of Confederate president Jefferson Davis, as Davis had stated them to Gilmore and Jaquess in Richmond soon before this.

As for Greeley, it was beginning to occur to him that he had gotten in way over his head. In a combination of his eagerness for peace and his desire to bring off a diplomatic coup, he may well have failed to explain to the Confederate representatives the basis on which Lincoln had said talks could begin. On the day after Hay arrived at Niagara, Greeley left for New York City and the editorial offices of his enormously influential *Tribune*. While Hay tried to unravel what had really been said and written by the principal parties before he arrived, still hoping for some indication that one or more Confederate emissaries might accompany him to Washington to open talks on the basis laid down by Lincoln, Clay and another of his colleagues exploited the situation by sending a letter to Colorado Jewett. In it, they deplored what they described as "the change made by the president in his instructions to convey [Confederate] commissioners to Washington for negotiations, unconditionally." Lincoln had of course set down the firmest of conditions, but this was just a foretaste of the propaganda benefits the agents in Canada hoped to reap from even those overtures that had been made.

On the one hand, Lincoln had information and a continuing correspondence—Confederates to Greeley, petulant letters from Greeley to Lincoln saying he had been misunderstood, exploited, betrayed—that might prove once and for all that negotiations with the Confederacy were impossible. On the other, Greeley was in no mood to be seen as having foolishly entered into an irresponsible relationship with dubious individuals and leading them to think that Lincoln would meet them without preconditions.

Lincoln decided that it was time to tell his principal advisers about this increasingly messy situation. At a cabinet meeting on July 22, Attorney General Bates noted in his diary, Lincoln "read us all the letters" thus far written or received concerning what Bates called the Confederate "(pretended) attempt to negotiate for peace . . . by the agency of that meddlesome blockhead Jewitt [Jewett] and Horace Greel[e]y." All this was new to Bates; he added, "I am surprised to find the Prest. green enough to be entrapped in such a correspondence; but being in, his letters seem to me cautious and prudent."

As a lawyer, Bates regarded these letters as evidence, and quickly concluded this:

> *I consider it a very serious affair—a double trick.—On the part of the Rebel Commissioners (now at Niagara, on the Canadian side) the hope might have been entertained that a show of negotiation for peace might produce a truce, relax the war, and give them a breathing spell, at this critical moment of their fate.*

The other side of the "double trick," as the attorney general saw it, was that if "the President, I fear, is afraid of the *Tribune*"—Greeley's paper—then Greeley, "having, vainly, exhausted his strength against Lincoln's candidacy, he now, adopts the candidate [Lincoln] . . . and plays the next best game, i.e. tries to convert him to his own use. . . ."

One thing seemed inevitable: it was only a matter of time until some person or entity—a Confederate in Canada, Greeley, some Northern newspaper other than Greeley's *Tribune*, or perhaps one of Lincoln's well-meaning allies—would break into print with a version of what had happened and what it meant

III

In these last days of July, Washington found itself free of crises in its immediate vicinity. In Georgia, Sherman had fought his way through to a standoff in which his powerful forces ringed Atlanta while the Confederates still defiantly held the city. Grant continued to fight Lee in Virginia and political intrigues continued to brew, but in Washington itself the atmosphere was of relative calm before a building storm. Patriots throughout the North might think of their capital with its marble dome as symbolizing a place whose life was as noble as some of the ideals for which Union soldiers were dying, but that was not the reality. Brigadier General William E. Doster was uniquely positioned to see the seamy side of Washington. As the military provost marshal, he was the city's police chief, as far as many thousands of Union Army personnel were involved. Almost in tones of wonder, he later described the scale on which prostitution existed in this metropolis where he had responsibilities for keeping order.

No one who has not witnessed it can believe the freedom with which this business was carried on and patronized at this time in Washington. Keepers of brothels from New York, Philadelphia, Baltimore, and even the Western cities of St. Louis, and Chicago, were attracted hither by the chance of making money, and occupied entire blocks on the south side of Pennsylvania Avenue. Four hundred and fifty houses registered were in Washington alone. . . . All of them were crowded at night. Even in the day it was not unusual to see a long row of saddled horses standing before such resorts.

In the spirit of giving credit where it was due, Doster said that everyone cooperated with his efforts to inspect and maintain order in these establishments.

The keepers were, or course, most complaisant to the police. The moment the tramp of the patrol was heard before the door, they made the girls open every room door to the guard. Of course, it was impossible to do more for this evil than to keep it in check. But the demoralizing influence of war is so great that it was no uncommon sight to see young men of good families riding side by side with these characters in the most public parts of Pennsylvania Avenue, and even taking them to the theater.

Gambling places abounded. Doster discovered that some of the brothels and gambling halls operated "under the patronage of leading people in the United States," and that the largest and most elaborate gambling hall was under the protection of people "of too high a character to be overcome by a subordinate officer of the army" such as himself. Nonetheless, while Doster could never get this biggest place closed down, he frequently engaged those running it in an inconvenient game of cat and mouse.

They had the saloon upstairs, entered through a winding passage, and through one outer and three inner doors, at each of which stood a watchman, communicating with a guard on the pavement outside. At the slightest approach of alarm, the signal was given and passed upstairs, the dealer hid his cards and chips, and the inmates escaped through a passage in the rear.

The doors were then opened and showed nothing but a splendidly furnished suite of rooms, with chairs in crimson, and richly framed oil paintings on the walls, and a supper table laden with delicacies of food and wine, superior to any that could be procured elsewhere in the city.

In somewhat bemused fashion, Doster described the bribes offered him, on one occasion in the form of "a roll of one thousand dollar treasury notes and a cluster diamond ring," to assist in matters ranging from looking the other way as weapons were smuggled to the Confederacy, to freeing a Union officer accused of a crime who was awaiting trial in the Old Capitol Prison. In the latter case, it was spelled out for Doster: "I could either connive at his escape, or prevent his trial, or influence the War Department to release him, or, if it came to the worst, pack the court with officers directed to acquit."

To their surprise, some of those attempting to bribe Doster found themselves behind bars. In writing of his position in wartime Washington, he explained that if he had wished to make a fortune, he could have done so in a different way and with virtually no risk. He had control of all this:

. . . the disposition and sale of the vast amount of confiscated Government stores, which were uninventoried, and of which I had the disposal without being responsible to anybody, —depots of clothing, ships and cargoes of smuggled goods, Confederate and Government money—horses, medicines, and a thousand valuable things I could ship North and sell, and keep the money, without the knowledge of any one. So, in purchasing

stores for the contrabands [a term used to refer to freed slaves], that was
entirely my business, and I was not obliged to render any one an account
of what I did, or to whom or how much I paid.

Although there was nothing illegal about it, various foreign military
adventurers who came to Washington seeking significant rank in the
Union Army thought this highly visible chief of the military police could
help them. "It was a singular thing," Doster wrote, "to see how many En-
glishmen applied to me for assistance to commissions, on the ground that
they had participated in the charge of the Light Brigade at Balaclava,
considering the number who fell in the charge."

AT THE WHITE House, the young painter Francis Carpenter had, after
what he described as "six months' incessant labor," come close to putting
the final touches on his big painting of Lincoln with his cabinet gathered
around him when he signed the Emancipation Proclamation. Now, at the
end of a cabinet meeting in late July, "the President and the Cabinet, at
the close of the regular session, adjourned in a body to the State Dining-
room, to view the work, at last in a condition to receive criticism." As
Carpenter anxiously awaited the reaction, "sitting in the middle of the
group, the President expressed his 'unschooled' opinion, as he called it,
of the result, in terms which could not but have afforded the deepest gratification to any artist."

By arrangement, Carpenter was to return to his home in New York
City, taking the painting with him. For the two days before that, Lincoln
had it put on display in the East Room so that the public could come and
see it. "During this time," Carpenter noted, "the house was thronged
with visitors, the porters estimating their number each day at several
thousands."

As the last visitors left on the second afternoon, with the painting by
itself in the suddenly silent East Room, Carpenter planned "to have the
canvas taken down and rolled up during the night for transportation to
New York," but he waited, hoping to have a chance to "say a last word to
Mr. Lincoln previous to his leaving for the Soldiers' Home, where the
family were then staying."

At four o'clock Lincoln's carriage came up to the door, his cavalry escort clattering along beside it. "Knowing that the President would soon

appear," Carpenter said, "I stepped out under the portico to wait for him."

Then—and this was the last time the young painter would ever talk with Lincoln—he saw once more the other side of the man he had come to admire so much: not the statesman who signed documents affecting the lives of millions, not the president who had soldiers of the largest army on earth waiting for him to step into his carriage, but the poor boy from the Illinois frontier who never forgot what it was to be an ordinary citizen who needed the help of those more powerful than himself.

> Presently I caught sight of his unmistakable figure standing half-way between the portico and the gateway leading to the War Department[,] leaning against the iron fence,—one arm thrown over the railing and one foot on the stone coping which supports it, evidently having been intercepted, on his way in from the War Department, by a plain-looking man, who was giving him, very diffidently, an account of a difficulty which he had been unable to have rectified.

Carpenter walked a bit closer to Lincoln, noting that the president "said very little to the man, but was intently studying the expression of his face while he was narrating his trouble." The presidential carriage and the men and horses of the United States Cavalry's "Black Horse Troop" could wait; everything could wait.

> . . . Mr. Lincoln said to him, "Have you a card?" The man searched his pockets, but finding none, a gentleman standing near, who had heard the question, came forward and said, "Here is one, Mr. President." . . . Taking the card and a pencil, Mr. Lincoln sat down upon the low stone coping, presenting almost the appearance of sitting upon the pavement itself, and wrote upon the card to the proper official to "examine this man's case."
>
> While [Lincoln was] writing this, I observed several persons passing through the promenade smiling, at what I presume they thought the undignified appearance of the head of a nation, who, however, seemed utterly unconscious, either of any impropriety in the action, or of attracting any attention. . . . Rising to his feet he handed the man the card, with a word of direction, and then turning to me said: "Well Carpenter, I must go in and take one more look at the picture before you leave us."

The president and the painter walked into the now-deserted East Room, to the painting; Lincoln, "sitting down in front of it, remained for some time in silence." After a while, they had this quiet exchange:

> *I said that I had at last worked out my idea, as he expressed it at our first interview, and would now be glad to hear his final suggestions and criticism.*
>
> *"There is little to find fault with," he replied; "the portraiture is the main thing, and that seems to me absolutely perfect."*

Lincoln then singled out a detail that had a significance Carpenter may not have understood. He noted that in portraying the details of his office, Carpenter had changed the title of a book that leaned against a chair leg. It had been, Lincoln said, what he thought was probably "an old volume of *United States Statutes*." Carpenter agreed that Lincoln was right, and told the president, "at the last moment I learned that you frequently consulted, during the period you were preparing the Proclamation[,] Solicitor Whiting's work on the 'War Powers of the President,' and as Emancipation was the result in fact of a military necessity, the book seemed to me to be just the thing to go in there; so I simply changed the title, leaving the old sheepskin cover as it was."

Lincoln said he would like a change to be made, not in the book's title, but its appearance. "Now[,] Whiting's book is not a regular law-book." It was a critical distinction: there was nothing in the many volumes of *United States Statutes* that empowered Lincoln to begin freeing slaves without a constitutional amendment; in developing the Emancipation Proclamation he had indeed relied on the concept of "emergency war powers," a term nowhere to be found in the Constitution. Referring to the presence of this book in the painting, Lincoln added, "It is all very well that it should be there, but I suggest that as you have changed the title, you change the character of the binding."

Immediately agreeing to paint the book's cover differently when he got to New York, Carpenter asked, "Is there anything else that you would like changed or added?"

> *"No," he replied, and then repeated very emphatically the expression he used when the design was first sketched upon the canvas: "It is as good as it can be made."*

I then referred at some length, to the enthusiasm in which the picture was conceived and had been executed, concluding with an expression of my profound appreciation of the very unusual opportunity afforded me in the prosecution of the work, and his unvarying kindness and consideration through the many weeks of our intercourse.

He listened pensively, — almost passively, to me, — his eyes fastened upon the picture. As I finished he turned, and in his simple-hearted, earnest way, said: "Carpenter, I believe that I am about as glad over the success of this work as you are."

And with these words in my ear, President and painter separated.

IV

For those anxiously watching the course of the war and the relative strength and ability of the Union and Confederate forces, an enormously significant event was about to take place. On Thursday, July 28, Union engineering troops carried out the order to "charge"—fill with four tons of explosives—the mine they had successfully tunneled out beneath the dominant Confederate position at Elliott's Salient on the Petersburg lines. General Burnside rode to Meade's headquarters to report that this had been done and to have a final discussion, two days before the attack, about the plan to exploit the sudden break in the enemy front that the massive blast would cause. When the explosion went off at first light, as many as 20,000 Federal troops would start attacking in successive waves, scheduled to rush across the hundred or so yards separating them from the destroyed Confederate redoubt. If they could pour swiftly through this breach in the enemy defenses and keep going into the city, they might seize Petersburg and significantly alter the course of the war.

This meeting between Meade and Burnside, and another the next day, did not go well. Neither man could forget that Burnside had once commanded the Army of the Potomac now led by Meade. Although Burnside had fully agreed to serve under Meade, there was also the tricky chain-of-command situation caused by Burnside's seniority, and Grant's practice of sending separate but complementary orders to both men. Meade informed Burnside that, with Grant's agreement, he was changing the previous decision to have the attack led by Burnside's division of United States Colored Troops. Meade had earlier expressed to Burnside his mistrust of these black units because of their lack of combat experience, but he now had Grant's backing on policy grounds. Grant later said this:

> *General Burnside wanted to put his colored division in front, and I believe if he had done so it would have been a success. Still I agreed with General Meade in his objection to that plan . . . [if] it should be a failure, it would then be said, and very properly, that we were shoving those people ahead to get killed because we did not care anything about them. But that could not be said if we put white troops in front.*

Burnside wanted his division of Colored Troops to lead the attack for reasons that had nothing to do with their race. Of his four divisions, the other three composed of white soldiers, they were by far the most rested; they had been told they were going to lead, they had been trained in what to do, and they were eager to show they could do it well. On this afternoon before the dawn attack, still trying to persuade Meade that he should be allowed to use his Fourth Division, the black troops, as his spearhead, he said that "I reminded him of the fact that the three white divisions had for forty days been in the immediate presence of the enemy, and at no point of the line could a man raise his head above the parapet without being fired at. . . ." He added that these units had been losing "thirty to sixty men daily," that their food had been poor, and that "they had had very few, if any, opportunities of washing . . . in my opinion, they were not in a condition to make a vigorous charge."

Meade listened, and closed the discussion with: "No, general, the order is final; you must detail one of your white divisions to take the advance."

Burnside returned to his headquarters. Assembling his four division commanders, he informed them of the change of plan. It was now afternoon, and the mine was to go off at three-thirty the following morning. All four of his generals, including Brigadier General Edward Ferrero, the white commander of the Fourth Division, still felt that the black troops should make the assault, but Burnside explained that the decision was out of his hands. It was, however, imperative to choose the leading division immediately, so that its troops could get into position overnight, to lead the assault.

Burnside had no preference as to which of the three white divisions should go first. He asked their commanders if one or more of them would volunteer. None of the three did. "I finally decided," he said, "that I would allow the leading division to be designated by lot." This was not to decide at all; Burnside put three straws of different lengths into an upended Union Army officer's hat, and each general, looking away as he put his hand into it, drew one out.

The short straw, designating who would lead, came out in the hand of Brigadier General James Ledlie, commander of the First Division; when he saw it, one of his staff said, he described himself to the others as the "unlucky victim." Ledlie was one more political general, originally appointed as a major in 1861 because of his connections in New York City. Although he had been rising in the army for three years, his service was in quiet coast artillery posts, and to this time he had seen virtually no combat. He had performed acceptably in largely administrative tasks; Burnside, under whose authority Ledlie had only recently come, was under the impression that when Ledlie finally received command of an infantry brigade during the past May, he had handled it commendably.

Burnside was badly misinformed about the man who, by picking the shortest of three straws, had become a key figure in a surprise attack of the greatest importance. At an engagement two months before at Ox Ford, Virginia, Ledlie was drunk; lost in some martial fantasy, he gave the order for an unnecessary attack. While he remained at the rear in a stupor, four Massachusetts infantry regiments charged a superior Confederate force that cut them down from the protection of formidable earthworks. Then, in the midst of a thunderstorm and with Ledlie having no more to do with the conduct of the battle than if he had been back in Washington, the Confederates launched a counterattack, capturing 150 men and sending the Union brigade running from the field.

Somehow, Burnside never learned of Ledlie's cowardly performance and disastrous lack of judgment, and during the past two months Ledlie had been promoted to command the 5,000 men he was to handle the following morning. His officers were accustomed to seeing him drunk while on duty. Now, as sunset neared, Burnside again reviewed the plan of attack. Ledlie may have been drunk during this talk, perhaps accounting for how little he remembered of his instructions the next day, and the other three generals displayed little confidence in what the dawn might bring.

Despite the confusion on the Union side, as the night went on the

Confederates, just a hundred yards off, had no idea of what was in store for them. During the thirty-five days since the Pennsylvania miners started digging the tunnel, there had been various sounds that seemed to be coming from underground in the area. The Confederates had even dug several "listening shafts," tunnels that they hoped might locate or even intersect with or collapse the horizontal shaft that they suspected was under construction, but they never found it.

The tunnel itself was a wonder. In the middle of a siege, with both sides firing artillery that shook the earth, the prewar mining engineer Lieutenant Colonel Henry Pleasants had brought forward, 20 feet under the surface of the battlefield, a shaft 510 feet long. It was a tunnel cut through the earth in the shape of a triangle between 5 and 6 feet high, about 54 inches wide at the bottom, and 2 feet wide at the top. As this narrow tunnel was dug toward the enemy line, lumber to build the roof and walls to keep it from collapsing had to be carried in and set in place, and ventilation and drainage had to be provided. Only two men at a time could do the digging at the inner end; once they filled a crate holding 4 cubic feet of earth, they would stagger out carrying it, and another pair of workers would take their places.

To accomplish this, Pleasants used, at one time or another, all the men of the 48th Pennsylvania. In one report, he said, "There are 210 men employed every twenty-four hours," but these words gave no indication of the physical exertion and mental stress endured by these men, who knew that at any moment the tunnel could collapse and bury them alive. They emerged from their three-hour shifts walking stooped over, covered with clay, their hands bruised and sometimes bloody, with their heads scraped from constant bumping against the rough timbers of the low ceiling. In all, these men from Pennsylvania brought out 18,000 cubic feet of earth, and at one moment discovered and carried out a bone so large that one of the regiment's officers confidently identified it as being a mastodon's thighbone. At the end of a month, they had set the stage for what would be the largest man-made explosion in the Western Hemisphere to that time.

AT THREE-FIFTEEN ON the morning of July 30, Lieutenant Colonel Henry Pleasants lit the long cordlike fuse that would set off the four tons of gunpowder. The explosion was to occur at three-thirty, and he calculated that the hissing, smoldering flame would take fifteen minutes to burn its way to the powder waiting to be ignited.

At three-twenty, Burnside received a telegram from Meade's chief of staff, saying, "As it is still so dark, the commanding general says you can postpone firing the mine if you think proper." With the fuse already burning, Burnside simply replied without explanation that the detonation would occur as scheduled.

It did not. Not at three-thirty, or at three forty-five, or at four. Meade's chief of staff soon sent a terse command: "The commanding general directs that if your mine has failed that you make an assault at once, opening your [artillery] batteries."

Here was not only suspense and confusion, but an element of madness. At the moment, no one could say if the smoldering fuse might not yet detonate the charge calculated to do enormous damage to everything above it. If Burnside ordered his thousands of men to dash across the hundred yards to Elliott's Salient, they might share the fate planned for its Confederate defenders. What was needed was an act of purest heroism, and it came swiftly. Sergeant Henry Reese, a Welsh coal miner from Minersville, Pennsylvania, volunteered to go into the tunnel with a lantern, find out what was happening with that fuse, and correct the situation if he could. To his relief, he found that the fuse had gone dead about 60 feet short of the tons of powder and was not about to complete its function belatedly and blow him to shreds. At the same time, he realized that, while he had a lantern that could relight the fuse, he did not have a knife with which to resplice the three cords needed to take the flame on from the junction where it had burnt out. As he started back along the tunnel, he encountered a second volunteer, Lieutenant Jacob Doughty, a boilermaker from Pottsville, Pennsylvania, who was bringing in extra lengths of fuse, and had a pocketknife.

The two men made the necessary repairs, but they understood that they now faced a new chance of sudden ghastly death: once they lit the repaired fuse, 60 feet from the four tons of powder, they had to sprint the 440 feet to the end of the tunnel while the flame had a seventh of that distance to go in the opposite direction before it set off a blast that might kill them in one of several ways before they got to open air.

They just made it. At 4:44 A.M., the mine went off. Any number of officers and men recorded what they experienced. A soldier of the 20th

Michigan looking out at the Confederate redoubt felt "a jar like an earth-quake," and saw this:

> *. . . a heaving and lifting of the fort and the hill on which it stood; then a monstrous tongue of flame shot fully two hundred feet in the air, followed by a vast column of white smoke . . . then a great spout or fountain of red earth rose to a great height, mingled with men and guns, timbers and planks, and every other kind of debris, all ascending, spreading, whirling, scattering . . .*

A soldier from New York recorded that "the air was filled with earth, cannon, caissons, sand-bags and living men," and a man from Maine remembered the sky being filled with "Earth, stones, timbers, arms, legs, guns unlimbered and bodies unlimbed." On the Confederate side, an adjutant of an artillery battalion saw the wreckage "hurtling down with a roaring sound showers of stones, broken timbers, and blackened human limbs."

No one on either side had ever seen anything like it; not the veteran Regulars who had fought in Mexico or in the Indian wars on the frontier—no one. Decades later, men who until that moment in the war had seen only corpses that looked like heaps of old clothes scattered on the ground would write vividly about human bodies rising in the air, coming apart as they did, heads going one way, arms another, legs spinning off by themselves, a man's trunk tumbling out of the sky like a thick log.

After gaping at this for a few seconds, the Union soldiers poised to attack realized that this debris could fall on them, too—a mass of clay as large as a hut dropped from the sky along with any number of other large objects that could kill a man. Major William H. Powell of Ledlie's staff described the troops' reaction: "This caused them to break and scatter to the rear, and about ten minutes were consumed re-forming for the attack." Initially, the Confederates still alive on each side of the wide hole in the front were paralyzed. Even as they saw Ledlie's reformed First Division start to come out of the Union positions, few fired their muskets at the Union soldiers; Pleasants later said that for more than an hour "not a shot was fired by their artillery."

The trouble for the advancing Union soldiers began as soon as they entered the area of what became known as the Crater. What Burnside had wanted was not for them to go down into this huge, suddenly-created pit, 30 feet deep, 60 feet across and 200 feet long, but to move around its edges and head for Cemetery Hill, a high point beyond it from which an assault into Petersburg could be launched.

Whatever Burnside expected, Brigadier General Ledlie never conveyed a useful order, nor did he do any leading. Ledlie remained in a "bomb-proof," a sandbagged bunker 165 feet behind the line from which his men started their move to the Crater, and never went nearer the enemy than that. For much of the day, he was joined by General Ferrero, the white commanding officer of the Colored Troops, and on at least one occasion a surgeon of a Michigan regiment "gave them rum"—at their request. This doctor also later testified that "General Ledlie . . . said he had the malaria and was struck by a spent [musket] ball," adding that Ledlie said he needed to find his subordinate, Colonel William Bartlett, "as he wanted to turn the command over to him and go to the rear." Somewhat later, Major Powell, who had twice risked his life running back and forth from the Union lines to the Crater to bring back firsthand information on which Ledlie might base orders, came into the bomb-proof, which had no view of the action. He explained to Ledlie the need to broaden the front "on the right and left of the crater," rather than piling additional men in there or expecting them to be able to use the Crater as a place from which to launch an attack up Cemetery Hill. Powell found Ledlie simply responding to him with "an order to go back and tell the brigade commanders to get their men out [of the Crater] and press forward to Cemetery Hill." Powell had this reaction:

> *This talk and these orders, coming from a commander sitting in a bomb-proof inside the Union lines, were disgusting. I returned again to the crater and delivered the orders, which I knew beforehand could not possibly be obeyed; and I told General Ledlie so before I left him.*

When the Union troops had first come to the edge of the Crater, Powell later wrote, "the whole scene of the explosion struck every one with astonishment as we arrived at the crest of the debris." Going down into the wreckage, a soldier from Massachusetts encountered Confederate survivors, "half buried[,] the bodies of soldiers still alive, which caused us for a while to help them out and give a drink of water to revive them." Ironically, this enormous explosion, an ultimate act of war, had turned warriors into men instinctively engaging in acts of humanity. Helping these shocked and wounded Confederates, they lost a vital half an hour or more that could have been used to exploit the surprise the blast created.

As they began to look past the scene of tangled enemy dead and wounded on the Crater floor, the First Division troops became aware of an appalling obstacle. Instead of having sides that gently sloped up to a rim, the far side of this huge hole that had been supposed to be a gateway through the Confederate defenses had steep walls of slippery earth 30 feet high, "composed of jagged masses of clay projecting from loose sand." Scaling ladders were needed; there were none. Men tried to climb what was in effect a cliff; finding no good place on its face to pull themselves up using their hands and feet, some turned their backs to this unevenly protruding wall, dug their heels into it, and attempted to scale it that way. A few succeeded, but most of them were shot as they appeared coming over the rim with their heads facing away from the enemy, with no chance to bring their rifles into immediate action. Major Powell said, "Every organization melted away, as soon as it entered this hole in the ground, into a mass of human beings clinging by toes and heels to its almost perpendicular sides. If a man was shot on the crest he fell and rolled to the bottom of the pit."

Less than an hour had passed since the explosion; more and more units of the First Division came over from the Union positions as ordered, and poured into the giant hole. By now some Confederates were firing down into it from the rim, with a few Union soldiers returning fire from below. The situation was described by Captain (later Brevet Brigadier General) Stephen M. Weld:

> *Here, in the crater was a confused mob of men continually increasing by fresh arrivals. Of course, nothing could be seen from this crater of the situation around us. Any attempt to move forward from this crater was absolutely hopeless. The men could not be got forward. It was a perfect mob. . . . To ask men to go forward in such a condition was useless. Each one felt as if he were to encounter the whole Confederate force alone and unsupported. The moral backing of an organized body of men, in which each would sustain his companions on either side, was wanting.*

About forty-five minutes after the blast, Colonel Henry G. Thomas, the white officer commanding the 2nd Brigade of the division of Colored Troops, was sitting in the Union entrenchments, waiting to take his men over to the Crater after his division's 1st Brigade went in. In his account of what happened, Thomas said he heard the "quiet voice" of someone who had arrived on horseback asking, "Who commands this brigade?"

> *"I do," I replied. Rising, and turning toward the voice, I saw General Grant. He was in his usual dress: a broad-brimmed felt hat and the ordinary coat of a private. He wore no sword. Colonel Horace Porter of his staff and a single orderly accompanied him.*
>
> *"Well," said the general, slowly and thoughtfully, as if communing with himself rather than addressing a subordinate, "Why are you not in?"*
>
> *Pointing to the First Brigade just in my front, I replied, "My orders are to follow that brigade." Feeling that golden opportunities might be slipping away from us, I added, "Will you give me the order to go in right now?"*
>
> *After a moment's hesitation, [Grant answered] in the same slow and hesitating manner, "No, you may keep the orders you have." Then, turning his horse's head, he rode away at a walk.*

Grant's presence revealed his instinct for when to come forward from headquarters often far back of the lines to observe a situation for himself. By contrast, it was ten minutes later that Burnside received a telegram from a staff officer at the headquarters of Meade, who had a more immediate responsibility than Grant for what was happening. It said: "The commanding general learns that your troops are halting at the works where the mine exploded. He directs that all your troops be pushed forward to the crest at once." Twenty minutes after that, at 6 A.M., this came in, directly from Meade and not from anyone on his staff.

> *Prisoners say there is no line in their rear, and that their men were falling back when ours advanced. . . . Our chance is now; push your men forward at all hazards (black and white), and don't lose time in making formations, but rush for the crest.*

The "crest" to which Meade referred was not the rim of the Crater, but the ridge of Cemetery Hill beyond it. By this time the situation had taken on a life of its own. A few of Burnside's units were moving on either side of the Crater, trying to reach that ridge, but Burnside responded to Meade's exhortation to throw every unit straight into the battle: ten minutes later, one of Burnside's staff replied directly to Meade, reporting that "General Burnside says that he has given orders to all his division commanders to push everything in at once." This meant that the great majority of Burnside's men, now including the black units, continued to enter what was developing into an increasingly crowded death trap.

In addition to everything else that was going wrong, both Meade and Burnside had lost control of the situation. They were relying on subordinate generals who were either unable to lead because of the confusion, or unwilling to lead. Two who were obviously unwilling, Ledlie and Ferrero, sat in their bomb-proof shelter while their men were in combat 200 yards from them.

Soon after Grant rode to the front to see the situation for himself, he dismounted some 300 yards from the earthworks in which Burnside had his headquarters. Grant's aide Horace Porter described the general-in-chief's next movements, which were made under enemy fire.

> *General Grant now began to edge his way vigorously to the front through the lines of the assaulting columns as they poured out of the rifle-pits and crawled over the obstructions. It was one of the warmest days of the entire summer, and even at this early hour of the morning the heat was suffocating. The general wore his blue blouse and a pair of blue trousers—in fact, the uniform of a private except for the shoulder-straps. . . . None of the men seemed to recognize the plainly dressed man who was elbowing past them energetically, and whose face was covered with dust and streaked with perspiration. . . .*

Burnside, Horace Porter recalled, "was not a little astonished to see the general approach on foot from such a direction, [and] climb over the parapet. . . ." Grant was his usual direct self. Speaking quickly to Burnside, he said, "The entire opportunity has been lost. There is now no chance of success. These troops must be immediately withdrawn. It is slaughter to leave them here."

Burnside presumably acknowledged the order; Grant left, but what passed back and forth between Meade and Burnside was something far from the effective communication that Grant wanted. At some point,

Meade had sent a runner to Burnside saying, "Do you mean to say that your officers and men will not obey your orders to advance? If not, what is the obstacle? Tell me the truth." This prompted Burnside, in the middle of a battle, to reply, "I have never, in any report, said anything different from what I conceive to be the truth. Were it not insubordinate, I would say that the latter remark of your note was unofficerlike and ungentlemanly." Whatever else was happening, neither Burnside nor Meade was trying to call off the attack.

Even getting to the Crater had become hazardous. The 5,000 men of the First Division had crossed the hundred yards from the Union lines with few casualties while the Confederates were still shocked and disorganized, but when the Second Division's 45th Pennsylvania followed them, they encountered a "severe fire from the enemy's works on the right and left [of the Crater]. The whole space was swept with canister, grape[shot] and musketry."

A better situation temporarily developed on the right, or northern, side of the Crater, when a force including the Indian snipers of the 1st Michigan Sharpshooters captured an enemy trench, took some prisoners, and turned two Confederate cannon around and began firing at other Confederate positions. Some of the black troops managed to get into the area beyond the Crater, "where they captured some 200-odd prisoners and a stand of colors, and recaptured a stand of colors belonging to a white regiment." Amid the chaos, some individuals acted heroically. Serving in a company that had captured a Confederate trench, a Lieutenant Pennell from a Massachusetts regiment picked up a fallen battle flag. A battle flag did far more than identify a regiment: it was its honor, its soul. Determined to have his men rise out of the captured trench and continue to advance, he leapt out of the trench by himself and ran along in front of it, carrying the battle flag and exhorting them to charge.

> *With his sword uplifted in his right hand and the banner in his left, he sought to call out the men along the whole line of the parapet. In a moment, a musketry fire was focused upon him, whirling him round and round several times before he fell. Of commanding figure, his bravery was so conspicuous that . . . a number of his men were shot because spellbound, they forgot their own shelter in watching this superb boy, who was the only child of an old Massachusetts clergyman.*

There were other remarkable efforts, one ending in mute shock. At a time when just to reach the Crater meant to lose many men from the Confederate crossfire now coming from the still-intact enemy trenches to its right and left, Lieutenant James H. Clark of the 115th New York saw his regimental color sergeant unfurl the unit's battle flag. The sergeant pointed toward the enemy, shouted, "Forward, Hundred and Fifteenth!" and led the charge that carried them into the Crater. Once in there, Clark first came into an area where, "amid gun carriages and timbers, lay the naked corpses of the South Carolinians blown up by powder." Then he saw what appeared to be "a large body of Union soldiers, lying as though in line of battle waiting for the command to move forward." Clark thought it was an entire regiment or even a brigade—certainly a thousand or more men. Upon coming closer:

What is our horror to find that they are all Union dead! There they lay both white and black, not singly or scattering, but in long rows; in whole companies. . . . The ground is blue with Union dead.

By now some of the fighting had spread across an area of a square mile, but by far the largest number of Union troops still milled about in the Crater itself. Both on the edges of the Crater and beyond, the Confederates had become aware that black soldiers were part of the force attacking them. Early in the action, some of the Colored Troops had shouted as their battle cry, "Remember Fort Pillow!"—the engagement in Tennessee fifteen weeks before in which the evidence was that the Confederates had murdered black Union troops after they surrendered. As soon as the defenders heard this shout, it caused a vehement, violent response: in words nearly identical to those said to have been shouted at Fort Pillow, a Confederate captain yelled, "Kill 'em! Shoot 'em! Kill the damned niggers!" That officer died moments later, stabbed by a black soldier's bayonet, and the feelings on both sides grew increasingly vicious: the commander of some Virginia infantrymen told them, "Boys, you have hot work ahead; they are negroes and show no quarter."

The thought that to be captured by the black soldiers was to be killed by them guaranteed more murder. Confederate artillery general Porter Alexander wrote, "Some of the Negro prisoners, who were originally allowed to surrender by some soldiers, were afterward shot by others"; another Confederate officer said of the fate of black prisoners, "I think about two hundred negroes got into our lines. . . . I don't believe that much over half of these ever reached the rear. You could see them lying dead all over the route to the rear."

At eight in the morning, some three hours after the action began, Robert E. Lee joined Beauregard at the house of a family named Gee, on high ground 500 yards back of the Crater, that was being used as a Confederate forward headquarters. Grant had returned to his headquarters, and Meade and even Burnside were much farther from the action than the vantage point now possessed by this remarkable pair of Confederate generals. In addition to the combination of ability and experience these two leaders possessed, Lee had ordered forward two brigades commanded by Brigadier General William Mahone, a VMI graduate who had distinguished himself at Fredericksburg, Chancellorsville, Gettysburg, the Wilderness, and Spotsylvania, and who before the day was out would receive a battlefield promotion to major general bestowed on him by Lee. (Trying to organize his units for a counterattack, Mahone encountered terrified fleeing Confederate soldiers who told them that their trenches had been overrun by black soldiers who "gave no quarter.") To back up the efforts of the Army of Northern Virginia regiments under Mahone, Lee brought up more cannons under the command of William Pegram, his young chief of artillery, and was personally advising where some of them should be placed.

While these Confederate leaders prepared to exploit the situation to the utmost, some Union wounded were able to hobble out of the Crater and cross back to the lines from which they had started. Some were simply relieved to be out of that hell, one shouting, "I'm all right, boys! This is good for thirty days' sick leave," but most were in far worse condition, "their pinched faces telling the effort they were making to suppress groans; others, with the ashy hue of death already gathering on their faces, were largely past pain. Many, out of their senses through agony, were moaning or bellowing like wild beasts." This last July day in a Virginia summer was becoming frightfully hot: a weird mist shrouded the Crater, a steamy cloud composed not only of gunsmoke, but coming from the labored breath and sweat of a huge crowd of frightened men. One soldier remembered being so jammed against those around him that he could not raise his hands, either to use his musket or to surrender if that is what he decided to do. Some of those packed in became so thirsty that they went mad, and others risked their lives going back and forth to the Union lines under intense fire to bring back filled canteens of water for their comrades.

At this point, in the Crater the bodies of "White men and negroes lay indiscriminately together, piled up three and four deep." Some 15,000 Union troops had now entered the bloody pit, and under these conditions there was no hope of reorganizing their original formations: to attempt to do that in the Crater now, a Union staff officer said, would have been "as utterly impracticable as it would be to marshal bees into line after upsetting the hive, and equally impracticable to re-form outside the crater, under the severe fire in front and rear, as it would be to hold a dress parade in the face of a charging enemy." A corporal from New Hampshire, looking down into the Crater from a captured Confederate trench to one side of it, saw the Union troops below as "a mass of worms crawling over each other." From near the rim facing the Confederates, some of the Indian sharpshooters were firing at the enemy and scoring hits, and a sergeant from Connecticut firing from the edge of the rim hit five men before a musket ball chopped off two of his fingers, but the Confederate artillery was now firing right into the Crater from various angles. Mortars were an ideal weapon for dropping cannonballs straight down onto the Union soldiers; the Confederate gunners smiled at how little powder was needed just to loft their shots into the air in an arc above the Crater, with no need to propel them even as far as the Union lines from which the attack had begun. Another battery of cannon designed for direct fire was being brought into place on higher ground that offered the opportunity to shoot straight into the Crater, and would soon begin slamming more than 500 shells into it.

At nine-thirty in the morning, almost five hours after the explosion went off, Burnside received this from Meade's chief of staff.

The major-general commanding has heard that the result of your attack has been a repulse, and directs that, if in your judgment nothing further can be effected, you withdraw to your own line, taking every precaution to get the men back safely.

Burnside still thought something could be accomplished—as events were soon to show, some Union troops could still show remarkable courage, and on the Confederate side Mahone was worried that there still could be a major advance from the Crater—but fifteen minutes after this message, Meade's chief of staff sent a direct order telling Burnside to "withdraw to your own intrenchments." Burnside thereupon rode to Meade's headquarters and argued that the enemy line could still be broken as originally planned, at some point near the Crater. Meade insisted on a withdrawal, but, in response to Burnside's claim that to retreat across the open ground under enemy fire at that moment would be suicide, modified his order to the extent of giving Burnside latitude as to when that retreat should be made.

In the Crater, the Union effort had come to its last and bloodiest gasp. A brigade of Confederates from Alabama advanced to the rim. They found so many muskets with bayonets on them lying on the ground that they threw them down into the Crater as if they were spears, and found the Federal troops throwing them right back. Then the Alabamans leapt down into the pit themselves and into what one of them called "that awful hand to hand struggle of which history tells you." Most of the Union troops fell back. Some of the white soldiers, afraid that the Confederates would kill them if they were captured fighting beside the Colored Troops, began trying to kill these fellow Union soldiers: a white officer wrote his family that "the men was bound not to be taken prisoner among them niggers."

As the defense in this part of the Crater collapsed, a group of some 30 Union soldiers who had surrendered were told to come over the rim, and were ordered to march to the Confederate rear. Union artillerymen thought that they were more Confederates, and opened fire on them. As one of the Confederates guarding them remembered it, "One poor fellow had his arm shot off just as he started to the rear, and . . . said: 'I could bear it better if my own men had not done it.'"

Large numbers of Union troops were managing to make their way back across the hundred yards they had crossed coming the other way hours before. Most made it; the Confederate artillery was busily supporting the two brigades, the one from Alabama and now an additional one from Georgia, that were in and around the Crater trying to finish off the remaining Northern soldiers.

In one area of the Crater where the men from Georgia and Alabama had not penetrated, the remaining Union defenders came up with a remarkable way of protecting themselves. Confederate cannon were now blasting canister shot down the length of two trenches leading into the

Lincoln in 1863, showing the physical effects upon him of two years of the constant strain of wartime leadership. His private secretary John Hay said, "Under this frightful ordeal . . . he aged with great rapidity." In early 1864 Lincoln told a friend, "This war is eating my life out."

Mary Todd Lincoln. A disturbed and difficult woman who once bought four hundred pairs of gloves in three months, she was deeply devoted to her husband. When he was shot by John Wilkes Booth, Mary cradled the mortally wounded president in her arms, shrieking, "Why didn't he shoot me!"

Lincoln in the linen coat he wore in hot weather. This was the type of hat he was wearing when he was shot at one August night in 1864 while entering the grounds of the Soldiers' Home, riding back from the White House to his and Mary's summer retreat. The bullet passed through the low crown of the hat, just above his skull.

Lincoln with his two principal private secretaries, John Nicolay and John Hay, who in private referred to Lincoln as "The Tycoon," and called Mary "The Hell-Cat."

Lincoln's Secretary of the Treasury Salmon P. Chase schemed unsuccessfully to replace Lincoln as a candidate in the 1864 presidential campaign.

Secretary of State William H. Seward, who became the president's close and supportive friend. Lincoln, who had never been out of the United States, was wise to choose as his secretary of state a man who had traveled to eleven foreign countries, speaking with influential persons in all of them.

General Robert E. Lee, a brilliant leader and the South's ultimate gentleman. One of his colonels said that, of all the officers on either side, he was "head and shoulders above every other in *audacity*." The men of Lee's Army of Northern Virginia loved him.

Jefferson Davis. To the end, he insisted that the Confederate States of America had the right to be a separate nation that could keep practicing slavery.

Confederate general Jubal Early. Throughout 1864 his forces threatened Washington; in July he made a bold attack that reached the capital's last lines of defense.

General Ulysses S. Grant. He started the war commanding a thousand men and rose to be the Union's general-in-chief, waging titanic battles against Robert E. Lee in Virginia during the bloody summer of 1864.

11

Secretary of War Edwin M. Stanton. Crusty, domineering, an obsessive worker, he stood by Lincoln's deathbed sobbing convulsively and said at the end, "Now he belongs to the ages."

12

Navy Secretary Gideon Welles kept a diary that gives a unique behind-the-scenes account of the tumultuous political and military events of 1864.

B. F. Butler. Lincoln appointed this prominent Democrat as a general for political reasons. His military performance was so inept that Grant finally asked that he be sent home to Massachusetts "for the good of the service."

Sojourner Truth. The most famous black woman of her era, she was a freed slave who worked on behalf of her people. When Sojourner visited Lincoln in the White House in 1864, she told him, "You are the best president who has ever taken the seat."

The black leader Frederick Douglass criticized some of Lincoln's handling of racial issues, but, shaking his hand hours after hearing his Second Inaugural Address and its message, "With malice toward none; with charity for all," he said of the speech, "Mr. Lincoln, it was a sacred effort."

Union general George B. Mc-Clellan. Relieved of command by Lincoln for having "the slows" in attacking Confederate forces early in the war, in 1864 he emerged as his unsuccessful Democratic opponent for president.

Short and fiery, General Philip Sheridan finally cleared Jubal Early out of Virginia's Shenandoah Valley. "Sheridan's Ride," the poem that immortalized his dramatic gallop from Winchester to save the day at Cedar Creek, inspired the North and added to the tide of military and political success that Lincoln experienced at the end of 1864.

General William Tecumseh Sherman. At a critical point in the 1864 presidential campaign, Sherman's capture of Atlanta as September began reversed the sinking public support for Lincoln and his administration.

The Republican elephant made its debut in this issue of *Father Abraham*, the newspaper put out by the Republican/National Union Party during the shifting fortunes of the 1864 presidential campaign.

VOL. XIV.—NO. 4096.

VICTORY!

GLORIOUS RESULT YESTERDAY.

Election of Lincoln and Johnson.

Terrible Defeat of McClellan.

THE UNION TRIUMPHANT.

New-England a Solid Phalanx.

New-York for Lincoln and Fenton

Defeat of Governor Seymour and His Friends.

The New York Times proclaims Lincoln's reelection.

Lincoln said that this photograph, taken in January of 1864, was his favorite picture of himself. It captures the essence of the strong, patient, indomitable leader who saved the Union.

northern side of the Crater. Ordered to build some sort of breastworks at the end of these alleyways to block this withering fire, some surviving Colored Troops began piling up the big blocks of clay that had been broken lose by the initial explosion, but it was all going too slowly. Then someone shouted, "Put in the dead men!" Everyone, white and black soldiers, started dragging corpses into position to be used as sandbags, and some bodies outside the rim were pulled into position along its edge. A few of the surviving Union riflemen shoved these bodies into position as a makeshift low parapet; then these diehard defenders, including Indians of the 1st Michigan Sharpshooters, used their hands to dig into the clay soil beneath their dead comrades and made little openings through which they continued firing at the enemy.

This continued—a skirmish here, a man falling there, groups making their way back to the Union lines—until two in the afternoon. Finally, in addition to the acres of dead and wounded, several hundred white Northern troops able to fight remained in the Crater, weapons still in their hands. Their officers could see that further resistance was useless, but mistrust on both sides was high; certainly these white Union troops had seen and heard enough about prisoners of all kinds being killed. A few Union soldiers called out their willingness to give up, but their cries just brought more of the violence that had gone on for about seven hours. A white lieutenant of the 13th United States Colored Troops had been watching the Indian snipers of the 1st Michigan Sharpshooter in action and described them as having done "splendid work." Now, when they were surrounded and with little ammunition left, he said this happened. "Some of them were mortally wounded, and drawing their blouses over their faces, they chanted a death song and died—four of them in a group."

The impasse was broken by Adjutant Morgan Cleveland of the 8th Alabama Regiment. Over the sound of the exchange of musket fire, he shouted, "Why in hell don't you fellows surrender?"

A Union colonel shouted back, "Why in the hell don't you let us?"

The shooting stopped. Slowly, dazed men rose from where they had been firing. In another minute, these last several hundred Union soldiers laid down their arms. In 450 minutes, almost 4,000 men of the Army of the Potomac had been killed, wounded, or captured. Despite their not having been sent in first as planned, the Colored Troops suffered the most, with 1,327 casualties. Of the close to 400 black soldiers who were captured, the evidence was that Confederate soldiers murdered 150 of them after they surrendered.

It had in some ways been the Union Army's worst day in thirty-nine months of war. First Bull Run had been a terrible rout; Lee and "Stonewall" Jackson had inflicted a decisive defeat at Chancellorsville; more men had been lost in the first hour at Cold Harbor or in three hours at Fredericksburg than during the entire day at the Crater; but for the North this was a peculiarly humiliating, revealing, emotionally scarring disaster. After three years of costly fighting, for the second time in six weeks the Union Army had thrown away a chance to seize Petersburg and dramatically change the course of the war. The day after the battle, Lee wrote his wife, Mary, a few details, saying of the enemy, "He has suffered severely." In Washington, Navy Secretary Welles noted that after receiving a report of the action from Grant, Secretary of War Stanton seemed "uncertain and confused." The *New York Times* got it partly right, using the terms "desperate attempt," "failure of the attempt," and "disaster and defeat," but also carried a subheadline, "The Colored Troops Charged with the Failure," when in fact the black soldiers had performed neither better nor worse than the white troops. Subsequently the *Times* summed it up for what it had been and what it meant, stating, "The shameful slaughter of our troops at Petersburgh [*sic*] on the 30th of July is looked for here, as elsewhere in the country, with feverish anxiety."

The full professional estimate of what had happened could best be seen and sensed at Grant's headquarters at City Point. Two days after the battle, Lieutenant Colonel Theodore Bowers of his staff wrote that "Gen. Grant and Porter returned this morning . . . as the evidences of the disgraceful conduct of all concerned develop and thicken, Grant grows sicker at heart. . . ." Bowers noted that later that day Meade arrived: "He feels very bad, and insists on a full investigation of the whole affair." The next day, August 2, Bowers added, writing at 8:15 A.M., "Grant is unwell this morning—so unwell that he has not yet left his bed. His illness is real, and I think resulted from his grief at the disaster."

At two o'clock that afternoon, Grant wired a report to Halleck, using the word "disaster" and adding, "It was the saddest affair I have witnessed in this war." Seven hours later, he sent Halleck a second telegram, saying, "I have the honor to request that the President may direct a Court of Inquiry to assemble without delay" to establish the facts concerning "the unsuccessful assault on the enemys [*sic*] position in front of Petersburg" and to determine "whether any officer or officers are answerable for the failure."

The Battle of the Crater ended Ambrose Burnside's military career. The Court of Inquiry, presided over by three generals, found that Burnside had in various ways "failed to obey the orders of the commanding general [Meade]," and that his actions resulted in—the real case against him—"affording time for the enemy to recover from his surprise, concentrate his fire, and bring his troops to operate against the Union troops assembled uselessly in the crater." The court did not accuse him of insubordination or deliberate dereliction of duty, but clearly identified him as being incompetent. Grant quietly saw to the rest: Burnside found himself on leave and never again held command during the war. Being Burnside, he tried to get a new assignment from Grant, who said flatly that he had nothing available. Then he went to Lincoln, complaining about the court's verdict and his forced inactivity; perhaps hoping to maneuver Lincoln into some form of reinstating him, he asked the president to accept his resignation from the Army. Lincoln declined to do that. Lincoln and Grant left Burnside in the same position that General George B. McClellan had been placed in two and a half years before: on extended leave, awaiting orders that would never come.

Meade, who had asked Grant to start the military inquiry into the performance of Burnside and other generals during the battle, eventually found himself being questioned by the congressional Joint Committee on the Conduct of the War. While the proceedings of the Court of Inquiry had been conducted by the Army, the civilian Joint Committee brought to its hearings the political bias of its Radical Republican majority.

Quite apart from his responsibility in the Battle of the Crater, Meade had good reason to worry about his appearance before the committee. Among its clear prejudices was that against West Pointers: the members felt that even academy graduates from the North were likely to be Southern sympathizers at heart, men who had little interest in the issue of slavery and retained friendly feelings for their brother officers of the prewar Regular Army who had chosen to fight for the Confederacy. They also saw the career army men as being indifferent to democratic institutions and giving little support to the American tradition of civilian control over the military. Meade, who had been summoned to appear after the Fredericksburg defeat, testifying two months before his victory at Gettysburg, had then said in a letter, "I sometimes feel very nervous about my position, [the committee is] knocking over generals at such a rate."

His nervousness was justified: while Meade and Burnside were both West Pointers, Burnside had endeared himself to the Radicals by his early advocacy of emancipation and his action the year before in arresting the arch-Copperhead congressman Clement L. Vallandigham on grounds of seditious activity. (Meade, along with Grant, Sherman, and most of the senior Union generals with the exception of Frémont and B. F. Butler, had consistently remained silent concerning emancipation and the future of American slaves.) When Lincoln had removed Burnside from command of the Army of the Potomac in January of 1863, the Joint Committee had gathered testimony favorable to Burnside during its unsuccessful effort to persuade Lincoln to reverse his decision to relieve Burnside.

Beyond the question of military merit, Meade had an ugly temper and had alienated many of his fellow generals, as well as some of the press. He also had family and personal connections with the South that were anathema to the Radicals. His sister Elizabeth had married a man who went on to own a slave-worked plantation in Mississippi over which she presided as mistress, and his sister-in-law Sarah was married to Henry A. Wise, a Confederate general who when he was the prewar governor of Virginia signed the death warrant of John Brown, the Radicals' abolitionist martyr.

Grant, on the other hand, had an admiration for Meade that grew when Meade graciously told Grant, after he was appointed general-in-chief, that he would certainly understand if Grant wanted to replace him as commander of the Army of the Potomac, putting in his place a general such as Sherman, with whom Grant had worked so successfully in the West. "I assured him," Grant said in recalling the moment, "that I had no thought of substituting anyone for him," and added that this "gave me an even more favorable opinion of Meade than did his great victory at Gettysburg. . . ."

By contrast, Radical senator Morton S. Wilkinson of Minnesota had spoken against Meade on the Senate floor when the honors of Gettysburg were being reassessed, and on March 3 of this year Wilkinson, along with Joint Committee members Senator Zachariah Chandler of Michigan and Representative Ben Wade of Ohio, had visited the president, unsuccessfully asking him to relieve Meade. The effort against Meade had not stopped there: not long before the Crater battle, Chandler and Wilkinson had arrived at the Army of the Potomac's headquarters at City Point on what was supposedly an inspection trip, but their mission proved to be that of trying to persuade Grant to remove Meade—an attempt that failed with Grant as it had with Lincoln.

When the Joint Committee finally issued its findings, it blamed Meade for not letting the division of black troops lead the assault as originally planned. There was minor censure of Burnside for allowing the division of white troops that did lead to be chosen literally by chance—the drawing of straws from a hat. Grant, who later told a journalist, "I had a great fondness for Meade," was angered by the committee's action in shifting the responsibility for what he called the "stupendous failure" of the Crater battle from Burnside to Meade. He suggested to Meade that the best way to set the record straight was to court-martial Burnside. That would put the matter back into Army hands, and Grant felt that, whatever came of charges against Burnside, Meade's name would be cleared. Meade asked Grant not to pursue that option.

As all this post-Crater activity ran its course, the reputations of Meade and Burnside suffered, both for good reason, but Burnside was finished, while Meade remained the commander of the Army of the Potomac. Perhaps the fairest judgment of Burnside's performance came from Grant's aide Colonel Cyrus B. Comstock, who said of the man who once commanded the Army of the Potomac, "He is not competent to command a corps . . . poor Burn." As for Ledlie, the division commander who had cowered in the bomb-proof shelter all day as his men died 200 and 300 yards from him, it was some time before Grant ordered Meade to relieve him of command. That may have been motivated by a desire to stop drawing attention to Union failures, but Ledlie, who could have faced charges ensuring a conviction that would have sent him to a military prison, was simply allowed to resign his commission.

IN THE CATASTROPHE of the Crater, the only group to improve its already fine reputation was Company K of the 1st Michigan Sharpshooters. Small as their numbers were, the Indians had impressed everyone who saw them in action, one Union officer saying of their performance at the Crater, "the Indians showed great coolness." One of them was twenty-eight-year-old Sergeant Thomas Ke-chi-ti-go, a large, powerfully muscled

Chippewa whose white comrades called him "Big Tom." At the beginning of the war, he had led five of his fellow braves to a recruiting station in Saginaw, Michigan, only to find that the Michigan legislature had decided that Indians were not fit to serve in the Union Army. Two years and hundreds of thousands of Northern casualties later, recruiters in Michigan were finding that few white men were volunteering, and the legislature decided that Indians were acceptable after all. The men of the tribes quickly came forward, Ke-chi-ti-go again bringing a group with him and being named a sergeant in Company K. (Soon the Detroit newspapers were making weekly mention that "another fine little squad" of Indians had arrived to be sworn into the Army.) Once in action, "Big Tom" and his fellow soldiers of Company K quickly proved to be the best skirmishers in what was a superior regiment. Seeing that the Confederates' butternut-colored uniforms blended in with the background of earth and trees better than did the Union Army's blue, they taught everyone in the regiment to go out and roll in the dirt and even in the mud, and the resulting natural camouflage reduced their casualties. In addition to that, Big Tom Ke-chi-ti-go, whose left arm was broken by a shell fragment at Spotsylvania eleven weeks before the Battle of the Crater, "ordered each brave to cover his head and breast with twigs and leaves to prevent contrast of color with their surroundings." All of this eagerness to serve, and skill and valor in battle, impressed the Indians' white comrades. Nineteen-year-old Private Amos Farling wrote, "If the Indian is so willing to shed his blood in defense of the country which he can scarcely call his own, how much more readily should we take up arms and go forth to do service in a cause so near and dear to us."

AUGUST:
THE DARKEST MONTH

In the North, belief in Lincoln and the Union Army's effectiveness plummeted. As August began, the slaughter at Cold Harbor was less than two months in the past; the first failure to take Petersburg had occurred six weeks before, and Sherman's repulse at Kennesaw Mountain in Georgia had come at the end of June. The news of Jubal Early's attack on Washington was only three weeks old, and accounts of the Crater disaster were appearing on front pages throughout the country.

It was hard to think that other things could have gone seriously wrong for the Union cause on the day of the "stupendous failure" of the Crater battle, but something else did. At five-thirty that morning, forty-five minutes after the explosion went off under the Confederate lines at Petersburg, Jubal Early's cavalry, never having been chased south after his bold and bloody raid on Washington, suddenly rode into the undefended town of Chambersburg, Pennsylvania, sixty miles north of Washington and twelve miles west of the scene of the Union victory at Gettysburg thirteen months before. The Confederate commanders told the residents that if they could not produce an "assessment" of $100,000 in gold or $500,000 in greenbacks, they would burn down their town. The citizens could not come up with such a sum; three and a half hours later, the raiders told the 3,000 people living in Chambersburg to evacuate their homes and businesses, and started setting fires that destroyed two-thirds of the town.

There were a few Northern military successes—on August 5, a fleet under Admiral David Farragut fought the battle of Mobile Bay, during which, when warned of submerged mines, also known as "torpedoes," he shouted, "Damn the torpedoes! Full speed ahead!" That was heroic and momentarily heartening, but the overall military prospect remained bleak. The Northern public thirsted for more than a successful naval battle and the subsequent capture by land forces of a strategically situated port on the Gulf of Mexico; a larger victory was needed, a breakthrough whose significance everyone in both the North and South could grasp. With reason, the *New York World* asked, "Who shall revive the withered hopes that bloomed at the opening of Grant's campaign?"

Paralleling this, and inevitably mixed with it, was the political situation. The prospects for Lincoln's reelection weakened by the day. With the presidential election some hundred days off and congressional and gubernatorial elections in six states sooner than that, it was proving true that the vote would be a referendum on the war. The Radicals were still hoping to find someone to oppose Lincoln as a third-party candidate. Names and rumors flew through the air: Frémont, still the official candidate named by the disorganized crowd that met at Cleveland as the Radical Democracy Party, might gain far stronger Radical support. Lincoln heard that one or more factions opposed to his reelection might be approaching Grant to be their candidate; Grant's popularity had waned, but his current military fortunes could change, and he could receive votes while serving as general-in-chief. Even Chase, busy traveling through New England as he visited with influential Radical Republicans, might reappear, running for any group that would have him. The War Democrats felt they had a strong candidate in what would be the Democratic Party's inevitable choice of McClellan at their convention in Chicago; the Peace Democrats and Copperheads would probably have to go along with McClellan, while counting on the Copperhead leader Vallandigham to frame a party platform that would set the stage for swift peace negotiations on terms generous to the Confederacy. (Vallandigham, legally back in the United States after his exile in Canada, was already proclaiming his views to audiences eager to hear him. On August 3, speaking to a crowd of 20,000 at Peoria, Illinois—the gathering became known as the "Copperhead Convention," although it did not in fact nominate anyone—he urged immediate talks to end the war.)

Beyond that welter of overt political activity, there remained the threat of armed uprisings in states such as Illinois and Indiana, fomented by Confederate agents aided by armed militant Copperheads. (Whatever Vallandigham might or might not have had to do with it, Lincoln's operative Leonard Swett, writing his wife about subversive activity from the Astor House in New York City, told her, "We seized this morning three thousand pistols going to Indiana for distribution." He added, "The most fearful things are probable."

For the North, there was no good news in sight. The war was going badly; during August, Union casualties suffered in the year's campaigns reached 90,000, and there was increasing opposition to Lincoln's call for an additional half-million recruits. The voting public, heartily sick of bloodshed, became mistrustful of statements coming out of Washington. There had been the premature claims of the capture of Petersburg, but the Confederate flag still waved above that indomitable southern city. Now the *National Intelligencer*, getting wind of Greeley's confused activities at Niagara Falls, came out with a report that negotiations for a possible peace were under way; the murky story further undermined public confidence in Lincoln's administration.

More unsettling news came from the financial markets of New York: speculation in gold indicated fears that the North's economy might collapse. The national debt was at its highest, the public credit at its lowest, and the treasury was running out of money paying for a war that appeared to be at a stalemate. In foreign business dealings involving valuations of the dollar, it dropped to 37 cents, a new wartime low. From Warsaw, Illinois, where he was on leave attending to family business, John Hay wrote his fellow presidential secretary, John Nicolay, that "the worst thing I have noticed is that prominent & wealthy Republicans" who wanted Lincoln to be reelected "are getting distrustful of the issue and forcing off their greenbacks into land at fancy prices"—acting on the theory that land would still possess value even if a change of administration brought about repudiation of government securities.

Yet one more election issue was increasingly coming into play. David Croly, the managing editor of the bitterly anti-administration New York *World*, had written a pamphlet that proved to be the greatest Trojan horse in the history of American political campaigns. Published anonymously and sold in modest numbers for twenty-five cents a copy, it was titled, *Miscegenation: The Theory of the Blending of the Races, Applied to the American White Man and Negro.* (To this time, the word used for the mixing of races was "amalgamation." Now Croly and a colleague invented a new word that sounded more menacing: combining the Latin words *miscere*, to mix, and *genus*, race, they came up with "miscegenation.") Ostensibly a scientific study proving that individuals and societies benefited from the practice of intermarriage between races, this tract's target was Lincoln. In the guise of congratulating Lincoln on the Emancipation Proclamation and his efforts to end slavery, it praised him for ushering in a new era of American civilization in which racial problems would be solved by greatly increased cohabitation between whites and newly freed slaves: "When the President proclaimed Emancipation he also proclaimed the mingling of the races." Within a few generations everyone in the United States would look the same and be the same. "If any fact is well established in history," this 72-page treatise stated, "it is that the miscegenetic or mixed races are much superior, mentally, physically, and morally, to those pure or unmixed." Indeed, as one of the chapter headings put it, "The Blending of Diverse Bloods [is] Essential to American Progress."

Croly did not care about how many copies his *Miscegenation* sold. Since having them printed in December of 1863, he had been sending them to famous abolitionists, in the hope that those men and women would endorse its ideas. The support Croly most hoped for was that of Lincoln, whose copy was sent to the White House. The scheme was to garner any statements of approval and give them wide publicity. As an ardent Copperhead, the author was playing on the racist feelings of so many in the North who backed the effort to preserve the Union, but had much less interest in freeing the slaves, and were disgusted by the idea of intermarriage. It might be possible to bring great numbers of Republican voters into the Democratic ranks if Lincoln could be shown to back such assertions as the one that, in the future, "the most perfect and highest type of manhood will not be white or black, but brown, or colored." Among the election issues already before the public was the civil status of freed slaves—were they to be given the vote, and if so, when? Now Croly linked a victory for Lincoln to what his thesis claimed its societal results would be. Born in Ireland, he was well aware of the tension felt between Irish immigrants and the freed blacks with whom they shared some of the North's worst slums. (According to the census of 1860, of the 813,000 people then living in New York City, 203,000 of them were born in Ireland.) Predicting a mixing of races unthinkable to the Irish and in no way attractive to the blacks, he wrote:

The fusion, whenever it takes place will be of infinite service to the Irish.
They are a brutal race and lower in civilization than the negro. . . . Take
an equal number of negroes and Irish from among the lowest communi-
ties of the city of New York, and the former will be found far superior to
the latter in cleanliness, education, moral feelings, beauty of form and
feature, and natural sense.

Having stirred up all that, along with memories of Irish slum dwellers
killing blacks during New York's Draft Riots and the white workingman's
fear of increased labor competition from freed slaves, Croly devoted a
chapter to "The Love of the Blonde for the Black." Here all whites were
included in feeling an attraction "founded upon natural law. We love our
opposites." From this he proceeded to play on the white man's reaction to
the thought of the black man as his sexual rival, setting the drama in the
South. "The mothers and daughters of the aristocratic slaveholders are
thrilled with a strange delight by daily contact with their dusky servitors
. . . It is idle for the Southern woman to deny it . . . she loves the black
man." This, Croly held, led her to wear lush colors and large pieces of
jewelry that pleased the male household slaves. "The Southern beauty, as
she parades her bright dresses and inappropriate colors in our Northern
cities and watering-places, proclaims by every massive ornament in her
shining hair, and by every yellow shade in the wavy folds of her dress, 'I
love the black man.'"

Asians were also introduced into the equation. With an eye to the
white voters of California, there was the prediction that after blacks and
whites had been sufficiently mixed, there would be this:

The next step will be the opening of California to the teeming millions of
eastern Asia. The patience, the industry, the ingenuity, the organizing
power, the skill in the mechanic arts, which characterize the Japanese and
Chinese, must be translated to our soil not merely by the emigration of the
inhabitants of those nations, but by their incorporation with the composite
race which will hereafter rule this continent.

As 1864 unfolded, this hoax failed to gain the backing of prominent
abolitionists, but a number of Democrat-supporting newspapers began
quoting the pamphlet as proof that Lincoln and his party intended to im-

pose these ideas upon the nation. The New York *Daily News* stated flatly that the Republican Party had enshrined miscegenation as its "doctrine and dogma," and the New York *Weekly Day-Book* printed for its readers a poem that characterized the supposed Lincoln-created future in these words:

> *Fill with mulattoes and mongrels the nation,*
> *THIS IS THE MEANING OF MISCEGENATION.*

Among the many pieces churned out to exploit this issue was a Democratic Party election pamphlet, "The Lincoln Catechism," a long satirical diatribe in which these questions and answers appeared.

> *Does the Republican party intend to change the name of the United States?*
> *It does.*
> *What do they intend to call it?*
> *New Africa.*

The overall effort was to place the miscegenation issue into the context of the election being a referendum on the war, with the "Peace Democrats" reiterating that white men were dying for blacks. In this, they could express views sympathetic to Croly's *Miscegenation*, in which the reader was told that the war was "a war for the negro. Not simply for his personal rights or physical freedom—it is a war if you please, of amalgamation, so called—a war looking, as its final fruit, to the mingling of the white and black."

It would remain impossible to quantify the effects of Croly's pseudo-scientific work, but the attention it created became one more obstacle lying between Abraham Lincoln and a second term. As for the Confederates, their armies were capable of striking severe blows as they had recently shown, but the hopes of their statesmen were shifting to the prospect of a Democratic election victory, followed by negotiations for peace. Jefferson Davis urged that the fighting continue "until Mr. Lincoln's time is out." Then, he said, the North "might compromise."

Looking at all this—the bad war news, the growing disaffection of the general public, and the array of opposition to Lincoln, even within his own party—the mainstream Republicans saw his chances for a second term disappearing before their eyes. On some days, Lincoln felt he might indeed lose, but his inner strength did not desert him; the man of whom a Chicago reporter long ago said "There is no backdown in Old Abe" intended to play the cards he was dealt. That included rock-ribbed support for his general-in-chief, the object of a great deal of criticism himself. When Grant received Halleck's warning that some of his troops might have to be withdrawn from facing Lee to go north and guard against Copperhead uprisings and antidraft riots, he responded to Halleck by saying he hoped that Lincoln would have the governors of northern states use their militias to quell such activity. That would enable him to continue battling Lee with all the men he had. (Grant also pointed out that if he had to reduce the forces opposing Lee in northern Virginia, the Confederate commander would immediately send reinforcements south to try to break Sherman's stalled siege of Atlanta.) Lincoln saw Grant's message to Halleck, and reassured him with this:

> *I have seen your despatch expressing your unwillingness to break your hold where you are. Neither am I willing. Hold on with a bull-dog gripe* [sic]*, and chew & choke, as much as possible.*
>
> A. Lincoln

The telegram delighted Grant; laughing, he showed it to his staff officers who walked over to see what had so pleased their usually undemonstrative chief, and said, "The president has more nerve than any of his advisers."

Lincoln kept coming in to the White House every morning from the Soldiers' Home, often dealing with great issues and individual human situations in quick succession. On August 5—the day Farragut shouted, "Damn the torpedoes!"—Lincoln met with General Philip Sheridan. Grant wanted his promising cavalry commander to go into the Shenandoah Valley and bring an end to the long series of Confederate eruptions from there, the most recent ones being Jubal Early's raid on Washington and the burning of Chambersburg. Lincoln wanted the same result, but thought the thirty-three-year-old Sheridan a bit young for the task that had in the past three years literally and figuratively defeated Union generals Frémont, Banks, Shields, Sigel, and Hunter. Sheridan may have looked even younger than his age—he was 5 feet 5, and never weighed more than 140 pounds—but his aggressiveness was exactly what Grant wanted; he never forgot that in the victory at Chattanooga, of all his generals who took Missionary Ridge, it was only Sheridan who continued to chase the retreating Confederates through the night until two in the morning. In Sheridan's meeting with Lincoln, Stanton, and Halleck, Lincoln told Sheridan frankly that he and Stanton thought him too young for this critical assignment, but were deferring to Grant. Then they made it clear to him that if he failed, it might be the final piece of news that would give the Democrats victory in the election. (Sheridan understood what he had been told, writing that "the defeat of my army might be followed by the overthrow of the party in power.")

The same day brought a different matter to Lincoln's attention. Secretary of the Navy Gideon Welles's son Tom, who had joined the army less than a month before, was now a lieutenant serving on the staff of General Edward O. C. Ord, commander of the Eighteenth Corps fighting at Petersburg. In the evening, he sent his father an out-of-channels telegram, concerning Colonel Griffin A. Stedman of Hartford, Connecticut, commander of the 11th Connecticut Volunteers, who had just been gravely wounded by a shot that passed through his stomach. Stedman had been recommended several times for promotion to brevet brigadier general, the brevet rank being conferred as an honor for distinguished service and requiring the personal approval of the president. That evening, Stedman was dying, and as Tom told his father, "will probably not survive the night." As Welles wrote in his diary, his son's telegram went on to say that General Ord, commander of the Eighteenth Corps in which Stedman served, "desired his promotion without delay, that it might be received before his death, and wishing me to call at once on the President." Welles rushed to the White House and showed the telegram to Lincoln, who swiftly wrote on it the endorsement, "I shall be glad to have this done." After that, Welles said, "I then, at his request, went to Secretary Stanton, who met me in the right spirit." Lincoln's approval of the promotion was telegraphed to Ord's headquarters; before Stedman died the next morning, he knew he had been made a general.

While he was still in the area of the White House and neighboring War Office, Welles became privy to other matters. Lincoln's controversial postmaster Montgomery Blair arrived, and Lincoln read them a telegram from Greeley. Now that the public was hearing various versions of what had taken place at Niagara Falls, Greeley wanted the entire correspondence published. Lincoln agreed in principle, but as Welles said, wanted Greeley to "erase some of the lamentations in his longest letter." The matter was on its way to resolution: with a few omissions that Greeley reluctantly approved, the correspondence was soon published in the *New York Times*. (Welles commented that Lincoln's doing this "was undoubtedly an adroit party movement on the part of the President that rebuked and embarrassed Greeley and defeated a wily intrigue"—the effort to make it look as if Lincoln would never enter into any kind of peace talks.) The published correspondence did, however, make it clear as never before that Lincoln demanded the end of slavery as part of any peace settlement—a position many Democrats opposed.

As if that were not enough for one prolonged visit to the White House, yet a different and damaging subject came under discussion. Ever since Lincoln had used his "pocket veto" to stop passage of the Radicals' bill that set forth what a postwar reconstruction of the Confederate state governments should be, Congressman Henry Winter Davis and Senator Ben Wade had been plotting political revenge. Now, using Greeley's *New York Tribune*, they had issued what became known as the Wade-Davis Manifesto, a blazing personal attack on Lincoln. They began by tearing into his efforts to create pro-Union state governments in Arkansas and Louisiana as lands fell into the hands of advancing Federal forces, claiming that these were "mere oligarchies" whose sole purpose was to give Lincoln some favorable electoral votes in the coming election. Then they moved to their argument that only the Congress, and not the White House, had the right to enact the kind of postwar programs that Lincoln had reserved to himself through his claim of "emergency war powers" and his veto. "A more studied outrage on the legislative authority of the people has never been perpetrated," they declared, and went on in a prosecutorial tone that led the *New York World* to tell its readers that the Congress, now back in session, might soon participate in an extraordinary drama: "Wade's charge amounts to an impeachment, and may be followed by one."

Through all these August days, during what Welles aptly called "an infinity of party and personal intrigue"—he even thought that Senator Ben Wade had turned out to be another "aspiring factionalist" who "has been bitten with the Presidential fever . . . with a vague, indefinite hope that he may be successful"—Lincoln remained strong. His spirit and thinking at this difficult time impressed Joseph T. Mills, a circuit judge from Wisconsin, who accompanied First Assistant Postmaster General Alexander Williams Randall, a former governor of that state, to confer with the president at his request. Lincoln had received a letter from a Wisconsin newspaper editor, a man whose words represented a body of opinion throughout the country that Lincoln wanted to influence favorably if he could. The man had described his position candidly.

> *I am a War Democrat, and the editor of a Democratic newspaper. I have sustained your Administration . . . because it is the legally constituted government. I have sustained its war policy, not because I endorsed it entire, but because it presented the only available method of putting down the rebellion.*

Now, however, the news of Lincoln's peace terms as stated in the published Niagara correspondence left him understanding that "no steps can be taken towards peace . . . unless accompanied by an abandonment of slavery." The editor threw right at Lincoln a slightly paraphrased version of his own words, written two years before when he was developing the Emancipation Proclamation: ". . . your assurance that if you could save the Union without freeing any slave, you would do it; if you could save it by freeing [all] the slaves, you would do it; and if you could do it by freeing some, and leaving others alone, you would also do that."

The letter closed by asking if Lincoln could suggest "some interpretation" of his present policy that could create "tenable ground on which we War Democrats may stand."

The purpose of this meeting was to discuss an answer that Lincoln had drafted, an answer that might brings hundreds of thousands of voters to his side. Judge Mills had never met Lincoln, and described his first reaction to him: "The President was free and animated, in conversation. I was astonished at his elasticity of spirits." Before discussing the topic that had prompted the president to ask Randall and Mills to meet with him, Randall urged Lincoln to take a vacation. The pressures of working in the "shop" had at times caused Lincoln's secretaries Nicolay and Hay to become sick; in each case they had recovered their strength and returned, but Lincoln kept right on with his punishing schedule. Randall now asked, "Why can't you, Mister President, seek some place of retirement for a few weeks? You would be reinvigorated."

"Aye," Lincoln answered, "[even] three weeks would do me no good—my thoughts, my solicitude for this great country, follow me where ever I go." Dropping the subject of his taking a vacation, Lincoln went on: "I don't think it is personal vanity or ambition—but I cannot but feel that the weal or woe of this great nation will be decided in the approaching canvass [election]. My own experience has convinced me that there is no program intended by the democratic party but that will result in the dismemberment of the Union."

Whether or not "personal vanity or ambition" underlay his remarks, it was clear that Lincoln believed that, if anything could work, he had the right approach. If the Democrats won in November, they might well start talks with the Confederates that could result in a peace leaving the Confederacy as an independent nation—the "dismemberment of the Union" to which he alluded. And if the Radicals ran a candidate and prevailed, they would insist on an unnecessarily harsh peace.

Then, as if taking to himself, Lincoln went to the subject of what should be in his reply to the editor from Wisconsin. He spoke as a man who fully agreed that he had indeed said what the man who wrote the letter said he had, about freeing some slaves and not others. The presidential oath contained not a word about abolishing slavery. His highest duty was to protect the Union, and he had often stated that if he could not do that, the cause of freeing the slaves was lost in any case. Now he told Randall and Mills that if he were to accede to some Democrats who in the interest of a swift peace wanted him to "return to slavery" even those former slaves who had joined the Union Army, "I should be damned in time and in eternity for so doing." Beyond this declaration of principle, in continuing his monologue he also set forth some of his practical reasons for freeing the slaves. Referring to the United States Colored Troops, he told Randall and Mills:

> There are now between one and two hundred thousand black men now in the service of the Union. . . . Abandon all the posts now possessed by these black men, surrender all these advantages to the enemy, and we would be compelled to abandon the war in three weeks . . . no human power can subdue this rebellion without using the Emancipation lever as I have done. Freedom has given us the control of two hundred thousand able bodied men, born and raised on southern soil. It will give us more yet. Just

so much it has subtracted from the strength of our enemies. . . . My ene-
mies condemn my emancipation policy. Let them prove by the history of
this war, that we can restore the Union without it.

After soliciting the views of Randall and Mills, Lincoln tried to revise the draft he had already written, to be sent to the editor in Wisconsin. His first draft had been made in pencil; the second he wrote in ink. In it, he offered these ambiguous words: "To me it seems plain that saying re-union and abandonment of slavery would be considered if offered [by the Confederates], is not saying that nothing *else*, or *less*, would be considered, if offered." With those words, at least hinting that he might enter talks without preconditions, he seemed to give the editor from Wisconsin an "interpretation" that might provide "the tenable ground on which we War Democrats wish to stand." There the matter rested, but only for the moment. As for Judge Mills, he said this of his first time in Lincoln's presence:

The President appeared not to be the pleasant joker I had expected to see,
but a man of deep convictions and an unutterable yearning for the success
of the Union cause. His voice was pleasant — his manner earnest and cor-
dial. As I heard a vindication of his policy from his own lips, I could not
but feel that his mind grew in stature like his body, and that those huge
Atlantian shoulders were fit to bear the weight of mightiest monarchies.

Later that same day, Lincoln spoke with a man who may have greatly influenced some of his thinking on this crucial issue. Also at his request, the black leader and spokesman Frederick Douglass came to see him. It is not clear whether he showed Douglass a draft of his reply to the editor in Wisconsin concerning the peace terms he might be willing to accept, but he certainly discussed its contents with him.

As he presented this to Douglass, the former slave became angry at the idea of Lincoln's even considering a peace plan that did not specifically include abolition. He saw it as a betrayal of principle and an act that would lose rather than gain votes. "It would be taken as a complete surrender of your antislavery policy," Douglass warned him, "and do you serious damage."

Lincoln left no notes of that meeting, but in a letter Douglass sent a friend, he said that Lincoln was in an "alarmed condition," and wanted the nation's black leaders to "inform the slaves in the Rebel States . . . as to what will be their probable condition should peace be concluded while they remain within the Rebel lines. . . . And more especially to urge upon them the necessity of making their escape." Lincoln, who was at the moment exploring the idea of a more conciliatory peace settlement himself, was warning Douglass that if he lost the election a Democratic administration would be just that much more likely to settle for a "soft peace" that could leave millions of blacks in slavery. True though that might be, in saying this to Douglass he was energizing black leaders to support him, even in terms of his simply being the better of two choices.

As they parted, Lincoln asked Douglass to come up with a plan to aid more slaves to escape to the Union-occupied areas of the South. Douglass set to work on this, although events were to change some of what was needed. He found Lincoln charming, personally courteous and respectful, but felt as before that in the overall reality of Northern society, "The Negro is the deformed child, which is put out of the room when company comes."

WHATEVER CONCESSIONS TO the South Lincoln might be considering, there could be no doubt that he was losing ground with the Northern voting public. Some opposition newspapers pounced on him as soon as the Wade-Davis Manifesto appeared. The day after the manifesto came out in Greeley's *Tribune*, the *New York Herald* led the attack, saying of Lincoln: "As President of the United States he must have enough sense to see and acknowledge he has been an egregious failure. One thing must be self-evident to him, and that is that under no circumstances can he hope to be the next President of the United States." He should, the paper insisted, "retire from the position to which, in an evil hour, he was exalted." Manton Marble's anti-Lincoln *World*, of New York, a paper with national circulation, published editorial attacks on him, one of which ended with this prediction of his political fate: "The people of the loyal states will teach him, they will not supply men and treasure to prosecute a war in the interest of the black race." Changing its mood the *World* also musingly saw Lincoln as a victim of friend and foe alike: "It would be difficult to determine which are more damaging . . . the heavy blows in front which his manly opponents are dealing, or the stabs in the back inflicted by his professed friends." The paper also saw him as being damned by faint praise; of the support given Lincoln by the pro-administration *New York Times*, whose editor, Henry Raymond, Lincoln described as being "my lieutenant general in Congress," the *World* said that the *Times* "does not exactly pronounce him a fool, but does the nearest thing to it in referring to him as a man of open nature." The *New York Herald* took another crack at Lincoln with this: "His election was a rash experiment, his administration is a deplorable failure."

The Confederate press leapt into the situation, the *Richmond Examiner* writing this, which Manton Marble of the *World* swiftly reprinted for his national audience: "The fact begins to shine out clear . . . that Abraham Lincoln is lost; that he will never be president again . . . the obscene ape of Illinois is about to be deposed from the Washington purple, and the White House will echo to his little jokes no more."

The growing disapproval of Lincoln was not restricted to the big Northern newspapers. The German-language *Illinois Staats-Anzeiger*, which Lincoln had once secretly owned, buying it in 1860 to influence the important German-American vote and then selling it before his election, had already broken with him; the paper told its readers this: "Reviewing the history of the past four years, nothing is left us but to cut loose decidedly from Lincoln and his policy and to *protest against his re-election under all circumstances and at any price.*"

Among individuals who would be voting, some of the soldiers of the Union Army began to doubt Lincoln; many of them had fond memories of McClellan and did not understand the extent to which "Little Mac" had failed when he commanded the Army of the Potomac. An artilleryman from Rhode Island wrote his sister that "little mac will be president if the soldiers can vote," and a soldier serving with Sherman's forces besieging Atlanta wrote home that "Mr. Lincoln is becoming almost daily more unpopular." A Wisconsin volunteer, also writing his sister during these hot August days, told her, "I don't believe that President Lincoln has committed as many unpopular acts in such a short time, as he has since he has been renominated." Private George Parks of the 24th New York Cavalry Volunteers described his views in some detail.

> *The soldiers are discontented and think the war has lasted long enough and if a peace man is nominated for the Presidency he would have the strong support of the army. . . . I do not look upon Father Abraham in the same light as when home. My politics have undergone some changes and*

Abe and no more of his stripe get my vote this fall. The army are strongly in favor of a peace man and I hope . . . the war is stopped. If you underwent what I have you would say the same.

With little time left to regain ground before the Democratic Convention in Chicago, Lincoln began hearing directly from those upon whom he had relied as political allies. According to New York Republican boss Thurlow Weed, within a week of the publication of the Wade-Davis Manifesto he called on Lincoln at the White House and told him that his election had become impossible. Then Weed wrote a letter to General B. F. Butler, whom Lincoln had sounded out earlier in the year as a possible vice-presidential candidate. (In declining the overture, Butler had described the position of vice president in scornful terms, but he did not include the presidency as a position in which he had no interest.) In his letter to Butler, Weed told him, "Lincoln is gone, I suppose you know as well as I." Weed was unhappy with Lincoln for insisting on the abolition of slavery as a condition for peace talks and was even ready to consider a Democrat; above all, he wanted a presidential candidate who would stand on the Crittenden resolution of 1861, put forward by Congressman John Jordan Crittenden of Kentucky, which had stated that the only reason for going to war was to preserve the Union and said nothing about slavery.

Lincoln would hear from other politicians; in the meantime, his secretary John Nicolay received a note from a friend of his who was a reporter for the *Philadelphia North American*. It read, "A friend of mine just in from the West says that a Petition is going the rounds, & very numerously signed asking Mr. Lincoln to resign being a candidate." Referring to Governor John A. Andrew of Massachusetts, a Radical Republican, Puleston added, "Gov. Andrew's private secretary is there helping to circulate it." The fact that the governor of Massachusetts had his private secretary traveling out of the state to aid a drive demanding that Lincoln withdraw from the campaign indicated the speed and scope with which the forces opposing him were organizing themselves.

All of this brought Lincoln to the point that, in order to bring the war to an end while he was still president and could control some terms for peace, he gave serious consideration to trying to bribe the Confederacy to give up slavery and the concept of being a separate nation. When his Pennsylvania Republican ally Alexander McClure came to see him in the White House, he said that Lincoln "took from a corner of his desk a paper written out in his handwriting, proposing to pay to the South $400,000,000 as compensation for their slaves on condition that the states should return to their allegiance to the government and accept Emancipation." (This was the same idea that had been suggested to Lincoln by Greeley a few weeks before.) To McClure, Lincoln seemed tortured; he wrote that Lincoln said to him:

> *If I could only get this proposition before the Southern people, I believe they would accept it. . . . One hundred days of war would cost us the $400,000,000 I would propose to give for Emancipation and a restored Republic, not to speak of the priceless sacrifice of life and the additional sacrifice of property; but were I to make this offer now it would defeat me inevitably and probably defeat Emancipation.*

McClure worried about Lincoln: "I had seen him many times when army disasters shadowed the land and oppressed him with sorrow, But I never saw him so profoundly moved with grief as he was on that day, when there seemed to be not even a silvery lining to the political cloud that hung over him." Strong as Lincoln was, it seemed to the troops on guard at Soldiers' Home that in the evenings he wandered around at something of a loss. (Mary was sometimes away during what she described as being this "very warm & dusty" Washington summer, spending time in the cool climate of Vermont with their son Tad and occasionally making trips to New York during which she indulged herself in the expensive compulsive shopping whose costs she concealed from her husband.) These sentries often saw him by himself, reading the Bible. When a reporter from the *Boston Journal* told him, "You are wearing yourself down with work," Lincoln replied: "I can't work less. But it isn't that. Work never troubled me. Things look badly, and I can't avoid anxiety." He added, "I feel a presentiment that I shall not outlast the rebellion. When it is over, my work will be done."

If Lincoln wished to hear something pleasant during these increasingly difficult days, that happened when he sent his friend Colonel John Eaton to Grant's City Point headquarters to see if there was any truth to the rumors that Grant might be interested in the presidency himself. When Eaton broached that subject as they sat talking, Grant slammed his hand down on the arm of his chair and exclaimed, "They can't do it! They can't compel me to do it!" Grant was as loyal to Lincoln as Lincoln was to him. In a way that made it clear he had indeed been approached, Grant explained that, as Eaton reported to Lincoln on returning to Washington, he considered it as important for Lincoln to be reelected as it was for the army to be "successful in the field." Lincoln's relief was palpable: "I told you," he said to Eaton. "They could not get him to run until he had closed out the rebellion." (The "until" was interesting. Both Lincoln and Mary thought that Grant might be a successful future presidential candidate; some months after this, in a conversation with Grant's wife, Julia, Mary tactlessly burst out with, "I suppose you think you'll get to the White House yourself, don't you?")

That was the end of the good news for Lincoln, both the things that he learned and those hidden from him at the moment. Henry Raymond of the *Times* aptly described Lincoln's position, caught between Radical Republicans on the one hand and so many of the Democrats on the other: "One denounces Mr. Lincoln because he didn't abolish Slavery soon enough—another because he assumed to touch it at all."

Within a few days, an assortment of political figures, ranging from Lincoln's Radical opponents to veteran mainstream Republicans who had given up on him, met at the house of New York City's mayor, George Opdyke. Among them were Congressman Henry Winter Davis of the Wade-Davis Manifesto, former congressman Roscoe Conkling of New York, and John Austin Stevens, the treasurer of the Republican National Committee. An interesting figure present was an eminent New York lawyer and legal reformer, the Radical Republican David Dudley Field, who was acting as a political adviser to Frémont, the nominee of the Radical Democracy Party that had met in Cleveland in May. Lesser figures arrived, representing Benjamin F. Butler and Salmon P. Chase. (Of Chase, Gideon Welles said at this point, "I doubt not that his ambitions are unextinguished.") Others not there but active in the quickly organized alliance were Senator Charles Sumner of Massachusetts, a friend of Mary Lincoln's, and Massachusetts governor John A. Andrew.

An example of what Welles had called "an infinity of party and personal intrigue" was the offstage presence not only of Greeley, who wrote Opdyke that "Mr. Lincoln is already beaten. He cannot be elected," but of Weed, who wrote Seward that "the People are wild for Peace. They are told that the President will only listen to terms of Peace on condition [that] Slavery be abandoned." Yet another man keeping in touch with this group was *New York Times* editor Henry Raymond, the Republican/National Union Party chairman.

Men like Weed and Raymond exemplified the political equivalent of the adage that business is business. Raymond, whose *Times* almost always supported Lincoln, had even put together a laudatory election-year book about him that was published in May, 496 pages that included a sketch of his life and a collection of his speeches, letters, and proclamations. He was still nominally Lincoln's campaign manger insofar as he had one, but his job as party chairman was to get into office a president who was not a Democrat, and what he was hearing from Republicans around the country was that Lincoln's candidacy was in trouble and probably doomed. Not all the men who met or were represented at Opdyke's house were committed to the program the leaders of this group now set forth, but several of them put out an announcement that there would be a new political convention, in effect a Radical Republican convention, in Cincinnati on September 28. Some of them used circumspect language about their intentions in doing this, but Henry Winter Davis put it plainly: the idea was "to get rid of Mr[.] Lincoln and name new candidates."

Lincoln, who had first been elected to the Illinois legislature exactly thirty years before and reached the presidency in 1860 through a combination of unlikely circumstances, knew that he was in the political battle of his life. He tried to bring to his side everyone he could, even sending word through a go-between to a long-ago friend, now opposed to his reelection, from the days when they were young men back on the Illinois frontier. He asked the intermediary to remind his friend that he had once saved him from a beating by a bully, grabbing the man by the throat and ending the uneven struggle. "Tell Clark I interfered and stood by him in a fight at New Salem and that I am in a big fight now, and I want him to stand by me." At the same time, Lincoln kept on doing all the other things he thought he should do, and here his beliefs shone through. Speaking from the White House steps to the men of the 166th Ohio, a "Hundred Days" regiment returning home at the expiration of its duties, he thanked them for their service and impressed upon them his conviction that "the nation is worth fighting for." Reminding them of "our birthright" of freedom and the opportunities possible in a democratic society, he said:

> *I happen temporarily to occupy this big White House. I am a living witness that any one of your children may look to come here as my father's child has. It is in order that each of you may have through this free government which we have enjoyed, an open field and a fair chance for your*

industry, enterprise and intelligence; that you may all have equal privileges in the race of life with all its desirable human aspirations. . . . It is for this the struggle should be maintained . . . to secure such an inestimable jewel.

With all the gravity of the hour, Lincoln was still able at times to have enjoyable talks with his friends, both at the White House and out at the Soldiers' Home in the evenings. Lincoln's closest friend among the capital's journalists was Noah Brooks of the *Sacramento Daily Union*, a thirty-four-year-old reporter who had begun life in the port of Castine on the coast of Maine. Moving to Illinois, where in 1856 he met Lincoln, and then on to California, he had after the death of his wife and a baby during childbirth in 1862 come east to Washington to report on the wartime scene. His stories, filed under the byline "Castine," presented an intimate view of life in the White House, where he was welcome because of his pleasant personality and the fact that he strongly supported Lincoln and his administration.

It was in chatting with Brooks that Lincoln chose to correct some misconceptions about himself. Most people thought that he invented the jokes and stories he told. Not so, said Lincoln. "I don't make the stories mine by telling them. I am only a retail dealer." He went on to say, as Brooks later wrote, "he never forgot a good story," but, "so far as he knew, about only one-sixth of all those that had been credited to him had ever been told by him."

As for the stories Lincoln particularly liked, Brooks said, "Anything that savored of the wit and humor of the soldiers was especially welcome to Lincoln . . . any incident that showed that 'the boys' were mirthful and jolly in their privations seemed to commend itself to him." Brooks chose this example of a Union soldier's reaction to something done by a Confederate soldier, a "Johnny Reb," as told by Lincoln.

. . . [The story of] a soldier at the battle of Chancellorsville, whose regiment, waiting to be called into the fight, was taking coffee. The hero of the story put his lips to a crockery mug, which he had carried, with infinite care, through several campaigns. A stray bullet, just missing the coffee-drinker's head, dashed the mug into fragments and left only its handle on his finger. Turning his head in that direction, the soldier angrily growled, "Johnny, you can't do that again!"

Brooks said that, relating this story, Lincoln commented, "It seems as if neither death nor danger could quench the grim humor of the American soldier."

On another occasion, talking with Brooks and some others, Lincoln put to rest the myth of "Abe the Rail-Splitter." He said that his work as a woodsman had been in felling trees; he was proud of how well he did that, but "he did not remember splitting many rails in his life."

Someone reminded him that he had authenticated some rails as of his splitting, during the Lincoln-Hamlin [1860 presidential] campaign.

"No, I didn't," he replied. "They brought those rails in where I was, with a great hurrah, and what I did say was that if I ever split any rails on the piece of ground that those rails came from, and I was not sure whether I had or not, I *was* sure that they were the rails."

Brooks was also struck by Lincoln's use or omission of certain terms. "He always used the phrase, 'since I came into this place,' instead of 'since I became President.' The war he usually spoke of as 'this great trouble,' and he almost never alluded to the enemy as 'Confederates,' or 'the Confederate government,' but he used the word 'rebel' in his talk and his letters."

In his conversation with Brooks, Lincoln mused about what he would like to do after "this great trouble" ended. Referring as he often did to Mary as "Mother," he one day said to Brooks, "When we leave this place . . . I guess mother will be satisfied with six months or so in Europe. After that, I should really like to go to California and have a look at the Pacific coast." Brooks added that Lincoln had a more than passing interest in seeing California, a state to which he had never been.

> . . . *he fixed his eyes on California as a place of permanent residence. He thought that that country offered better opportunities for his two boys, one of whom was then in college, than the older states. He had heard so much of the delightful climate and the abundant natural productions of California that he had a strong desire to visit the state, and remain there if he were satisfied with the results of his observations.*

Lincoln's friends such as Brooks admired his combination of mind and spirit, the seamless way in which he dealt with politics, history, the beauty of language, and his belief in justice and the American future, but they seldom caught a glimpse of his instinctive grasp of scientific matters. That aspect of Lincoln was appreciated in the nearby War Department Telegraph Office. Samuel F. B. Morse had invented the telegraph in 1837, but few Americans had any idea of how this technology worked, or displayed any interest in learning about it. In the telegraph office, Lincoln would chat with cipher-clerks such as Charles A. Tinker, whom he had met in 1857, four years before the war. At that time, Tinker was working as a telegraph operator at the Tazewell House, a hotel in Pekin, Illinois, in an office that acted as headquarters for a circuit court in which Lincoln made frequent appearances. Another of the War Department cipher-clerks, David Homer Bates, later explained how Lincoln and Tinker first became acquainted.

> *On one occasion, after watching young Tinker's manipulation of the Morse key, and seeing him write down an incoming message, which he received by sound, an unusual accomplishment in those early days, Lincoln asked him to explain the operation of this new and mysterious force.*
>
> *Tinker gladly complied. . . . Lincoln seemed greatly interested in this explanation, and asked pertinent questions showing an observing mind already well furnished with knowledge of collateral facts and natural phenomena; and that he comprehended quite readily the operation of the telegraph. . . . it should be remembered that before that time wires had been extended west of the Alleghany [sic] Mountains only five or six years.*

That Lincoln had been able to understand the manipulation of an electrical current was not astonishing, but on an occasion when Bates was alone with Lincoln in the War Department Telegraph Office, the president "began to talk of the functions of the eye and brain when one was reading aloud from a printed page." Lincoln expanded on this, "remarking upon the curious fact that the eye is capable of receiving simultaneously several distinct impressions or a series of impressions constantly changing as one continues to read across the page, and that these numerous and sometimes radically different impressions are communicated from eye to brain and then back to the vocal organs by means of the most delicate nerves."

Here, Lincoln had by himself arrived at observations and conclusions paralleling the most sophisticated contemporary scientific experiments.

In other words, he added, communications are being transmitted continuously and simultaneously in both directions between the outer and inner senses. He likened this mysterious, instantaneous and two-fold operation to the telegraph, although as regards the dual process it should be remembered that the invention of duplex telegraphy was not brought into use until more than ten years after this interesting discourse of Lincoln in the presence of his solitary auditor.

II

During these hot August evenings of 1864, with Mary away so much of the time, after working late in his "shop" at the White House, Lincoln would sometimes ride out to the Soldiers' Home by himself on "Old Abe," his favorite horse. At eleven o'clock on one of these nights, Private John W. Nichols of the 150th Pennsylvania Infantry was standing guard at the large gate to the grounds of the Soldiers' Home when he heard a shot in the darkness. A moment later, Lincoln and his out-of-control horse came galloping up the twisting driveway from the main road; the alarmed private saw that Lincoln was "bareheaded." When he and the other sentries asked Lincoln what had happened, Lincoln replied, as Nichols later related it, that someone "had fired off a gun at the foot of the hill," causing Old Abe to bolt so swiftly that it "jerked his hat off." As Lincoln rode on at a slower pace toward the presidential house, Nichols and another soldier went down to the main road. There they found Lincoln's hat; there was a hole on each side of its crown where a bullet had passed through it, inches above his skull.

The next day, when Private Nichols returned Lincoln's hat to him, the president said, "rather unconcernedly," as Nichols put it, that he wanted the incident "kept quiet." At the White House, he had a talk with Ward Lamon, his old Illinois crony whom he had made Washington's Federal marshal and the man who sometimes acted as his bodyguard. Lamon, who along with Stanton had been urging Lincoln to make greater use of the protection available to him, was staggered to hear Lincoln say, "I can't bring myself to believe that any one has shot at me or will deliberately shoot at me with the deliberate purpose of killing me." Speaking of the wooded countryside and rural cottages in the area of the Soldiers' Home, Lincoln added, "It may be that some one on his return from a day's hunt . . . fired off his gun as a precautionary measure of safety after reaching his house"—a practice in which the weapon is fired toward the sky, and a most unlikely way of producing a trajectory that would send a bullet horizontally through the air several feet above the ground. In any case, Lincoln told Lamon, "No good can result at this time from giving it publicity." Finally admitting that it could have been an assassination attempt, Lincoln said, in what Lamon thought was a most unsuitable spirit of levity, that on thinking it over, "I was left in doubt whether death was more desirable from being thrown from a runaway federal horse, or as the tragic result of a rifle-ball fired by a disloyal bushwhacker in the middle of the night."

Lamon, already in despair over both the lax and inefficient security measures he seemed unable to improve and Lincoln's casual attitude toward his own safety, was giving thought to telling his old friend that he would no longer act as his bodyguard. He had already threatened to quit once, when he learned that Lincoln had gone to the theater accompanied only by Senator Charles Sumner and the aged Prussian minister, Baron Gerolt, "neither of whom," Lamon said, "could defend himself against an assault from any able-bodied woman in this city."

In fact, the danger to Lincoln was growing faster than either of them realized. One of the problems in assessing the threat was the vagueness of the information. As far back as March, the *New York Tribune* had reported rumors of a plot to kidnap Lincoln; this was the same idea that the actor John Wilkes Booth already entertained, but the rumors did not identify the conspirators. In July, a letter to the White House from a "Lizzie W. S." warned the president against just the sort of attempt made on him in the near-miss shooting: "If you value your life! *do*, I entreat of you, *discontinue* your visits outside of the City." A newspaper in Wisconsin, one edited by a rabid Copperhead unlike the responsible "War Democrat" who had queried Lincoln, even called for his death: the *La Crosse Democrat* stated, printing it in italics for emphasis, that if Lincoln were reelected, "*We hope that a bold hand will be found to plunge the dagger into the Tyrant's heart for the public welfare.*"

Whether or not the kidnapping plot mentioned earlier by the *New York Herald* was the same, in mid-August Booth arrived at Barnum's

Hotel in Baltimore. (Actors and actresses were allowed to move freely through the Union and Confederate lines, free to give performances in Savannah or Richmond one month, and in Philadelphia or New York or some other Northern city the next. By 1864, the twenty-five-year-old Booth, rabid on the subject of Lincoln, was appearing almost exclusively in cities under Federal military control.) He began to recruit men to try to capture Lincoln while he was going to or from the Soldiers' Home. While Booth was not in the cast of any plays presented in Washington during this time, there is an account of a conversation that took place at a billiard table in the capital at some point after Early's raid in July. Booth said to his fellow billiard players, who may not have fully understood his meaning, "Abe's contract is nearly up, and whether he is reelected or not, he'll get his goose cooked."

III

On August 17, with the Democratic convention in Chicago eleven days away, the *New York Times* ran a piece on its front page titled "The Trying Time for the Union Party" that presented the case for supporting Lincoln and his policies. Timely and well expressed, it was written by the paper's founder and editor, Henry Raymond, who was at the same time getting ready to write a letter to Lincoln telling him that he was on his way to defeat. Nonetheless, Raymond set forth the challenge to his and Lincoln's Republican/National Union Party, and the reasons to support the president. Referring to the Radical opposition by speaking of "this great danger of dissension in the Union party," he went on to say this, lumping all Democrats together as "Copperheads" as he gave his view of the coming September and October:

> . . . *the Copperheads, it is certain, will attack with greater insidiousness and ranker virulence than ever before. They know this is their last chance. . . . What the Copperheads can ever do, they must attempt during the first two Fall months. The Union party should prepare itself for a political campaign, after the Copperhead nomination is made, of an intensity never perhaps equaled in the political history of the country. It is foolish to calculate upon their inability to agree upon a common candidate. With all their discord, hatred of the Union party is still their master passion.*

Then Raymond analyzed the Confederate hope to have the Democrats win the election and begin talks leading to a "soft peace." "Next to peace, they desire of all things—the very thing for which Northern Copperheads are constantly clamoring—an armistice and time to talk." Raymond wanted to make sure that his readers understood what that would mean.

An armistice means, of course, delay, and delay is the very thing for which LEE is now fighting. He has been doing all along what jockies [sic] call "riding a waiting race." The end and aim of all his strategy . . . has been to oppose barriers to the Northern advance . . . the South is in possession of the object in dispute. In merely holding her territory and keeping her Government unbroken, her aim is attained. She holds, before the world and before us, the position of a de facto *independent power . . . an armistice, therefore . . . would serve precisely the same purpose for Lee as a line of entrenchments, and a still better one, for it would entail no fatigue on his men.*

Raymond came to his summation. He felt that, once at a peace table, the people of the North would never be willing to resume the bloodshed. If the firing ceased and talks began, the Confederacy would remain "in existence, and because in existence, still triumphant. A battle won could not give LEE more than this, for he does not seek the conquest of the North."

Accurate as this estimate and prediction was, it did little to stiffen the will of many Republicans, including those in Lincoln's administration. Four days after Raymond's piece appeared, 2,000 Confederate cavalrymen under the command of the legendary raider Nathan Bedford Forrest swept into Memphis at first light, almost captured two Union generals who fled the city as they came in, and held Memphis for most of the day. As had been the case with Jubal Early's burning of Chambersburg, the idea that the Confederates could capture even for a day a city that had passed into Union hands twenty-six months before was profoundly discouraging. Tremendous effort had been put into trying to outmaneuver, outwit, and kill or capture Forrest, to no avail; as an immediate result of this setback, Federal operations in the area were put into a more defensive pattern, giving Forrest more opportunities to attack the supply lines on which Sherman's forces besieging Atlanta depended. At the same time, news came from Grant's front that in an action south of Petersburg, Union troops had repelled a Confederate counterattack, but in doing so lost 4,445 of the 20,000 Union troops engaged.

Prominent men who had until now stood by Lincoln began to have their doubts about him. One of his closest friends was Orville Browning, the former senator from Lincoln's own state of Illinois. Browning, who with his wife had, at the Lincolns' request, stayed at the White House during their dying son Willie's last days, wrote a friend that he had never "been able to persuade myself that he was big enough for the position." He added, "Still, I thought he might be able to get through, as many a boy [gets] through college, without disgrace, and without knowledge; and I fear he is a failure." Joseph Medill, the powerful editor of the *Chicago Tribune* and a man who had supported Lincoln ever since writing an enthusiastic report of his 1858 "House Divided" speech (in which Lincoln said of the prewar nation as secession loomed, "A house divided against itself cannot stand"), now said privately of Republican fortunes: "Thanks to Mr. Lincoln's blunders & follies we will be kicked out of the White House." Lincoln's staunch political operative Leonard Swett was in New York trying to rally support for Lincoln from within the Republican National Committee but wrote his wife: "There is not much hope. Unless material changes can be wrought, Lincoln's election is beyond any possible hope. It is probably clean gone now." He added in another letter, referring to militant Copperhead activity, "We are in the midst of conspiracies equal to the French Revolution." More bad news came in: a man trying to work for the Republican cause in New York wrote to Gideon Welles, "There are no Lincoln men. . . . We know not which way to turn." Lincoln's secretary Nicolay, never giving up hope for him, nonetheless described recent days as being almost "a disastrous panic—a sort of political Bull Run." In a conversation with a Radical, Lincoln asked for his support in the coming weeks, and the man replied, "No, sir. . . . Unless you clean these men away who surround you, [and] do something with your army, you will be beaten overwhelmingly."

Lincoln took that just as it was given. "You think I don't know I am going to be beaten," he told the Radical, "*but I do* and unless some great change takes place *badly beaten*."

The last week of August marked a singularly complicated point in the intricacies of all that Lincoln confronted. He read a letter from Henry Raymond, sent from New York City on August 22. The chairman of his party and the man who was his campaign chairman said:

> *I feel compelled to drop you a line concerning the political condition of the country. I am in active correspondence with your staunchest friends in every state and from them I hear but one report. The tide is setting strongly against us. [Illinois congressman] Hon. E. B. Washburne writes that "were an election to be held now in Illinois we should be beaten." Mr. Cameron [Simon Cameron, former governor of Pennsylvania and Lincoln's first secretary of war] writes that Pennsylvania is against us. Gov. Morton writes that nothing but the most strenuous efforts can carry Indiana. This State, according to the best information I can get, would go 50,000 against us to-morrow. And so the rest.*

Raymond recommended that Lincoln bite the bullet. He should "at once" appoint a commissioner to make "*distinct proffers of peace to* [Jefferson] *Davis, as the head of the rebel armies, on the sole condition of acknowledging the supremacy of the constitution*"—in short, say nothing about slavery. Raymond believed the overture would be rejected; that would "dispel all the delusions about peace that prevail in the North," and "unite the North as nothing since the firing on Fort Sumter has hitherto done."

This, coming from his party chairman and the editor of the *New York Times* and dated six days before the Democratic convention would open in Chicago, evidently impressed Lincoln more than anything else had. To this point, he had drafted a response to the editor in Wisconsin, intimating that he might enter peace talks without conditions, but he had not sent that letter. Now he started to draft a letter of instructions to Raymond that went much further, in terms of potential compromise. He wanted Raymond, acting on his behalf, to pass through the Union and Confederate lines under a flag of truce, and go to Jefferson Davis in Richmond. Telling him to address Davis in "entirely respectful terms," he added, ". . . you will propose, on behalf of this government, that upon the restoration of the Union and the national authority, the war shall cease at once, all remaining questions to be left for adjustment by peaceful modes."

There it stood, in the form of a draft written in Lincoln's hand and yet to be signed by him. If the Confederate States would stop fighting and resume their prewar status as part of the Union, "all remaining questions," slavery obviously being paramount, would be peacefully settled. Lincoln offered even more: "If the presentation of any terms embracing the restoration of the Union be declined, you will then request to be informed what terms of peace . . . would be accepted."

Lincoln was placing on paper the battle for his soul. He wanted to continue as president, and believed that he could lead the Union better than any other contender of any party or faction. He was determined to uphold his oath to preserve the Union. With his Emancipation Proclamation, he had done more than anyone in American history to bring about the end of slavery, yet he was preparing to offer Jefferson Davis peace talks for which the abandonment of slavery was not a precondition. He could not read Jefferson Davis's mind; if Davis, despite his rhetoric, had reached a conclusion that the South would inevitably lose the war, he might think the white people of the South would be better served by reentering the Union with the institution of slavery subject to "adjustment by peaceful modes." The Confederacy would cease to exist, as it would with a military defeat, but the South's slave-labor-based economy and social fabric might to some extent survive at a peace table if talks began now. And, as Raymond had pointed out, if Davis rejected this overture, the fact that Lincoln made the offer might well give him the votes of the War Democrats who backed him as a war leader but not as a champion of freeing the slaves.

No one could know just how this inner battle of Lincoln's was progressing, but on Tuesday, August 23, he involved himself in an extraordinary act that demonstrated his belief that someone other than himself would become the next president. When the members of his cabinet assembled for one of their afternoon meetings, they found Lincoln asking each of them to sign, without knowing what it said, a folded-over and sealed document. What Lincoln had written that morning, what they could not see and what he was asking them to endorse by placing their signatures on it, was this statement.

> *This morning, as for some days past, it seems exceedingly likely that this Administration will not be re-elected. Then it will be my duty to so cooperate with the President elect, as to save the Union between the election and the inauguration; as he will have secured his election on such ground that he can not possibly save it afterwards.*

Lincoln was pledging all of them to guarantee an orderly transfer of power in the event of his "exceedingly likely" defeat. Two days after that, the executive committee of the Republican National Committee, led by Raymond, met with Lincoln in the White House. Lincoln, backed by Seward, Stanton, and the new Secretary of the Treasury Fessenden, debated the idea of sending Raymond on the peace mission to Jefferson Davis—something Lincoln had now decided against. According to Nicolay, after hearing what Lincoln and his cabinet members had to say, Raymond "very readily concurred with them in the opinion that to follow his plan of sending a commission to Richmond would be worse than losing the Presidential contest—it would be ignominiously surrendering it in advance." Writing of this later, Nicolay said that Raymond and his Republican National Committee colleagues went back to New York "encouraged and cheered," but that day, in a letter to Hay, who was combining a vacation in Illinois with taking political soundings there, Nicolay said this of the overall picture: "Hell is to pay. . . . Everything is darkness and doubt and discouragement."

IV

On August 28, three days after Nicolay wrote of Republican "doubt and discouragement," many thousands of Democrats converged on Chicago for their convention, due to begin the next morning. The eleven train lines running into the city's stations brought in dignitaries, delegates, and spectators; the flamingly pro-Democrat *Chicago Times* said that the city was playing host to "the largest and most enthusiastic gathering ever held upon American soil." Noah Brooks was there as a reporter but was also acting as an unofficial observer for Lincoln at his "express wish." He arrived to find a city "all alive with flags, banners, processions, music, cheers, and butternuts"—the last being a synonym for the Copperheads, seen by Republicans as in effect wearing the butternut-colored uniforms of Confederate soldiers. The correspondent for the *New York Times* in Chicago echoed the theme of anticipation, reporting "much excitement in our city." Speaking of the Democrats, the reporter said, "Many of the great lights of the party are here, and the wires are being industriously pulled." He went on to describe the reception being accorded to former

Congressman Clement Vallandigham of Ohio, who had been arrested for seditious activity fifteen months before, released to the Confederates, spirited off to Canada, and had now come to Chicago to take a leading role at the convention. "VALLANDIGHAM is here, and excites as much curiosity as a loosed elephant would in our streets. Crowds follow him wherever he goes—they enter his hotel with him, and are clamorous for a speech."

Vallandigham was there in his more peaceful guise, but the extremist Copperheads who wanted to foment an uprising hoped to carry out their postponed plan to use the convention confusion to free the 10,000 Confederate prisoners at Camp Douglas, just outside the city. A contingent of 62 Confederate agents, men in civilian clothes who had at different times escaped from Northern prisoner-of-war camps, arrived from Canada, led by two of the plotters, Thomas H. Hines and John B. Castleman. The night before the convention began, Hines and Castleman met with the leaders of the thousands of Sons of Liberty who lived in the Chicago area and were supposed to start a revolt that would take some of the states of the Old Northwest out of the Union. They found that the local leaders had men throughout the city willing to act, but that there was no organization, no plan to mobilize, no method for issuing orders to the scattered groups. Within thirty hours, they would call off their effort and head back to Canada, determined to carry out violent attacks later in the autumn.

The next morning, Monday, August 29, crowds began pouring into the Wigwam, a huge two-story wooden building that stood beside Lake Michigan. (The Indian name was chosen for its meaning, "a place of temporary shelter," and had nothing to do with its boxlike appearance.) This structure had been built in 1860 specifically to hold that year's Republican National Convention, which nominated Lincoln. By noon, a capacity crowd of 12,000 had assembled. The New York financier and Democratic Party chairman August Belmont called the convention to order and launched into a speech emphasizing the themes upon which he hoped the ideologically divided factions could agree. Stressing that Lincoln's "four years of misrule" had the nation on a "downward course," Belmont told the delegates that his reelection would be a "calamity," and added this.

The administration cannot save the Union. We can. Mr. Lincoln views many things above the Union. We put the Union first of all. He thinks a proclamation [the Emancipation Proclamation] worth more than peace. We think the blood of our people more precious than edicts of the President.

Belmont called for unity: "We are here not as war democrats or peace democrats, but as citizens of the great Republic, which we will strive to bring back to its former greatness and prosperity." In the first mention of a "soft peace" and efforts to restore the status of the Confederate States, he referred to the American flag and the prewar nation, saying that re-union could be accomplished "without one single star taken from the brilliant constellation that once encircled its youthful brow."

The convention moved into the executive phase of naming committees, and reconvened at ten the next morning. Governor Horatio Seymour of New York, the convention chairman and a leading Radical sometimes mentioned for the presidency himself, was escorted to the podium through the applauding crowd. He continued the exhortations begun by Belmont the previous day: "This administration cannot now save this Union," he told the delegates, and proceeded to hold out an olive branch to the South.

We demand no conditions for the restoration of our Union. We are shack-led with no hatreds, no prejudices, no passions. We wish for fraternal relationship with the people of the South. We demand for them what we demand for ourselves — the full recognition of States. We mean that every State on our nation's banner shall shine with one and the same lustre.

At four o'clock that afternoon, the committee on resolutions presented the party platform. A key member of the committee was the Copperheads' hero Vallandigham, who stood before the crowd as the author of the most controversial resolution in the party's six-plank platform. Characterizing Lincoln as a tyrant, this second resolution said that his administration had done nothing but spill blood in its "experiment of war," and that the only sane course after three years of pointless fighting was to make "immediate efforts . . . for a cessation of hostilities." Another resolution called for the administration to resume the exchange of prisoners of war. (The practice of exchanging prisoners had been stopped by Grant and approved by Lincoln because the North could replace captured soldiers in a way that the South no longer could.) Yet another resolution pledged, as the Republicans had in Baltimore, to provide extensive future care and benefits for the soldiers of the Union Army.

Even in the midst of the momentum and enthusiasm of this second day of the convention, some of the old Democratic political hands saw that Vallandigham's resolution committing the party to "immediate" peace talks was sure to cause trouble. Lincoln's observer Noah Brooks studied the faces of some political veterans as they listened to Vallandigham. August Belmont, he said, "looked profoundly sad." Ohio Democratic congressman Samuel S. Cox, known as "Sunset Cox" because he loved describing sunsets, hung his head, "a picture of despair." Nonetheless, not a single delegate rose to start a debate about any part of the party platform; it received swift approval as the convention exploded in cheers.

With evening, the delegates proceeded to their central task: nominating their candidate for president of the United States. The momentum slowed. For weeks most of the delegates had been waiting eagerly to cast their ballots for George B. McClellan, the War Democrat who had decided not to attend but expected to hear good news soon, perhaps to be telegraphed to him at his house in New Jersey that night. Now two individuals began to criticize him, prompting others to begin a furious defense of McClellan. Congressman Benjamin Harris of Maryland, a Peace Democrat, rose to point out some of McClellan's record early in the war. If Lincoln was a tyrant, he asked, what did the delegates think of McClellan's action in September of 1861, when he ordered his soldiers to disband and arrest the Border State of Maryland's legislature, making certain that none of them should escape? And when Lincoln suspended habeas corpus in Maryland thirty days later, who had willingly carried out his order? McClellan. As a soldier, McClellan had "been defeated everywhere"; as a citizen, he had acted as an "assassin of States rights"—the very thing this convention claimed it was determined to restore. "You ask me," he said, "to go home to Maryland . . . and going forward to the polls, vote for George B. McClellan, the very man who destroyed her liberties . . . I cannot do it. I never will do it."

This produced catcalls and indignant shouted demands that Harris be ejected, but also brought forth cheers. When a delegate from New York standing near him yelled, "You're a damned traitor!" Harris punched him to the ground. As order was finally restored, with some delegates pointing out that it was getting dark and "there is no way to light this building," Congressman Alexander Long of Ohio continued the attack on McClellan, calling him more of a tyrant than Lincoln. "George B. McClellan has not contented himself with the arrest of a citizen here and there and incarcerating him in a bastile, but has arrested an entire legislature. . . . He is the worst man you could put upon the ticket having the name of democrat." As others spoke defending McClellan, with heckling voices in the background, it became so dark that Horatio Seymour finally announced that "it is utterly impossible to transact business in this confusion" and adjourned the session.

The next morning, the balloting began: after just one round, McClellan had 174 votes, more than the 151 required to nominate him. Seymour, whose name had also been put forward, withdrew, and on the second ballot McClellan received 202½ votes, out of some 250 eligible to be cast.

McClellan was the Democratic Party nominee. Outside the Wigwam, a battery of cannon thundered. Inside, a band played "Hail to the Chief." Through a crowd behaving "like bedlamites," a group of delegates carried to the podium a huge banner prepared for this moment and put it in place: it read MCCLELLAN, OUR COUNTRY'S HOPE AND PRIDE.

Vallandigham stepped forward on the stage, to cheers, and successfully moved that the vote be made unanimous. One after another, men who had opposed McClellan came up and made speeches endorsing him. Then "Sunset" Cox opened the nominations for vice president. Within an hour, the delegates had settled for Congressman George H. Pendleton of Ohio, a dedicated Peace Democrat whose nomination was a sop to the Copperhead wing of the party.

There was a last, unusual motion. Charles A. Wickliffe of Kentucky, a former congressman and governor of that state and a man known in Washington as "Old Kentucky," prevailed on the delegates to close their convention without a formal adjournment. Thus, although the nominations were settled upon and everyone was going home, the convention could be recalled by the Democratic National Committee at any time. The move sprang from the Copperheads' fear that McClellan, a War Democrat, would accept the nomination but reject Vallandigham's "peace plank," the resolution in the party platform calling for "immediate efforts" to begin peace talks. Wickliffe's unprecedented move left the door open for the Copperheads to make a last-ditch effort: if McClellan accepted the nomination and rejected the platform, they could in theory start beating the drums to reopen these proceedings and try to nominate a trustworthy Peace Democrat like Governor Seymour of New York.

And so it was over in Chicago, but amid the general celebration some men worried. The delegates seemed happy with this ticket pairing the War Democrat McClellan and the Peace Democrat Pendleton, but August Belmont saw Pendleton as a nonentity who had spent his time in Congress trying to thwart the Union's efforts to win the war. As Noah Brooks walked out of the Wigwam on his way to report to Lincoln in Washington, he heard a Peace Democrat from Indiana say that McClellan was himself a cipher, and Pendleton a "putty head."

Predictably, the nation's press lined up along party lines, but the ever-capricious Horace Greeley, who had begged Lincoln to do everything possible to start peace talks, now said this through the pages of his *New York Tribune*: "In short, if Mr. Jeff. Davis had been platform-maker for the Chicago Convention, he could not have treated himself more tenderly nor his enterprise more gently than they have been in the actual Platform."

McClellan had a lot to think about, so much to resolve, that for a week after he was informed of his nomination he sent no word to Democratic Party officials. As he considered his situation while sitting in his house in New Jersey, letters and telegrams poured in from Democrats, all assuming that he would accept the nomination. The great issue was the party's "peace plank." Many urged him to disavow the call for "immediate efforts" to begin peace talks; the *New York Evening Post* gave voice to these War Democrats when it told its readers, "It is impossible to vote for General McClellan, or any other candidate . . . on that Chicago platform." Speaking for the Peace Democrats, Vallandigham wrote McClellan that he should accept the platform as written, and "not insinuate even a little war" into his letter of acceptance.

As McClellan spent his days deciding how he wished to respond, just what position to take, something happened at a place six hundred miles from Chicago that changed everything for Abraham Lincoln.

ELEVEN

SIX WORDS
FROM SHERMAN

At six in the morning on Saturday, September 3, General Sherman sent a telegram north from Georgia that said, "Atlanta is ours, and fairly won." Here was the great and unmistakable success for which the North had hungered: Union soldiers had captured the Southern city second in importance only to Richmond, a vital manufacturing center and strategic rail hub in the heart of the Confederacy. Triumphant joy exploded in every Northern city and town; church bells rang; bands played. Grant sent a message in code to his friend Sherman, telling him that, "in honor of your great victory," he had ordered every piece of artillery on the Petersburg front to fire a salute, using real cannonballs aimed at the enemy lines. He added, "The salute will be fired within an hour amidst great rejoicing."

On the same day that Sherman's telegram reached Washington, Lincoln issued a "Proclamation of Thanksgiving and Prayer," citing "the glorious achievements of the Army under Major General Sherman in the State of Georgia, resulting in the capture of the City of Atlanta." To Sherman, he wrote an "Order of Thanks" in which he said, "The marches, battles, sieges, and other military operations that have signalized this campaign must render it famous in the annals of war, and have entitled those who have participated therein to the applause and thanks of the nation." Later, when Grant could pause from giving all the orders necessitated by this and other developments, he wired Sherman, "I feel you have accomplished the most gigantic undertak[ing] given to any General in this War and with a skill and ability that will be acknowledged in history as unsurpassed if not unequalled."

The editors of Northern papers leapt on this victory even more swiftly than they had rushed to kick Lincoln when he was down. Joseph Medill of the *Chicago Tribune*, who had recently said, "Thanks to Mr. Lincoln's blunders & follies we will be kicked out of the White House," dashed into print with this: "Union Men! The dark days are over. We see our way out. . . . Thanks be to God! The Republic is safe!" The Southern press did not deceive its readers: in Georgia, the *Augusta Chronicle & Sentinel* came out with, "We have suffered a great disaster. We cannot conceal from ourselves the magnitude of the loss we have sustained." That loss had many aspects. Some of the Confederate high command had seen the defense of Atlanta as a political as well as a military priority: General Joseph E. Johnston said later that his goal was to keep Sherman from taking Atlanta before November, and thus help the Democrats "to carry the presidential election . . . [which] would have brought the war to an immediate close."

For the moment, nothing was going right for the Confederates; the day after Sherman sent north his "Atlanta is ours" message, their famous guerrilla cavalry raider, John Hunt Morgan of Kentucky, died at Greeneville, Tennessee, killed in an early morning ambush just like those he had often set himself. As Northern papers carried all this news, Greeley, now sailing before a rising wind, acted as if he had never wanted peace talks and eventually came out with this indignant editorial statement: "An armistice! The idea of one springs from folly or treason."

It remained for the *New York Times* to put things into perspective. Four days after Sherman's telegram from Atlanta thrilled the North and gave it new strength, the paper came out with an editorial titled "The Political Prospect."

The skies begin to brighten. The clouds that lowered over the Union cause a month ago are breaking away . . . a profound despondency had taken hold of the public mind . . . the enemies of the Administration were open and loud in their predictions of disaster to the Union cause.

Now all this is changed. The public temper is buoyant and hopeful. The friends of the Government, the defenders of the Constitution, the supporters of the Union ticket, are full of courage and confidence. Their faith in the flag has revived, and they are ready and eager to do battle under its starry folds for the Union and the Constitution. . . .

The coming election season was indeed to be a referendum on the war; referring back to Lincoln's election in 1860, the *Times* saw the situation in these terms: "The great contest is now to be closed as it was begun, at the ballot-box." This underestimated Confederate tenacity on the battlefield and, on the home front, the *Charleston Courier* told its readers to "prepare to pass through more months of blood and tears and suffering"—but large blocs of Northern voters were swinging back to Lincoln, whose sense of humor still survived. When he learned that after six days McClellan had not yet replied to the Democratic leadership regarding his nomination, Lincoln said, thinking back upon McClellan's chronic slow movements and reluctance to engage the enemy, "Oh, he's intrenching."

As the Democrats waited to hear from McClellan, it became clear that the Radical Republicans had overplayed their hand. Weeks before this, starting in states such as Senator Ben Wade's own Ohio, newspapers like the *Cleveland Herald* and the *Columbus Crisis* began to criticize the Wade-Davis Manifesto and to defend Lincoln. The *New York Times* and the *Detroit Advertiser & Tribune* each printed a letter from Gerrit Smith, a leading abolitionist, reformer, and philanthropist from upstate New York, endorsing Lincoln. In 1853, Smith had been elected to the House of Representatives as an independent, serving one term. His was a compelling voice, one that Radicals could not ignore. Smith, a friend and benefactor of Frederick Douglass and a man who had been the presidential candidate of different parties and splinter groups in the elections of 1848, 1856, and 1860, differed with Lincoln on a number of issues, but believed that "the eve of the Presidential election" was no time to be attacking the one man who could both preserve the Union and end slavery. Wade and Davis, who wished to be seen as leading abolitionists, found their attacks on Lincoln severely criticized by the editors of the *National Anti-Slavery Standard* as well as by the *New York Tribune* and the *Washington Chronicle*. A combination of other papers joined in, some with Democratic loyalties that were ready to slam any part of the Republican Party, and others who were Republican in sympathy but thought the party's Radical wing must be brought to heel. Wade, Davis, and the leading Radicals found themselves the object of counterattacks in the pages of the *New York Evening*

Post, the *Chicago Tribune*, the *Milwaukee Sentinel*, the *Boston Daily Advertiser*, the *Albany Evening Journal*, the *Philadelphia Age*, and the widely read *Harper's Weekly*.

Sherman's taking Atlanta at just this moment stopped Lincoln's slide toward what he had termed his "exceedingly likely" defeat by the Democrats, and this reaction to the Wade-Davis assault upon him broadened his support within the Republican ranks. What would happen in the contest with the Democrats had yet to unfold, but the Radicals began to realize that they had no realistic chance to replace Lincoln as the Republican candidate: they had to back him, or risk helping a Democrat win the White House.

As the Radicals started coming back to Lincoln, the Democrats heard from McClellan. Whether Sherman's capture of Atlanta influenced him to any extent was unknown, but he accepted the nomination and rejected the "peace plank." After wrestling through six drafts of what he wanted to say, working on the wording with his friend Samuel L. M. Barlow, a New York corporation lawyer and a Democratic leader, five days after the news of Sherman's victory he presented his letter of acceptance to the Chicago convention committee that nominated him. In it he said that any peace talks with Confederate representatives could begin only on the understanding that the rebel states had to rejoin the Union: "I could not look in the face my gallant comrades . . . who have survived so many bloody battles, and tell them that their labors and the sacrifice of so many of our slain and wounded had been in vain. . . ." On the other hand, acting on Barlow's strong recommendation, McClellan was careful to avoid using the words "war" and "slavery," neither of which appeared in his letter. Indeed, his acceptance could be read as saying that what to do about slavery could wait: "The Union is the one condition of peace. We ask no more." The day after McClellan made his letter public, he wrote his wife Ellen that "the effect thus far has been electric"—vintage McClellan self-esteem, and not an accurate reflection of the Democrats' sturdy willingness to continue working to defeat Lincoln in an election now less than eight weeks away. (One effect it had, possibly beneficial to the Democratic Party as a whole, was that once the Copperhead leader Vallandigham learned that McClellan had rejected the "peace plank," he canceled a speaking trip he had planned to make on McClellan's behalf.)

Bit by bit, more good news came in for Lincoln. The first of the five state elections to be held this autumn took place on September 6, three days after Sherman's telegram and two days before McClellan delivered his letter of acceptance. In Vermont, the Republican/National Union Party candidate for governor and its candidates for Congress were elected by a decisive majority of 20,000 votes; in the state legislature, Republicans triumphed by a 5 to 1 ratio. A week later, in Maine, the Republicans reelected the governor with another 20,000-vote majority and sent an entirely Republican congressional delegation to Washington. These were traditional Republican strongholds: the prospect in Indiana was far from bright, and one could only guess what might happen in Pennsylvania, but in trying to reinvent themselves in mid-campaign, the Radicals were strengthening Lincoln's chances.

Good news of a sort came in a different way. On September 22, John C. Frémont, the third-party candidate nominated by the Radical Democracy Party at its ad hoc convention in Cleveland back in May, withdrew from the presidential race. This would bring to Lincoln's side more voters who did not like him but who could not accept the Democratic Party's ambivalence about slavery. Frémont, who could not like Lincoln—the man who had ended his career as a major general by sending him home to "await orders" in the same status that had finished McClellan's active service—announced that he was ending his candidacy, "not to aid in the triumph of Mr. Lincoln, but to do my part towards preventing the election of the Democratic candidate." As a parting remark, he added that Lincoln's presidency "has been politically, militarily, and financially a failure," but that its "necessary continuance" was still better than having a defeatist Democratic administration.

Frémont's departure may have been part of a backroom deal with Lincoln. For a long time, the Radicals had seen Postmaster General Montgomery Blair as the man they wanted to force out of the cabinet. The Blairs had been loyal Lincoln supporters, but Montgomery remained a controversial figure who had become a growing problem for the president—a problem that did not lessen when he was quoted as saying after Jubal Early's raid that the Union generals defending Washington were "poltroons." A sometimes abrasive man, Blair was clearly opposed to slavery but felt that freed slaves should be segregated and not have the vote. His belief that blacks and whites could never live together successfully led him to want freed blacks sent to colonies of their own in Latin America—an idea that Lincoln himself had considered. The Radicals saw Blair as a traitor, a man who had among other political betrayals opposed the banishment of the Copperhead leader Vallandigham. At the Republican/National Union Party convention in Baltimore, the Radicals had managed to put into the party platform its sixth resolution, seemingly innocent language saying that there should be harmony among the highest government officials—certainly not the case when Blair mistrusted Seward and intensely disliked Stanton and then-Secretary of the Treasury Chase, who was always the Radicals' darling.

The inclusion of that sixth resolution had in itself been the result of a deal—if the Radicals promised to support Lincoln during the Baltimore convention, the controversial Radical delegation from Missouri would be seated, and they could also have their sixth resolution, which they saw as setting the stage for a future move to unseat Blair.

The time for that move had come. Its history provides a lesson in political choreography. As soon as Zachariah Chandler, the Radical senator from Michigan, learned that McClellan was officially the Democratic nominee, he began jumping on trains. He went first to Ohio, and talked with his friend Senator Ben Wade. The outlines of a deal took shape: Lincoln, already under pressure from many mainstream Republicans to remove Blair, might finally be ready to drop him, in return for the promise of the Radicals' support in the weeks before the November balloting. After getting Wade's agreement to his scheme, Chandler went to Washington and had an exploratory talk with Lincoln, who acted like a man ready to deal. Next, Chandler visited the other half of the "Wade-Davis" team, conferring with Congressman Henry Winter Davis in Maryland. Davis came on board.

Chandler thought that Frémont was the missing piece. If Frémont would pull out of the race, then he could go back to Lincoln with a real package. With Frémont out, there would be no Radical third-party candidate to vote for, no one who could siphon off what could be a significant and possibly critical bloc of votes for Lincoln. It would be solely a Lincoln-McClellan contest, and Wade and Davis, hitherto Lincoln's most virulent Radical critics, would support him.

Chandler went to New York twice and talked several times with Frémont. They met in the offices of Frémont's adviser David Dudley Field, the famous lawyer who had been one of the prominent anti-Lincoln Republicans who had met at New York Mayor George Opdyke's house to, as Davis put it, "get rid of Mr. Lincoln and name new candidates." According to one account, Chandler told Frémont that he had been authorized by Lincoln to say that if he withdrew from the race, Lincoln would place him back in the kind of military command from which he had removed him in June of 1862 and would also drop Blair from his cabinet. Frémont's wife Jessie said that her husband found this to be a dishonorable offer. Regarding the bargain involving a new military command or firing Blair as a quid pro quo, she said, "The latter part of the proposition General Frémont at once declined. . . . But he took the question of withdrawing as a candidate, under consideration"—in short, he would think about giving up his candidacy without expecting anything in return. (Frémont had already been hearing from those who wanted him to step out of the race, including his friend the poet John Greenleaf Whittier.)

Chandler never claimed that Frémont agreed to anything, but the chronology of the last parts of all this is suggestive. His final talk with Frémont took place on September 21; on September 22, Chandler was on his way to Washington from New York to see Lincoln again when Frémont issued his statement that he was no longer a candidate for the presidency.

However it had come about, a deal was a deal. On September 23, Lincoln wrote this to Blair:

> *You have generously said to me more than once that whenever your resignation could be a relief to me, it was at my disposal. The time has come. You very well know that this proceeds from no dissatisfaction of mine with you personally or officially. Your uniform kindness has been unsurpassed by that of any friend.*

Blair understood the situation, liked Lincoln, and wanted him to be reelected. He replied, in the same spirit: "I can not take leave of you without renewing the expressions of my gratitude for the uniform kindness which has marked your course towards [me]. . . ."

The next day, Lincoln wired William Dennison, the former Republican governor of Ohio, the man who served as permanent chairman of the Baltimore convention that renominated Lincoln, "Mr. Blair has resigned, and I appoint you Post-Master General. Come on immediately." Things unimaginable a month before began to happen. Both Wade and Davis hit the campaign trail, urging voters to reelect Lincoln, although Wade wrote Chandler that he wished he were doing it "for a better man." Greeley, always dancing somewhere on the political stage, had his *Tribune* out there saying of Lincoln in capital letters, "We MUST re-elect him, and, God helping us, we WILL." To make sure he got credit for what he was doing, he wrote Lincoln's secretary, Nicolay, "I shall fight like a savage in this campaign."

Most prominent Radicals scurried for political shelter. The idea of holding a Radical convention in Cincinnati to nominate a third-party candidate (or possibly get behind the now-void Frémont candidacy) vanished. Varying views came to light: editor James Gordon Bennett of the *New York Herald*, who had called Lincoln a "Presidential pygmy" but whose paper remained neutral regarding the overall contest, deplored the choice offered the public, calling Lincoln and McClellan "Two men of mediocre talent." Bennett cherished the wild hope that, no matter whom the voters chose in November, the electoral college would defy history and its appropriate function and name Ulysses S. Grant as President of the United States. In the meantime, Bennett continued his practice of firing at targets of opportunity: five days before the Democrats had poured into the Wigwam to begin their convention, he had predicted the Radical retreat. Among those who would "sneak back to old Abe, or be left out in the cold," he named Ben Wade, Henry Winter Davis, Greeley, Henry J. Raymond, George Opdyke, and Salmon P. Chase: "We shall soon see them skedaddling for the Lincoln train." They and their political bedfellows would, Bennett said, "all make tracks for Old Abe's plantation." Soon they would be doing this for Lincoln:

> . . . *crowing, and blowing, and vowing, and writhing, and swearing and stumping the States on his side, declaring that he, and he alone, is the hope of the nation, the bugaboo of Jeff Davis, the first of conservatives, the best of abolitionists, the most honest of politicians, the purest of patriots. . . . The spectacle will be ridiculous, but it is inevitable.*

One of those who had come to terms with the situation was Salmon P. Chase, who finally realized that he had no more cards to play. He would always feel at heart that he would have made a better president than Lincoln, but to support Lincoln now, he said, "seems to me to be the only path of patriotic duty." With that, he started making speeches for Lincoln in Indiana and Kentucky, as well as in Ohio, the state that had in the past sent him to Washington as a senator and elected him as governor.

II

With the political battle lines drawn and the presidential campaign start-ing in earnest, Lincoln still had the unending responsibilities of conduct-ing the war and dealing with the public.

An interesting visitor entered his office. She was Mary Ellen Wise, one of several hundred women, North and South, who had during the course of the war disguised their gender to join the army. In 1862, then less than eighteen, she enlisted in the 34th Indiana Volunteer Infantry, and served as a foot soldier. Participating in a number of battles, Mary Ellen received two minor wounds that required treatment, but the medical personnel did not recognize that she was a woman. There is no record of how many more battles she fought in after that, but the odds of being seriously wounded caught up with her: a musket ball tore through her shoulder, and when they took off her uniform in the hospital as they prepared to operate, it became clear that the patient was a woman.

Mary Ellen required months of treatment to recover. When the time came to be mustered out, she was told that, although she had been paid until the time she was wounded, she was entitled to none of the back pay she had accumulated since then, because she had enlisted under false pretenses.

Unable to recover that money from any military authority, Mary Ellen came to Washington. Now wearing women's clothes and still tanned from her years of campaigning, she sat for a while in the anteroom to Lincoln's office and in due course was admitted to see him. As soon as she sat down and explained her situation, Lincoln "blazed with anger." He told her that if she could not get her pay any other way he would give her the money himself, but the instructions that he wrote to the paymaster gen-eral swiftly produced Mary Ellen's back pay.

One could not say that her subsequent time in civilian life got off to a good start. Soon after her audience with Lincoln, Mary Ellen married a Sergeant Lloyd Forehand, in Washington; some weeks later, the *Wash-ington Star* reported this.

[She] was arrested yesterday . . . on the complaint of her husband, who charged that she had followed him for several days with a pistol and threatening to take his life. . . . Her husband did not wish to prose-

cute her, but only wanted to be safe. Justice Handy dismissed her to leave the city on the first train, and she took her departure in the 6 P.M. train.

With that, Mary Ellen disappears from view.

Another sort of young woman appeared at the White House. Colonel Thomas H. Ford, the former lieutenant governor of Ohio whom Lincoln had sent to B. F. Butler in March to sound out his interest in becoming vice president, had an appointment to see Lincoln at six in the evening. When he came through the door of the White House, he found what he described as a "poorly clad young woman who was violently sobbing." Ford stopped and asked her what was wrong. Speaking with a foreign accent, she told him that she and her brother, both orphans, had come to America before the war. At some point, the brother had enlisted in the Union Army, and, as Ford put it, "through bad influences, was induced to desert." He had been caught, tried, and was soon to be executed by a firing squad.

The girl had been able to find a number of her brother's comrades who were still serving honorably, and they had signed a petition asking that he be pardoned. She had been at the White House for two days trying to get in to see the president and show him the petition, and now "had been ordered away."

Colonel Ford told her that he did not know what he could do for her, but that he had an appointment with Lincoln and thought he could at least get her into the president's office. Just as they reached the door of the "shop," Lincoln came out. Seeing Ford and not noticing the girl, he explained that he had been so busy that he never had lunch; if Ford would just go in, he would eat something quickly and be back.

Once inside the empty office, Ford told her this: "Now, my good girl, I want you to muster all the courage you have in the world. When the President comes back he will sit down in that arm-chair. I shall get up to speak to him, and as I do you must force yourself between us, and insist on an examination of your papers, telling him it is a case of life and death, and admits of no delay."

The girl may not have understood every word, but when Lincoln returned she did exactly as told.

Mr. Lincoln was at first somewhat surprised at the apparent forwardness of the young woman, but observing her distressed appearance, he ... commenced an examination of the document she had placed in his hands. Glancing from it to the face of the petitioner, whose tears had broken forth afresh, he studied its expression for a moment, and then his eye fell upon her scanty but neat dress. Instantly his face lighted up.

Neither the former lieutenant governor of Ohio nor the orphan immigrant girl understood just what they were seeing. This was the president of the United States, standing in the mansion whose rooms were often thronged by bejeweled ladies wearing elaborate dresses with hoop skirts, but this was also the penniless boy from a frontier where thousands of farm girls would never have a hoop skirt and went barefoot until winter. Lincoln had also grasped the fact that she had come to see him by herself, and that Ford had seen her crying and brought her in. "My poor girl," he said, "you have come here with no governor, or senator, or member of congress, to plead your cause. You seem honest and truthful; and"—Ford said that Lincoln spoke the next words 'with great emphasis'—"you don't wear '*hoops*'; and I will be whipped but I will pardon your brother!"

And in this same office, during these momentous days Lincoln used a different side of his vocabulary. Eliza P. Gurney, a Quaker, sent him a letter written on a spiritual plane far above the current rough-and-tumble of politics and the realities of constant bloody war. Her thoughts concerned the struggle to bring slavery to an end.

I believe the prayer of many thousands whose heart thou hast gladdened by the praiseworthy and successful effort 'to burst the bands of wickedness, and let the oppressed go free' that the Almighty ... may strengthen thee to accomplish all the blessed purposes, which, in the unerring counsel of his will and wisdom, I do assuredly believe he did design to making thee instrumental in accomplishing. ...

Lincoln wanted this woman to know that he understood her religious convictions. He wrote her in reply, "Your people—the Friends—have had, and are having, a very great trial. On principle, and faith, opposed to both war and oppression, they can only oppose oppression by war. In this hard dilemma, some have chosen one horn and some the other"—some Quakers had chosen to fight, and others refused to do so, no matter what that might bring upon them.

Lincoln had in large part avoided taking legal action against pacifists who protested the war because of their religious beliefs, and reaffirmed that now. "For those appealing to me on conscientious grounds, I have done, and shall do, the best I could and can, in my own conscience, under my oath to the law." He moved beyond that, in presenting his view of the spiritual and temporal framework in which he found himself having to act.

We hoped for a happy termination of this terrible war long before this; but God knows best, and has ruled otherwise. We shall yet acknowledge his wisdom and our own error therein. Meanwhile we must work earnestly in the best light He gives us, trusting that so working still conduces to the great ends He ordains.

Lincoln closed this line of thought with the ancient hope that an omniscient God would turn human suffering into benefits that justified the sacrifice. "Surely He intends some great good to follow this mighty convulsion, which no mortal could make, and no mortal could stay."

TWELVE

SHERIDAN GOES IN;
LINCOLN GETS OUT
THE VOTE

After Lincoln and Stanton deferred to Grant in giving an officer as young as Sheridan one of the Union Army's most important missions, the thirty-three-year-old major general started preparing for his task. His assignment was to slam shut Washington's "back door"—the Shenandoah Valley, the area in which "Stonewall" Jackson had waged his brilliant Valley Campaign, the broad avenue that opened Maryland and Pennsylvania to Lee, the place from which Jubal Early struck swiftly during his raid on the capital in July. Early had regrouped in the Valley he knew so well, strengthened by reinforcements sent him by Lee from the Petersburg-Richmond front.

Sheridan understood the importance of his impending confrontation with Early's Army of the Valley. He had not forgotten that in his meeting with Lincoln and Stanton they had explained that more than the strategic Shenandoah Valley was at stake. Sheridan knew that even after Farragut's "Damn the torpedoes!" victory at Mobile and Sherman's all-important capture of Atlanta, if he led his forces to disaster in an area near the nation's capital, that could still lose Lincoln the election and might result in peace talks that would give the Confederacy much of what it wanted. As for other important strategic aspects of the constantly contested Valley, from their present area of control the Confederates were able to block the shortest east-west transportation routes from Baltimore to the Ohio River.

Jubal Early, usually so sensitive to both opportunity and danger, seemed to underestimate his prospective young opponent, who had graduated from West Point sixteen years after he did and was still a cadet when Early was a major fighting in the Mexican War. Observing some of Sheridan's initial movements, including his withdrawal from a position he had previously occupied, Early decided that Sheridan, like the other Union generals he had outmaneuvered and outfought, lacked a spirit of "enterprise" and "possessed an excessive caution which amounted to timidity."

The young general Early was talking about did not lack enterprise. When Lee and Grant fought at Spotsylvania three months before, Grant had turned Sheridan loose with a force of 13,000 cavalrymen and horse artillery units to make a ride around Lee's entire army, swinging near Richmond and winning four battles in fifteen days, including the engagement at Yellow Tavern in which Lee's cavalry leader "Jeb" Stuart was killed. What held Sheridan back now was not "timidity," but Grant's intention to keep sending him regiments until Sheridan had a strong numerical advantage for the clash he would soon experience, fighting against some of the South's best combat leaders and veteran enlisted men.

In addition to building up Sheridan's Army of the Shenandoah, Grant imbued him with a harsh philosophy. Earlier, when he sent General David Hunter into the Valley, Grant had stressed his concept of "total war"— the Valley was a key to military movements, but its 2,250 square miles also served as a major source of food for an entire region of the Confederacy and produced the rations consumed by much of Lee's Army of Northern Virginia. In words later changed in various ways and attributed to several individuals, Grant told Hunter that his troops should destroy crops, take what cattle they needed, drive the rest far into the mountains, and "eat out Virginia clear and clean as far as they go, so that crows flying over it [the Valley] for the balance of the season will have to carry their provender with them." Hunter had failed and been moved up to a face-saving administrative position in which he nominally commanded Sheridan, but Grant stressed the same concepts to Sheridan: in "pushing up" the Valley, he told him, "it is desirable that nothing should be left that would invite the enemy to return . . . we are determined to stop them at all hazards." Emphasizing the overall policy, he added, "Do all the damage to railroads and crops you can. . . . If the war is to last another year, we want the Shenandoah Valley to remain a barren waste."

For the moment, Grant was trying to strike a balance that would help Sheridan: he kept strengthening Sheridan's force, and he also sensed that his own war of attrition against Lee at Petersburg and Richmond might soon force Lee to call back from the Valley the reinforcements he had sent to Early. "Watch closely," Grant wired Sheridan, and if he saw this start to happen, "push with all vigor. Give the enemy no rest." No one ever accused Grant of ambiguity: Grant told Sheridan that if he saw a chance to strike Early while he was in motion and vulnerable, "when he moves, follow him up, being ready at all times to pounce upon him."

In Washington, Lincoln felt pressure from those who saw Sheridan as another in the succession of Union generals who went into the Valley and sat there until the Confederates chose to drive them back the way they came. Usually averse to giving his commanders specific advice, on September 12 Lincoln sent Grant this, regarding his view of the situation:

Sheridan and Early are facing each other at a dead lock. Could we not pick up a regiment here and there, to the number of say ten thousand men, and quietly, but suddenly concentrate them at Sheridan's camp and enable him to make a strike?

The next day, Grant replied, "It has been my intention for a week . . . to see Sheridan and arrange what was necessary to start Early out of the Valley. It seems to me it can be successfully done." Now, knowing that the commander-in-chief wanted action as soon as possible, Grant arrived at Charles Town, Virginia, on September 17 with a detailed plan of battle for Sheridan folded in the pocket of his greatcoat. He found that Sheridan had what appeared to be a better one, based on knowledge he had been accumulating about the terrain that lay ahead of him and some fresh intelligence that reached him in an interesting way. Thomas Laws, a middle-aged black man who acted as an intelligence courier, had arrived at Sheridan's headquarters with a message wrapped in tinfoil concealed under his tongue. (Laws's standing instructions were that, if stopped for questioning, he was to swallow whatever message he carried.) The message came from a twenty-six-year-old Quaker schoolteacher named Rebecca Wright who lived in Winchester, Virginia, the town fifty-two miles from Washington then possessed by the Confederates that had changed hands seventy-three times. A lady loyal to the Union, Rebecca had by chance fallen into conversation with a Confederate officer in a social situation and learned some things. Never trained as a spy, she sent Sheridan a model intelligence report, alerting him to just the kind of opportunity "to pounce" that Grant had mentioned.

> *I have no communication whatever with the rebels, but will tell you what I know. The division of General Kershaw, and Cutshaw's artillery, twelve guns and men, General Anderson commanding, have been sent away, and no more are expected, as they cannot be spared from Richmond. I do not know how the troops are situated, but the force is much smaller than represented. I will take pleasure hereafter in learning all that I can of their strength and position, and the bearer may call again.*

Using a map as he spoke, Sheridan outlined his plan, which Grant listened to quietly without touching his own plan, still in his pocket. When Sheridan finished, Grant asked him, speaking of a time three days away, "Could you be ready to move by next Tuesday?"

Without hesitation, Sheridan replied, "I can be off before daylight on Monday."

Grant nodded, said "Go in," and headed back to his headquarters 135 miles away at City Point. Unfortunately for the Union cause, Confederate intelligence reported that Grant had come to Charles Town to confer with Sheridan; something big must be coming, and soon. Sheridan's chance to "pounce" vanished.

If Early could have seen Philip Sheridan and his Army of the Shenandoah as they neared Winchester at dawn on Monday, September 19, the thought of "timidity" would not have come to his mind. Sheridan was mounted on his horse Rienzi, a black gelding of Morgan stock which stood seventeen hands high, a charger of extraordinary speed and strength whose normal walking gait was five miles an hour and whose great size made Sheridan look shorter than he was. Any diminutive impression ceased there; with his flushed red complexion, waxed black mustache, and flashing brown eyes, Sheridan, most of whose weight seemed to be in his broad shoulders and deep chest, radiated a fierce desire to do battle. He had the superiority in numbers that Grant wished him to have: the leading elements of his force of 37,000 approaching Winchester from the north and east were already skirmishing with the pickets posted in front of Early's defenders, who were estimated to number between 12,000 to 17,000. Fully as important as the total numbers was that 7,000 of Sheridan's men were cavalry.

"A glaring and blood-red sun" rose on a clear day. Sheridan nearly lost this battle at Winchester before it was really underway. He approached the town and its defenses with three parallel columns, but in an effort to maintain some measure of surprise and to protect the largest part of his force from prematurely crossing open fields where the defenders could cut them down, he sent his middle column, the 25,000 men of the Sixth and Nineteenth Corps, up the Berryville Pike. This road, leading straight to Winchester, ran through a two-mile canyon. It was a risky commitment of so many men, but might have worked except for a decision made by Sheridan's subordinate Major General Horatio Wright, commander of the Sixth Corps. These were the veteran troops wearing the Greek Cross insignia who had arrived by ship at Washington just in time to oppose Early's raid in July. Wright decided to bring his entire wagon train with him in this opening move. The result was reminiscent of the situation that Grant and Meade had created in the first hours of their march through the Wilderness; the supply wagons held back the faster moving combat units that were supposed to get through swiftly to engage the enemy.

The situation quickly became chaotic. A soldier from Vermont described the miles-long tangle of wagons and ambulances as a "stupid, mischievous clutter." While the main body worked its disordered way through the canyon—at one point two major generals were shouting at each other about which units should go first—the Confederates did not wait to bring everything to a test. In the open country north and south of the canyon, skirmishing intensified, and when the Sixth and Nineteenth corps finally emerged from the canyon, a mistake clearly attributable to Sheridan imperiled the entire operation. In making his battle plan, he had misread a map. As a result, the Sixth and Nineteenth corps, supposed to line up beside each other in one long Union line of battle, came onto the field in such a way that it left a large gap between these two major units.

Seizing the opportunity, the Confederates began an attack to exploit that advantage. The artillery on both sides was already raking the battlefield; a Union survivor later wrote home that the Confederate artillery "walked death in our ranks." An early casualty was Confederate Major General Robert Rodes, commanding one of the two divisions making this swift and skillful effort to keep the Union line broken in two. Rodes sat on his black stallion, shouting, "Charge them, boys! Charge them!" as he watched his division send thousands of Union troops reeling backward into the shelter of some woods. As he shouted, a steel splinter from an exploding shell cut into his head behind his left ear, throwing him off his horse to the ground, dead.

At this moment Sheridan, mounted on Rienzi, was on a knoll back of the center of the Union line. Just ahead of him, facing the enemy but not yet committed to battle, stood the division of the veteran Sixth Corps he had held in reserve, led by his friend Major General David Russell. In the prewar Regular Army, when Sheridan served as a lieutenant in the 4th Infantry Regiment, Russell had been his company commander. Earlier in this action, when Russell, who wanted to get right into the battle, saw that Sheridan was putting his division in reserve, he asked, "Phil, why do you put me in the rear?"

"Because I know," Sheridan had answered, "what I shall have there in a commanding officer if the line should break at or near that point."

Exactly that situation had occurred. Sheridan was slow to see this potential disaster happening on the battlefield, but now he ordered his former superior to advance and fill the wide, immensely vulnerable space in the Union line. Russell's men charged, saving the situation. For half an hour the two sides fired their weapons at each other at close range. Moving along just behind his men's line of battle on horseback, Russell was wounded in the chest. He concealed the wound and kept on giving orders for hours, until a fragment of shrapnel cut through his heart and killed him.

Some of the fighting turned into small actions—Sheridan's West Point roommate George Crook, in command of a collection of veteran units known as the Army of West Virginia, said that at one point "every man was fighting on his own hook"—but there were major attacks and counterattacks as well, and the battle moved increasingly onto terrain where Sheridan's far larger cavalry units could strike effectively. By five in the afternoon, Sheridan's superior numbers were part of what was helping to compensate for his earlier mistakes. He had created the situation in which the "stupid, mischievous clutter" in the canyon could occur, and he had been slow to shore up the gap in his line that cost many casualties, including his friend Russell's death. However, as the fighting went on, hour after bloody hour, with the outnumbered Confederates fighting bravely and often brilliantly, Sheridan began to get an ever-stronger grip on his army—a sense of the battle, of where to reinforce, where to redirect a line of attack, where to take advantage of a retreating movement.

In addition to the good, quick decisions he was now making, Sheridan's battlefield presence communicated itself to his men. At some point after one in the afternoon, he had come down from the knoll where he could see much of the battlefield. With aides galloping back and forth bringing him reports from different areas, he began riding up and down the Union line directly behind his men who were in combat, letting them know he was there. When a Confederate cannonball struck between his horse Rienzi's legs without harming him or Rienzi, he shouted, "Damn close, but we'll lick hell out of them yet!" Amid the blasts of cannon and the snapping sound of enemy bullets, he rode along with the light of battle in his eye, causing one of his soldiers to think he "looked as happy as a schoolboy." One member of the company later reported that when some men of the 49th Pennsylvania gathered around him, he called out to them over the blasting gunfire, "Boys the only way we have to Do is to Kill every Son of a Bitch." Riding up to Brigadier General Alfred Torbert, who commanded one of his two cavalry divisions, he ordered him to attack with this exhortation: "Press them, General, they'll run. Press them, General, I know they'll run."

Captain George B. Sanford of Torbert's staff said this of Sheridan's effect on officers and men alike:

> *In action . . . the whole man seemed to expand physically and mentally. His influence on his men was like an electric shock, and he was the only commander I have ever met whose personal appearance in the field was an immediate and positive stimulus to battle. . . .*
>
> *Many of our generals were more warmly beloved by the soldiers, but none, to the best of my belief, carried such a convincing air of success to the minds of his men, or could get the last drop of strength out of their bodies. . . . They simply believed he was going to win, and every man apparently was determined to be on hand to see him do it.*

The end came quickly. Philip Sheridan knew how to use cavalry as an irresistible force. At this moment in the late afternoon, Jubal Early's regiments were still intact, bravely standing their ground in an L-shaped line on high, flat fields east of Winchester. A spectacularly dramatic scene unfolded. In the light before sunset, 7,000 Union horsemen assembled two miles north of Jubal Early's left flank. With their battle standards unfurled and every man's saber sparkling in the last direct sunlight, this mounted mass began their advance, with their horses moving first at a walk, then at the trot, and then finally cantering, shaking the ground and creating a rumble like an earthquake. "Every man's saber was waving above his head," a soldier of a New York cavalry regiment said, "and with a savage yell, we swept down. . . ."

Confederate soldiers who had fought since early morning and who still waited, watching this charge in the vain hope that their own greatly outnumbered cavalry would dash out to counter it, finally could not keep their places. First, a few men turned and ran, a man here and a man there. Then groups began to run, and finally it was everyone, every man for himself, running in the direction of Winchester.

It became a rout. A Union soldier wrote his wife, "I never seen any men Run faster than the Rebels run last Munday after we got them drivin out on the open plaine. It was fun To see them Running." Because the collapse was so swift and the darkness came on quickly, thousands of the Confederates managed to get through the narrow streets and alleys of Winchester, and escaped to the south through the night.

Unlike Sheridan's actions after the Confederate retreat over the top of Missionary Ridge at Chattanooga, when he went on chasing his foes until two in the morning, he gave the order to reorganize around Winchester. Needing a place to sit and write a telegram to Grant, he presented himself at the house of Rebecca Wright, the Quaker schoolmistress who had sent him the intelligence about Early's forces. Meeting her for the first time at the end of this day of battle, he greeted her with an enthusiastic "Hurrah for this loyal girl!" Then he sat down in the schoolroom in her house to write his telegram to Grant. Dating it "Winchester, 7:30 P.M.," he said that he and his men had fought Early in "a most stubborn" battle and "completely defeated him."

It had been an important victory, but bought at a high price. Sheridan's army had suffered 5,000 casualties; of the nearly 4,000 men lost by Early, close to 2,000 were listed as missing, and it could never be determined how many of those missing were killed or wounded and how many captured. (Lee's nephew Fitzhugh Lee was seriously wounded after having three horses shot from under him.)

At dawn, Sheridan began to follow the retreating Confederates, but as his men moved up the valley, a "special artist" came upon a ghastly act taking place on the battlefield of the day before. The man was James E. Taylor of *Frank Leslie's Illustrated Newspaper*, a Northern paper of wide circulation that printed engravings made from the on-the-scene drawings of the war made by its staff artists such as Taylor, a man who had himself served in the Union Army during the first two years of fighting. Moving through woods strewn with corpses of men who had died the previous day, he saw some ten Union soldiers gathered about a Confederate officer who was alive and lying on the ground. Both of the man's eyes had been shot out, and as the helpless man lay there, some of the Union enlisted man were bending over and going through his pockets, robbing the blind man as he begged them not to take his belongings. "Familiar as I was with the horrors of the Battlefield," Taylor wrote, "this scene capped the climax in my experience. Going through [the possessions of] dead men was legitimate, but this passed the limits."

Three days after his victory at Winchester, Sheridan resumed battle with Early, who had dug in at Fishers Hill, a massive natural formation sixteen miles to the south that overlooked Strasburg, Virginia. Here, Sheridan's men prevailed again. One account gave this description of his foot soldiers in action.

> ". . . *taking up the charge, [they] descended into the ravine on Tumbling Run, with a headlong rush over fields, walls, rocks, and felled trees. Making their way across the brook, they were soon scrambling up heights that it had seemed madness to attack, while Sheridan and his admirable staff were on every part of the line, shouting, "Forward! Forward everything!" And to all inquiries the reply was still, "Go on, don't stop, go on!"*

Another soldier who watched Sheridan cheering on his exhausted infantrymen after they knocked the Confederates off the top of the hill and started chasing them down the other side said that he shouted, "Run boys, run! Don't wait to form! Don't let 'em stop! If you can't run, then holler!"

As at Missionary Ridge, the pursuit went on through the night, this time in a heavy rain. The next day, to Sheridan's "astonishment and chagrin," he found that two of his cavalry commanders had failed to move into positions where they could have cut off Early's retreating men, probably finishing them once and for all. By midnight, one of those leaders, Brigadier General William Woods Averell, was relieved of command by Sheridan, and left the next morning.

Jubal Early and his Army of the Valley had gotten away, shocked and badly battered—one in three of the men who had started the battle at Winchester were gone—but were still a force capable of regrouping farther up the Valley, low in morale but able to fight again. Early gave Lee an unsparing appraisal: "My troops are very much shattered, the men, very much exhausted, and many of them without shoes." Lee, writing in response to Governor William Smith of Virginia, who wanted Early relieved of command forthwith, said of Early's defeats at Winchester and Fishers Hill, "I lament those disasters as much as yourself," but in effect added that he had no one better available to replace him. Jubal Early started right to work, determined to give Sheridan another surprise.

Sheridan wrote of these four days, from the first guns firing at Winchester to the Confederate flight down the back of Fishers Hill, "Our success was very great, yet I had anticipated results still more pregnant." In a sense, Sheridan was a minority of one: everyone else who wanted the Union to win the war saw the four days as an unqualified success, although for Grant a battle was always just one more step on a bloody road.

The morning after the battle at Winchester, Lincoln wired Sheridan in code, "Have just heard of your great victory. God bless you all, officers and men. Strongly inclined to come up and see you." At 2 P.M. that afternoon, Grant telegraphed Sheridan from City Point, "I have just received news of your great victory and ordered the Armies here to fire a salute of one hundred (100) guns in honor of it at 7 A.M. tomorrow morning—If practicable push your success and make all you can of it." Two nights later, when Grant learned that Sheridan had indeed pushed his success and won at Fishers Hill, he wrote him again, summing up the past days with this:

I congratulate you and the Army serving under you for the great victory just achieved. It has been most opportune in point of time and in effect. It

*will open again to the Government and the public the very important
line of [rail]road from Baltimore to the Ohio and also the Chesapeake
Canal. Better still, it wipes out much of the stain upon our arms by previous disasters in that locality.*

May your good work continue is now the prayer of all loyal men.

U. S. Grant
Lt. Gen.

II

The year 1864 had come to a turning point. Less than a month before
Lincoln wired Sheridan that he had "just heard of your great victory," he
had written his memorandum, signed by his cabinet, in which he said, "it
seems exceedingly likely that this Administration will not be re-elected."
Since then, Sherman had taken Atlanta, and Sheridan had, as his opponent Early said, "shattered" the Confederate Army of the Valley. Military
success reversed the declining Northern public confidence in Lincoln
and his administration. The price of gold, the precious commodity into
which many speculators and investors put their money when things
looked black, dropped 20 percent in a few days, and the value of the large
issues of Confederate bonds held by banks in Europe fell.

Even now, nothing could be taken for granted. At the Tuesday afternoon cabinet meeting on September 20, the day after Sheridan's victory
at Winchester, there was news of a different kind. Secretary of the Navy
Welles noted in his diary that Secretary of War Stanton "unfolded and
read a telegram, stating that two steamers had been captured on Lake
Erie by Rebels from Canada. This he said was a matter that immediately
concerned the State and Navy Departments." Secretary of State Seward
explained that the United States had a treaty with Canada; more facts
were needed to establish in whose waters this had occurred, and where
the ships and people involved were at the moment. The information soon
came in, and Welles added this:

. . . some Rebel refugees had come aboard the packet-boat Parsons *at
Malden [Fort Malden, Ontario], the boat being on her way from Detroit
to Sandusky [Ohio]; had risen on the officers and crew and seized
the boat, had subsequently seized and sunk the* [Island Queen],

then run their own boat into a Canada port and disabled and then deserted her.

While more information was being called for, Welles and Stanton had a conversation between themselves. Welles, who had been in Lincoln's cabinet since the beginning of his administration, had by now observed Stanton at scores of cabinet meetings during the thirty-three months since Stanton became secretary of war and disliked him intensely. Lincoln valued his hardworking secretary of war enormously, but Welles said of Stanton in a crisis, "He is always in an excited panic, a sensational condition, at such times." Stanton now thought that the Confederate raiders still had one vessel in action, and, according to Welles, told him that the ship "was rushing over the lake and all our vast shipping on the [Great] Lakes was at its mercy." Welles took another view:

I remarked that we had best keep within the terms of the treaty, and call on the British authorities to do their duty. I remarked this was a piece of robbery and could not be considered in any other light; that the robbers had come from Canada, and risen upon the vessel upon which they had embarked, and had fled into Canada with the stolen property. The State Department had, or should have, the situation in hand.

As Welles had thought, "the flurry was pretty well over, and the fuss ended." The Confederates had indeed hoped for more than had happened, and this seizure of vessels on Lake Erie was only part of a more far-reaching scheme. Although the Copperhead movement had originated and grown in the North, during 1864 the Confederacy had begun an energetic effort to support aspects of it. In February, the Confederate Congress passed a bill in closed session that authorized the spending of 5 million U.S. dollars for a Secret Service fund to finance covert actions that would undermine the Union war effort, those actions to include destroying "the enemy's property, by land and sea."

As part of this, in late April, Jefferson Davis signed a letter commissioning Jacob Thompson of Mississippi, a former congressman from that state as well as its former governor, to "proceed at once to Canada, there to carry out the instructions you have received from me verbally." Thompson, who had been the prewar secretary of the interior under President Buchanan, evidently had carte blanche to further "the interests of the Confederate States of America" as he saw the opportunity and was given considerable sums of money to do that. He had been one of the shadowy agents, not empowered to negotiate terms of peace, with whom Horace Greeley dealt at Niagara Falls, and he had advanced money to organize the "Copperhead Convention" held at Peoria in early August. Thompson had also given $40,000 to the campaign for governor being made by Congressman James C. Robinson of Illinois, a dedicated Peace Democrat. The Copperhead leader Vallandigham initiated him into the militant Sons of Liberty; Thompson ardently wished for the "Northwest Conspiracy" to succeed in detaching several states of the Union to create a "Western Confederacy," and his activities took him into a potentially more violent realm.

Thompson had as a major objective the capture of the Federal gunboat *Michigan*, the only American warship on the Great Lakes. That vessel would then be used to attack Johnson's Island in Lake Erie, spearheading the effort to free the thousands of Confederate prisoners held there and arm them. Working with the militant Copperheads of the region, they would create a revolution, forcing the Union to a peace table.

Using language such as "By the authority in me vested" and "assigned to the secret detached service mentioned," Thompson turned this mission over to officers of the Confederate States Navy operating clandestinely in Canada. They recruited the men who were to act as a pirate crew—Confederate prisoners of war who had escaped from the camps in which they were confined and fled into Canada. There was also an effort to plant a Confederate agent aboard the *Michigan*, a man who was to try bribing the crew into some form of mutiny or surrender. At this point a figure not in the Confederate scheme came into the picture: a man appeared in the offices of the Union Army provost marshal in Detroit, said that he was a "refugee rebel soldier," and gave the information that "the officers and men of the steamer *Michigan* had been tampered with," and an effort would be made "in expectation of getting possession of your steamer." Whatever the accuracy of this man's account, it put the Federal authorities on alert.

A fiasco resulted, beginning with the fact that only one or two Confederate officers and some twenty men undertook the mission. Having seized the *Philo Parsons*, a combination of ferryboat and light cargo vessel, and the similar *Island Queen*, they had all their captured passengers, including women, aboard the *Parsons*, and, possibly because they did not have enough crew for both ships, had to cast the *Island Queen* adrift. It never became clear just what precipitated a peaceful mutiny among the Confederate pirate crew, but sixteen of them signed a letter to their captain, John Y. Beall of the Confederate States Navy, expressing their admiration for his "gentlemanly bearing, skill, and courage," but indicating that they were convinced that "the enemy is already appraised of our approach" and that there was no possibility of success. They concluded that, in this venture, "having already captured two boats, we respectfully decline to prosecute it any further." Captain Beall aborted the mission and landed both his rebellious crew and his prisoners in Canada, where his crew managed to become as invisible as they had been before they made this attempt. Barren as these results were—despite the initial reports, both captured ships were able to resume their normal passenger and freight service within six days—some of the Confederate agents and militant Copperheads continued to plan future attacks.

III

On Saturday, October 1, a unique ceremony took place in Lincoln's White House office. Under the Enrollment Act passed in March of 1863, the Union had begun its military draft. The act permitted a man to avoid military service by hiring a substitute for $300 to take his place. At fifty-five, Lincoln was ten years senior to the oldest men eligible to be conscripted, but he wanted to support a new program, through which men older than forty-five, many of them prominent citizens, could pay $500 and send into the army a man who was a "representative" rather than a substitute.

In Washington, the job of finding someone to enter the Union Army on Lincoln's behalf fell to Noble D. Larner, a local politician. As he walked down Pennsylvania Avenue, he saw a youth, short in stature but muscular, coming the other way beside a man who proved to be his father. Larner introduced himself and said, "I am looking for a young man to represent the President in the Army as a recruit. Will you accept?"

The person he had approached, twenty-year-old John Staples, a minor who needed parental permission to enlist, answered "If my father consents." His father, standing beside him, agreed; the three men walked down to the provost marshal's office, where John Staples was sworn into the Union Army.

This was not young Staples's first experience with the military. A native of Stroudsburg, Pennsylvania, he had gone into the army in late 1862 as a substitute and served for five months before being discharged for having "a broken down constitution" as a result of typhoid fever he contracted serving in North Carolina. He had recovered, and since April he and his father had been working together as carpenters at the government's vessel repair yard in Georgetown.

Lincoln was told about Staples being sworn in and saw an opportunity to publicize this program of sending forward "representative recruits." (Among those overage Northerners who did this were the poet Henry Wadsworth Longfellow, the man of letters James Russell Lowell, and Edward Everett, who had held the positions of secretary of state, senator from Massachusetts, and president of Harvard College, and was the famous orator who spoke for two hours at the dedication of the cemetery at Gettysburg, the occasion on which Lincoln delivered his immortal 272-word address in three minutes.)

Thus, the meeting on October 1. Wearing his new blue private's uniform, John Staples entered the "shop," accompanied by his father, his recruiter Noble D. Larner, and the provost marshal general of the Union Army, James Barnet Fry, whose duties included recruiting and the enforcement of the draft. (Others may have been present, including journalists; two stories about the occasion appeared in the *Washington Star*.) Lincoln shook hands with Private Staples, who stood about a foot shorter than he, and said that Staples looked like a fine young man who was sure to do his duty well. After Larner presented Lincoln with a certificate of thanks for participating in the program, everyone shook hands; as they parted, Lincoln told Staples that he hoped that in his army service he would be "one of the fortunate ones."

That proved to be true. Staples reported for duty to a sergeant who looked at this short private who represented the 6-foot-4 president and said, "Aren't you just the first instalment?" Without any influence apparently being exerted to keep the president's "representative" from being killed, wounded, or captured, Staples was assigned to a unit defending Washington that was stationed just across the Potomac River, in Alexandria, and served there safely.

• • •

THE LINCOLNS HAD not yet moved back to the White House from the Soldiers' Home, and in the evenings Lincoln made his way out there. Stanton and Washington's district marshal Ward Lamon were gradually increasing the number of guards at both the White House and the Soldiers' Home, as well as stressing to Lincoln the importance of his being protected by his cavalry escort. It may have been that on some nights Lincoln still managed to walk out of the White House, mount one of the horses available to him, and ride out by himself.

Whether accompanied or alone, he occasionally stopped at Iowa Circle, later known as Logan Circle, where the army had its Contraband Camp headquarters. This was where escaped slaves, their status as citizens not yet fully established, could receive papers guaranteeing them military protection. Many of them lived here in long two-story wooden military barracks, as individuals or as families. One of the leaders of this community was a black woman known as "Aunt Mary" Dines—an interesting surname, since she was a cook, sometimes working for the Lincolns at the White House and sometimes at the Soldiers' Home.

Those who saw Lincoln at Iowa Circle saw him as no one else did. He enjoyed listening to the singing during the evening under the trees. He could not read music, and could not carry a tune, but he loved simple songs like the old Scottish ballad "Annie Laurie." Here he stood in the campfire shadows and sang along in a raspy monotone. "Aunt Mary" remembered an evening when she led the singing and Lincoln joined in. Together, he and the black refugees sang "America," with its words beginning, "My country 'tis of thee, sweet land of liberty," and then "Nobody Knows the Trouble I've Seen." After that, when they finished "Every Time I Feel the Spirit," Lincoln wiped tears from his face. He remained silent with his head bowed as the black people around him sang "Thank God I Am Free at Last." He joined them in singing "John Brown's Body," and went on his way.

"Aunt Mary" was one of the people in the Lincolns' lives who had a strong wish to protect them. Another was Rebecca Pomroy, a nurse from Massachusetts with extensive experience at Washington's Columbia College Hospital, who spent some time at the White House taking care of Mary Lincoln after her son Willie died, and also aided in her treatment after she was thrown from a carriage in the accident in 1863 that appeared to be an effort to hurt or kill Lincoln. Rebecca also helped take care of Tad from time to time, and got to know the Lincolns so well that at one point Lincoln, noticing that she was looking haggard from her regular hospital duties (at one time she was responsible for ninety-one beds), arranged for her to spend some days of vacation with the presidential family. Just how much time she spent at the White House in 1864 was not clear, but during these October days she wrote this:

> *Aunt Mary, from Mrs. Lincoln, called to have me go out to the Soldiers'* *Home and spend a few days with the family. She says that the President* *has had several threatening letters, his house is guarded all round the* *outside, and a private guard in the house.*

Almost nothing ever came to light concerning these "threatening letters," but the time they were supposed to have been received coincided with a later claim by a man named Thomas N. Conrad. He wrote that he had been a spy, authorized by the Confederate secretary of war James A. Seddon to organize and execute a plan to kidnap Lincoln as he went out to the Soldiers' Home "in the cool of evening." Conrad said that he and two or three fellow conspirators came to Washington in late September and followed Lincoln's carriage along the winding wooded roads several times in a carriage of their own, waiting for their opportunity:

> *It was all planned out to the last detail, and the minute the driver of Mr.* *Lincoln's carriage passed into the forest, he should be made to stop by* *means of a pistol at his head, and Mr. Lincoln, served in the same manner, would be compelled to cross from his carriage to the close vehicle.*

Conrad claimed that he eventually had to abort the scheme when Lincoln started having strong nightly protection from his cavalry escort, something that had been available to the president for a long time but which had clearly not been on hand the night two months before when Lincoln was shot at as he approached the Soldiers' Home riding on Old Abe. Conrad stayed in Washington until November 10, two days after Election Day; after leaving, he described his thwarted efforts to abduct Lincoln as a "humiliating failure."

There was supposedly yet another similar scheme, in which a Confederate cavalry officer, Bradley T. Johnson, was to "make a dash" at kidnapping Lincoln, a plan abandoned when Johnson received orders in June of 1864 to report to Jubal Early for service in the Valley. If true, this meant that John Wilkes Booth, who during 1864 focused on the idea of seizing the president and holding him as a hostage, was one of three people with the same idea, each unaware of the other.

IV

With crucial gubernatorial and congressional elections in Indiana, Ohio, and Pennsylvania less than two weeks away, to be followed by the presidential election four weeks after that, Lincoln and his Republican/ National Union Party greatly expanded the efforts they had been making all year. It was not the custom for a president seeking reelection to go around the country giving campaign speeches, but from inside the White House Lincoln worked hard to get out the vote. He saw the three state elections scheduled for October 11 as being in many ways as important as the presidential election in November. Those results would influence voters in other states throughout the North and would be the first solid indication of whether the post-Atlanta-victory change in public support would keep him in the White House. (Both parties gave the October contests the same significance: a Democratic leader in Pennsylvania wrote his national chairman August Belmont, "The party carrying the state in October will carry it in November. . . . All depends on October," and a friend of Lincoln's adjutant general Joseph Holt wrote of the overall election that the Democrats "are entering into this contest like a pack of ravenous wolves.")

Lincoln believed that, despite the enthusiasm shown for McClellan by many of the soldiers who had served under him in the Army of the Potomac early in the war, most of the soldiers in the Union Army who were eligible to vote would cast their ballots for him rather than for "Little Mac." He tried this out on Henry Wing, the young *New York Tribune* reporter who had brought him the first news from the Wilderness; true to their compact with each other, whenever Henry came back to Washington from Grant's front in Virginia, he would go to the White House and answer Lincoln's questions about how he thought the war was really going.

"Henry," Lincoln said, "I would rather be defeated with the soldier vote than elected without it."

"You will have it, Mister Lincoln," Henry replied. "You will have it. They'll vote as they shoot."

There had not been a wartime election since 1812, and, although absentee ballots were employed in American elections as early as colonial times, this was their first widespread use. In the coming October state elections the soldiers from Ohio and Pennsylvania could vote in the field wherever they were, but Indiana had not passed the special legislation required for that, and the only way for soldiers from Indiana to vote was to do so within their state. On September 12, Indiana's governor Oliver Morton and Indiana's congressional delegation joined in sending Stanton a request that 15,000 soldiers from Indiana be furloughed home long enough to vote. Stanton agreed that Indiana's hundred-day volunteers could return, but this did not come near the 15,000 figure. On September 19, while Sherman was still resting and refitting his army around Atlanta before continuing to campaign through the South, Lincoln sent him this.

> *The State election of Indiana occurs on the 11th of October, and the loss of it to the friends of the Government would go far towards losing the whole Union cause. . . . Indiana is the only important State, voting in October, whose soldiers cannot vote in the field. Any thing you can safely do to let her soldiers, or any part of them, go home and vote at the State election, will be greatly in point. They need not remain for the Presidential election, but may return to you at once. This is in no sense, an order, but is intended merely to impress you with the importance, to the army itself, of your doing all you safely can, yourself being the judge of what you can safely do.*

Sherman did not want to send any men away from his main force; how many he might have sent in response to this would remain a question, because Confederate general John Bell Hood, who had replaced Joseph E. Johnston and had a total strength of 40,000 men, began making moves against Sherman's hundred-mile-long lines of communication and supply that stretched back from recently captured Atlanta to Chattanooga. Sherman decided not to detach men who were fit for duty, but under the pressure from Lincoln, Stanton, and the Indiana leaders, a compromise was reached. Nearly 9,000 wounded or sick Indiana soldiers of Sherman's command who were able to leave military hospitals received furloughs to go home and vote; many officers, and a few small units stationed near Indiana, were also released for this purpose, and Major Generals Frank John Logan and Francis Preston Blair, Jr., were permitted to spend time giving campaign speeches in Indiana and adjoining states. (In what was presumably a bureaucratic blunder, a Vermont regiment serving in Sherman's Army of the West found itself lining up at ballot boxes in Indiana, and the men from Vermont, along with some from Massachusetts, dutifully voted in the Indiana election.)

In the political maneuvering during the weeks before the election season began, the Democrats expressed worry that their party representatives would be excluded from taking "tickets" [ballots] into the military polling places and to act as de facto poll watchers. Democratic Party chairman August Belmont raised this subject in a letter to Stanton, and the secretary of war sent it along to Grant. Responding to Stanton, Grant set forth his overall views concerning the correct policy for the soldiers of the Union Army who were to vote by absentee ballot. He believed strongly in their right to do this:

> *In performing this sacred duty, they should not be deprived of a most precious privilege. They have as much right to demand that their votes shall be counted, in their choice of rulers, as those citizens, who remain at home; Nay more, for they have sacrificed more for their country.*

Having said that, Grant insisted that no electioneering should be allowed. He wrote in part that there should be "no political meetings, no harangues from soldiers or citizens and no canvassing of camps or regiments for votes. I do not see why a single individual, not belonging to the Armies, should be admitted into their lines, to deliver tickets."

Stanton and Grant worked out a practice by which Democratic Party workers could be present during the voting, but not all the absentee ballots would actually be cast in the field. In a letter home, an artillery officer described the required procedure for the men from New York State: "Quite a form has to be gone through by New York soldiers who vote, giving power of attorney to some legal voter where they reside to cast their votes for them, taking an oath that they are legal voters etc. all of which requires a good deal of writing."

In other aspects of preelection strategy, questions had already arisen as to what constituted permissible political activity at government workplaces that employed civilians. As far back as late August, Secretary of the Navy Welles was approached by Mary Lincoln's New York City friend Abram Wakeman, the influential Republican postmaster who had quietly refinanced the bills she had run up with some of the city's leading merchants so that Lincoln would not learn of her extravagant shopping sprees. (Wakeman's position vis-à-vis the Lincolns was remarkable; on the one hand, Lincoln trusted him in many delicate and important political situations, while at the same time he evidently never learned of Wakeman's efforts on Mary's behalf. For different reasons, both Lincolns wanted his advancement, and on September 7, Lincoln named him to the lucrative Customs House job of surveyor of the Port of New York, the position Wakeman long had wished to have.)

In this August meeting, Wakeman complained to Welles about the situation at the Brooklyn Navy Yard, the Navy's largest installation, which had 6,000 employees and an annual payroll of $4 million. Wakeman told Welles that the admiral in charge of the yard had broken up a meeting in which one of the principal civilian managers there "had gathered two or three hundred workmen together, and was organizing them with a view to raise funds [for Lincoln's campaign] and get them on the right track." Welles, a Republican from Connecticut who always found the ethics of the New York Republican machine dubious, replied that he approved of the admiral's action and that "there ought to be no gathering of workmen in working hours and while under government pay for party schemes." He noted that Wakeman "was a little staggered by my words . . . insisted we could not succeed without doing these things, that other parties had done them, and we must."

Welles maintained his position, which led to a tense mid-September meeting in his office with Burton C. Cook of Illinois, a member of the Republican National Committee, and three other men, including a former congressman in whose district the navy yard was located. They advanced on Welles from a different direction, saying that "a majority of the men in the Yard are Copperheads, opposed to the Administration," and that "Mr. Davidson, the Assistant Naval Constructor . . . would not dismiss, or give permission to dismiss," anyone who was a Democrat. These Republicans finally came to what Welles said they really wanted to do: "If allowed to go into the yard they could better organize, and it would help them much . . . if they could go near the paymaster when he was paying the men off, and get the assessment off each man, it would greatly aid them"

In response to all this, Welles went so far as to say he would review the complaints about favoring dockyard workers who were Democrats but forbade any effort to extract political contributions at the pay table. He wrote, perhaps naïvely: "I told them it would help them to no votes. The man who was compelled to pay a party tax could not love the party who taxed him. His contribution must, like his vote, come voluntarily, and they must persuade and convince him[,] to make him earnest and effective."

Welles saw all this as proof of the corruption of New York Republicans. Making a diary entry concerning Henry Raymond, who was himself running for Congress, Welles said this of key leaders of the New York committee, a group with which Secretary of State Seward, a former governor of New York, was strongly affiliated.

> *Raymond has in party matters neither honesty nor principle himself, and believes that no one else has. He would compel men to vote, and would buy up leaders. . . . This fellow, trained in the vicious New York school of politics . . . is spending much of his time in Washington, working upon the President. . . . [New York political boss Thurlow] Weed, worse than Seward, is Raymond's prompter, and the debaucher of New York politics.*

In light of all that was going on, the Republican effort at the Brooklyn shipyard was only an indication of the scale on which party discipline was being enforced, patronage dispensed, and political contributions demanded. When Lincoln was elected in November of 1860, unprecedented numbers of patronage appointments were made, but now the Republicans had been in power for four years, controlling the government's executive departments. Lincoln had learned that it was unwise to appoint generals who had little or no military experience, but after his nomination the past June he began an effort to seduce the opposition press. Through Wakeman, it was put to James Gordon Bennett of the *New York Herald* that Lincoln intended to offer him an attractive appointment, the exact position not being specified in the first overtures. What Lincoln had in mind was minister to France, but when Bennett seemed unresponsive, the matter came to an end. (Nonetheless, despite some caustic editorials, Bennett kept the *Herald* neutral during the campaign, to Lincoln's benefit. Lincoln eventually made him a formal offer of the Paris post, and Bennett turned it down.) Next on Lincoln's list of the editors he wanted to tame or at least appease was Horace Greeley of the *Tribune*. Postmaster General Montgomery Blair was already under fire, with the Radicals wanting him to be dismissed. It would be seven more weeks before Lincoln let Blair go, but through another intermediary he offered that cabinet-level postmaster appointment to Greeley, who had always wanted a high government position. Greeley, like Bennett, simply did not respond to the offer, and subsequent events left him no option but to back Lincoln.

Lincoln found other matters easier to solve. In a case of party discipline, he came to the aid of a Radical, before the time in 1864 when Radicals found they had no alternative but to support him. Congressman George Julian of Indiana went to Lincoln with a complaint about Commissioner of Patents David P. Holloway, one of Lincoln's appointees. Holloway, serving in Washington, came from Julian's congressional district in Indiana and was one of the editors of a Republican newspaper there. Although Julian was the official Republican candidate for reelection to Congress from that district, Holloway, in Julian's words, "refused to recognize me as the party candidate, and kept the name of my defeated [in the party caucus] competitor standing in his newspaper."

When Julian told Lincoln about this, he received a quick, definitive reply: "Your nomination is as binding on Republicans as mine, and you can rest assured that Mr. Holloway shall support you, openly and unconditionally, or lose his head."

Lincoln had a good memory for those who had in his view gone too far, even allowing for the rough-and-tumble of politics. One was Republican senator Samuel C. Pomeroy of Kansas, the Radical whose Pomeroy Circular distributed back in February had opposed Lincoln's renomination and urged support for Chase. Subsequently, as Lincoln's secretary John Hay put it, Pomeroy "asked an appointment of the President for the purpose of getting some offices [patronage positions]. He is getting starved out. . . . He did not get any." When Charles Gibson, whom Lincoln had appointed as solicitor of the United States Court of Claims, resigned his position because he said his principles forbade his supporting the president for reelection, Lincoln shot back, having John Hay write on his behalf that he "could never learn of his giving much attention to the duties of his office," and that he thought little of "this studied attempt of Mr. Gibson's to stab him."

In the broad picture, it was impossible for Lincoln not to know what was being done behind the scenes in the reelection campaign. As far back as March, long before his renomination, three members of his cabinet, Seward, Usher, and Blair, had made contributions of $500 each toward his reelection. Now the Republican/National Union fundraisers assessed each member of the cabinet $250. In these autumn weeks, readers in the strongly contested state of Indiana could learn this, sent by a Washington correspondent to the *Indianapolis State Journal*:

> *The National Republican Committee has taken full possession of all the Capitol buildings, and the committee rooms of the Senate and House of Representatives are filled with clerks, busy in mailing Lincoln documents all over the loyal States.*
>
> *One hundred of these clerks there employed, I am assured, have been detailed from the government department, and continue to draw their salaries while engaged in re-electing Abraham Lincoln. . . .*
>
> *The Post Office Department, of course, is attending to the lion's share of this work. Eighty bags of mail matter, all concerning Lincoln documents, are daily sent to Sherman's army.*

In addition to these mass mailings, individual Republican officeholders in many places sent out great quantities of campaign literature to soldiers; one official was said to have supervised the distribution of a million documents.

The fundraising effort worked in tandem with this. From the time of Lincoln's election in 1860, many individuals who then received jobs had been paying in the 10 percent of their payroll checks that they understood they must contribute. Now, however, under the aegis of Raymond, "assessments" were levied on many workers in more menial jobs who had not previously been dunned for political contributions. All employees in the New York Customs House were informed that they would now contribute "an average three per cent of their yearly pay," and on September 30 they were told that the Republican bag men "will be found at the basement room formerly occupied by the United States measurers, from 9 A.M. to 3 o'clock P.M., this day, and to-morrow." To make sure that everyone paid in something, a levy of 5 percent of their salaries was placed on all workers in the War, Treasury and Post Office departments.

Working closely with the party's National Committee was the Union Executive Congressional Committee, organized for the election season and composed of three Republican senators and three Republican members of the House. Using the postage-free franking privileges of Senator James Harlan of Iowa, whom Lincoln later rewarded with an important post, they sent out a dunning letter to every postmaster in the nation, telling the recipient that "the Committee, presuming you will esteem it a privilege to do something in aid of a work so vital to our country, have assessed you . . ."—this followed by a figure ranging from $5 to $150, depending on the size of the post office and the postmaster's salary. The letter also solicited "suggestions as to the canvass [getting out the vote] in your locality." This committee also sent out other campaign literature. On September 15, when its work had barely begun, Congressman Elihu B. Washburne of Illinois, Grant's political backer from the war's outset and the committee's senior member in the House, reported, "We are now sending out from fifty to a hundred thousand documents a day."

Coordinating all this, Raymond acted not only as a fundraiser, but as an axman, and became for the moment an extraordinarily powerful figure. Welles never clarified what he meant in saying that Raymond "is spending much of his time in Washington, working upon the President," but when men refused to pay up, Raymond demanded that they be removed forthwith, and there is no record of Lincoln doing anything to curb that.

This penalizing of those who failed to demonstrate party loyalty extended even to some officers of the Union Army. A colonel who had attended the Democratic convention found himself sidelined from active duty, and action on a number of promotions, either bestowed or not given, appears to have been based on party allegiance. In his diary, John Hay gave two examples of this occurring at the highest level. Talking with Secretary of War Stanton, he mentioned that he had heard that a regiment commanded by a colonel named Dandy was "all for McClellan." When he added that Dandy wanted to be promoted to brigadier general, he got this sarcastic response from Stanton: " 'He will get it,' said the Secretary, puffing a long blue spiral wreath of smoke from his lips. Colonel Dandy's dream of [a general's] stars passed away in that smoke." Stanton mentioned to Hay what had happened to a nephew of Governor John C. Brough of Ohio "that I placed at Louisville and made a Colonel," in a safe and comfortable position as a quartermaster. When the man was found to be betting against Republican Governor Morton of Indiana in the upcoming election, Stanton said, "I reduced [him] to a Captain and ordered him South the other day."

Regarding Lincoln's opponent General McClellan, Stanton felt that if a general entered politics, he must expect to be handled roughly. On June 15, well before McClellan was the Democratic nominee but when he was already seen as the Democrats' likely choice, McClellan gave an address at West Point. This speech, while in a sense not political, was used by the Democrats at the Chicago convention; copies of it were given to every arriving delegate as part of a package labeled "McClellan's Platform." After McClellan's appearance at West Point, the three officers of the committee that invited him to speak, one of them the academy's superintendent, were transferred or dismissed from the service by Stanton. Like Lincoln, McClellan made virtually no public appearances once he was nominated, but he felt certain that he and other Democratic leaders including the Democratic vice-presidential nominee George H. Pendleton were being followed by detectives acting under War Department direction.

There were those who felt that Stanton was acting as a shadow campaign manager for Lincoln, and being fully as effective in his own way as Henry J. Raymond was in his official capacity. While remaining tantalizing circumspect about the details, Assistant Secretary of War Charles A. Dana, a man in a position to know, many years later wrote this about Stanton's behind-the-scenes activities in Lincoln's campaign.

> *In all my experience I have never witnessed any other election that had so much politics in it. All the resources of partisan science, backed by the vast and widespread expenditures of the War Department, then about a million a day, had been employed by the astute and relentless man at the head of the War Office; and he did it with a pertinacity and skill that have never been surpassed. Of course no great step had been taken without the knowledge and consent of Mr. Lincoln, himself a politician of a very fertile and superior order; but the engineer whose hand was never taken off the machine, was Mr. Stanton; and his ardent and excitable nature was kept at fever heat to the very last moment of the contest, and thereafter.*

Stanton was clearly willing to confront civilian authority, as well as to impose his rule in matters involving military officers. An example of his autocratic methods, although not one involving expenditure of the rivers of money at his disposal, came when Democratic governor Horatio Seymour of New York sent a commission to Washington to ensure that all the soldiers there who were Democrats voted. Stanton had the commissioners jailed, not to be released until after the election.

Regarding men of the Union Army who could aid his campaign, Lincoln gladly accepted the offer of the influential Brigadier General Carl Schurz to go out and make speeches on his behalf. Schurz's performance as a general would be a subject of debate, but the Democrats had no one to counter this "eloquent Teuton," as John Hay called him. Speaking in his native German, Schurz exhorted the large and important body of German-American voters to support the president.

In other areas of the presidential race, the Lincoln forces, sometimes referred to throughout the campaign as the National Union Party and often simply as the Republicans they largely were, had a fully organized speakers bureau. On September 25, sixteen days before the October state elections, a Democrat in Indiana worriedly reported, "The Republicans have sent out *twenty* new speakers. Gov. And. Johnson, candidate for V.P., is among them." The speakers bureau had a unique offering for selected audiences: the black leader Frederick Douglass. He still had reservations about Lincoln, but felt that every vote for Lincoln was a vote against slavery and intended to work hard in that effort. His itinerary reflected racial feeling: the farther north he was sent, the less likely he was to trigger the animosity not only felt in Border States such as Maryland and Kentucky, but in the southern parts of states such as Indiana and Illinois. A campaign worker in Chicago wrote Congressman Washburne that Douglass "would do pretty well in some parts of Wisconsin," but thought he should postpone appearing in Illinois "for fear that our people would be driven off by the cry of 'Nigger' and a prejudice be raised in the Southern portion of the State."

The Democrats were fighting back. The *New York Times* reported that in Indiana, "Rebels expelled from Kentucky have been brought by thousands across the Ohio to give their votes against the Government," and that in Pennsylvania, "*hundreds of thousands of dollars* have been sent there within the last ten days." In addition to sending individual speakers around the country, both parties held mass rallies. On September 17, the

Democrats brought together a crowd in the capital that the *New York Herald* called "the largest ever assembled in Washington in opposition to any administration," and on the same night in New York City the Democrats drew thousands to Union Square for what the *Herald* called "a demonstration, an exhibition of numerical power, a display of force, strength and enthusiasm such as is seldom seen even in this city." Ten days later a young Republican firebrand named Abram Dittenhoefer harangued a crowd in the 2,000-seat auditorium of Manhattan's Cooper Institute, telling them that McClellan was "the leader of the Confederate forces"—a preposterous statement, but one playing on the Republican theme that to be a Democrat was to be a traitor. Besides the speechmaking and mass mailings, the Republicans had started a pro-Lincoln campaign newspaper, *Father Abraham*, scheduled to cease publication as soon as the election was over.

In the effort to raise money, Raymond and his New York team were now reaching well beyond what could be extracted from government employees at all levels. Executives of businesses that had received government contracts received letters asking for funds, written under the letterhead "Rooms of the National Union Executive Committee." Sent from New York's large and fashionable Astor House hotel and signed by Raymond, these solicitations read in part, "I take it for granted you appreciate the necessity of sustaining the government in its contest with the rebellion, and of electing a Union candidate in November, the only mode of carrying the war to a successful close, and of restoring a peace which shall also restore the Union." The letter made it clear that Raymond was running Lincoln's campaign: "Please remit whatever you feel inclined to give in a check, payable to my order as treasurer of the national executive committee."

Businessmen responded quickly. William E. Dodge, Jr., of the Phelps, Dodge mining and metal manufacturing company, wrote Raymond from the corporation's headquarters near Wall Street, "I enclose check for $3000—from members of our firm who sympathize most heartily with the good cause in which your Committee is working. We shall be glad to do more if necessary." This produced an example of cause and effect: William E. Dodge, Sr., received the Republican/National Union nomination to run for Congress from Manhattan's Eighth Congressional District.

The cumulative results of all these "assessments" and solicitations put the New York Republican organization into a position to aid the party in other states. The chairman of the Union Republican State Committee of New Hampshire, writing from his state capital of Concord, acknowledged receipt of a total of $10,000—a Union private's annual pay came to $156—and Raymond was able to send funds to Lincoln's own state of Illinois.

Whether or not all this was what Welles meant by Raymond's "working upon" Lincoln, there was no question that in some matters the president remained ready, sometimes reluctantly, to accommodate his powerful New York operatives. At the end of August, in response to a request made by Raymond, Weed, and New York senator Edwin D. Morgan, he had agreed to release from prison a man who, in Lincoln's words, "came from the rebel lines into ours with a written contract to furnish large supplies to the rebels, was arrested with the contract in his possession, and has been sentenced to imprisonment for it." Lincoln, a lawyer who had argued criminal as well as civil cases, made it clear that he thought the argument being made by the New Yorkers for a pardon relied on the "very absurd and improbable story" that the merchant was using this contract "as a means for escaping from the rebel lines." In giving them what they wanted, he asked them not to insult his intelligence: "Now, if Senator Morgan, and Mr. Weed, and Mr. Raymond, will not argue with me that I *ought* to release this man, but will, in writing on this sheet, simply request me to do it, I will do it solely in deference to their wishes.")

From the White House, Lincoln kept monitoring every part of the complex national political situation. Some of the information he received came in interesting ways: when his secretary John Nicolay traveled on a train from Pittsburgh to Harrisburg, Pennsylvania, two weeks after Sherman took Atlanta and shortly before Frémont withdrew from the race, he went through the cars, polling the male passengers as to whom they intended to vote for in November. The results, which Lincoln jotted down in a memorandum, were Lincoln 172, McClellan 66, and Frémont 7, with no one on the train evidently declining to participate.

By this time, Lincoln had done all that he could regarding the impending state elections and was focusing on the presidential election in November. On Monday, October 2, he met with William McKee, editor of the *Missouri Democrat*, a paper whose name did not reflect its editorial sympathies, to discuss political developments in St. Louis, and two days later he asked Nicolay to travel to St. Louis to learn more about the pre-election views of Union sympathizers there.

Later in the week, he held a discussion with a delegation from Kentucky about the critical situation in that border state, which would not vote until November and was a place where he was sure to lose. On July 5, at a time when many Confederate guerrilla raids were causing great unrest there, Lincoln had given Union general Stephen Burbridge the order to declare martial law and to suspend habeas corpus throughout the state. Soon after that, an additional series of raids prompted Burbridge to issue his notorious Order No. 59, which stated that whenever an unarmed Union civilian was killed in one of these raids, four guerrillas who were prisoners would be shot to death in retaliation. In all, some fifty captive Confederates were chosen at random under this measure and executed.

With Kentucky now being treated primarily not as a state, but as a military district under Burbridge's despotic rule, the general suppressed anti-Lincoln newspapers and started arresting candidates for office whom he deemed to be unsuitable. Burbridge also embarked on measures to intimidate any Democratic voters who came to the polls—something that angered Kentuckians, who had seen this before during the congressional elections of 1862. Lincoln, who knew there was no chance he could win Kentucky, eventually came to realize that he had an "imbecile commander" on his hands but continued the suspension of *habeas corpus* and did not remove Burbridge for another four months. (Burbridge left no doubt as to how he saw things, and wrote this to Lincoln from Lexington, Kentucky: "A vigorous policy against rebel sympathizers in this state must be pursued & if I have erred I fear I have made too few arrests instead of too many.") During this first week in October, Lincoln also reviewed the situation in Louisiana, a place where there was less unrest than in Kentucky, hundreds of miles to its north. The pro-Union government in Louisiana, which represented half the state's area and two-thirds of its population, would not have its electoral votes counted because of congressional opposition to Lincoln's views on Reconstruction.

V

On Monday, October 10, the day before the critical contests in Indiana, Ohio, and Pennsylvania, Lincoln began moving through one of his remarkably varied schedules. That night, several thousand people were to assemble at Baltimore's Monument Square in a mass meeting to support the ratification of Maryland's new constitution, the key provision of which, as Lincoln put it, "provides for the extinction of slavery." The vote to adopt or reject it would be held in three days. Writing a statement to be taken to Baltimore and read there at the mass meeting, Lincoln said:

> *I presume it is no secret, that I wish success to this provision. I desire it on every consideration. I wish all men to be free. . . . I wish to see, in process of disappearing, that only thing which ever could bring this nation to civil war. . . . I only add that I shall be gratified exceedingly if the good people of the State shall, by their votes, ratify the new constitution.*

After that, Lincoln devoted two and a half hours in the "shop" to a talk with Congressman William D. Kelley, from Philadelphia. It was not clear whether Lincoln's secretary Hay was paraphrasing the president's reaction to the meeting or simply commenting on his own behalf, but Hay wrote to Nicolay, who was taking political soundings in St. Louis, that Kelley "seemed to be in a great hurry, as he only staid [*sic*] two hours and a half, and didn't talk about himself more than nine-tenths of the time."

In fact, Lincoln and Kelley may have been doing some last-minute horse-trading about the political situation in Kelley's state of Pennsylvania, which Lincoln believed he had to win in November even if he could not win there the next day. The situation demonstrated how far and in what ways Lincoln's influence extended. Kelley was an undoubted Radical, but he and Lincoln had always been on good terms, and Kelley certainly owed Lincoln a favor or two. Back in June, Lincoln had stopped the Philadelphia postmaster Cornelius A. Walborn from having his 200 to 300 postal employees work against Kelley's reelection, which was now certain to occur the next day. The president had done this at the urging of his friend and political confidant John Forney, who had in earlier years been owner and editor of the *Philadelphia Pennsylvanian*. Forney had then moved to Washington, where he became an editorial writer for the *Washington Daily Union*, a paper of which he became part owner, and subsequently moved back to Philadelphia and started that city's *Press*. When Lincoln was elected in 1860, Forney, a War Democrat who was by now a man to reckon with in Pennsylvania as well as in Washington, had asked for an administrative appointment, and Lincoln had helped him get the votes necessary to become secretary of the Senate. The duties of the position left Forney time to start the *Washington Sunday Chronicle*; at Lincoln's suggestion, in 1862 Forney turned this into a daily paper, the pro-administration *Chronicle*, which distributed many thousands of copies a day to the Army of the Potomac.

Whatever went on between Lincoln and Kelley during those two and a half hours, Lincoln next met with Welles, to straighten out a situation in which more than 1,100 United States Marines, when they enlisted, had been promised a bounty of $100—something sailors had not received when they volunteered for the United States Navy. Welles was concerned about the effect on the sailors' morale if this commitment to the Marines was kept without an equal bounty being paid to many thousands of sailors. On looking into the legality of the matter, Welles concluded that the Marines "must be paid the bounty or discharged. I thought it best to re-examine the whole subject with the president. He concurs with me and decides it is best to pay the bounty." (For the moment, apparently none of the sailors in the Navy learned about this.)

As he continued dealing with the various matters before him just on this one day, Lincoln sent off a communication to the House Judiciary Committee, which had before it the question of whether the civilian owners of houses destroyed by Union artillery fire in the defense of Washington during Jubal Early's raid could receive compensation under a claim of "the taking of private property for public use," or for "losses and damages by war." The committee had heard that Lincoln had been there during that battle and had given permission to bombard the houses, and wanted a statement from him. Evidently unsure of precisely where he had been on the day he came under enemy fire, he wrote:

I was present at Fort Stevens (I think) on the afternoon of July 12th. 1864, when some houses in front were shelled by our guns, and under-standing that the Military officers in command thought the shelling of the houses proper and necessary, I certainly gave my approbation to its being done.

A. Lincoln

VI

On the morning of Tuesday, October 11, with voters in the state elections already going to the polls in Indiana, Ohio, and Pennsylvania, Lincoln walked into the office of Secretary of the Navy Gideon Welles. He had with him Secretary of State Seward, a former governor of New York State as well as one of its former United States senators, and a man always interested in furthering the interests of New York Republicans. They were there to discuss what the secretary of the navy found to be an interesting request, as he described it, "relative to New York voters in the Navy." Looking a month ahead to the presidential election, they asked Welles for this: "Wanted one of our boats to be placed at the disposal of the New York [electoral] commission to gather votes in the Mississippi Squadron." The idea was to have a ship go around to other ships, rounding up the ballots of sailors from New York State serving aboard warships in the Gulf of Mexico and gunboats on the Mississippi.

Of the entire business of getting out the military and naval vote by extraordinary measures, Welles remarked in his diary that "The subject is one that has not impressed me favorably . . . and yet it seems ungracious to oppose it." He came up with a solution that evidently satisfied Lincoln and Seward, but would also give sailors from every state equal treatment. When Charles Jones, the chairman of New York State's National Union (Republican) Central Committee, arrived in his office later in the day saying he wanted to sail with the fleet and extend this voting at sea to the "blockading squadrons" off the East Coast, Welles gave him "permission to go by the *Circassian*," a swift vessel used for carrying dispatches, and then "directed commanders to extend facilities to all voters."

AT ABOUT EIGHT o'clock that evening, Lincoln and his secretary John Hay left the White House and walked over to the War Department, ready to read the returns in the state elections just finishing in Indiana, Ohio, and Pennsylvania, whenever they arrived by telegraph. They found that Stanton, evidently fearing violent acts against the War Department building or its occupants, had locked the door and taken the keys upstairs with him. He had, however, left a messenger there, shivering as he walked back and forth in the moonlight on this cold night, and this man took them around to the side of the building occupied by the Navy Department, where they were let in through a side door. Lincoln, Stanton, and Hay settled down in the telegraph office.

As the evening went on, the first returns came in from Ohio. A most interesting Republican from there was elected to Congress on his first try: Rutherford B. Hayes, a four-times wounded colonel, soon to be a brigadier general. He had run for office while in uniform and was still serving under Philip Sheridan in the Valley; Hayes would go on to become the nineteenth president of the United States. The news from Ohio was good; surprisingly, strongly contested Indiana also began to turn out well for Lincoln.

The returns from Pennsylvania came in slowly and inconclusively. Interspersed with the ballots being cast in those three states were results from the soldiers from Ohio and Pennsylvania who could vote wherever they were. Lincoln's friend the reporter Henry Wing had been right when he said, "They'll vote the way they shoot." Hay noted of the early military vote, "the Ohio troops about ten to one for [National] Union [Party] and the Pennsylvanians less than three to one." The military result from the District of Columbia at Carver Army Hospital, a place where Lincoln and Mary, and Stanton, had visited the patients, "gave the heaviest opposition vote—about one out of three." When Lincoln read this tally, he turned to his secretary of war and said, "That's hard on us, Stanton—they know us better than the others." (As for others who saw much of Lincoln, Company K of the 150th Pennsylvania Volunteer Infantry, assigned to guard Lincoln at the Soldiers' Home and the White House, voted Republican, 63 to 11.)

During a lull between the incoming results, Lincoln took from his pocket a collection of stories by his favorite humorist, David R. Locke, who published his satirical letters under the pen name of Petroleum V. Nasby. He began reading what Hay described as "several chapters" aloud to his audience, which consisted of Hay, Secretary of War Stanton, Assistant Secretary of War Charles A. Dana, and the young military telegraph operators. One of these youths, David Homer Bates, who had heard Lincoln read Locke-Nasby's pieces aloud before, described the things the president enjoyed.

Some of Nasby's letters were irresistibly funny, especially those relating to the continuous struggle for the post-office at "Confedrit Cross Roads," and to the backwardness of some of our generals. Others referred to the

great excitement caused by the discovery of flowing oil-fields in Pennsyl-
vania, whereby great and sudden wealth had come to many formerly poor
farmers and others in that region. One catch phrase which Lincoln espe-
cially enjoyed repeating was, "Oil's well that ends well."

Hay, who found the readings "immensely amusing," said that Stanton and Dana "enjoyed them scarcely less than the president, who read on, *con amore*, until nine o'clock." Lincoln waited in the telegraph office past midnight, unsure of the overall result. He was particularly concerned about how the slowly arriving messages from Pennsylvania might turn out; in terms of electoral votes in the presidential election twenty-eight days away, to lose momentum now in Pennsylvania would be worse than losing Indiana. Finally, he sent his Pennsylvania operative and former secretary of war Simon Cameron this message.

Am leaving office to go home. How does it stand now?
A. Lincoln

The morning brought no reply from Cameron, but good news started coming in, first from Ohio. Lincoln's party had carried the state with an imposing majority of 50,000 votes. This was a smaller margin than he had received in the presidential election that took him to the White House in 1860, but the effect on Ohio's representation in the House of Representatives was that of a tidal wave. Before this state election, Ohio had fourteen Democratic congressmen and five Republicans. Now it would have seventeen Republicans in Congress, and only two Democrats. Among those unseated was "Sunset" Cox, who at the Democratic convention had hung his head in "a picture of despair" as the delegates accepted Vallandigham's resolution that the party commit itself to "immediate" peace talks. That had indeed become a defining issue, helping to bring him and other incumbents down; the Republican *Ohio State Journal* bade "Sunset" farewell with, "So good night, Mr. Cox."

Next came the news from Indiana, a state where the voting had worried Lincoln so much. The margin of victory was less than in Ohio—27,000 votes—but Governor Oliver Morton, who had fought the Copperhead ferment there with an arsenal of executive weapons that included the recent arrest and trial of several leaders of the Sons of Liberty, was reelected. Lincoln sent Morton a telegram saying, "Bravo, for Indiana, and for yourself personally." Indiana Republicans picked up four seats in Congress, and its legislature, dominated until this election by Democrats who had at one time created a situation in which Morton had no power to enact taxes to support the war effort, now had sixty Republicans and forty Democrats.

Pennsylvania remained in doubt. The soldier vote kept coming in from far-flung units, but it became clear that it would be days, perhaps weeks, before the overall result there could be tabulated. Both parties immediately began to act as if there were no doubt they had won in Pennsylvania, but the closeness of the returns demonstrated that the state would be strongly contested in November.

In the middle of all this, on the night after the three crucial state elections, Chief Justice Roger Brooke Taney died at his home on Indiana Avenue in Washington. Born a year after the signing of the Declaration of Independence, he was eighty-seven. Known for his ruling in the Dred Scott case that held that slaves were not citizens and had no standing to sue in a federal court, earlier in his life this native of Maryland had worked to improve the conditions of slaves and freed blacks, and had freed his own slaves long before the Civil War. Starting his public career at the time of the War of 1812, he had subsequently served in the Maryland senate and then as the state's attorney general. Taney went on to be the nation's secretary of the treasury and attorney general before being appointed chief justice of the Supreme Court by Andrew Jackson in 1835 and confirmed in the post the next year.

Taney's death now, after serving for twenty-eight years as chief justice, both swearing in Lincoln at his first inauguration and repeatedly clashing with him on constitutional issues, caused a feeling of relief among Republicans. That opinion was expressed by the New York socialite and diarist George Templeton Strong, chairman of the semiofficial United States Sanitary Commission that helped care for the Union sick and wounded, when he said, "Better late than never." Far harsher judgments were passed, but the ever-decent Welles did his best to give Taney his due:

> *That he had many good qualities and possessed ability, I do not doubt; that he rendered service in Jackson's administration is true, and during most of his judicial life he was upright and just. But the course pursued in*

the Dred Scott case and all the attending circumstances forfeited respect
for him as a man or a judge.

The immediate situation called for a decision as to what form of last
respects should be paid to an unpopular and in many ways discredited
chief justice of the Supreme Court. This judge, sworn in by Andrew Jackson, was a lifelong devout Roman Catholic. After a simple service at his
house in Washington, his body was to be taken to Frederick, Maryland,
where a requiem mass would be sung in the small Jesuit Church of St.
John's, which Taney had helped to build sixty years before. Then he
would be buried next to his mother's grave.

Lincoln consulted Welles as to what should be done. Thus far, as
Welles noted in his diary, "Seward thought it was his duty to attend the
funeral in this city but not farther, and advised that the President should
also." On the other hand, Attorney General Edward Bates, as the Federal
government's senior lawyer, felt that he should accompany the body on
the train to Maryland, and attend the funeral mass and burial. Welles told
Lincoln, "I thought the suggestions in regard to himself and Messrs.
Seward and Bates very well, and it would be best not to take official action
but to let each member of the Cabinet act his pleasure. For my own part,
I felt little inclined to participate."

The brief service at Taney's house began at 6 A.M., with Lincoln and
three of his cabinet attending, along with Taney's family and friends.
Then everyone entered carriages that followed a hearse to the nearby
rairoad station, and Lincoln waited until the train pulled out, carrying
Taney's casket and those closest to him. Bates, the only member of the
cabinet to attend the funeral in Frederick, was also the only cabinet member to have worked closely with Taney, and admired him more than did
the others. On the day after Taney died, Bates wrote in his diary some
praise and an inaccurate prediction:

> *He was a man of great and varied talent; a model of a presiding officer;*
> *and the last specimen within my knowledge, of a graceful and polished old*
> *fashioned gentleman.*
>
> *The luster of his fame, as a lawyer and a judge, is for the present,*
> *dimmed by the bitterness of party feeling arising out of his unfortunate*
> *judgment in the Dred Scott case. That was a great error; but it ought not*
> *and will not, for long, tarnish his otherwise well earned fame.*

In terms of presidential patronage, Taney's death gave Lincoln the opportunity to name a new justice of the Supreme Court—a permanent position far more prestigious than the other government posts that so many had sought during this election year. Lincoln had the option of giving a justice already on the court the chief justice position and bringing in another man as one of the nine justices, or to appoint someone not on the court directly as chief justice. John Hay would write to Nicolay, "It is a matter of the greatest importance that Mr. Lincoln has ever decided."

There was no lack of interest in the position. Justice Noah H. Swayne of Ohio had come onto the Court in 1862 through a campaign of self-promotion he began on the day in 1861 that Justice John McLean, another Ohioan, died. Before that day was out, Swayne had written then-Secretary of the Treasury Chase, another prominent figure from Ohio, "If you can deem it proper to give me your friendly support you will lay me under a lasting obligation." In a demonstration of how these things were done, Swayne picked up backing from Ohio's then-Governor William Dennison, now Lincoln's new postmaster general replacing Montgomery Blair, and, most importantly, Senator Ben Wade of Ohio, who was indebted to Swayne for the work he was doing to get him re-elected to the Senate in the election of 1862. Lincoln had appointed Swayne to the Court, and now Swayne wanted to be its chief justice.

Another man, also on the Court and wanting to lead it, was David Davis, Lincoln's old lawyer friend from Illinois whom he had rewarded for being his campaign manager in 1860 by naming him to the Court. Now Davis was immediately and strongly backed to become chief justice by James Gordon Bennett, who started filling the pages of his *New York Herald* with reasons why Lincoln should name him. A man who had performed great service to Lincoln and the Union also jumped into the picture: Secretary of War Stanton, also from Ohio. In prewar days, he had won a national reputation as an eminent lawyer; named as attorney general by President Buchanan in December of 1860 when Lincoln was president-elect and the secession crisis deepened, with the backing of War Democrats he had become Lincoln's secretary of war when he dismissed Cameron in 1862. Stanton wasted no time letting his interest be known: on the day after Taney's death, Supreme Court Justice Robert C. Grier, who had been on the court for eighteen years, wrote him, "I think that the President owes it to you." Stanton's wife, Ellen, enlisted former

Illinois senator Orville Browning to work on his behalf; when Browning went to his friend Lincoln's office to do this high policy-level lobbying for Stanton, Lincoln told him that Attorney General Bates was also asking for the position. From New York, Thurlow Weed started pushing for William M. Evarts, a Republican lawyer of great attainments, and the New York Court of Appeals sent Lincoln a letter unanimously endorsing Evarts.

Montgomery Blair, who had left the office of postmaster general gracefully when Lincoln asked him to do that, also wanted the high court post. An able lawyer who in prewar years had routinely argued cases before the Supreme Court, he had important backing, including that of his influential father, Lincoln's friend Francis P. Blair, Sr., who wrote Lincoln, "I think Montgomery's unswerving support of your administration in all its aspects coupled with his unfaltering attachment to you personally fits him to be your representative at the head of that Bench."

And then there was Salmon P. Chase, who had been startled this past June when Lincoln finally called his hand and accepted his fourth resignation as secretary of the treasury. The man who Welles thought still had "unextinguished" ambitions would indeed have preferred the presidency, but encouraged the supporters who now started working on his behalf. Two days after Taney died, Mary Lincoln's friend Radical Republican senator Charles Sumner of Massachusetts wrote Chase that he had written Lincoln "without delay," reminding the president of what he had said to Congressman Samuel Hooper the past spring: when Taney died, he intended to name Chase as his successor. To Chase, Sumner wrote, concerning a nomination Lincoln had yet to make, "Of course you will accept." Chase replied with the understatement that if the position were offered, "it is certainly not wrong to say to you that I would accept." (Although Mary Lincoln enjoyed the company of Sumner, a charming and erudite bachelor, she did not share his enthusiasm for Chase, who she rightly felt had given her husband so much trouble. She soon said to Francis P. Blair, Sr., "Mr. Blair, Chase and his friends are besieging my husband for the Chief-Justiceship. I wish you could prevent them.") When Chase sent Lincoln a friendly letter without mentioning the vacancy on the court, the president chuckled and handed the letter to Nicolay with the instruction, "File this with his other recommendations."

All these hats landed in the ring within a few days of Taney's death. Hay made this diary entry on the day after Taney died:

Already (before his poor old clay is cold) they are beginning to canvass vigorously for his successor. Chase men say the place is promised to their magnifico. . . .

I talked with the president one moment. He says he does not think he will make the appointment immediately. He will be, he says, rather "shut pan" in the matter at present.

On the day after Taney died, Maryland cast its ballots on the issue of adopting a new constitution that would abolish slavery. In a state that had many ties to the South and with many of its citizens still sympathetic to the Confederate cause, the civilian voters rejected the new constitution, 29,536 to 27,541. It was the absentee ballots from soldiers that changed things: they voted overwhelmingly to abolish slavery, 2,633 to 263, bringing the Maryland Constitution of 1864 into force on October 13 by a margin of 375 votes out of a total of 59,973 ballots cast.

On the night that these votes were being tallied in Baltimore, Lincoln was back in the War Department Telegraph Office. Young David Homer Bates was on duty, along with Major Thomas Eckert, chief of the War Department telegraph staff, and said that the "cipher operators were all there."

. . . we could not fail to notice that the President looked unusually weary and depressed as he sat down to scan the political field and consider the probabilities of his re-election, three weeks later.

After the results of the State elections two days before had been discussed, the conversation begun by him turned to the Presidential election, and he expressed himself as being not at all sure of re-election . . . after pondering the matter a short while, he reached for a cipher telegraph blank and wrote his own careful estimate of the electoral vote. . . .

He entered in one column the names of the eight States which he conceded to the McClellan-Pendleton ticket, giving them 114 electoral votes. In a second column he had entered the names of the States which he felt sure would cast 117 votes for the Administration. This showed only three more votes than he allowed McClellan. He did this from memory, making no mistake in the number of electoral votes to which each State was entitled, excepting that he omitted Nevada, which was about to come into the Union, and her three votes were added [in Lncoln's column] in Eckert's handwriting.

Lincoln was calculating a margin of victory thinner than the result of the Maryland vote for a new state constitution. He was being exceedingly cautious for the purposes of this calculation, ceding to McClellan not only the Border States, but also New York, Pennsylvania, Missouri, and his own state of Illinois. (By comparison, on this same day the clever Confederate agent Jacob Thompson, in Canada and still plotting destructive acts against the Union, wrote Jefferson Davis, "We now look upon the reelection of Lincoln as certain.") Lincoln knew that the results from the recent gubernatorial and congressional elections in Ohio and Indiana, with Pennsylvania still in doubt, indicated further success, but he also knew from a wealth of painful experience that a lot could happen in the twenty-three days before the election. In a speech to Marylanders living in Washington who came to serenade him at the White House in celebration of their new state constitution, Lincoln stressed that he was ready to accept defeat. In revealing and in some ways prophetic remarks, he stressed his commitment to an orderly transfer of power.

I therefore say, that if I shall live, I shall remain President until the fourth of next March; and that whoever shall be constitutionally elected therefore in November, shall be duly installed as President on the fourth of March; and that in the interval I shall do my utmost that whoever is to hold the helm for the next voyage, shall start with the best possible chance to save the ship.

Having expressed that, Lincoln made it equally clear that he believed that a vote for him would be best for the future of the United States. Referring to the choice before the public offered by the Democrats' "peace plank," he said:

If they should deliberately resolve to have immediate peace even at the loss of their country, and their liberty, I know not the power or the right to resist them. . . . I believe, however, they are still resolved to preserve their country and their liberty, and in this, in office or out of it, I am resolved to stand by them.

As for the Democrats, McClellan wrote to Democratic National Chairman August Belmont that he was receiving favorable reports concerning the forthcoming soldier vote, and wrote another political ally that Governor Horatio Seymour of New York had written him "that all is favorable in New York, & I hear that the Penna people feel very jubilant." He followed this, to the same correspondent, with, "All the news I hear is *very* favorable. There is every reason to be most hopeful."

VII

No one could ever say that Jubal Early did not try to thwart the Union war effort in every way he could. Since Sheridan defeated him at Winchester and Fishers Hill, he had been forced to watch from farther up the Shenandoah Valley as Sheridan's men wreaked havoc in its fertile areas. Bringing into horrid reality Grant's vision of making the Valley "a barren waste," starting on September 26 the Union cavalry began a period when, as a soldier from Rhode Island described it, "the fire demon reigned supreme." For ten days, Sheridan's men destroyed everything: barns, grist mills, factories, and some miles of railroad track. Whatever crops and livestock the Federal horsemen did not burn or kill were seized and carried off for the Union Army's food supply. Shocked and frightened residents saw the night skies of the Valley constantly bright from flames. Terrible reprisals and counterreprisals took place between Confederate John Singleton Mosby's guerilla Rangers and bands of Northern irregulars.

Starting at the end of September, Sheridan inexplicably and uncharacteristically began to change his immensely aggressive movements in the Valley. He kept up the destruction but, on October 1, wired Grant that he thought it best "to let the burning of the crops in the Valley be the end of this campaign, and let some of this army go somewhere else." Sheridan explained that he could not protect the undestroyed railroad lines in his possession, which might still prove useful, without weakening his overall force, and added that he no longer had the wagons required to carry the supplies for major movements. In accordance with this, he started pulling his forces back down the Valley, giving up some territory that his cavalrymen had scorched. His desire was to move his Army of the Shenandoah somewhat closer to Grant's much larger forces operating to the east.

Grant felt that Sheridan underestimated his own potential and had an exaggerated idea of what strength Early might have left, but he did not force the issue. After more fighting and Federal destruction in the Valley, there was still a difference of opinion between Grant and Sheridan concerning the strategy to be employed in northern Virginia.

Stanton entered the picture. Usually more of an administrator than a man wishing to influence military operations, he worried that Lee could profit from this, holding Grant and the Army of the Potomac locked along the Petersburg-Richmond line while Sheridan changed front to redirect his campaign. Stanton saw that the Union Army must keep up its momentum everywhere: Sherman was at Atlanta, with his next movements unclear, and Grant and Sheridan had to work together effectively in Virginia. On October 13, right after the state elections and Taney's death, Stanton was thinking about his chances of becoming chief justice, but that did not cloud his view of the war. He wired Sheridan that he should come to Washington. "If you can come here," he said, "a consultation on several points is extremely desirable. I propose to visit General Grant and would like to see you first."

Thus it was that Sheridan, taking four staff officers with him, started for Washington on October 15. He could not have picked a worse moment to do that. Lee was every bit as aggressive a general as Grant, and wanted Early to start something big, and soon. On October 12, he sent Early a dispatch from his headquarters in Petersburg that emphasized his wishes. Talking about the reinforcements he had sent Early, Lee said, "I have weakened myself very much to strengthen you. It was done with the expectation of enabling you to gain such success that you could return the troops if not rejoin me yourself." Lee laid down some recommendations concerning how Early should handle his force, but the thrust of what he said had an uncanny similarity to Grant's advice to Sheridan a month before when he told Sheridan to "pounce" on Early if he had the chance. Sensing that Sheridan might intend to make major adjustments in the placement of his army, Lee told Early that if he could catch Sheridan in a vulnerable situation, "you had better move against him and crush him." He also told Early that he thought he was overestimating Sheridan's strength (exactly what Grant felt that Sheridan was doing, in regard to Early) and that Early had a chance to strike an enormous blow for the Confederacy if he would just pull everything together. "With your united force," he said firmly, "it can be accomplished."

Early went to work. On Tuesday, October 18, while Sheridan was on the first leg of a two-day trip back to his army from meeting with Stanton in Washington and receiving permission to continue his repositioning, Early met with his generals near a massive land feature known as Massanutten Mountain, a forty-seven-mile-long ridge running from south to north in the Valley. Its northern end was just west of Fishers Hill. In keeping with his overall strategy, Sheridan had brought his 30,000-man army back down the valley past Fishers Hill, where he had completed his victory over Early at Winchester a month before, and had them encamped in defensive positions along Cedar Creek, a tributary of the North Fork of the Shenandoah River. Sheridan's army had 12,000 more men than Early had, and it seemed unlikely that even the resolute Early could make a major attack so soon after having his forces routed and scattered at Fishers Hill.

Early saw the possibility of approaching Cedar Creek through a plan conceived by his remarkable subordinate Major General John B. Gordon of Georgia, a man who entered the Confederate Army with no previous military training and became the captain of a company of volunteers called the "Raccoon Roughs." After promotions and service at Seven Pines and Antietam, Gordon went on to command a noted brigade of Georgians at Chancellorsville, Gettysburg, the Wilderness, and Spotsylvania, before becoming a division commander under Early in the Valley.

For two days, Gordon had been personally scouting the parts of Massanutten Mountain nearest the big Union encampment, while the rest of Early's army quietly came into the area and organized itself for an attack for which the orders had yet to be issued. Gordon came up with one of the most daring schemes of the war. The weakest point in Sheridan's positions along Cedar Creek was its left flank; from the defenders' point of view, it seemed almost impossible that the Confederates could approach from that direction in any strength. To mount an attack, many thousands of men would have to materialize from Massanutten Mountain ready for battle, cross the North Fork of the Shenandoah River, and continue on over open ground in battle formation.

Gordon had the answer. He would lead the 8,000 men of his Second Corps on a night march along a trail, one long treacherous part of it running along the Massanutten ridge, high above the Shenandoah's South Fork. Before dawn, they would come down from the slope, cross the North Fork at a shallow point, and hit the Union left flank with a surprise attack while it was still dark. The other major units would attack simultaneously from other directions, with one small unit assigned to dash toward Sheridan's headquarters, a limestone house in the middle of the Federal positions, and capture him. (The intelligence concerning the Union defenses was excellent, but Early had no idea that Sheridan was not there, and would be sleeping that night eleven miles north of Cedar Creek at Winchester, on his way back from Washington.) Every man had to be in place by 5 A.M., ready to attack. Early and his commanders knew they had a real chance to pull off a great, desperately needed coup, something to rival Chancellorsville, the Union defeat that left Lincoln pacing his office distractedly muttering, "What will the people say? What will the people say?"—perhaps "saying" it this time with their votes in the upcoming election.

For Early, it was truly a now-or-never moment. He understood the importance Lee attached to his achieving a major success, and he also knew that if his men were to continue functioning they had to break through to a part of the Valley where there was still some food. Sheridan had denuded much of the land through which Early's men had marched to attempt this massive strategic counterattack, and they were hungry. Early, his commanders, and most of the men understood that everything now depended on surprise: even a few hours' notice of this intricate approach through the night would leave them facing a superior force, well prepared to cut them down as they crossed a river and moved across the final stretches of open ground.

Under a moon three days past the full, Gordon's men silently moved single file for miles along the trail, sometimes beside the water and sometimes high on the ridge, a route so narrow it was known as a "pig's path." To make sure that not a single one of these thousands of men went astray, couriers from corps headquarters were posted like human signposts in the moonlight at some of the forks on the slopes. As his men kept on with their secret march along cliffs high above the river, Gordon described what he saw: ". . . the long gray line like a great serpent glided noiselessly along the dim pathway above the precipice."

The attack came off as planned. Emerging with fixed bayonets out of the still-dark fog along the riverbank at dawn, Gordon's thousands of men completely surprised the lightly defended Union left-flank positions. As the shooting began, most of the Northern soldiers were asleep in their tents. Many ran away wearing only their underwear. The fog filled with the eerie yip-yip-yip of the rebel yell. One Union soldier described that sound as "a regular wildcat screech," and another wrote: "You have to feel it, and if you say you did not feel it, you have *never* been there."

As the Union soldiers on the left flank fled, the other Confederate units attacked the larger Union forces stationed farther to the north on Cedar Creek, routing the 9,000-man Union Eighth Corps, which was soon followed to the rear by the smaller Nineteenth Corps. Only the Union soldiers farthest up the stream, the men of Horatio Wright's Sixth Corps, the troops who wore the Greek Cross insignia and had arrived in Washington to defend the capital during Early's July raid, pulled themselves together and started firing back, but in thirty minutes this attack out of the still-dark fog sent as many as 15,000 panic-stricken Federal troops reeling back to the north, reduced to what a witness described as "a disorganized, routed, demoralized, terrified mob." A soldier from New York said the men running were "simply insane with fear," and a volunteer from Vermont offered this explanation: "That these men were brave no one doubts; their previous brilliant conduct had amply shown it; but a night surprise, total and terrific, is too trying for the *morale* of the best troops in the world to survive."

On his way back to his army from Washington, Sheridan had spent the night at the house of a tobacco merchant named Lloyd Logan in Winchester. While away from his army, he had thought things were probably under control, but early on the day he reached Winchester he had been handed an intercepted Confederate message to Early from Longstreet. It told Early that he was on the way with a powerful reinforcement; Early should "Be ready to move as soon as my forces join you and we will crush Sheridan." Sheridan thought this was probably a ruse, as it was, but it prompted him to send a message to Sixth Corps commander Horatio Wright, in whose charge he had left his Army of the Shenandoah. He told Wright to "make your position strong . . . look well to your ground and be well prepared." Wright replied that everything was quiet and that he would make a personal reconnaissance at dawn the next day—the time for which the rebel attack was planned, by which time any scouting would be too late. Feeling that things were under control and knowing that he was only twelve miles from his army's encampment, Sheridan went to sleep in Winchester.

At dawn, an officer of Sheridan's staff awoke him with the report that cannons could be heard firing from the direction of Cedar Creek. At this point, Sheridan evidently did not hear the cannons himself. Thinking that this was probably part of a reconnaissance in force that Wright might have under way, Sheridan was not worried. He dressed and went down to breakfast. As he ate and dealt with paperwork, the same officer of his staff brought him more reports of gunfire to the south. Sheridan asked the man if he thought it sounded as if a battle was under way and was told the shooting did not sound widespread.

At nine o'clock, Sheridan mounted Rienzi; with his staff he rode south out of Winchester, picking up his escort of 300 horsemen from the 17th Pennsylvania Cavalry. By now, the cannon fire was loud and frequent; using a technique he had learned during his prewar Indian-fighting days in the West, Sheridan dismounted and knelt down, putting his ear to the ground to judge the distance from which the sound of explosions was coming. That settled it: not only was a battle under way, but the guns were moving his way moment by moment, indicating that his men were retreating before a rapid Confederate advance.

Coming over to the top of a rise in the road, Sheridan's staff officer Lieutenant Colonel James Forsyth said they encountered "the appalling spectacle of a panic-stricken army—hundreds of slightly wounded men, throngs of others unhurt but utterly demoralized, and baggage-wagons by the score, all pressing to the rear in hopeless confusion."

For a moment, Sheridan considered whether he should stop right there, rally these troops, and prepare to make this a line of defense into which everyone else retreating this way could be placed. But that was not Philip Sheridan. Ordering two of his staff and twenty Pennsylvania troopers to follow him, Sheridan spurred Rienzi toward Cedar Creek; a young orderly galloped behind him, carrying a swallow-tailed cavalry standard, a battle flag displaying the two stars that identified the man riding ahead of it as a major general. Sheridan and Rienzi picked up a 50-yard lead on the others, blazing toward his army.

Long lines of discouraged Union soldiers were coming the other way, most of them no longer terrified, weapons in their hands but separated from their officers and looking for leadership. Without stopping, Sheridan waved his campaign hat as he thundered past, shouting, "Come on back, boys! Give 'em hell, God damn 'em! We'll make coffee out of Cedar Creek tonight!" Men started to turn around and go back the way they had come; as he galloped along, Sheridan shouted to others, "Come on back! Face the other way. We're going to lick those fellows out of their boots!" More men turned around, but at points along the road there was such confusion, so many cannon mixed up with ambulances and supply wagons, all still retreating, that Sheridan and his small galloping group had to veer off the road and dash through fields just to keep going. Nonetheless, many men were eager to reorganize and go back and fight. Twenty-one-year-old Captain William McKinley of Brigadier General George Crook's staff caught sight of Sheridan's two-star flag racing south; the future twenty-fifth president of the United States, who had earlier served in the Valley under future president Rutherford B. Hayes, knew that the speeding flag expressed an order: Follow me into battle, every man of you. McKinley quickly began spreading the word to head back toward Cedar Creek.

As he galloped into an area three miles north of Cedar Creek, Sheridan saw his rear guard making a stand behind a slapped-together barricade of fence rails. (They had found some time to do this because many of Early's hungry men had stopped to loot the rations in the Union encampment.) Sheridan announced his arrival in the most dramatic way imaginable. He soared above the barricade on his massive black horse, landing in an open area. Wheeling Rienzi around where his soldiers could see him for a hundred yards in either direction, he bellowed, "Men, by God, we'll whip 'em yet! We'll sleep in our old tents tonight!"

He was ready to die for them; they were ready to die for him. A roar went up along the line. A major who witnessed it said that a change took place "instantly." "Hope and confidence returned at a bound. . . . Now we all burned to attack the enemy, to drive him back, to retrieve our honor and sleep in our old camps that night. And every man knew that Sheridan would do it."

There was hard fighting ahead, with many losses on both sides, but first Sheridan divided his time between consulting with his officers, reorganizing the situation, and letting the rest of his men, many of whom kept coming back from their retreat, see that he was indeed there. The re-forming line of Sheridan's army stretched through the woods north of Cedar Creek; at noon, with his hat in his hand, Sheridan started riding past regiment after regiment, producing what another witness called "a deafening cheer." He stopped repeatedly to tell men who crowded around him that it was their turn now, and promised them that they would sleep that night in the tents they had abandoned at dawn. Then he continued the placement of units that had been scattered during the morning.

At four in the afternoon, Sheridan launched his massive counterattack. As in the final hour at the Winchester battle, he did everything he could to strike fear into the enemy and throw everything he had into one massive assault. Two hundred buglers sounded the call to charge, and thousands of men moved forward. A soldier from New York observed that the troops fought with the spirit that Sheridan's dramatic leadership gave them: "The men were inspired with new hope, and they went in with a will." For half an hour, the outnumbered Confederates stood their ground bravely, and then they broke. Sheridan rode forward among his advancing men, shouting "Give 'em hell!" and "Put a twist on 'em!" An eighteen-year-old captain from South Carolina bitterly called the retreat "the grandest stampede of the Southern Army." The gallant and able Confederate leader John Gordon said, "Regiment after regiment, brigade after brigade, in rapid succession was crushed . . . the superb commands crumbled to pieces." For an hour, singly and in groups, Early's defeated soldiers kept dashing back through the waters of Cedar Creek, which they had forded so silently and skillfully in the foggy dawn. By five-thirty, Sheridan had kept his promise to his men that they would again be in their encampment, but in keeping with Grant's philosophy that a battle was never over and a routed enemy must be pursued, Sheridan did what he had done at Chattanooga's Missionary Ridge the year before. He sent his cavalry across Cedar Creek, and they chased the retreating Confederates until between ten and eleven that night.

Once again, Early had to write Lee a painful report: he went into some detail, but summed it up with, "The state of things was distressing and mortifying beyond measure." He would be criticized, but he also said something to Lee that no one in the North or South could ever deny: "I have labored faithfully to gain success." During the course of 1864, Early and his men would march 1,670 miles in and around the Shenandoah Valley, with his units participating in 75 engagements.

It had been a remarkable day. A soldier from New Hampshire wrote of Sheridan, "We believe that not another man in America could have got that victory out of that army." At ten that night, Sheridan sent a coded telegram to Grant from Cedar Creek. Not a man to minimize his accomplishments, he indicated what he had done, and praised his soldiers.

I have the honor to report that my army at Cedar Creek was attacked this morning and my left was turned and driven in confusion. In fact most of the line was driven in confusion with the loss of twenty pieces of artillery—I hastened from Winchester. . . . I here took the affair in hand . . . I attacked with great vigor driving and routing the enemy capturing according to last report forty three pieces of artillery and very many prisoners. . . . Affairs at time[s] looked badly but by the gallantry of our officers and men disaster has been converted into a splendid victory.

Sheridan would follow this with a later message saying in part, "For ten miles on the line of retreat the roads and country were covered with small arms [muskets] thrown away by the flying rebels," but he added soberly, "My loss in killed and wounded will be between three and four thousand." (Early lost just under 3,000.)

By the time these totals were established, Sheridan's fame had surpassed that of Meade, the victor at Gettysburg, and was second only to that of Grant and Sherman. Putting aside any recent differences concerning strategy in northern Virginia, on the day after Cedar Creek, Grant wired this from his City Point headquarters to Stanton, who along with Lincoln had thought Sheridan too young to command the Army of the Shenandoah: "I had a salute of one hundred guns from each of the Armies here fired in honor of Sheridan's last victory. Turning what bid fare [*sic*] to be a disaster into glorious victory stamps Sheridan what I have always thought of him, one of the ablest of Generals."

The news came to Lincoln at an interesting time. The day after Cedar Creek, he had issued the "Proclamation of Thanksgiving" suggested to him by a woman the year before, the day for the holiday to be then and thereafter, as the document put it, "the last Thursday in November." The next evening, citizens of Washington converged on the White House to celebrate Sheridan's victory. The *Chronicle* described the spectacle.

[A torchlight parade] passed through the grounds in front of the Presidential Mansion, where a large crowd had gathered, and kept up a continual blaze of light with rockets, blue-lights, Roman-candles, &c., lighting up the upper windows under the portico, at which stood the President and "little Thad [Tad]." . . . After the procession had left the grounds, the crowd called loudly for the President, and he responded. . . .

Lincoln was exhausted and had not planned to speak, but, in begin-ning his short response to this demonstration, he told the crowd, "I pro-pose that you give three hearty cheers for Sheridan." That done, he added, "While we are at it we may well consider how fortunate it was for the Sesech [the secessionist Confederate soldiers] that Sheridan was a very little man. If he had been a large man, there is no knowing what he would have done with them." Lincoln finished with this: "I propose three cheers for General Grant, who knew to what use to put Sheridan; three cheers for all our noble commanders and the soldiers and sailors; three cheers for people everywhere who cheer the soldiers and sailors of the Union—and now, good night." The following day, Lincoln wrote Sheridan, "With great pleasure I tender to you and your brave army, the thanks of the Nation, and my own personal admiration and gratitude, for the month's operations in the Shenandoah Valley; and particularly for the splendid work of October 19, 1864."

Four nights after Cedar Creek, Sheridan was asleep in the limestone house at Belle Grove, the headquarters that a special Confederate unit had been assigned to raid in an attempt to capture him in the dawn attack, when an aide awakened him. Assistant Secretary of War Charles A. Dana had arrived from Washington and wanted to see him immediately. It was some hours after midnight. Not too happy about being gotten out of bed, Sheridan appeared; Dana told him that his commission as major general of Volunteers would soon be changed to the more prestigious and perma-nent rank of major general in the Regular Army—an extraordinary honor for an officer just eleven years out of West Point.

The next day, Sheridan invited Dana to accompany him as he visited the different units of his army. "I was struck," Dana wrote, "in riding through the lines, by the universal demonstration of personal affection for Sheridan." Dana had seen many of the Union Army's commands, and the relationship of enlisted men and officers to their generals, but he said to Sheridan of this warmth and enthusiasm, "I have never seen anything like it. Tell me what is the reason?"

The exchange that ensued revealed Sheridan as something other than a fearless swashbuckler. When he said "My practice has always been to fight in the front rank," Dana remarked that Sheridan could easily be killed doing that.

Sheridan agreed, but said, "That is the reason the men like me. They know that when the hard pinch comes I am exposed just as much as any of them."

Dana asked, "But are you never afraid?"

"If I was I should not be ashamed of it," Sheridan said. "If I should follow my natural impulse, I should run away always at the beginning of the danger; the men who say they are never afraid in a battle do not tell the truth."

Sheridan, who had been cautioned by Lincoln and Stanton that if he marched his Army of the Shenandoah into a disaster it could lose the election for "the party in power," had not only won a great victory just before the presidential election, but his swift and dramatic ride on Rienzi from Winchester to Cedar Creek produced something else. Moved by the story of Cedar Creek, a minor poet named Thomas Buchanan Read wrote a poem to which he gave the title "Sheridan's Ride." On the night of November 1, seven days before the election, the famous actor James E. Murdoch first presented it in an emotional reading before a crowd in Cincinnati's Pike Opera Hall gathered there for a Sanitary Commission fair—one of the events held in Northern cities to benefit sick and wounded soldiers. "Sheridan's Ride" received an immense ovation and immediately began appearing in newspapers throughout the Union. The poet had the distance from Winchester to Cedar Creek wrong—it was eleven miles, not twenty—but he certainly brought forth the American response to the idea of the cavalry coming to the rescue—in this case, one bold cavalryman on a splendid black horse.

Rienzi was the hero of the seven stanzas, dashing toward the sound of the guns as he carried Sheridan ever closer to Cedar Creek. At the end of thirty-two lines, "Every nerve of the charger was strained to full play/With Sheridan only ten miles away." Another eight lines, and "He is snuffing the smoke of the roaring fray/With Sheridan only five miles away." Rienzi speaks; Sheridan does not. When Rienzi gallops onto the scene at Cedar Creek, "He seemed to the whole great army to say: 'I have brought you Sheridan all the way/From Winchester down to save the day.'"

The public went wild over the final verse.

Hurrah! Hurrah for Sheridan!
Hurrah for horse and man!
And when their statues are placed on high

Under the dome of the Union sky,
The American soldier's Temple of Fame;
There, with the glorious general's name,
Be it said, in letters both bold and bright:
"Here is the steed that saved the day
By carrying Sheridan into the fight,
From Winchester — twenty miles away!"

At a tent headquarters in the Valley, Sheridan did not know of the poem until an officer brought him one of the many papers in which it was appearing. As he became aware of the surge of patriotic feeling and support for "the party in power" that the poem was producing, Sheridan observed of the public reaction, "The thing they seem to like best about it is the horse." Writing to the poet, he said, using the word "genius" loosely and perhaps sensing that this poem would be recited by generations of schoolboys in the North, "Your genius has put us into the same boat for the long journey, and we must try to take along the black horse."

THIRTEEN

THE FINAL MILE TO THE POLLS: ROCKS, SMOOTH PLACES, PUZZLES

On the day that Sheridan's men fought the battle of Cedar Creek in Virginia, the long arm of the Confederacy struck in an entirely different area. For more than a week, polite and friendly young men in hunting clothes had been checking into a hotel at St. Albans, Vermont, a quiet town fifteen miles south of the Canadian border. The gathering grew to be twenty-five in number; they explained that they had come from St. John's, in Canada, to participate in a hunting trip.

At three in the afternoon on October 20, these hunters split into three groups and entered the town's three banks. They drew their pistols, identified themselves as Confederate soldiers, and walked out with a total of $208,000, to be used to finance guerrilla activities. As these men, who had escaped to Canada from Northern prisoner-of-war camps, stole horses for their flight back across the border, some townsmen resisted; one resident was killed and another wounded. In Canada, the authorities arrested the raiders and returned the $88,000 found on them when they were jailed. A diplomatic contretemps ensued—the Canadian government freed the Confederates, saying that Canada was neutral and that these men were soldiers acting under military orders—but the far larger result was that the Northern public demanded additional protection, which could come only from Union soldiers who were needed far to the south.

Generals as well as civilians worried about being unprepared for surprise attacks far from the battlefronts. The day before the raid on St. Albans, Major General John A. Dix, in command at New York City, wrote Grant that he had only a few hundred men to protect against violence in a city that he described as having "more disaffection and disloyalty, independent of the elements of mischief and disturbance always present here, than in any other city in the Union." There were credible reports of potential trouble: Seward wrote New York mayor George Opdyke that he had received information about a well-organized plot to set large fires and cause other disruption in Manhattan at the time of the election.

This led to Grant's giving General B. F. Butler an assignment for which he was singularly well suited. After correspondence with Dix, Meade, and Stanton, Grant wired Butler on November 1, a week before the election, saying that he had a request from Stanton "asking me to send more troops to the City of New York, and if possible to let you go there until after the election." Butler wired Grant two hours later, "Will start in an hour."

Butler, the ultimate political appointee as a general and an officer who had repeatedly demonstrated varying degrees of ineptitude as a combat leader, was perfect for the task of keeping order in this city where draft riots had left a hundred dead the year before. A skilled Massachusetts politician who knew how to play off the New York factions, he locked down Manhattan before anyone knew what had happened. Persuading Grant that General Dix should remain in official command while he had hands-on authority over "the troops sent to preserve peace in the State of New York," Butler commandeered the large Hoffman House hotel for his headquarters. In a quick showdown, he ordered a major general of state militia not to mobilize his less disciplined and somewhat unreliable troops. Fully aware that there were "several thousand secessionists" in the city, he came up with a brilliant way of maximizing the services of both the Navy and the veteran soldiers who had been assigned to him but had not yet arrived.

> *I made an arrangement with the manager of the Western Union Telegraph Company to bring into a room at my headquarters adjoining my office telegraph lines from more than sixty points. There was one line from High Bridge, where a gunboat was stationed, lest somebody should attempt to break an aqueduct which brought water into the city. There*

was another line from a gunboat anchored opposite Mackerelville, which was supposed to contain the worst population in New York; and still another from a gunboat anchored so as to cover the Sub-Treasury Building and the Customs House on Wall Street and the United States Arsenal.

Butler's masterstroke involved the ferryboats that operated from nine docks at different points around Manhattan Island.

The ferry-boats could each accommodate more than a regiment of infantry in their saloons, and . . . as many as four pieces of artillery and their equipment. I determined therefore to take possession of four of the larger ferry-boats, and place two on the North [Hudson] River and two on the east [East River] side of the city. . . . From my headquarters I could communicate with them by the telegraph lines, so that in case of a gathering of rioters in any part of the city I could throw four regiments there, if need be, in less time than I could march them from any place of encampment in the city.

Thus, with these forces soon in place and working closely with New York's police department—he had one of his army officers, in plain clothes, ready to stand by with detectives at each polling place—Butler had prepared for violence, but he had an added instinct for how to make his authoritative presence known. Hearing rumors that he was staying inside his headquarters for fear he "should be assassinated," he had an aide reserve a box at the opera. Wearing a new uniform, Butler appeared there, where he and his staff were "received with some applause." During the intermission, it was reported to him that the Democratic national chairman and New York millionaire August Belmont was also at the performance, and that Belmont was offering a double-barreled bet to anyone who would take it: "a thousand dollars that the election would go for McClellan, and another thousand that gold would go up to 300 by the morning of the election." Butler sent word from his box to Belmont's that he would take that bet, "but Mr. Belmont declined." To reinforce the image of who was in charge in New York City, he and his staff went riding in Central Park, their horses looking worn and tired after military campaigning and "having met bad weather at sea" while being shipped to the city. Butler commented that he and those officers, several in uniforms they had been wearing at the front, looked like a set of desperadoes. He said, "We might have been stopped by the police," except for "our well-blacked cavalry boots, and our wicked-looking sabers clanking against the spur and stirrup, and the neatly cased revolvers fast to the belt on the left side."

Moving swiftly in what was in essence a one-man military occupation of Manhattan, the next evening Butler began his intervention in the workings of August Belmont's world of Wall Street. Getting off a train from Washington, John A. Stewart, the Federal assistant treasurer in New York, went straight to the Hoffmann House to tell Butler of a conversation he had had with Lincoln earlier in the day. When Stewart explained to Lincoln that speculators in New York had it in their power to conspire and "throw the price of gold no one knows how high," a situation that he told the president would "bankrupt any treasury," Lincoln replied: "General Butler is in command in New York. I don't see exactly what he can do, but if anything can be done, he is the man to do it, and I wish he would do anything that he believes will be for the good of the country. Say this from me to him."

The next day, Butler summoned to his headquarters H. J. Lyons, a businessman from a firm in Montreal who had been in New York for eleven months. Stewart had given Butler documents indicating that in the past two weeks Lyons had, according to Butler, "bought and paid for and sent out of the country upwards of twelve million dollars of gold," and had in vaults in New York more than "three million dollars in gold." When Butler asked him, "Is that so?" Lyons answered, "I cannot give the actual amount from memory, but you are substantially correct."

Butler had learned a lot during his years in Boston as a politician, and had also been a successful criminal lawyer. He laid out what could be done to Lyons, who replied, "Then I suppose I am to be arrested, General?"

Here it came: a deal. Butler explained it.

No, Mr. Lyons. . . . To punish you is not my business now, providing you will aid me in preventing the success of this conspiracy to raise the price of gold to three hundred. You can do it, and if you will keep gold down [until the day after the election] . . . I will give you my honor that you shall go where you please and take your gold with you . . . if the election is determined in favor of Lincoln it is of no consequence where the gold goes after that. . . . I make no threats, but I do tell you that if gold goes to three hun-

dred on election morning I shall know it, and I shall also know where to
find you and your gold.

Lyons understood. "I think, General, I will sell all my gold right off." Butler gave him a secular benediction: "I think that would be wise, and I will approve of it." The price of gold stayed within the limits Butler set. What the financial and political worlds learned of this private arrangement never became known, but prominent New Yorkers, Democrats as well as Republicans, were grateful for all that did and did not happen during Butler's time in the city. There would be some violence—nothing like what they believed would have occurred if he had not been running things from the Hoffman House—and before he left they held a large and lavish banquet in his honor at the elegant new Fifth Avenue Hotel.

II

In his office, Lincoln continued to balance his time between the election bearing down on him and the continuing duties of his office. In these days before the election, he signed a document, "Approval of First Hundred Miles of Union Pacific Railroad," which refined the previously undetermined route: it was to start west from the existing railhead at Omaha, Nebraska. At this time, too, postal money orders were instituted; devised to help soldiers send part of their pay home or to enable their families to send them money, they also served the entire population. In an entirely different area of what he considered to be his responsibility to the public, he wrote thanking a Mrs. George W. Swift, of Falmouth, Massachusetts, for "Your complimentary little poem, asking for my autograph. . . . I thank you for it, and cheerfully comply with your request."

Inevitably, the combination of the political and the military, present in Lincoln's life every day of 1864, influenced virtually all that he said and did. When the 189th New York Volunteers were paraded in front of the White House on their way to the Virginia front, Lincoln addressed them from the steps. He began with this politically nonpartisan observation: "It is said that we have the best [form of] Government the world has ever known, and I am glad to meet you, the supporters of that Government. To you who render the hardest work in its support should be given the greatest credit." Few mainstream Democrats could have taken issue with that, but a sentence later Lincoln added this: "While others differ with the Administration and, perhaps, [have done so] honestly, the soldiers have sustained it; they have not only fought right, they have voted right, and I for one thank you for it."

Something else, that on the surface seemed simply to involve the westward growth of the nation, was Lincoln's "Proclamation Admitting Nevada into the Union," which he signed on October 31, a week before the election. (To become official, the entire text of the constitution of the new state had to be received in Washington; it was said to be the longest telegram ever sent, to that date.) From the Republican point of view, this was by no means government business as usual; as soon as Lincoln signed that document, Nevada residents could vote in the election now eight days away, and it seemed certain that they and their three electoral votes would be for Lincoln.

The sense of humor that had seen Lincoln through so much showed itself in an endorsement he penned on a letter that Seward had sent over for him to see, a letter written by an unidentified man who told the secretary of state that in this last phase, the Democrats' "opposition policy for the Presidential Campaign will be to *abstain from voting*." Concentrating on the word "abstain," Lincoln jotted down his reaction to this improbable scenario: "More likely to abstain from *stopping* once they get at it, until they shall have voted several times each." In yet another comment, when Congressman Elihu Washburne wrote him a letter from Illinois saying, "There is imminent danger of losing the State," Lincoln wrote on the envelope the dismissive observation "Stampeded."

A matter unlike others was the subject of a letter written to Lincoln from New York on October 26 by Myer Isaacs of New York City. Isaacs, then twenty-three years old, was the son of a prominent New York rabbi. A lawyer who had graduated at the top of his class at New York University, Isaacs was the secretary of the Board of Delegates of American Israelites, started by his father in 1859 to be what Myer called the "central organization" of the American Jewish community. He wrote to Lincoln on learning that a group of Jews had met with the president at the White House some days before. Isaacs characterized it as being a "visitation" to Lincoln "on the part of persons claiming to represent the Israelites of New York or the United States and pledging the 'Jewish vote' to your support, and, I am informed, succeeding in a deception that resulted in their pecuniary profit."

This was a supposition that Lincoln had made a deal, in some way buying the "Jewish vote." Isaacs went on to say that, while he believed that most American Jews supported Lincoln, "There is no 'Jewish vote'— if there were, it could not be bought." He felt that Lincoln had "been imposed upon by irresponsible men" who had no authority to make "any such representations as those understood to have been made."

The only detailed description of this meeting came from Noah Brooks, the California journalist and Lincoln's friend, who was frequently in the White House. Referring to events of October 18, he wrote this, which appeared in the *Sacramento Daily Union*.

> *Yesterday a deputation of Jews from Chicago, New York, Philadelphia and Boston called upon the President to present him with an address, assuring him that their people, as a body, were in favor of his re-election. These men were chiefly priests, and assured the President that they had heretofore mingled in politics, and that the address presented had been read and adopted in their synagogues throughout the country.*
>
> *The President thanked them for their good wishes and promises, and reminded them that he was only the exponent of the wishes and opinions of a portion of the loyal States, and while he was President had no right to seek personal political favors at the hands of any, but believed that the support of the principles of the so-called Union party of the country . . . was a more effectual way of putting down the rebellion than the contrary course.*
>
> *The delegation departed, hugely pleased at their reception, and wonderfully surprised at the frank, simple way with which the President disposed of their address.*

After this description of the meeting, Brooks added this personal observation, which appeared in the California paper as part of the story. "We might be induced to give more weight to this unusual movement, were it not for the fact that men of Hebraic descent are, (in these parts at least), notoriously given to Copperhead—not to say secesh [secessionist]— proclivities."

The letter from Isaacs about the meeting described by Brooks arrived in the White House mail on November 1; on Lincoln's instructions, John Hay answered it the same day, and said:

You are in error in the assumptions you make in regard to the circumstances of the recent interview to which you refer, between certain gentlemen of the Hebrew faith, and the President. No pledge of the Jewish vote was made by these gentlemen and no inducements or promises were extended to them by the President, and received no such response as you seem to suppose.

The President deems this response due to you, and thanks you for your letter.

That letter written by Hay dealt with a specific letter of concern, but another letter was also written from New York on October 26, by Samuel A. Lewis, who was associated with an interesting figure named Isachar Zacharie, Lincoln's podiatrist. The London-born Zacharie, who had treated the feet of Stanton, Seward, and a number of Union generals, first worked on the president's feet in 1862; during their conversations, he gained Lincoln's confidence. The president had sometimes discussed with him the concerns of American Jews, and evidently used Zacharie in one or more missions to ascertain conditions in New Orleans. (There was also a less authenticated account that, acting as an informal emissary, Zacharie had a meeting in Richmond with the Confederate secretary of state Judah P. Benjamin, who was also Jewish, to discuss possible ways of ending the war.)

In this letter to Lincoln that arrived about the same time that the one from Isaacs did, it became clear that Zacharie's friend Lewis had heard of the same White House meeting that had troubled Isaacs. He explained that he was acting on behalf of Zacharie, who "will be away frequently between now and the election," and said that, according to "our friend Dr. Zacharie . . . some parties representing themselves as 'a committee from the Jews' had called on you to solicit contributions. . . ." At that point, however, Lewis's letter diverged from that sent by Isaacs. He indicated that his interest was not in alerting Lincoln to any unauthorized financial solicitation; speaking for himself, Zacharie, and perhaps others, Lewis said: "We propose to give—not to take—I would esteem it a favor should any Jewish committee call on you . . . if you would send them to me . . . I will furnish them such amounts as we see can be used to advantage."

This letter from Lewis was apparently part of an ongoing effort by

Zacharie to be something of a freelance election campaign manager for Lincoln among communities of American Jews. On September 19, soon before the October state elections, Lincoln had written a letter to Zacharie. Addressed "Dr. Zacharie" and with the salutation "Dear Sir," it said, "I thank you again for the deep interest you have constantly taken in the Union cause. The personal matter on behalf of your friend which you mentioned will be fully and fairly considered when presented." Signed "Yours truly," by Lincoln, it elicited this reply, written from New York two days later.

> Dear Friend,
> Yours of the 19th came duly to hand, it has had the desired effect, with the friend of the Partie [sic].
> I leave tomorrow for the interior of Pennsylvania, may go as far as Ohio. One thing to be done, and that is for you to impress on the minds of your friends for them not to be to[o] sure.

Just how much time Zacharie spent away from New York during the preelection weeks is not certain, but he was back when he wrote this to Lincoln on November 3, five days before the public would go to the polls.

> I just returned to this city after a trip of nine days through Pennsylvania and New York state, and I am happy to inform you that I have done much good, I now think all is Right. . . . As regards the Isrelites [sic] with but few Exceptions, they will vote for you. . . . I understand them well, and have taken the precaution—to see that they do as they have promised—I have secured good and trustworthy men to—attend them on Election Day—My Men have been all the week seeing that their masses are properly Registered—so that all will go right on the 8th inst. [Election Day.]

There is no record of an answer being made to Zacharie's letter, but he remained *persona grata* with Lincoln; within weeks, the president would secure a pass from Stanton that enabled Zacharie to visit members of his family in a part of the South newly under Union control.

• • •

IN THESE DAYS before the election, Lincoln met in the "shop" with his most remarkable visitor yet: the freed slave Sojourner Truth, 6 feet tall and sixty-seven years old. Here was a woman who knew what it was to be sold at a slave auction as a child of nine; to be whipped; to work endless hours stooped in cotton fields. Preacher, lecturer on abolition, activist for women's rights, during the war she had been making her own efforts for the Union cause. After being arrested in Indiana early in the war for making an antislavery and pro-Union speech, in Michigan she had devoted herself to caring for the 1st Michigan Regiment of the United States Colored Troops. She had given speeches throughout the North, urging black men to enlist in the Union Army; her grandson was in the 54th Massachusetts, the most famous of the black regiments. The subject of a romanticized article in the *Atlantic Monthly* written by Harriet Becher Stowe, the author of *Uncle Tom's Cabin*, Sojourner had come to Washington to work among freed slaves at a government refugee camp at Freedmen's Village in Arlington Heights, across the river from Washington. She would soon engage in what was in effect a one-woman battle against the segregation practiced by the conductors of the city's streetcars, a struggle with hard-won results: she had one conductor dismissed for keeping her from boarding a car, and had another dismissed and convicted of assault and battery for dislocating her right shoulder when he tried to throw her off a car she had entered. (In yet another incident, when a conductor threatened to put her off a car, a Union general who was aboard rose and intervened on her behalf.)

A legendary figure and a passionate orator, Sojourner had come to national attention during the "Women's Convention" of white and black women held in Akron, Ohio, ten years before the war. When a man who saw himself as sympathetic to the plight of women spoke of their physical weakness, Sojourner, then fifty-four, rose up, tall and rangy. She launched into a fiery impromptu speech, crying out: "And ain't I a woman? Look at me! Look at my arm! I have ploughed and planted, and gathered into barns, and no man could head me! And ain't I a woman? I could work as much and eat as much as a man—when I could get it—and bear the lash as well!" Her eloquent outburst, all of it sent throughout the country by newspapers as the "Ain't I a Woman?" speech, struck a chord with white women as well as blacks and made her the best-known black woman in the nation.

Despite all that she had experienced, Sojourner was an almost reverent supporter of Lincoln, and, accompanied by her white abolitionist friend Lucy Colman, she came to see him, both to promote her own work helping the freed people, and to tell him that she considered him to be the savior of the nation's blacks. Soon thereafter, she sent a letter to a friend about her experience at the White House. (In a sense, there were two Sojourners: the former field hand to whom "ain't" came naturally, and the skillful self-taught writer who described this meeting with a man who learned to read by the light from a fireplace in a frontier cabin.)

Upon entering his reception room we found about a dozen persons in waiting, among them two colored women. I had quite a pleasant time waiting until he was disengaged, and enjoyed his conversation with others; he showed as much kindness and consideration to the colored persons as to the whites—if there was any difference, more. One case was that of a colored woman who was sick and likely to be turned out of her house on account of her inability to pay her rent. The president listened to her with much attention, and spoke to her with kindness and tenderness. He said he had given so much he could give no more, but told her where to go and get the money, and asked Mrs. C[olman], who accompanied me, to assist her, which she [later] did.

When Lincoln turned his complete attention to Sojourner and her companion, she said this to him:

Mr. President, when you first took your seat I feared you would be torn to pieces, for I likened you unto Daniel, who was thrown into the lions' den; and if the lions did not tear you into pieces, I knew it would be God that saved you; and I said that if He spared me I would see you before the four years expired, and He has done so, and now I am here to see you for myself.

Sojourner said that she next told Lincoln, "I appreciate you, for you are the best President who has ever taken the seat." He gave her this reply: "I expect you have reference to my having emancipated the slaves in my proclamation." In her account, she told how he expanded on that.

"But," said he, mentioning the names of several of his predecessors (and among them emphatically that of Washington), "they were all just as

good, and would have done just as I did if the time had come. If the people
across the river (pointing across the Potomac) had behaved themselves, I
could not have done what I have done; but they did not, and I was com-
pelled to do these things."

He then showed me the Bible presented to him by the colored people of
Baltimore. . . . After I had looked it over, I said to him: "This is beautiful
indeed; the colored people have given this to the Head of the Government,
and that Government once sanctioned laws that would not permit its
people to learn enough to enable them to read this Book. And for what?
Let them answer who can."

Sojourner had brought her autograph book with her. She had in it the
signatures of many famous people, but now she received the one she
wanted most.

He took up my little book, and with the same hand that signed the death-
warrant of slavery, he wrote as follows:—

For Aunty Sojourner Truth,
Oct. 29, 1864   A. LINCOLN

Lucy Colman later described Lincoln's attitude toward Sojourner
during this meeting as one of condescension, calling her " 'Aunty' . . . as
he would his washerwoman," but that is not how Sojourner felt.

As I was taking my leave, he arose and shook my hand, and said he would
be pleased to have me call again. I felt that I was in the presence of a
friend, and now I thank God that I always have advocated his cause, and
have done it openly and boldly. I shall feel still more in duty bound to do so
in time to come. May God assist me.

III

Unlike the later practice of casting a secret ballot in a voting booth, in
these years a registered voter would enter a polling place, have his name
checked against a list, and then be asked whether he wanted a Republican
or a Democrat party ballot. He would be handed the ballot, sign it, and
drop it into the box bearing the name of the party of his choice.

As these ballots were being printed and distributed to polling places as far from each other as Maine and California, on November 3, with the election five days away, a soldier came to the White House to see the president. He had received leave to go home and vote, but when he got as far as Washington on the first leg of his journey, he found crowds of travelers backed up at the railroad stations. More than 18,000 people, most of them government employees, were trying to get to the states in which they were registered to vote and, for the moment, not enough trains were available to keep taking them out of the city.

Once this enlisted man entered Lincoln's office and sat down with him, he explained that he intended to vote for McClellan but was having trouble finding transportation. Rather than asking this man why he should receive preferential treatment, Lincoln decided to help this soldier vote for his presidential opponent, and quickly wrote to Stanton, "This man wants to go home and vote. Sec. of War please see him."

In these final days before the election, the Republican elephant made his debut. The campaign newspaper *Father Abraham* was out with a full-page cartoon featuring an elephant striding across the page from right to left, the blanket on its back proclaiming, PENN'A 20,000!

This referred to the final margin of Republican/National Union Party victory from the October state election in Pennsylvania; the elephant held in his trunk a streaming banner that said THE ELEPHANT IS COMING! Above that, in the largest type on the page, was VICTORY! VICTORY! Although this elephant looked like a cheerful, high-stepping creature, the image of the elephant carried a deeper symbolism; soldiers approaching battle referred to the totality of the experience as "meeting the elephant."

Beneath this triumphant elephant, slamming home the theme of Republican-is-Patriotic, was the capitalized refrain from a popular song: "We'll Rally Round the Flag, Boys, Rally once again, Shouting the Battle Cry of Freedom!" On down the page, referring to the October elections and Maryland's ratification of its new antislavery constitution, was this message:

VICTORY IN PENNSYLVANIA!
VICTORY IN INDIANA!
VICTORY IN OHIO!

VICTORY IN MARYLAND, AND
VICTORY ALONG THE LINE!

As for the fate of Lincoln's opponent McClellan, capital letters at the top of the page announced:

"LITTLE MAC" OFF THE TRACK!

Interestingly, the name of Lincoln did not appear anywhere on the page, and a reference to "glorious Union victory" was the only variation of the name of the National Union/Republican Party. (In the small type at the bottom of the page, however, there was a brief derogatory reference to Copperheads.)

IT HAD ALL finally come down to this week beginning Monday, November 7. So much had happened in 1864, starting with Lincoln's first endorsements from New York in January, five months before he was nominated. Figures and events had come and gone; Frémont and the wild-and-woolly Cleveland convention; Salmon P. Chase and the Radical efforts to, as Congressman Henry Winter Davis had put it back in August, "get rid of Mr. Lincoln and name new candidates." Lincoln had been nominated at Baltimore in June, after the bloody fighting in the Wilderness and Spotsylvania, and just as the news of Grant's disaster at Cold Harbor came into the headlines. Sherman was thrown back at Kennesaw Mountain in Georgia on June 27. By July 12, Jubal Early was attacking Fort Stevens on the north side of Washington; the horror of the Battle of the Crater at Petersburg came at the end of that month. As his political fortunes plummeted, on August 23 Lincoln had written and had his cabinet sign, unseen, the reverse side of his memorandum in which he said, "it seems exceedingly probable that this Administration will not be re-elected."

Nine days after that, Sherman took Atlanta, starting the shift in public opinion that Sheridan accelerated by his victories in the Shenandoah Valley at Winchester and Cedar Creek. Copperhead activity still had not ceased; on the Wednesday before this momentous week in November began, Seward informed both the mayor of New York, and General

B. F. Butler, preserving order there, of intelligence received from Canada that Confederate agents intended to burn the city on Election Day.

It had been the greatest seesaw year in American political history, and now on Monday, November 7, the states of the Union were poised to go to the polls. In New York, Henry Raymond prepared this, to appear in the next day's *New York Times*:

> *The day has come—the day of fate. Before the morning's sun sets, the destinies of the republic . . . are to be settled. . . . We are making this decision, not for ourselves simply. We are settling the lot of the generations that shall come after us.*

In Washington, the seat of the Union, an eerie quiet settled on the streets. It was grey; a heavy rain kept falling; all the senators and congressmen and many members of their staffs had gone to their home states to vote. The government offices were closing early.

By contrast, in Richmond, ninety-five miles to the south, the Confederate Congress was convening for its second session of the year. For months, the people of Richmond had gone about their daily business to the sound of cannon fire a few miles away. Among the Southern legislators arriving at their Capitol were two who had lost a leg in the war. Confederate military reverses had produced some hostility toward Jefferson Davis; there was a greater willingness to consider peace negotiations, but as a body the Confederate Congress was prepared to fight on.

The principal activity in this opening session was to receive President Davis's Message to Congress. As was done in Washington, this was submitted in writing annually by the president, who did not attend, to be read to the joint session of the Confederate Senate and House. (Only in later years did American presidents personally deliver what became known as the State of the Union Address.)

In this year's message, Davis continued the optimistic tone he had maintained through recent defeats and difficulties. After Sherman took Atlanta, he told a Confederate congressman, "Sherman's army can be driven out of Georgia, perhaps destroyed." On the day that Sheridan followed up his victory at Winchester by routing Early's force at Fishers Hill, Davis said at a meeting in Georgia, "Friends are drawn together in adversity. Our cause is not lost. Sherman cannot keep [open] his long line of communication, and retreat, sooner or later, he must." He added that he would talk with General John Bell Hood about retaking all of Georgia, and closed with, "Let no one despond." A few days after that, addressing the people of Columbia, South Carolina, he pictured Sherman at Atlanta, deep in territory hostile to him, as being surrounded by Confederate forces destined to prevail: if the soldiers available to support Hood "will give him their strength, I see no chance for Sherman to escape from a disgraceful retreat." He took his rallying cry to Augusta, Georgia. Flanked by Generals Beauregard and Hardee, he assured a cheering crowd that they were part of a "free and independent people," and struck this note:

> *Never before was I so confident that energy, harmony and determination would rid the country of its enemy and give to the women of the land that peace that their good deeds have so well deserved. . . . We must beat Sherman, we must march into Tennessee . . . we must push the enemy back to the banks of the Ohio.*

Now, in his message, Jefferson Davis made the case that the loss of Atlanta, or any other Southern city, could be overcome. No single defeat could bring the South to its knees: "There are no vital points on the preservation of which the continued existence of the Confederacy depends." If properly organized, there would be enough military supplies, and enough food for both the soldiers and the general population. Touching on the Confederacy's economy, he found it "far from discouraging."

In what the Confederate Congress heard, some of Davis's words sounded plausible to many of the legislators, and some did not. The South was running out of soldiers; in May, the age limits had been changed so that males aged seventeen to fifty could be drafted, and there were many deserters. Food supplies in the Shenandoah Valley were being destroyed and, on their march south from Chattanooga to Atlanta, Sherman's soldiers had scarcely begun the kind of looting that would become commonplace. Still, the Confederacy had come this far, living on courage and hope: hope that Lee could come up with another Chancellorsville; hope that Sherman had in fact overextended himself in Georgia; hope that enough Northerners were so sick of the war that they would settle for a peace acceptable to the South. These Confederate senators and congressmen wanted to believe that Davis was right, that endurance and valor could produce near-miracles, that in the end a people who would not give up could not be defeated.

For the first time, Davis proposed something that would have been unthinkable earlier in the struggle. He recommended that the Confederate government buy 40,000 slaves from their owners, use them in the Confederate army as manual laborers and possibly even as soldiers, and free them whenever the war ended. The inconsistency of this was not lost on the legislators, who saw the irony of asking slaves to fight to preserve slavery. One Confederate congressman commented, "We have been denying all along that freedom is a good thing for the negro; yet now we propose to give him that freedom in return for enlistment in our armies."

The message from Davis ended with language making clear that he still wanted a separate nation and that, as an independent nation, the Confederacy would be entitled to have its own institutions, including slavery. He said that his government wanted a negotiated peace, and at the same time stated that such a peace must recognize the Confederacy's independence, and not lead to "our unconditional submission and degradation."

In Washington, amid the continuing rain on the eve of the day millions would vote for him or for McClellan, Lincoln performed the most prosaic of tasks. He had been too busy to deposit two of his monthly paychecks, for slightly different amounts, one made out to him by the Treasury in April and one in July. The two checks came to a total of $4,040, a bit less than a sixth of his annual salary of $25,000. He deposited them in Washington's Riggs Bank.

At the end of this day, still in his office in the evening, he received a visit from Elizabeth Comstock, an English-born Quaker minister and pacifist who gave speeches advocating the cause of abolition, women's rights, temperance, and prison reform.

A widow, during the year she had been tending to the needs of the wounded at Washington's Armory Square Hospital, the place that treated the most gravely wounded, including those with head wounds and almost all amputees. Her meeting with Lincoln seems to have been an informal service of worship. She read to him from the Bible. The only specific verse she is known to have read him, Isaiah 9:13, says in part, "For the people turneth not unto him that smiteth them." Possibly, Elizabeth Comstock saw that as a prophecy that the people *would* turn to Lincoln, in the momentous event to unfold the next day. The one published report of this evening meeting, presumably her own account of it, appeared in the *Armory Square Hospital Gazette*, and read, "Mr. Lincoln was highly gratified with the interview, and before taking her leave she kneeled in prayer, while he joined her in the reverend [*sic*] attitude."

FOURTEEN

THE FORTY-EIGHT-HOUR ELECTION DAY

O n the morning of Election Day, the White House was silent. The rain continued to fall. The city lay motionless, chill and dreary; a banker wrote a friend: "The streets wear a quiet Sunday air—in the Department building[s], the empty corridors respond to the foot fall of the solitary visitor; the hotels are almost tenantless." In his diary, John Hay offered an additional reason why the White House was particularly empty: "Everybody in Washington, not at home [in their home state] voting, seems ashamed of it and stays away from the President."

With almost no one waiting outside his office, and knowing there would be no election results until much later in the day, Lincoln settled down to deal with whatever business might arise.

A woman entered to ask for what was called a special exchange. A member of her family, Captain William A. Collins of the 10th Wisconsin Infantry, had been captured by the Confederates. In some instances, it was possible to arrange for the exchange of a specifically identified Union prisoner in return for the release of a similarly known Confederate. In other cases, often when a Northern family knew a similarly situated Southern family, informal arrangements were made for each to take special care of the other's still-imprisoned relative without his being released. After meeting with this lady, Lincoln sent one of his brief requests for action to the Union's commissioner for the exchange of prisoners, sixty-six-year-old Major General Ethan Allen Hitchcock, grandson of Ethan Allen, the Revolutionary War leader of Vermont's Green Mountain Boys. It read simply: "Will Gen. Hitchcock please see & hear this lady about a special exchange."

Next, Lincoln turned to a unique matter. He had in front of him a telegram from Republican Congressman Alexander H. Rice, the former mayor of Boston, telling him that Carlos Pierce, a prominent citizen of that city, had just given Lincoln a "Mammoth Ox" named "General Grant." The animal was in Boston. Would Lincoln donate it, Rice asked, to be auctioned off at the National Sailors' Fair for the benefit of sick and wounded sailors that would start in Boston the following day?

Lincoln wired back, "Yours received. I have no other notice that the ox is mine. If it be really so I present it to the Sailors' Fair, as a contribution." He followed this with another communication, wishing the organizers of the Sailors' Fair success, adding "With the old fame of the Navy, made brighter in the present war, you cannot fail. . . . To all from Rear Admiral, to honest Jack [Tar] I tender the Nation's admiration and gratitude." (The "Mammoth Ox" brought "upwards of Three Thousand two hundred dollars.")

The rain may have stopped for a time—it was pouring again by evening—and Lincoln's eleven-year-old son Tad came into his office and told him that he must go to the window and see what was happening on the south lawn. When Lincoln looked out, he saw the detachment of foot soldiers from the 150th Pennsylvania who acted as his bodyguard lined up, ready to step forward to ballot boxes and vote under the supervision of a commission sent to Washington from Pennsylvania. Strutting around among them was a turkey named Jack, whose life Tad had saved the year before when he begged his father not to have Jack killed for Christmas dinner.

Lincoln turned to Tad and playfully asked, "What business has the turkey stalking around the polls in that way? Does he vote?"

Without missing a beat, Tad replied, "No. He's not of age."

(In the October elections, when these soldiers from Pennsylvania had voted for state governor and for their representatives in Congress, the vote had been 63 for the Republican candidates and 11 for the Democrats, but now, voting for president, they voted unanimously for Lincoln.)

At noon Lincoln spent time talking with Noah Brooks, who described the White House as being "singularly deserted." Brooks found Lincoln by himself, worrying about how the election would really go. Lincoln said to Brooks that he had been "just enough of a politician to know there was not much doubt about the results of the Baltimore convention" at which he was nominated, "but about this thing I am very far from being certain. I wish I was certain."

Out in the nation, the voters were going to the polls. In Sturbridge, Massachusetts, 104-year-old John Phillips, accompanied by his 79-year-old son Edward, was carried into the town hall in a chair. A group of Union soldiers escorted him as they passed between "two unfurled flags of his country, bearing on them the Stars and Stripes; all within, at the time rising, with uncovered heads, to do him homage." Phillips had voted for George Washington for president. Now, "when offered two votes, to take his choice, he said: 'I vote for Abraham Lincoln.'" Down in the Shenandoah Valley, Private Wilbur Fisk of the 2nd Vermont, serving under Sheridan, gave considerable thought to what it meant to be voting.

> *Thousands of bits of paper are falling into ballot-boxes today, all over the country. It is a little thing, and can be done very easily, but mighty consequences may hang on the result. It is almost a new thing in the history of the world, when such great results as whether this country shall be governed by one principle, or another in almost complete hostility to it, can be decided by such simple means.*
>
> *God hasten the day when all questions may be decided in the same way, and then war, with its terrible list of horrors, will be remembered as one of the evils buried forever in the grim Past.*

In Georgia's notorious Andersonville Prison, Union soldiers who were prisoners, but not as sick or as starved as many had become, held their own informal election. Perhaps unaware that, with Lincoln's knowledge and tacit approval, Grant had instituted a policy of no general exchange of prisoners in order to deny the South any replenishment of its quickly shrinking manpower, these men, like the Vermont soldier, saw their action in idealistic terms. Sergeant Lucius W. Barber of Marengo, Illinois, who had enlisted in the 15th Illinois Volunteer Infantry twenty-five days after Fort Sumter was fired on in 1861, made this entry in the diary he had kept through thirty-nine months of battles and his recently-begun captivity:

This day, fraught with so deep an interest to every American heart, dawned unpleasant and rainy. The great issue to be decided today will engross the whole attention of lovers of liberty and free government throughout the civilized world.

*   ...A vote was taken in our detachment. There were two hundred and twenty-four votes cast. Lincoln received one hundred and eighty-eight and McClellan thirty-six. Over one-half the men did not vote. Our rations continue very scarce.*

In New York City, where so much trouble had been expected, B. F. Butler's plans for keeping order would succeed completely. In all of Manhattan, only one voting irregularity was reported, and that was one to gladden Butler's heart. Earlier in the day, when August Belmont, chairman of the Democratic National Committee, stepped forward to vote for McClellan, his vote was challenged on the grounds that he had bet on the election. So, of course, had thousands of other people, but the millionaire Belmont had done his betting so publicly and so often that the officials at the polling place told him they were challenging his right to vote. As Butler put it, "under that challenge he declined to vote."

Tuesday afternoon was the time scheduled for cabinet meetings, and Lincoln sat down at the head of the long black walnut table in his office. Only two members were there: Navy Secretary Welles and Attorney General Bates. Stanton was "sick abed with chills and fever," and Seward was home in Aurora, New York, to vote. Secretary of the Interior John Usher was voting in Indiana, and the new postmaster general, William Dennison, was casting his vote in Ohio. William Fessenden, who had taken over the Treasury when Lincoln finally dropped Chase, was in Manhattan, "shut up with New York financiers" in an effort to secure more loans so that the government could continue to pay the costs of the war.

After a cabinet meeting during which evidently nothing was accomplished, Lincoln, still in the White House, finally heard something specific about the election. Noah Brooks said, "The first gun came from Indiana, Indianapolis sending word about half-past-six in the evening that a gain of 1,500 in that city had been made for Lincoln." This was followed by a sliver of news from Nicolay, who had been doing everything he could for the Lincoln effort in Illinois. With the polls still open in Springfield, the state capital where Lincoln and Mary had lived and where he had practiced law and served his political apprenticeship in the Assembly, he was leading by 20 votes. Also, during the course of the day and well before the overall results of the election could be known, McClellan sent a letter to Adjutant General Lorenzo Thomas, resigning from the Army; in the event that he was elected, there would be no difficulty about a general serving as president.

At about seven, Lincoln and Hay walked over to the War Department in conditions much like those they had encountered on October 11 when the returns of the state elections came in. Hay described the way the historic evening began.

> *The night was rainy, steamy, and dark. We splashed through the grounds to the side door of the War Department where a soaked and steaming sentinel was standing in his own vapor with his huddled-up frame covered with a rubber cloak. Inside a half-dozen idle orderlies, upstairs the clerks of the telegraph.*

As Lincoln entered the telegraph office, he was handed a wire from his friend John Forney, the publisher of the *Washington Chronicle* and a man singularly well connected in Pennsylvania, claiming a lead of 10,000 votes in Philadelphia. Lincoln remarked skeptically, "Forney is a little excitable," and turned his attention to a message just in from Baltimore that read, "15,000 in the city, 5,000 in the state. All hail, Free Maryland!" Next came two telegrams arriving simultaneously from Massachusetts, one from Alexander Rice of Boston saying he had won reelection as mayor by 4,000 votes, and another from Senator Charles Sumner saying that Lincoln had won in Boston by 5,000. Hay said that, after looking this over, "The President sent over the first fruits to Mrs. Lincoln. He said, 'She is more anxious than I.'"

Noah Brooks had come in and was present when Lincoln read what was apparently another telegram from Forney, saying that Pennsylvania appeared sure to go for the Republicans. According to Brooks, Lincoln had this reaction: " 'As Pennsylvania goes, so goes the Union, they say,' remarked Father Abraham, and he looked solemn, as he seemed to see another term of office looming before him."

Nothing more came in for a time. New Jersey gained a Republican seat, but there was, as Brooks understood the situation there, "a fair prospect of the State going for McClellan." Finally, some news arrived from

New York, a state in which the Raymond-Weed Republican machine was fighting it out to the end with the forces of Democratic governor Horatio Seymour and Democratic National Chairman August Belmont. The wire claimed that Lincoln was ahead in the state by 10,000 votes. "I don't believe that," Lincoln remarked, indicating that he thought his lead would be smaller, if he was even in the lead.

As Lincoln waited for results, so did crowds around the nation. In Manhattan, after the polls closed and it was dark, thousands congregated in Printing House Square, where employees of the *Times* and the *Tribune* appeared and reappeared from their offices to post incoming results on bulletin boards. The *Herald* portrayed the scene outside its windows, saying that the crowd stood "in solid phalanx, as compactly and regularly arranged as a regiment in the field, swaying and moving as one immense body." The Democrats, expecting New York City to vote strongly for the McClellan-Pendleton ticket, were ready to celebrate at Tammany Hall, while the Republicans were holding a rally at the Cooper Institute; Republican (Union Party) National Chairman Henry Raymond, himself waiting to see if he would be elected to Congress, prepared a victory party at the Astor House. In Philadelphia, halls were filled with partisans waiting for results; torchlight parades of both parties were passing through the streets, led by bands and carrying banners, including a Republican one emblazoned with WE ARE COMING FATHER ABRAHAM, WITH AN OVERWHELMING MAJORITY.

Many men came to the War Department in Washington, including Navy Secretary Welles and his assistant secretary, Gustavus Fox. When Assistant Secretary of War Charles Dana came in out of the rain, he found that Stanton, who had missed the afternoon cabinet meeting "sick abed with chills and a fever," had recovered sufficiently to be present. Lincoln, "apparently as serene as a summer morning," was alone with Stanton in his large private office, and Dana joined them. Major (later Brevet Brigadier General) Thomas Eckert, who had started running the telegraph office as a captain and continued to manage it superlatively well (and never wore a uniform), kept coming in with telegrams. They brought good news, but the storm outside, as well as storms in other places, was delaying the transmission and reception of messages from more distant states.

In spite of these delays, Dana already thought that Lincoln was elected, but during a lull in the incoming bulletins, Lincoln did what he had done during the night of the October state elections. He pulled out what Dana described as "a thin yellow-covered pamphlet," which proved to contain the writings of his favorite humorist, David R. Locke, writing as "Petroleum V. Nasby." In what happened next, the recollections of Hay and Dana appear to differ. According to Hay, on that October night of the state elections, when Lincoln read Locke-Nasby's work aloud, Stanton and Dana "enjoyed them scarcely less than [did] the president." Tonight, however, Dana's account was that when Lincoln asked him, "Have you ever read anything of Petroleum V. Nasby?" he answered, "No, Sir," adding that he knew that some of the famous pieces were written from "Confederate Crossroads" and that some had appeared in the *Toledo Blade*—a reply that would seem a bit sketchy if Lincoln had read the man's work to him three weeks before.

As Dana remembered it, Lincoln told him, "Pull up your chair and listen." Dana did: Lincoln "began to read aloud, to me only and not to Stanton, one after another of Petroleum's funny hits; and between each of them we had a quiet little laugh to ourselves." Stanton had a different reaction; "he had no sympathy with this amusement; in fact, his face wore its darkest expression."

When Major Eckert brought in a telegram that he indicated was important, Lincoln switched his attention to reading that; Dana recounted what happened then.

> *While he [Lincoln] was thus engaged, Mr. Stanton motioned me to come into General Eckert's room, and when the door was shut he broke out in a fury: "God damn it to hell, was there ever such nonsense? Was there ever such inability to appreciate what is going on in an awful crisis? Here is the fate of this whole republic at stake, and here is the man around whom it all centres, on whom it all depends, turning aside from this momentous, this incomparable issue, to read the God damned trash of a silly mountebank!"*

At some point after this, during which more good news kept coming in, Stanton had another chance to be angry. As Lincoln was looking over yet another telegram in Stanton's office, an orderly brought to Lincoln the card of a man waiting to see him. Lincoln said, "Show him in!" and handed the card to Stanton. Dana told what happened next.

> *Stanton read it, and, turning to me, exclaimed in a low voice, "God in heaven, it is Whitelaw Reid!"*

I understood at once the point of this explosion. Mr. Reid, who was then the correspondent of the Cincinnati Gazette *and a great friend of [former] Secretary Chase in Washington, was not liked by the Secretary of War. This dislike had gone so far that the doorkeepers at the War Department had received instructions that Mr. Reid was not to be admitted. But when he sent in his card to the President they could not refuse it. Mr. Reid came in and was greeted by Mr. Lincoln, but not by the Secretary.*

Reid was there in his capacity as a responsible and competitive journalist, trying to see, as Dana put it, if he could "obtain from headquarters and from the highest authority the assurance that the election had in fact certainly gone in favor of Lincoln." By then the confirmed tallies of votes, while incomplete, made it seem certain that Lincoln was on the way to winning enough states to assure him the electoral votes he needed. Talking with Reid, Lincoln was ready to project his own victory, although later that night he made the far more guarded statement, "I cannot at this hour say what has been the result of the election." When Lincoln went ahead and gave Reid the "assurance" he sought, the journalist expressed "thanks and congratulations" and walked out with his scoop—the news of Lincoln's reelection, coming from the mouth of the president himself.

The mood in the telegraph office became quietly jubilant; Massachusetts had gone for Lincoln by a whopping 80,000 votes, and when Horace Greeley wired from New York that Lincoln was ahead by 4,000 votes rather than the earlier figure of 10,000 that Lincoln had doubted, Lincoln believed that, although even then New York was not certain. Brooks said, "By midnight we were sure of Pennsylvania, the New England states, Maryland, Ohio, Indiana, Michigan, Wisconsin, and it then appeared [wrongly] that we should have Delaware."

It was time to celebrate. Hay said: "We had supper, provided by Eckert. The President went awkwardly and hospitably to work shoveling out the fried oysters. He was most agreeable and genial all the evening long in fact." After this midnight supper, several people left, but Lincoln stayed on, waiting for more news. At 1 A.M., a wire from Chicago got in through the storm, saying that Lincoln was ahead in Illinois by 20,000 votes. Hay reported that, despite the weather, "We got later in the evening a scattering despatch from the West . . . promising us Missouri certainly."

Then, Brooks said, "About two o'clock in the morning a messenger came over from the White House with the news that a crowd of Pennsylvanians were serenading his empty chamber."

There is some question as to whether Lincoln went over to the White House or whether the crowd came over to the War Department and he appeared at a window there (there is the possibility that he spoke two or three times), but, using some cues jotted down for him by Hay, he addressed and thanked these enthusiastic supporters. It was now that Lincoln told them, "I cannot at this hour say what has been the result of the election." However, showing that by this point he had no real doubt of the outcome, he told them that "this day's work . . . will be to the lasting advantage, if not the very salvation, of the country." He added: "All who have labored to-day in behalf of the Union organization, have wrought for the best interests of their country and the world, not only for the present, but for all future ages. I am thankful to God for this approval of the people."

As Hay was getting ready to go to bed in his room at the White House after this long day, Ward Lamon came in. Lincoln's appointee as Washington's federal marshal, and the man who acted as Lincoln's self-appointed bodyguard, he wanted, as Hay put it, "to talk over the Chief Justiceship." Lincoln had not yet filled the Supreme Court vacancy opened by Taney's death, and Lamon felt that it should go to Stanton. He was worried about what would happen if Lincoln named Chase; Hay said of their conversation that Lamon "thinks, as I am inclined to think, that the President cannot afford to place an enemy in a position so momentous for good or evil."

Hay's last description of the momentous day was this, about Lamon:

He took a glass of whiskey and then, refusing my offer of a bed, went out & rolling himself up in his cloak, lay down at the President's door; passing the night in that touching attitude of dumb fidelity, with a small arsenal of pistols & bowie knives around him. In the morning he went away leaving my blankets at the door, before I or the President were awake.

THE NEXT MORNING, with more election results still to be received, Lincoln did not go straight to the telegraph office, but went to his "shop" to attend to whatever awaited him there. His first visitor was an enlisted man with a problem. Within a minute, Lincoln sent him off with a self-explanatory note he had written and signed. Addressed to the Union Army's paymaster general, Timothy P. Andrews, it read: "This poor soldier is in distress because he can get no pay. Will Pay Master-General, please have him put on the right track to get his pay." Next he sent a reply to Benjamin B. French, the commissioner of public buildings, who considered Lincoln's election a *fait accompli*. In response to French's wish, he granted him permission "to give laborers at the White House a holiday."

After that, Lincoln went over to the War Department. He was intensely interested in the election results yet to be received, but, in addition to that, Stanton wanted to talk to him about a telegraphic exchange he had going on with B. F. Butler in New York City. As promised, the speculator H. J. Lyons had sold his gold before the election, averting a financial crisis, but, as Hay noted in his diary, "Butler wants to grab and incarcerate some [other] gold gamblers." Lincoln evidently ruled against doing this; Hay said of that, "The President doesn't like to sully victory with any harshness."

In the telegraph office, more news arrived. Hay noted that at 2 P.M. a wire came in that "reports a splendid set of majorities in Maryland reaching an aggregate of 10,000." On through the afternoon and evening, Lincoln read more telegrams confirming his victory. (One still not in was one that Hay recorded this way when it came: "Nicolay sent a superb dispatch from Illinois giving us 25,000 majority and ten [of fourteen] congressmen.") It was not the custom for a losing candidate to make a public concession; McClellan wrote his mother, "The smoke has cleared away, and we are beaten!"

Before the last votes were in, many newspapers and individuals started to get their stories and opinions into print. There were those who deplored the result: in Lincoln's town of Springfield, the *Illinois State Register* said that his reelection was "the heaviest calamity that ever befell this nation," but the *Boston Post*, which had backed McClellan, spoke for the concept of civic duty when it said editorially, "The ballot-box has spoken, and we abide the result." The South saw that any realistic hope for a negotiated peace was gone: in Virginia, the *Richmond Examiner* told its readers, "The Yankee nation has committed itself to the game of all or nothing, and so must we." Jefferson Davis remained defiant and determined, but Confederate soldiers who saw no point in further fighting began a surge of desertions.

Those who had supported Lincoln had reactions ranging from relief to joy, mixed with the sober realization that many men continued to be killed and wounded every day. Henry Raymond, now elected to Congress, reflected on the campaign in which he had been National Republican (National Union) party chairman. Forgetting or setting aside memories of the plight in which Lincoln and his party found themselves just ten weeks before, Raymond prepared for his *New York Times* the comment, "We accept it without surprise." Corporately, however, the paper was not blasé, running the headline "VICTORY!" with, beneath that, subheadlines that included "Glorious Result Yesterday," "Terrible Defeat of McClellan," and "The Union Triumphant."

Others would weigh in with their reactions; in the War Department, the tallies coming in from areas affected by the storm the day before continued to reveal a decisive victory, far more so in electoral votes than in the popular vote. When it was all in, Lincoln had 2,213,665 votes to McClellan's 1,802,237, leading McClellan by 10 percent in the popular vote, but the electoral vote was overwhelming—212 to 21. Lincoln and his party carried every state that voted, except New Jersey, Kentucky, and Delaware. There would be much analysis of how and why it all happened, but the soldier vote leapt out of the figures; many of those ballots were merged in state totals, but of the 150,635 identified, Lincoln would have 116,887, and McClellan would receive only 33,748. Reporter Henry Wing had been right when he told Lincoln "They'll vote the way they shoot."

Later that evening, having been told that a crowd would gather to serenade him at the White House when he returned from the War Department, Lincoln wrote out what he wanted to say instead of relying on his ability to speak from a few cues written for him by Hay, as he had the night before. Exhausted though Lincoln was, he took care as he wrote, underlining words he wished to emphasize. Under this pressure, he composed one of his best speeches, one that at times resonated with the same cadences that rang through his Gettysburg Address.

Noah Brooks described the scene that awaited Lincoln when he arrived after midnight.

... an impromptu procession, gay with banners and resplendent with lanterns and transparencies, marched up to the White House, the vast crowd surging around the great entrance, blocking up all of the semicircular avenue thereto as far as the eyes could reach. Brass bands brayed martial music on the air, enthusiastic sovereigns cheered to the echo, and the roar of cannon shook the sky, even to the breaking of the President's windows, greatly to the delight of the crowd and Master "Tad'" Lincoln, who was flying about from window to window, arranging a small illumination [setting candles in the windows] on his private account.

[Lincoln's] appearance at the window was the signal for a tremendous yell, and it was some time before the deafening cheers would permit him to proceed.

This was the nearest thing to an acceptance speech that Lincoln would give. As he intended, Lincoln did not give the suddenly silent and respectful crowd a sugar-coated victory oration. He set before them the great issues, the questions and answers through which they were living together.

It has long been a grave question whether any government, not too strong for the liberties of its people, can be strong enough to maintain its own existence, in great emergencies. On this point the present rebellion brought our republic to a severe test; and a presidential election ... added not a little to the strain. If the loyal people, united, were put to the utmost of their strength by the rebellion, must they not fail when divided, and partially paralyzed, by a political war among themselves?

Lincoln paused. He told the citizens looking up at him as he stood in the window, "But the election was a necessity." After another few silent seconds, he continued.

We can not have free government without elections, and if the rebellion could force us to forego, or postpone, a national election, it might fairly be said to have already conquered and ruined us. ... But the election, along with its incidental and undesirable strife, has done good too. It has demonstrated that a people's government can sustain a national election, in the midst of a great civil war. Until now it has not been known to the world that this was a possibility. It shows also how sound, *and how* strong *we still are.*

He did not want the crowd to disperse in the night without knowing what he wanted of them, what he wanted now from all Republicans, all Democrats. "But the rebellion continues; and now that the election is over, may not all, having a common interest, re-unite in a common country?" The crowd was hearing, without knowing it—perhaps Lincoln did not yet know it—the precursor to his sublime Second Inaugural speech, burning into history its words, "With malice towards none, with charity for all." Referring to his desire to join hands with those who had opposed him politically, he said this to his crowd of supporters: "May I ask those who have not differed with me, to join with me, in this same spirit towards those who have?"

It remained only to end this night as he and those cheering him would wish. He had in his remarks already said, "I am deeply sensible to the high compliment of a re-election," and had also spoken of being "duly grateful, as I trust, to Almighty God for having directed my countrymen to a right conclusion, as I think, for their own good."

He always thought of the Union fighting men, the ones who had the most to lose—their lives—by voting for the man who was determined to keep fighting to preserve the Union. They had voted for him, more than three to one. Finally, the exhausted Lincoln said this, before he stepped back from the window where he stood above his listeners, his voters, his people: "And now, let me close by asking three hearty cheers for our soldiers and seamen and their gallant and skilful commanders."

He had done it. When Mary Lincoln's black maid, Elizabeth Keckley, offered her congratulations, Mary answered, "Thank you, Elizabeth; but now that we have won the position, I almost wish it were otherwise. Mr. Lincoln is looking so broken-hearted, so completely worn out, I fear he will not get through the next four years."

It is not certain that Mary remembered at this moment something that occurred in their house in Illinois on the night of Lincoln's first election in 1860 when he knew he'd been elected, but after this second election night Lincoln told Brooks about it. On that evening, "I was well tired out, and went home to rest, throwing myself down on a lounge in my chamber." A mirror was opposite him, and in it he saw this: "My face, I noticed, had *two* separate and distinct images, the tip of the nose of one being about three inches from the tip of the other." When Lincoln stood up to look into the mirror closely, he saw only one face, but "on lying down again I saw it a second time—plainer, if possible, than before; and then I noticed that one of the faces was paler, say five shades, than the other."

Lincoln told Mary about it: "She thought it was a 'sign' that I was to be elected to a second term of office, and that the paleness of one of the faces was an omen that I should not see life through the last term."

II

At the next cabinet meeting after his reelection, Hay was present in his capacity as private secretary. In his diary, he told what happened.

> . . . the President took out a paper from his desk and said, "Gentlemen, do you remember last summer I asked you all to sign your names to the back of a paper of which I did not show you the inside? This is it. Now, Mr. Hay, see if you can get this open without tearing it?" He had pasted it up in so singular [a] style that it required some cutting to get it open.

When Hay handed it to Lincoln, the president read to his cabinet the words he had penned on the dark day of August 23, beginning with, "This morning, as for some days past, it seems exceedingly probable that this Administration will not be reelected."

Then Lincoln gave the cabinet an exact picture of what had been in his mind on that day. He reminded them that this was written six days before the Chicago convention, when he felt that he and his administration "seemed to have no friends." Lincoln said that he had assumed that McClellan would win in November and explained what he intended to do in the interim between the election and McClellan's inauguration.

> I would see him and talk matters over with him. I would say, "General, the election has demonstrated that you are stronger, have more influence with the American people than I. Now, let us together, you with your influence, and I with the executive power of the government, try to save the country. You raise as many troops as you possibly can for this final trial, and I will devote all my energies to assisting and finishing the war."

When Lincoln finished this description of what his intentions had then been, nine days before Sherman wired north that he had taken Atlanta, only Stanton made a comment. Obviously thinking back to McClellan's famous inactivity when he was general-in-chief, Stanton observed, "And the General would answer you, '*Yes, Yes,*' and the next day when you saw him again, and pressed these views upon him, he would say, '*Yes, Yes*'; and so on forever, and would have done nothing at all."

Now everything had changed. Across the country and in Europe, the news of Lincoln's reelection became the subject of newspaper stories and private judgments. The widely read *Harper's Weekly* began its lead story with a proclamation of triumph, but quickly moved to something more insightful than a recitation of electoral totals. Speaking of what the voice of the people had really said, it observed of Lincoln, "In himself, notwithstanding his unwearied patience, perfect fidelity, and remarkable sagacity, he is unimportant; but as the representative of the feeling and purpose of the American people he is the most important fact in the world."

The theme of Lincoln as being one with his people inspired three of the most fertile minds in the nation. Francis Lieber, the eminent German-born author, professor, and legal scholar (and the first man in America to call himself a political scientist), said the election was "one of the greatest national acts in all history." From New England, Ralph Waldo Emerson wrote, "Seldom in history was so much staked on a single vote—I suppose never in history." An unvarnished appreciation of Lincoln's accomplishment came from Walt Whitman, who had never met Lincoln, but who often watched him pass by.

I see the President often.... He has conscience and honesty and homely shrewdness; conceals an enormous tenacity under his mild, gawky Western manner. The difficulties of his situation have been unprecedented in the history of statesmanship. That he has conserved the government so far is a miracle.

Those were the appreciations expressed by great minds, but another and important kind of opinion kept arriving in the mailbags opened at the White House. One read:

Dear Sir. Please permit me though a poor man to congratulate you on your reelection as Chief Magistrate of the Nation for another four years,

for which I am truly thankful and your trustworthy servant will ever
pray that you may be able to bring this rebellion to an and [end] and we
again will be a happy and prosperous nation.

Very truly Your obedient servant
J. M. Belknap
Williston, Mass.

Those trying to analyze what had happened politically during the weeks leading up to the election gave credit to Sherman's capture of Atlanta and Sheridan's victories in the Shenandoah Valley, but it also became clear that the Democrats had mortally wounded themselves at their convention in Chicago. Even though McClellan had in effect repudiated the party's "peace plank," it had struck too defeatist a tone with the many voters that the party needed to keep or win over, and those who might like McClellan had little or no use for the vice-presidential nominee George H. Pendleton, a Copperhead congressman. From the moment the Democrats included the "peace plank" in their platform, the military vote began to collapse: a colonel in the Army of the Potomac, one of the many scores of thousands of officers and men who had become fond of McClellan when he commanded them, wrote his wife: "The nomination of McClellan is not well received in the army, from the fact that they put that abominable traitor, Pendleton, on as Vice President. The ticket has no chance here. McClellan's friends . . . have abandoned him." In another letter to his wife, written a few days later, he added, "I have not come across an officer or man who will vote for McClellan and Pendleton. Why, we don't touch the Chicago platform!" A soldier serving with Sherman wrote:

There were in the Western Army many McClellan men at the time of his
nomination, but since the platform was read and then to know that the
nomination of McClellan was made on the motion of that Traitor Val-
landigham is more than the admirers of little 'Mac' could stand and I can
assure that 'Mac' has lost thousands of votes within three weeks.

Another of Sherman's soldiers expressed a simple, heartfelt reason for voting for Lincoln. "We must have the man who dares to say: the Nation must live. We can trust ourselves to no other pilot."

When the result became clear, Ulysses S. Grant sent a telegram from his City Point headquarters to Stanton at the War Department. A man who so often understood the crux of a situation, he saw a result not readily visible to everyone. "Congratulate the President for me for the double victory." Lincoln had won, but so had the democratic process, and the character of the citizens. "The election having passed off quietly, no bloodshed or rioit [sic] throughout the land, is a victory worth more to the country than a battle won." Grant understood that the people of the Union had sent forth a message of discipline, determination, and loyalty to the procedures set forth in the Constitution; he finished with, "Rebeldom and Europe will so construe it."

The final reactions and opinions came from Lincoln himself. Brooks said of a moment in the War Department when it became obvious that Lincoln had won, "He took it very calmly—said that he was free to confess that he felt relieved of suspense, and was glad that the verdict of the people was so likely to be clear, full and unmistakable, for it then appeared that his majority in the electoral college would be immense." A day after that, Lincoln said to Brooks, "Being only mortal, after all, I should have been a little mortified if I had been beaten in a canvass before the people," but he added, "that sting would have been more than compensated [for] by the thought that all my official responsibilities were soon to be lifted off my back."

As a postmortem on the Democrats' campaign strategy, when John Nicolay returned from working to the last minute for Lincoln's reelection in contested Illinois, working so hard that he became sick for a few days, Lincoln told him: "I am here by the blunders of the Democrats. If, instead of resolving that the war was a failure, they had resolved that I was a failure, and denounced me for not prosecuting it more vigorously, I would not have been reelected."

FIFTEEN

AN EPIC YEAR BEGINS ITS DRAMATIC CLOSE

At seven in the morning on November 16, a week after Lincoln's electoral sweep, General Sherman rode his horse southeast out of Atlanta, at the head of one of the four powerful, well-armed columns into which he had divided his army of 62,000 men. Looking back, he saw a shocking scene: "Behind us lay Atlanta, smouldering and in ruins, the black smoke rising high in the air, and hanging like a pall over the city." Atlanta had been set afire twice: once at the end of August by the retreating Confederates, burning supplies to deny them to the Union forces, and now by Sherman's troops, to carry out his orders to destroy the commercial and manufacturing areas of the city. As he rode on, Sherman saw and heard this: "the white-topped wagons stretching away to the south," and the soldiers with their "gun-barrels glistening in the sun . . . marching steadily and rapidly, with a cheery look and a swinging pace. . . . Some band had, by accident, struck up the anthem of 'John Brown's soul goes marching on'; the men caught up the strain, and never before or since have I heard the chorus of 'Glory, glory, hallelujah!' done with more spirit."

The picture was one of a well-organized enormous march; it was that, but had been authorized only after an intense debate and a resolution of differences between Sherman on the one hand, and Grant, Lincoln, Halleck, and Stanton on the other. After capturing Atlanta, Sherman had sent word to Grant that as soon as he dealt with remaining Confederate forces in a large surrounding area, he wanted to march on to the southeast, going 225 miles through the heart of Georgia to the Atlantic, and end with the capture of the Confederate stronghold port of Savannah. Grant had grave doubts about that entire concept; Lincoln and Stanton had even stronger feelings as to whether Sherman's march should even be attempted—Lincoln later said that he was "*anxious*, if not fearful," about the venture, and Stanton wired Grant at City Point that "a mis step [*sic*] now by Sherman might be fatal to his army."

Whatever else Grant might permit his friend Sherman to do, he had priorities that he initially placed above what he thought of as being a high-risk major movement. Some immediate threats materialized: forces under Sherman first fought a number of engagements, including the successful defense on October 5 of a big Federal supply depot at Allatoona, Georgia, but even after that Grant thought that Sherman should march south to Mobile and crush the remaining Confederate strength on the Gulf coast. Sherman persuaded him that this was not essential and that he could successfully fight his way to the sea—Sherman told Grant, "I can make the march and make Georgia howl"—but Grant had only to look at a map to see additional threats. If Sherman headed for the Atlantic, he would be marching away from John Bell Hood's Army of Tennessee, which Hood was readying to take north into Tennessee where they would be opposed by the Union forces under George Thomas. Hood had at his disposal 33,000 foot soldiers and a powerful force of 6,000 cavalrymen under the command of the endlessly resourceful Nathan Bedford Forrest. Grant feared that if Hood could break through the forces under Thomas in northern Tennessee while Sherman was opening a greater distance between himself and Hood every day, it would create a potential disaster: Hood could move across the Tennessee border into Kentucky, and might push north across Kentucky and reach Cincinnati on the Ohio River. Grant wanted Sherman to "settle" Hood first, and then he could have his 225-mile march.

Sherman continued to argue with Grant by telegraph, saying that Thomas could handle Hood, and he added another reason. Not only could he make the march; he told Grant (in effect also talking to Lincoln, Stanton, and Halleck, all of whom intended to let Grant make the final decision) that this would break the South's heart. He intended to wage the kind of "total war" that Sheridan had engaged in during his burning of the Shenandoah Valley. He believed that his march, "even without a battle," would make "sensible men" throughout the South understand, as never before, that further resistance would be useless.

What Grant was seeing every day of the steadfast valor of Lee's Army of Northern Virginia left him doubtful that even making Georgia "howl" would bring the entire Confederacy to its knees, but he listened to Sherman's statement that in Georgia, "the utter destruction of its roads, houses and people will cripple their military resources." Finally, Grant made an act of faith in his friend, who had proven to be a splendid general. He wired Sherman, "I say, then, go on as you propose."

And so Sherman headed south. His men were hardened veterans, some of whom had been with Sherman since Shiloh, thirty-one months before. They marched with everything they needed, and not a thing more. Sherman cut his railroad links—he was not going to lessen his strength by dropping off detachments along the way to guard railroad lines, and he cut his telegraph links as well. No one, not Grant, not Stanton, not Halleck, was going to be able to find him. His army was taking along a twenty-day supply of food that included a herd of 3,000 beef cattle, but they were indeed going to live off the land.

This innovation of moving forward without supply lines behind him was not Sherman's invention. He had learned that it could be done by watching Grant do it in a prelude to the siege of Vicksburg. Before Grant moved forty miles from the Mississippi River in a preemptive strike on Jackson, Mississippi, he sent Sherman a message that they would start off with "what rations of hard bread, coffee & salt we can and make the [surrounding] country furnish the balance." Sherman was adapting that on a far larger scale, and he had with him men who believed completely in the lanky, dynamic, redheaded general they called "Uncle Billy." A sergeant from Iowa personified that confidence when he wrote in his diary, "Started this morning for the Southern coast, somewhere, and we don't care, as long as Sherman is leading us."

II

In the White House, Lincoln had responded to many congratulations on his reelection and was hard at work on the regular duties of his presidency. The Congress would not reconvene until December 5, but he was already working on his Message to Congress, to be sent to the Capitol and read to a joint session of the Senate and House. At cabinet meetings, Lincoln was asking his heads of government departments to prepare the annual reports on which he would base parts of his message. Noah Brooks watched Lincoln putting the message together.

> *It may be a matter of interest to know that the whole of the . . . message exists, or did exist, upon slips of pasteboard or boxboard. It is a favorite habit of the President, when writing anything requiring thought, to have a number of these slips of board near at hand, and, seated at ease in his armchair, he lays the slip on his knee and writes and rewrites in pencil what is afterward copied in his own hand with new changes and interlineations.*
>
> *Then, being "set up" by the printer with big "slugs" in the place of "leads," spaces of half an inch are left between each line in the proof. More corrections and interlineations are made, and from this patchwork the document is finally set up and printed.*

Lincoln continued to work frequently on his Message to Congress but, among other matters reaching his desk, the Office of the Adjutant General brought him a statement concerning the situation of a widow, Mrs. Lydia Bixby of Boston. Governor John A. Andrew of Massachusetts thought that Lincoln might want to write a letter to her, because he had been informed that she had lost five sons fighting in the Union Army. (The facts were wrong: only two of the five who had enlisted had died in battle, one had deserted, another either deserted or died in a Confederate prison camp, and a fifth completed his service with an honorable discharge.) Although Lincoln wrote her because of what seemed a singularly horrible tragedy, what he so eloquently expressed in his letter reflected his feelings about every parent's loss of a child. On November 21, addressing Mrs. Bixby as "Dear Madam," he said in part:

> *I feel how weak and fruitless must be any words of mine which should attempt to beguile you from the grief of a loss so overwhelming. But I cannot refrain from tendering the consolation that may be found in the thanks of the Republic they died to save.*
>
> *I pray that our Heavenly Father may assuage the anguish of your*

bereavement, and leave you only the cherished memory of the loved and lost, and the solemn pride that must be yours, to have laid so costly a sacrifice upon the altar of Freedom.

Yours very sincerely and respectfully,
A. Lincoln

LINCOLN'S REELECTION FAILED to bring an end to violent Confederate efforts to disrupt life in the North at places far from the fighting front. Once again, Confederate agents came down from Canada, this time to New York City. Carrying concealed packages of chemicals supposed to be extremely combustible, they checked into ten or more hotels and on the night of November 25 attempted to set the buildings afire. The effort failed. The chemicals literally fizzled; one account had it that the chemist who compounded the mixture had deliberately sabotaged the effort, and in any case the New York Fire Department arrived swiftly at each location. The one building that suffered serious damage was Barnum's American Museum, the city's greatest tourist attraction, visited annually by tens of thousands of visitors eager to see the collection of oddities assembled by the incomparable promoter P. T. Barnum. (The Confederate agent who set that fire, a man named R. C. Kennedy, was arrested, tried, and hanged.)

Four days after this, Lincoln took a role in a very different disposition of the case of a Confederate agent. A Captain John B. Castleman of John Hunt Morgan's Kentucky mounted scouts and raiders had been captured in Chicago at the time of the Democratic convention. He was charged with carrying plans to release Confederate prisoners held at prison camps in the area "and to assist the Sons of Liberty in a 'Northwestern Insurrection.'" A Confederate soldier captured while wearing civilian clothes was considered to be a spy, subject to the death penalty.

Fortunately for Castleman, his sister Virginia was married to Lincoln's friend Judge Samuel M. Breckinridge of St. Louis. Lincoln fixed the case: Castleman was released without trial, on condition that he leave the United States. (His banishment lasted for eighteen months, by which time the war had been over for a year.) In writing Breckinridge, Lincoln enclosed the order with which he had disposed of the case, and said, "Sam, this is for you and Virginia, entrusted in confidence." Castleman himself obviously knew that something had been done on his behalf, but first learned of Lincoln's involvement fifteen years later.

The day after Lincoln acted in that life-and-death matter, quite a different thing happened in the "shop." At ten in the morning, an assortment of men began coming in, curious to see a present about to be given to Lincoln. In due course the gift, along with the man presenting it, was brought in. The present was a chair made from elk antlers, and the man giving it was the celebrated California big game hunter Seth Kinman, a tall, erect man with a long grey beard who appeared wearing buckskins. Also noted for shooting grizzly bears and presenting their claws to famous people, Kinman had brought with him a fiddle he had made from the bleached bones of a mule who died on the plains, using its skull for the fiddle's body, and a rib and some hairs from the tail for the bow and the strings. He then played his instrument for Lincoln and this little White House audience, entertaining them with "Essence of Old Virginia" and what was probably the most unusual rendering of "John Brown's Body" they ever heard.

Lincoln made a brief and perhaps slightly bemused reply of thanks, saying that he would ask Kinman for the fiddle as an additional present but, since he could not play it, the fiddle would be better off with Kinman. The chair must have made an impression on Lincoln; within three weeks he was using it in making the point to a colleague that he would rather have eaten that chair, spiked antlers and all, than make an important appointment that he felt compelled to bestow.

SOMETHING ELSE OCCURRED in New York on the night that the Confederate agents failed in their attempt to start fires around the city. As a one-night benefit performance to pay for a statue of Shakespeare to be erected in Central Park, the Winter Garden Theatre on Broadway presented the Bard's *Julius Caesar*. For the only time in their careers, the actors Edwin, Junius, and John Wilkes Booth, all three brothers, with Edwin being the most famous, appeared in the same play. With their mother Mary Ann proudly watching them from a box above the stage, the three brothers took the three leading roles in the most celebrated play to portray a political assassination. The striking down of a Roman emperor is depicted as a patriotic act; with the slain emperor lying dead on the stage, Brutus loudly declares:

Liberty! Freedom! Tyranny is dead!
Run hence, proclaim, cry it about the streets.

During the play's second scene, there were cries that the theater was on fire. That proved not to be true, and the show went on, but in fact the LaFarge House, a hotel next door, was one of the targets the Confederate agents had chosen; like the efforts to burn down the other hotels, it failed.

At this point, John Wilkes Booth still had the idea of abducting Lincoln rather than killing him outright, but by now he had both gone to Canada fruitlessly looking for quasi-official support for his scheme and had recruited some men in and near Washington who seemed committed to the plan. The idea was still to seize Lincoln somewhere, get him into a carriage, and move him swiftly along back roads through the Union and Confederate lines, delivering him to Richmond, where he would be used as a bargaining chip for the resumption of the exchange of Confederate prisoners.

Booth had selected the men to handle different parts of his kidnapping. To grab Lincoln, put him in handcuffs, and get him into the escape carriage, he had two physically strong men from Baltimore, Samuel Arnold and Mike O'Laughlin, friends who had served in the same Confederate regiment earlier in the war. To help spirit the captured president south through the countryside, he had twenty-year-old John Surratt, who assisted in running what had been his family's tavern and post office in Surratsville, ten miles south of Washington. Surratsville had been in Union hands for most of the war, but the tavern acted as a place where Confederate spies and couriers stayed as they slipped back and forth between Washington and Richmond. John Surratt had perfect knowledge of all the least-watched back roads. (His mother, Mary Surratt, later hanged for her part in Lincoln's death, had moved on November 1 to Washington, where she started taking in boarders at a house owned by her late husband. It, too, became a safe house for Confederate agents passing in and out of the capital.) Thirty-one-year-old Thomas Harbin of Bryantown, Virginia, also on the route to Richmond, was familiar with Confederate mail drops hidden throughout a countryside he knew thoroughly. Both he and John Surratt would be expert guides. Booth's team would also have the resources of David Herold, a pharmacy clerk whom Booth saw as being generally useful. Booth had yet to bring into his web the conspirators who would actually play violent roles.

III

In northern Tennessee, on November 30, the forces under John Bell Hood and George Thomas fought a battle at Franklin, twenty miles south of Nashville. It was a battle that Grant had known must take place somewhere, ever since he let Sherman win the debate in which Lincoln later described himself as having been "*anxious*, if not fearful" about Sherman's proposed march from Atlanta to Savannah.

Grant had let Sherman start to the sea without first dealing definitively with Hood. After some delay, Hood marched north through Tennessee, headed for Nashville. Thomas's forces were moving toward Nashville themselves, intent on getting there first and strengthening its defenses. Along the way, there was much maneuvering, and minor engagements between units of Hood's Army of Tennessee and Thomas's Army of the Cumberland, but the goal was Nashville. Thomas reached it first and began hurriedly positioning his forces to thwart this attempt to retake territory that in some areas had been in Union hands for two or more years. If Hood could take Nashville, an ominous prospect would open for the North: Louisville, Cincinnati, and other virtually undefended cities would have to be protected, and the forces to do that might have to be drawn from battlefronts where they were now fully engaged. In terms of strategy, at this stage in the war it was more important for Thomas to hold Nashville than for Sherman to capture Savannah.

Two extraordinary commanders opposed each other in this separate campaign. Hood, a sad-eyed, 6-foot-2 Kentuckian with a lush beard, had graduated from West Point at the same time Sheridan did; the same age as Sheridan, he was equally aggressive but lacked his wisdom. He had been wounded in prewar fighting against the Indians, and first gained fame in this war commanding the valiant Texas Brigade, which he led at Gaine's Mill, Second Manassas, and Antietam. Hood was then badly wounded in the arm at Gettysburg; after losing his right leg at Chickamauga, he had to be strapped into the saddle to keep him from falling off his horse when he went into action. Both Lee and Grant had reservations about Hood, Lee saying, "Hood is a bold fighter . . . I am doubtful about other qualities necessary." Grant told his wife Julia about his reaction when Jefferson Davis ordered Hood to replace Joseph E. Johnston during the defense of Atlanta: "My satisfaction at Hood's being placed in command was this . . . [Johnston] was a most careful, brave, wise soldier. But Hood would dash out and fight every time we raised a flag before him, and that was just what we wanted."

Hood's forty-four-year-old adversary, George Thomas, another man over 6 feet tall, was a Virginian who had graduated from West Point in 1840. He ranked six places behind Sherman in that class. Twice brevetted for valor during the Mexican War, this Southerner's decision to stay in the Regular Army and fight for the Union may have been influenced by his beautiful Northern wife. In any event, it placed him at the center of bitter controversy; his sisters never spoke to him again, Confederates disdained him, and many Northerners had suspicions about this Virginian despite his great battlefield contributions to the Union cause. He fought at First Manassas, Shiloh, and other battles, and earned the name "The Rock of Chickamauga" for his effective and heroic actions in saving that Union defeat from becoming a complete disaster. Thomas then played an important role in Grant's victory at Chattanooga. In command of the Army of the Cumberland, his divisions had comprised half of the total force that Sherman led in his march south from Chattanooga to Atlanta.

Now, while Sherman marched through Georgia, Thomas, at Nashville, continued arranging his order of battle to try to stop Hood's northward march. As some of Thomas's columns of supply wagons continued to come through northern Tennessee, attempting to stay ahead of Hood, the part of Thomas's Army of the Cumberland under Brigadier General John Schofield reached the town of Franklin, still twenty miles short of Nashville. Schofield was a West Pointer, a thirty-three-year-old who had graduated with Hood and Sheridan, and had until now played successful second-tier roles as a commander. With just hours to do it, Schofield built three strong defensive lines at Franklin, putting in place earthworks on the outside of which the enemy would have to penetrate sharpened locust branches that acted as barbed wire. The mission thrust upon Schofield by circumstances was to delay Hood's advance, and to offer protection to the Union supply columns as they neared Franklin, hoping to get them inside the Union lines before the Confederates struck those long lines of slow-moving wagons.

Schofield succeeded in doing this, sending the wagons on to Nashville. Now Schofield, facing south with 32,000 men, and Hood, opposite him facing north with 38,000, had decisions to make. Thomas, still trying to complete his defenses at Nashville, wired Schofield that he hoped he could hold on at Franklin and delay Hood "for three more days." The outnumbered Schofield replied that he was lucky just to have made it to Franklin ahead of Hood. He told Thomas: "The slightest mistake on my part, or failure of a subordinate during the last three days might have proved disastrous."

The decision facing Hood was whether to attack Schofield immediately at Franklin or to let him cross the Harpeth River beyond that town and move north to join Thomas at Nashville. The generals advancing under Hood were worried about the expanse of flat land that lay between them and the defenses at Franklin. Remembering Gettysburg, where Lee's final fatal advance known as Pickett's Charge took place across three-quarters of a mile of open ground after a heavy preliminary artillery bombardment of the Union positions, they pointed out that here their men would have to cross two miles in full view of the enemy, and that they had few cannon available to soften up the Union lines. Hood's subordinate Major General Frank Cheatham told him, "I don't like the looks of this fight. The Federals are in an excellent position, and are well fortified." Hood answered, "I would prefer to fight them here when they have only eight hours to fortify, than to strike them at Nashville, where they have been strengthening themselves for three years or more."

With Schofield staying in place and Hood deciding to attack him, the men on both sides became part of one of the greatest and ultimately bloodiest panoramas of the war. At three-thirty in the afternoon on November 30, more than 20,000 Confederates lined up on open ground, bayonets fixed on their muskets. From east to west, the formation of men about to attack extended for three miles, with 125 regimental battle flags spaced out along that line, waving in a light breeze. When a signal flag was dropped from behind them on Winstead Hill, "the line moved forward steady as a clock." For one of the few times in the war, bands played as they advanced to within range of the Union artillery: Hood's men moved forward to the sounds of "Dixie," the Confederate "Bonnie Blue Flag," and "The Girl I Left Behind Me," the old Regular Army tune to which many officers on both sides had marched when they were cadets parading on the Plain at West Point. A Union soldier watching them all come said, "Nearer and nearer the Confederates approached with all the precision of a dress parade." Another Federal defender recalled, "It was a grand sight! For the moment we were spellbound with admiration, although they were our hated foes." He also observed this, as the soldiers in grey marched forward through the grass:

> *As forerunners well in advance, could be seen a line of rabbits, bounding along for a few leaps, and then would stop and look back and listen, but scamper off again . . . and quail by the thousands, in coveys here and there would rise and settle, and rise again to the warm sunlight, and finally they rose high in the air and whirred off to the gray skylight of the north.*

Then the fighting exploded, and raged on for five hours. Early in the battle, the Confederates captured a section of the defensive positions in the center of the Union line, but Brigadier General Emerson Opdyke of Ohio, acting on his own initiative, threw his reserve brigade into hand-to-hand fighting that blunted and finally threw back what looked as if it could become a Confederate breakthrough. The entire Union line stiffened; behind the strong earthworks, Schofield's men started pouring a murderous fire into a series of attacks by Hood's forces.

Despite the width of the attacking and defending lines, in one area of a few acres thousands of men became locked in combat at close quarters. As it became twilight, a fifteen-year-old drummer boy from a Missouri Confederate regiment attempted to attack a Union artillery piece single-handedly. With his drum slung on his back, he "thrust a fence rail into the mouth of a cannon thinking, by his brave act, to stop the use of that gun. It was heavily loaded at the time and was fired, tearing the poor boy to shreds, so that nothing was found of him." Captain Aaron Baldwin of the 6th Ohio light artillery kept firing at point-blank range into waves of Confederates. He later wrote, "At every discharge of my gun there were two distinct sounds, first the explosion, then the [shattering of] bones." Twenty-four-year-old Major Arthur MacArthur of the 12th Wisconsin, who would one day have a famous soldier son named Douglas, moved ahead on horseback, saber drawn, heading toward a Confederate major who was coming the other way with the staff of a Confederate battle flag gripped in one hand and a pistol in the other. Amid all the firing, MacArthur's horse was shot from under him and a bullet hit him in the shoulder. As he continued to fight his way forward on foot, the Confederate major shot him in the chest. MacArthur thrust his sword into the major's stomach; as the man went down, he shot MacArthur again, through the knee. (MacArthur recovered, and would end the war as a lieutenant colonel; staying in the United States Army, he rose to be a general, serving in both Cuba and the Philippines during the Spanish-American War.)

At nine that night, Hood called off his attacks; the firing back and forth finally died away at eleven. In the dark, Schofield withdrew across the Harpeth River and successfully made his way toward Thomas's forces at Nashville, but at that point neither he nor Thomas understood how badly the day's fighting had crippled Hood's Army of Tennessee. The Confederates had lost 6,252 men killed, wounded, or missing, two and a half times the number of Union casualties, but in this battle the numbers did not begin to tell the story. Who had won a battle was often measured by which force controlled the ground at the end of the day; the Confederates now held Franklin, but on the porch of a house in the town lay the bodies of five valuable Confederate generals, and a sixth had been mortally wounded and would die days later. It was the largest number of Confederate generals killed on a single day during the war. The greatest loss to the Confederacy was the death of Major General Patrick Ronayne Cleburne, the Irish-born soldier who began distinguishing himself at Shiloh, fought brilliantly at Chickamauga, threw back Sherman's attacks at Missionary Ridge during the Battle of Chattanooga, and had won for himself the reputation of being the "Stonewall Jackson of the West." In addition to the loss of generals, fifty-four of Hood's regimental commanders had been killed, wounded, or captured. On Schofield's night march north to join Thomas's forces in the stronger defensive positions Thomas had prepared at Nashville, the Union soldiers carried with them thirty-two Confederate regimental battle flags.

Despite ruinous losses, the ever-aggressive Hood was ready to push on toward Nashville; two days later, the first of his units began appearing south of the city. The credit for the action at Franklin rightly went to Schofield, but it was Thomas who reached Nashville ahead of Hood and started organizing and placing his forces in a way that could produce such a favorable result. At this moment, as December began, it seemed unthinkable that within two weeks Grant, Lincoln, and Stanton would be drafting an order relieving Thomas of command.

IV

On December 6, Lincoln's annual Message to Congress was read to a joint session of the House and Senate held in the House of Representatives. An immensely important document, summing up 1864 in so many ways, it was received this way: "A complete silence pervaded the vast hall and the breathless, crowded galleries"—visitors' galleries in which many women were present. Keeping with tradition, Lincoln was not there, but his voice permeated every paragraph of what he had synthesized from the materials brought to him in the "shop" across the past weeks.

Noah Brooks was in the visitors' gallery; the next day he wrote this description of the occasion for his newspaper in California. He began with the arrival of John Hay, carrying the official copy of the message:

> *Precisely at one o'clock yesterday the private secretary of the President appeared at the bar of the House of Representatives with the annual message of the President . . . in a few minutes, Clerk [of the House Edward] McPherson, in a loud and clear voice, took up the document and began with the terse and litany-like exordium: "Again the blessings of health and abundant harvests claim our profoundest gratitude to Almighty God." Simultaneously with the utterance of the words a host of small, agile pages [Congressional page boys] spread themselves all over the hall, laying upon the desks of the members printed copies of the message which were eagerly seized and read.*

The first topic of Lincoln's message dealt with foreign affairs, which he deemed to be "reasonably satisfactory." He described Mexico, where Maximilian's forces continued to fight the nationalists under Juárez, as being "a theatre of civil war." In what was technically true, although it did not reflect his administration's dislike for Maximilian's presence on an artificial Mexican throne, he said, "We have . . . strictly maintained neutrality between the belligerents." Regarding Canada, he did not mention the recent St. Albans raid or other forays from Canada by Confederate agents, but made it clear that the United States considered itself "at liberty to increase the naval armament upon the [Great] lakes" if needed. He felt that "the Colonial authorities of Canada . . . with the approval of the imperial [British] government . . . will take the necessary measures to prevent new incursions across the border."

• • •

While basing his worldview partly on Seward's information, Lincoln clearly saw a future with greater global communication. His message spoke with enthusiasm about "the proposed overland telegraph between America and Europe by way of Behring's [sic] Straits and Arctic Russia," and he added, "I learn, with much satisfaction, that the noble design of a telegraphic communication between the eastern coast of America and Great Britain has been renewed with full expectation of its early accomplishment."

Lincoln turned to an overall area in which no one in his administration had a broader vision than his: the nation's domestic future, a seamless web of increasing population, westward expansion, and increasing financial activity and industrial production. Calling the encouragement of immigration "this great national policy"—during the war, 615,000 men, women, and children had arrived—he said, "I regard our emigrants [sic] as one of the principal replenishing streams which are appointed by Providence to repair the ravages of internal war, and its wastes of national strength and health. All that is needed is to secure that stream in its present fullness." Discussing the economy, he presented some figures but referred his congressional audience to a separate detailed Treasury report, adding that more taxes were needed "to meet the expenses consequent upon the war." He suggested individual savings accounts "exempt from taxation" that would "enable every prudent person to set aside a small annuity against a possible day of want." In language and thought reminiscent of Benjamin Franklin, he summed up his thought on individual investment with this: "The great advantage of citizens being creditors as well as debtors, with relation to the public debt, is obvious. Men readily perceive that they cannot be much oppressed by a debt that they owe to themselves."

Even at this point in the message, it was clear that a lot of creative and productive thinking had gone on in the White House and in Lincoln's cabinet, apart from the conduct of the war and the nation's present and future political situation. Lincoln moved to something with far-reaching implications, and those who had known him for a long time could see in this the former Whig who believed in having strong institutions of central government.

The national banking system is proving to be acceptable to capitalists and to the people. On the twenty-fifth of November five hundred and eighty-

four national banks had been organized, a considerable number of which were conversions from State banks . . . it is hoped that, very soon, there will be in the United States, no banks of issue not authorized by Congress, and no bank-note circulation not secured by government. . . . The national system will create a reliable and permanent influence in support of the national credit, and protect people against losses in the use of paper money.

Then Lincoln spoke of the West. "The territories of the Union are generally in a condition of prosperous growth." Idaho and Montana had been "only partially organized," but Nevada had been admitted as a state. "The great enterprise of connecting the Pacific with the Atlantic States by railways and telegraph lines has been entered upon with a vigor that gives assurance of success." Apparently changing his earlier view that exploitation of gold being found this year in the West might unsettle the economy, Lincoln reported: "Numerous discoveries of gold, silver and cinnabar mines have been added to the many heretofore known[,] and the country occupied by the Sierra Nevada and Rocky mountains . . . now teems with enterprising labor . . . the product of the mines of precious metals in that region has, during the year, reached, if not exceeded, one hundred millions in value."

Now, some 4,000 words into the report, Lincoln wrote, "The war continues." Seeing the effects of war in the round, Lincoln pointed this out: "Since the last annual message all the important lines and positions then occupied by our troops have been maintained, and our arms have steadily advanced; thus liberating the regions left in rear; so that Missouri, Kentucky, Tennessee and parts of other States have again produced reasonably fair crops."

Sherman was much on Lincoln's mind: during these days, when a friend remarked that the president did not even notice that he had just spoken to him, Lincoln said in explanation, "I was thinking of a man down south." His message said this:

The most remarkable feature in the military operations of the year is General Sherman's attempted march of three hundred miles directly through the insurgent region. It tends to show a great increase of our relative strength that our General-in-Chief [Grant] should feel able to confront and hold in check every active force of the enemy, and yet to de-

tach a well-appointed large army to move on such an expedition. The re-
sult not yet being known, conjecture in regard to it is not here indulged.

Congressmen hearing this would not have sensed the debate that preceded Grant's finally giving Sherman permission to head for Savannah.
Even now, Lincoln spoke of the "attempted march," and "the result not
being known." He had deleted from a draft of the message this reference
to Grant: "We must conclude that he feels our cause could, if need be,
survive the loss of the whole detached force [62,000 men]; while, by the
risk, he takes a chance for the great advantages that would follow success."

Now the message came to political changes and results. When the
clerk of the House read Lincoln's reference to Maryland, which had voted
for a new antislavery constitution, Noah Brooks said that the man's voice
"rang out clarion-like with the words, 'Maryland is secure to liberty and
Union for all the future . . . rebellion will no more claim Maryland. Like
another foul spirit, being driven out, it may seek to tear her, but it will
woo her no more.' These triumphant and poetic words brought forth a
burst of applause."

Fully aware that many of the elected politicians who would hear what
he had to say had opposed him in the presidential election less than a
month past, Lincoln indulged himself in an unassailable statement rather
than any finger-pointing. "The most reliable indication of public purpose
in this country is derived through our popular elections." He used this
mention of his enormous electoral mandate to lobby for the passage of a
previously rejected "amendment of the Constitution abolishing slavery
throughout the United States. . . . I venture to recommend the reconsid-
eration and passage of the measure at the present session."

Lincoln's summation began with proof that, despite all the suffering,
the Union was stronger than ever. He admitted that he could not explain
the growth in population—immigration alone had certainly outstripped
battlefield losses—but he gave as just one example: "The number in organized territories is triple now what it was four years ago, while thousands,
white and black, join us [in the freed area] as the national arms press back
the insurgent lines." Combining population, agricultural products, coal
and other mineral mining: "The national resources, then, are unex-
hausted, and, as we believe, inexhaustible."

Lincoln presented a bright picture, but the guns were still firing, and men dying. Some senators and representatives listening to this remained Peace Democrats. Even those of the public who had voted for Lincoln yearned for peace, and nearly 2 million had not voted for him. There had been peace-feelers, mostly from the North; defiant statements continued to stream from Jefferson Davis, and brave men like those under Lee demonstrated every day that they would obey orders to fight on. The question remained, what to do now? Lincoln gave the Congress and the nation an eloquent answer, one that began with a painful reality concerning Jefferson Davis and moved to a note of hope.

> *The manner of continuing the effort remains to choose . . . it seems to me that no attempt at negotiation with the insurgent leader could result in any good. He would accept nothing short of the severance of the Union— precisely what we will not and cannot give. His declarations to this effect are explicit and oft-repeated. He does not deceive us. He affords us no excuse to deceive ourselves. He cannot voluntarily reaccept the Union; we cannot voluntarily yield it. . . . If we yield, we are beaten; if the Southern people fail him, he is beaten.*

Now Lincoln, knowing that his words would reach the South as well as the North, offered a different possibility. "What is true, however, of him who leads the insurrection, is not necessarily true of those who follow. Although he cannot accept the Union, they can . . . at any moment, have peace simply by laying down their arms and submitting to the national authority." All too prophetically, Lincoln in effect told the South that the longer it fought on, the greater would be the chances of a harsh period of postwar Reconstruction. He indicated that he was ready to continue a policy of "general pardon and amnesty" for everyone but the highest Confederate leaders, with that "door . . . still open to all," but he could foresee a situation in which "more rigorous measures than heretofore shall be adopted."

Much had been said about the constitutionality of the Emancipation Proclamation, and Lincoln himself had agreed that he had signed it as an executive "war powers" measure that could be revoked by a postwar Congress. It needed to be superseded by the constitutional amendment to abolish slavery that he had again urged the Congress to enact, but he wanted to make clear that, whatever the future congressional representatives of the public might do, he would never be part of any attempt to revoke his Proclamation. "If the people should, by whatever mode or means, make it an Executive duty to re-enslave such persons, another, and not I, must be their instrument to perform it."

Finally, Lincoln intended to cut through any possible ambiguities about the prospects for peace, and he used the last sentence of his message to do that. "In stating a single condition of peace, I mean simply to say that the war will cease on the part of the government, whenever it shall have ceased on the part of those who began it."

Brooks reported the reaction. "When the noble sentences which conclude the message were read there was a long, loud, and continued burst of applause, which the Speaker but feebly tried to still." Men of both parties "shook hands kindly and smilingly." They had heard the words of a masterful, optimistic, healing document. Lincoln had displayed statesmanship and stewardship; he had committed the Congress to nothing for which it was not ready; he had avoided partisanship. He said nothing about new or personally favored policies for Reconstruction, other than to suggest that Southerners would be well advised to end the war quickly. "The verdict of all men," Brooks wrote, "is that the message is immensely strengthening for the President, and that while it has all the dignity and polish of a first-rate state paper, it has strong common sense and practical knowledge of details which will commend the document to the minds of the 'simple people.'" Even the crusty arch-Radical congressman Thaddeus Stevens of Pennsylvania, eager to punish the South, concluded, according to Brooks, that "the message is the best and wisest the President has ever sent to Congress."

As if having his 6,000-word report read before every member of Congress were not enough for one day, Lincoln also sent this over to the Senate: "I nominate Salmon P. Chase of Ohio, to be Chief Justice of the Supreme Court of the United States, vice [succeeding] Roger B. Taney, deceased." Controversial though Chase had been, with much speculation concerning who would replace Taney and several men vying for the position, the Senate promptly and unanimously confirmed the appointment. That evening, Chase wrote Lincoln a note thanking him "for this mark of your confidence." In one more demonstration of how the man who had wanted so desperately to be president would say whatever he felt a situation demanded, Chase closed with, "Be assured that I prize your confidence & goodwill more than nomination or office."

There would be differing accounts of what Lincoln said about naming Chase. Without expressing a view on how Chase might perform, he told his friend Ward Lamon, "His *appointment* will satisfy the Radicals and after that they will not dare to kick up against any appointment I make." Chase's supporters praised Lincoln for his generosity of spirit in naming a man who, even though a member of his cabinet, had criticized him and worked against him. In two private conversations, Lincoln revealed what were probably his true feelings about appointing Chase. One friend recalled that, referring to the heated triangular irons used to press clothes, Lincoln said "he would sooner have eat flat irons than do it." Navy Secretary Welles wrote in his diary that, speaking of the chair made from elk antlers that was recently presented to him, "The President told [Democratic Senator Zachariah] Chandler of New Hampshire, who remonstrated against such selections, that he would rather have swallowed his buckhorn chair than to have nominated Chase."

At the end of this day when his message was read to Congress and Chase had been nominated and confirmed, Lincoln found a crowd outside the White House serenading him. He appeared at the windows and confessed to them that he really had nothing to say. As reported in the *New York Tribune*, this elicited "laughter and cheering." Lincoln evidently felt he should not leave the crowd with only that. He continued with, "I have no good news to tell you, and yet I have no bad news to tell. We have talked of elections until there is nothing more to say about them." Turning to the subject of the war, he said of Sherman, from whom nothing had been heard during the three weeks since he marched out of Atlanta, "The most interesting news we have is from Sherman. We all know where he went in at, but I can't tell where he will come out at." This brought "cheers and cries, 'he'll come out all right.'" The *Tribune* recorded Lincoln's final words to the crowd: "I will now close by proposing three cheers for Gen. Sherman and the army." (Privately, Lincoln had a colorful way of describing the strategy that he hoped was working, with Grant locking Lee in combat in northern Virginia while Sherman sliced through Georgia: "Grant has the bear by the hind leg while Sherman takes off its hide.")

As for what Sherman and his men were in fact doing, as they marched through Georgia they began to exceed what Sheridan had done in laying waste the Shenandoah Valley. The original orders to the troops were to limit foraging to supplies needed by the Union Army and to avoid entering Southern homes, but this restriction was soon ignored. The troops went quickly from destroying farm equipment, or burning a barn that stored crops that could feed Confederate soldiers, to looting houses. Sherman later wrote, "I know that in the beginning, I too had the old West Point notion that pillaging was a capital crime, and punished it by shooting," but soon "ceased to quarrel with our men about such minor things."

How ready Sherman was to abandon this policy could be seen by his earlier statement to Grant that in Georgia he could bring about "the utter destruction of its roads, houses and people." As his troops marched through weakly defended but intensely hostile territory, there were virtually no cases of rape, murder, or beating of civilians, but the Northern men became aware of the virulent hatred that most Southern women felt for those who were coming into their land and killing their men. (Sherman could see how he could be regarded as "the Vandal Chief," and wrote his wife Ellen, "They regard us as the Romans did the Goths, and the parallel is not unjust.")

Examples of how emotions on both sides could escalate occurred when a column of Sherman's men came to Milledgeville, Georgia. It was here that the troops saw for the first time some Union soldiers who had escaped from the Confederate prison camp at Andersonville. Starved and sick, with what a colonel from Indiana described as a "wild-animal stare" as they spoke, these living skeletons told tales of their mistreatment that quickly spread through Sherman's ranks. When a woman in Milledgeville came up to a Union soldier on the street and spat on him, he and the men with him did not touch her; they burnt down her house. At the same time, the troops learned that Jefferson Davis had issued orders to Confederate officers to block their advance by using "sub-terra shells [land mines]." Sherman's response was to issue this order: when his men suspected that land mines had been laid in front of them, they were to use Confederate prisoners to take the risks of digging them up.

The destruction became wide-scale. Houses began to be burnt, particularly large houses owned by slaveholders. At times, the columns into which Sherman had divided his army moved forward several miles apart. The headquarters companies of major units carried flares that could be shot aloft at night, so that each column would know where the others were. This proved to be unnecessary: the location of each advancing corps could be seen by the flames along its route.

From Sherman on down, most of the men in this army of veterans had hardened their hearts. Although they were encountering only light resistance, some of their comrades were being killed and wounded. Because this army had no rear bases with hospitals, maimed men had to be carried along day after day in jolting wagons, with no hope of receiving full medical attention until the march ended. Some Union troops were captured in surprise Confederate forays. Throughout the ranks, officers and men felt that accomplishing their mission swiftly, taking enemy territory and destroying whatever could sustain Confederate soldiers and Southern civilians, would bring the war to an end faster and with less bloodshed on both sides. A soldier from Wisconsin wrote his parents, "Anything and Everything, if it will help us and weaken them, is my motto." A man on this march later spoke of the ultimate goal: "The prevailing feeling among the men was a desire to finish the job; they wanted to get back home."

Mile by mile, the March to the Sea produced a terrible paradox. As Sherman's men captured hundreds of Southern plantations, many thousands of suddenly freed slaves, determined to stay close to the Union troops they hailed as their liberators, fell in with them on their march. The advancing columns were not equipped to handle this, although the soldiers fed these refugees who insisted on accompanying them. The first taste of freedom for these slaves involved scenes such as this, described by an officer from Indiana.

> It was very touching to see the vast number of colored women following us with babies in their arms, and little ones . . . clinging to their tattered skirts. One poor creature, while nobody was looking, hid two boys, five years old, in a wagon, intending, I suppose, that they should see the land of freedom if she couldn't. Babies tumbled from the backs of mules to which they had been told to cling, and were drowned in the swamps, while mothers stood by the roadside crying for their lost children and doubting whether to continue with the advancing army.

It seemed almost certain that a disaster of some size would attend this disorganized exodus, and it came about on December 8, at a place near Savannah called Ebeneezer Creek. Sherman was not present; the senior officer was Brigadier General Jefferson C. Davis, a man not related to the Confederate president. A column of Davis's Fourteenth Corps was on a pontoon bridge crossing a small but deep river called Ebeneezer Creek. Just behind them, a crowd of black refugees—men, women, and children—were on the riverbank, waiting their turn to follow them across. A unit of Confederate cavalry general Joseph Wheeler's horsemen appeared, galloping toward the end of this floating bridge that the vulnerable strung-out line of Union soldiers was still crossing.

Seeing this threat to the rear of his column, as soon as the last of his men crossed the bridge, Davis ordered it to be cut loose from the riverbank where the refugees were still waiting to cross to safety. Stranded there, the freed slaves were terrified that the Confederates riding down upon them would kill them for casting their lot with the Northern soldiers they saw as being their guardians. They began leaping into the water in an effort to escape by crossing the creek. Most could not swim: despite the efforts many Union soldiers made to save them, an undetermined but large number of black men, women, and children drowned.

It was only one incident in Sherman's massive march; when it was reported to him, he supported Davis's decision to cut loose a pontoon bridge to save his vulnerable troops from an attack by enemy horsemen who were right on their heels. Radicals in Congress saw this tragedy as demonstrating a cruel indifference to the blacks' fate, and as indicative of views Sherman had sometimes expressed as to their racial inferiority. Sherman's recorded thoughts included his belief that "the negro should be a free race, but not put on any equality with the Whites," and in a letter to an old friend in St. Louis he wrote, "A nigger as such is a most excellent fellow, but he is not fit to marry, to associate, or vote with me, or mine." Those opinions were widespread among whites in the North as well as the South but, ironically, Sherman was in fact doing more to free the slaves than anyone but Lincoln himself. The reports reaching Washington about Ebeneezer Creek subsequently prompted Stanton to conduct what became his own private inquiry into the matter. Twenty black leaders in the Savannah area, most of them ministers and none under duress, assured him that "we have confidence in General Sherman, and think what concerns us could not be in better hands." They also said of his handling of the complicated overall situation involving newly freed blacks: "His conduct and deportment toward us characterized him as a friend and a gentleman."

On December 10, Sherman reached Savannah. He had moved 62,000 men through 225 miles of enemy territory in twenty-four days. He soon had the port city surrounded on its landward sides and knew that the

United States Navy controlled the waters off the coast. Sherman decided not to attack, but to wait and see if Savannah's 18,000 defenders would surrender. A complicated situation confronted him. He had yet to accomplish a badly needed linking up with the navy's ships. Sherman's men would soon need more to eat, and for the moment they could not get any of the supplies and medical attention that those vessels could provide. In the inaccessible area of marshes and rice paddies surrounding Savannah, it was difficult to find any solid shoreline other than within the city itself. The ships cruising just off the coast were looking for Sherman; they knew his objective was Savannah, but to this moment not one soul outside his army knew the location of Sherman and his 62,000 men.

That problem was about to be solved. The Confederates' Fort McAllister, a lightly garrisoned post on the south bank of the Ogeechee River, below the city, protected the city's access to the Atlantic, and its twenty-three cannon denied any invading fleet the opportunity to come close enough to bombard it. Although keeping to his decision not to launch a major attack on Savannah itself, within three days Sherman had one of his divisions ready to storm the fort. Just before sunset on December 13, with his selected division about to make its attack, Sherman was watching from the roof of a rice mill beside the river. A Union steamship entered the mouth of the river; unsure of the situation, from downstream she used her signal flags to ask whoever might be there, "Is Fort McAllister taken?" Sherman signaled back, "Not yet, but in fifteen minutes it will be." Fifteen minutes later, after a tactically perfect attack, the fort surrendered.

Savannah's days were numbered. Sherman tightened the noose around the city, but wanted to spare the loss of his men's lives that would occur if a final attack had to be made across the rice paddies and marshes surrounding Savannah. He hoped to see a white flag wave above the city; knowing that might not happen, he left open for the more than 15,000 defenders a route of retreat to the north—a causeway that ran through the flooded rice fields.

V

As Sherman gave Savannah time to avoid destruction, a tense situation continued to unfold in both Nashville and Washington, one that revealed a lot about several people, including Lincoln. Despite his losses at Franklin, Hood had immediately pushed all his remaining forces into place in front of Nashville and started a siege of the city. Hood hoped that Thomas would come out from behind his defenses and attack him, possibly giving his Army of Tennessee the chance to inflict the kind of losses that Schofield had caused him to suffer at Franklin.

In Washington, Lincoln expected Thomas to go on the offensive immediately. There were things he did not know: at Nashville, unusually bad December weather covered the fields and roads with ice, and Thomas was busy incorporating into his Army of the Cumberland 15,000 reinforcements that had arrived from Kentucky. He was also waiting for his cavalry units to find additional horses that would bring them up to far greater strength than that of Hood's horsemen.

Taking stock of his situation, Thomas wired Chief-of-Staff Halleck in Washington that he wanted to wait a few days before attacking Hood. He might as well have fired a cannonball into the War Department. As soon as Stanton saw the telegram, he conferred with Lincoln, who was so unhappy about a delay that it prompted Stanton to fire off a message to Grant at City Point that said in part: "The President feels solicitous about the disposition of Thomas to lay in fortifications for an indefinite period. . . . This looks like the McClellan . . . strategy of do nothing and let the rebels raid the country. The President wishes you to consider the matter."

All this hit a nerve with Grant, who believed in attacking whenever that possibility presented itself, and still remembered Lincoln's impatience when he had not sent Sheridan into action in the Valley sooner than he did. On December 2, he fired off two telegrams to Thomas within two hours of each other, urging him to go on the offensive. That night, Thomas replied with a recital of his difficulties and promised to attempt an attack "in a few more days." Grant held off further urging for three days but then began increasing the pressure on Thomas. He began with a wire saying, "Hood should be attacked where he is. Time strengthens him, in all probability, as much as it does you." The next day, thinking of how Hood and Thomas had maneuvered against each other in what was a withdrawal north to Nashville, he warned against anything that could produce a retreat north of Nashville: "Attack at once. . . . There is great danger of delay resulting in a campaign back to the Ohio River." The day after that, Stanton, who was always conferring with Lincoln, fanned the flames with this, to Grant: "Thomas seems unwilling to attack because it is hazardous, as if all war is anything but hazardous." Grant answered with, "You probably saw my order to Thomas to attack? If he does not do it promptly I would recommend superceeding [*sic*] him by Schofield, leaving Thomas subordinate." A day later, he wired Halleck to start more reinforcements moving to support Thomas, adding, "If Thomas has not struck yet he ought to be ordered to hand his command over to Schofield"—odd language to use, considering that Grant had the right to issue that order himself. Demonstrating the ambivalent feeling he still had about what Thomas could do, he finished with, "There is no better man to repel an attack than Thomas—but I fear he is too cautious ever to take the initiative."

This produced a reply an hour later from Halleck: the Union Army's chief of staff was not a man to stick his neck out, and his office was next to Stanton's, where Lincoln was often to be found. "If you wish Genl Thomas to be relieved from command," this communication from Halleck to his superior read, "give the order. No one here will, I think, interfere . . . [but] no one here, as far as I am informed, wishes Genl Thomas' removal."

Here was the first of two mysteries. Why Lincoln, Stanton, and Halleck had gone from insisting that Thomas should attack, to remaining neutral about his being relieved when he did not, never became clear. It was all back on Grant's shoulders, with the implication that Lincoln was among those who did not wish "Genl Thomas's removal." On December 7, after five days of trying to get Thomas to advance on Hood, Grant wrote him in a message that combined concern and a touch of disdain, "Why not attack at once? By all means avoid the contingency of a footrace to see which, you or Hood, can beat [the other] to the Ohio." He even added, in an uncharacteristic wheedling tone, "Use the means at your command and you can do this and cause a rejocing [*sic*] that will resound from one end of the land to the other."

In Washington, Halleck became alarmed. He started ordering all the western commands to reinforce Thomas, and thought was given to asking various governors to start raising 60,000 men if Hood broke through at Nashville and kept on going to the Ohio River.

Now the second unusual element, one of intrigue, entered this troubling picture. As apprehension mounted in Washington, Schofield, the victor at Franklin, apparently went out of the chain of command to further undermine Grant's confidence in Thomas. At some point, he sent

Grant a telegram, a copy of which was found, saying, "Many officers here are of the opinion that Thomas is certainly too slow in his movements."

Uncertainty clouded much of what happened next. At 11 A.M. on December 9, a week after starting his efforts to put Thomas on the offensive, Grant wired Halleck, "Please telegraph orders relieving him at once and placing Schofield in command." Apparently, this also set in motion a directive from Lincoln relieving Thomas. Two hours after that, Grant received this from Thomas, who knew the authorities in Washington were displeased with him, but did not know he was about to be relieved.

I had nearly completed my preparations to attack the enemy tomorrow morning, but a terrible storm of freezing rain has come on to-day which will make it impossible for our men to fight to any advantage. I am therefore compelled to wait for the storm to break and make the attack immediately after . . .

Maj Genl Halleck informs me that you are very much dissatisfied with my delay in attacking. I can only say that I have done all in my power to prepare, and if you should find it necessary to relieve me I shall submit without a murmur.

Five and a half hours after receiving that, Grant decided not to relieve Thomas, wiring Halleck that he would "suspend the order relieving him until it is seen whether he will do anything." He also changed his mind about Schofield, and ordered Major General John Logan to start for Nashville, ready to take over from Thomas if necessary. Grant wanted action, whatever that required. It even occurred to him that Hood might try to pass right around Thomas, leaving him in his entrenchments at Nashville, and march on north. "If you delay attack longer," he told Thomas on December 11, "the mortifying spectacle will be witnessed of a rebel army moving for the Ohio River, and you will be forced to act, accepting such weather as you find. Let there be no further delay." He had already told Thomas that he was deferring an order to relieve him, and at the end of this message he repeated, "Delay no longer for weather or reinforcements."

At heart, Grant was always a man of action. After waiting three more days, on the morning of December 14 he sent a message in code from his City Point headquarters to his subordinate generals Meade and Ord, who were facing Lee on the Petersburg-Richmond line of battle. He told them, "I am unexpectedly called away," and gave them instructions on how to forward telegrams to him. Grant was calling himself away. He was going up to Washington, to talk things over at the War Department before heading west to Nashville and taking command there.

The weather accomplished what Grant, Lincoln, Stanton, and Halleck could not. On the afternoon of December 14, the day after Sherman's capture of Fort McAllister at Savannah, with the sun warm and skies suddenly clear at Nashville, Thomas assembled his corps commanders and handed them copies of his Special Field Order No. 342. In ten succinct paragraphs, he laid out his plan of battle. To Halleck in Washington, he sent this message: "The ice having melted away today, the enemy will be attacked tomorrow morning."

The next day, while Grant traveled to Washington, George Thomas demonstrated that he was not "too cautious ever to take the initiative." At eight in the morning, one of his divisions made a diversionary attack on Hood's right; at ten o'clock, two of his corps smashed into the center of Hood's line, and this was followed by Schofield hitting his left. Then the cavalry force that Thomas had waited to rebuild, now 12,000 horses and men, hooked around Hood's left and started getting behind the Confederates on that flank.

Considering the difference in size between the opposing armies—by waiting for infantry and cavalry reinforcements, Thomas was now able to throw nearly 50,000 men at Hood's 23,000—the Confederates did well to survive the day. That night, unsure whether Hood would continue to fall back as he had been forced to do, Thomas reverted to his cautious self and did not push forward in the dark. At nine that evening, he sent this report to Halleck: "I attacked the enemy's left this morning, and drove it from the [Cumberland] river, below the city, very nearly to the Franklin pike, a distance about eight miles." Thomas described the capture of an enemy field headquarters and two columns of supply wagons, and said his men took "between 800 and 1,000 prisoners and 16 pieces of artillery." He added, "The troops behaved splendidly, all taking their share in assaulting and carrying the enemy's breast-works. . . . I shall attack the enemy again to-morrow, if he stands to fight." Although this report of a victorious day was sent from Nashville at 9 P.M., it did not reach the War Department until 11:25.

• • •

During the evening of the day that Thomas had destroyed a good part of Hood's Army of Tennessee, with no word of that yet reaching Washington, Grant was at the War Department in conference with Lincoln, Stanton, and Halleck. Lincoln pointed out that Thomas, five hundred miles away at Nashville, had a better chance of judging the situation than they did as they sat in the War Department. By this time, Grant was determined to relieve Thomas, going to Nashville to do it; Lincoln reluctantly decided this was not the moment for the commander-in-chief to overrule his general-in-chief.

Everyone went their separate ways, Lincoln to the White House, Stanton being driven to his house in a carriage, and Grant to the Willard Hotel, intending to go on to the railroad station from which he would take a midnight train for Louisville, on his way to Nashville. Somewhat before Thomas's message arrived at eleven twenty-five, a brief report came into the War Department Telegraph Office from Captain John Van Duzer of Thomas's staff, giving some details of the day's fighting and saying, "although the battle is not yet decided the whole action today was splendidly successful."

This message was addressed to Major Eckert, who ran the telegraph office, and placed him in a difficult situation. He had in his hands the final order from Grant removing Thomas but realized that this could change everything. Eckert ran downstairs with the two telegrams in his hand— Grant's relieving Thomas, and the news of Thomas's success—and leapt into the converted ambulance wagon that was always kept near the door in case couriers had to take messages to destinations around the city. When the horses clattered up to Stanton's house, Stanton swiftly came out and got in, and off they went to the White House. On the way, Eckert told him about the news from Nashville and then took from his pocket the order from Grant, the one relieving Thomas of command. Stanton asked Eckert if he had sent it. Eckert answered that he had not, and added, "Mister Secretary, I fear that I have violated a military rule and have placed myself in a position to be court-martialed." The usually brusque and crusty Stanton put his arm around Eckert's shoulder and said, "Major, if they court-martial you, they will have to court-martial me."

When they reached the White House, this occurred, as later recounted by a man to whom Eckert described it.

Eckert says he will never forget the tall, ghostly form of Lincoln in his
night-dress, with a lighted candle in his hands, as he appeared at the head
of the second story landing when the two callers were ushered up-stairs by
the doorkeeper. The President was, of course, highly delighted to receive
the news of Thomas's victory.

As this went on at the White House, another copy of Van Duzer's message of success was handed to Grant at the Willard Hotel by Captain Samuel H. Beckwith of Grant's staff, a communications officer who expected to get on the train for Louisville with him in a few minutes. Grant looked at it and told him, "I guess we will not go to Nashville." He promptly sent Thomas a telegram that began, "I was just on my way to Nashville but receiving a dispatch from Van Duzer detailing your splendid success of to-day I will go no further." Then, in line with his philosophy that the battle was never over, he added, "Push the enemy now, and give him no rest until he is entirely destroyed." After some advice on how Thomas should do this, he closed his message with, "Much is now expected." Thirty minutes later, at midnight, Grant realized that he had said not a word of congratulations, and in the meantime he had received the report sent by Thomas himself from Nashville at nine o'clock. He replied to the a message from Thomas with, "I congratulate you and the Army under your command . . . and feel a conviction that to-morrow will add more fruits to your victory."

The next morning, Lincoln sent Thomas a response to the news that combined both praise and a reaction like Grant's. He started by saying, "Please accept for yourself, officers, and men, the nation's thanks for your good work of yesterday." Lincoln added, in language suggesting that he still worried about how aggressive Thomas really was and whether he would now go in for the kill, "You made a magnificent beginning. A grand consummation is within your easy reach. Do not let it slip."

By the time Thomas was able to digest these words of praise and exhortations for swift further action, he had effectively shattered Hood's Army of Tennessee. It had not been easy. The battle's second day was marked by the bravery shown in an attack on a Confederate-held hill by a brigade of United States Colored Troops. The defending Confederate general, Brigadier General James T. Holtzclaw, a veteran of the battles of Shiloh, Chickamauga, and Chattanooga, paid them this tribute:

At 12 P.M. the enemy made a most determined charge on my right. Plac-
ing a negro brigade in front they gallantly charged up to the abatis [a line
of obstacles in front of a trench], forty feet in front, and were killed by
hundreds. Pressed on by their white brethren in the rear they continued
to come up in masses to the abatis, but they came to die. I have seen most
of the battle-fields of the West, but never saw dead men thicker than in
front of my two right regiments.

Holtzclaw's superior, Major General Henry D. Clayton, was also
impressed by how these regiments kept pressing home their attacks:
"Five color-bearers with their colors were shot down in a few steps of the
works, one of which, having inscribed on its folds, 'Eighteenth Regiment,
U. S. Colored Infantry, Presented by the Colored Ladies of Murfrees-
borough [Tennessee],' was brought in."

At Franklin, the climactic scene had been one in which, under a clear
sky and with bands playing, a line of 20,000 Confederates moved forward
in perfect order to be slaughtered. Here the roles were reversed, with the
Union troops attacking but also being thrown back in places. The skies
were grey and it was starting to drizzle, but as at Franklin, it was possible
to have a panoramic view—a Union officer later wrote his wife that he
could see "every move, attack or retreat. It was magnificent; what a grand
sight it was." Behind his position, "We could see the [state] capitol all day,
and the churches."

In midafternoon, Hood's defenses began crumbling. Watching some
veteran Confederate troops struggling through a muddy field to get away
from a larger number of Union soldiers chasing them and "shooting as
fast as the Devil," a Confederate infantry officer saw this retreat through
knee-deep mud as symbolic: "I now felt that the Confederacy was indeed
gone up, and that we were a ruined people."

All of Thomas's units were now attacking, through heavy rain that
began to turn into snow. Watching the entire Army of the Cumberland
move forward, one of Thomas's staff officers saw this:

It was more like a scene in a spectacular drama than a real incident in
war. The hillside in front, still green, dotted with the boys in blue swarm-
ing up the slope; the dark background of high hills beyond; the lowering
clouds, the waving flags, the [gunpowder] smoke slowly rising through

*the leafless treetops and drifting across the valleys; the wonderful outburst
of musketry; the ecstatic cheers . . .*

As the retreat became for a time an every-man-for-himself flight,
Hood watched in near-despair, saying of that moment in the darkening
late afternoon, "I beheld for the first and only time a Confederate army
abandon the field in confusion." He gave orders that rallied a rearguard;
placing themselves along the Franklin Pike, the road up which they had
confidently marched from the south to Franklin two weeks before, these
units held back Thomas's men under a sky that cleared to reveal a frozen
moon.

As Hood retreated through Franklin and continued south, the weather
came to his aid. Thomas's heavier-laden troops, traveling on what
Thomas described as "mud roads completely sogged with heavy rains,"
could not catch up with men who had every incentive to stay ahead of
them. Hood's Army of Tennessee retreated completely out of Tennessee,
into Alabama. Once again, some complained of Thomas being slow, but
Grant, Lincoln, Stanton, and Halleck began to understand and appreciate what the "Rock of Chickamauga" had done. Thomas, a major general
of Volunteers, received the coveted promotion to the same (and permanent) rank in the Regular Army.

Southern newspapers denounced Hood, and a cry arose to bring back
Joseph E. Johnston, whom Hood had replaced before Atlanta fell. The
fickleness of military fame was demonstrated when Hood's old friend
from Texas, Confederate senator Louis Wigfall told friends in Richmond,
"Hood is dead, smashed, gone up, finished." Hood resigned from command of the Army of Tennessee, an act that reduced him one grade in
rank, but he would lead men again, during the Confederacy's dark hours
immediately to come.

LINCOLN'S
LAST CHRISTMAS

Even as Christmas neared, Lincoln continued to deal with matters brought about by his reelection. (Everyone, of course, assumed that he would be president for another four years.) As always happened at this point in a reelected administration, resignations came to the president's desk. To replace Attorney General Edward Bates, Lincoln named James Speed of Kentucky, brother of his old friend Joshua Speed; James had among other things helped keep Kentucky in the Union, and acted as an important link between Kentucky and Lincoln's administration. Lincoln had become dissatisfied with the performance of Secretary of the Interior John P. Usher of Indiana, who was politically loyal to him but largely ineffectual. Usher did not want to leave, but Lincoln intended to ask him to resign and had Senator James Harlan of Iowa in mind to replace him.

The scramble for lower-level appointments and reappointments further wearied the exhausted president. During the campaign, he had vigorously wielded the power to promise and reward but, having been reelected, he wished that the line of job-seekers at the "shop" door would vanish. Talking to Senator Daniel Clark of New Hampshire, he asked, "Can't you and others start a public sentiment in favor of making no changes in office except for good and sufficient causes?" He added something that he had always known, but annoyed him now: "To remove a man is very easy, but when I go to fill his place, there are *twenty* applicants, and of these I must make *nineteen* enemies."

Change was coming within the White House itself. Mary Lincoln may never have known that Lincoln's private secretaries John Nicolay and John Hay referred to her as the "hell-cat," but she disliked them as much as they did her. During a visit east by Lincoln's friend Anson G. Henry, Lincoln's former personal physician whom he had appointed as the surveyor general of Washington State, she schemed with Henry to replace Nicolay with the journalist Noah Brooks, who acquiesced in the matter. Despite Nicolay's devotion to Lincoln, nearly four years of Mary had made him ready to move on; he had been studying French, and Lincoln, who did not announce a replacement for Nicolay, secured him a position as consul to Paris, to begin some months into 1865. Nicolay's friend, White House roommate, and "shop" coworker Hay also had his eye on France; the future secretary of state, now twenty-six, received the position of first secretary of legation in Paris, to start once he had a new staff in place at the White House. (By 1870, both Nicolay and Hay were back in the United States, and would begin their years of collaboration in writing their study of Lincoln and his administration.)

The war continued its relentless demands. On December 19, Lincoln issued a call for 300,000 volunteers "to serve for one, two, and three years." As before, if not enough men stepped forward, the number needed could be made up through a draft. Casualties continued to pile up in Virginia, and many men who enlisted in 1861 were coming to the end of their three-year terms. (Although the Enrollment Act of 1863 gave the government the power to conscript, the number of men who continued to volunteer and those who furnished paid substitutes, plus those who were exempted from serving for physical and other reasons, meant that only 46,437 men were actually drafted into the service during the entire war.)

At the moment, Lincoln was not watching any military operation nearly as closely as he had the struggle for Nashville, but he knew B. F. Butler was involved in an effort in which, working with the Navy, he would try to seize the Confederate-held port of Wilmington, North Carolina. Butler had in part redeemed his earlier failures by his success in preventing violence in New York City during the election, but Grant still wanted to be rid of him. This movement on Wilmington would be Butler's last chance.

Lincoln continued to receive belated congratulations on his reelection and letters expressing high hopes for the success of his next term in office.

He gave particular instructions that one of these letters be saved, noting on it that the well-wisher from whom it came "is one of the best men in the world." It was from his friend Judge Samuel D. Lockwood, of Batavia, Illinois. Lockwood, now seventy-five and ailing, was a former Illinois attorney general and Supreme Court justice who, after he retired, had worked with Lincoln on Illinois Central Railroad legal matters. He wrote Lincoln this:

> . . . *I feel fully conscious that heavier burden's* [sic] *& responsibilities never rested on the mind and heart of any man, but I sincerely hope & believe, that you will come out of them all with an unblemished reputation & the complete establishment for our Country of the Glorious principle enunciated in the Declaration of Independence, "That all men are created equal." If such shall be the result of your sacrifices & labours, no man need ever aspire to a more beneficent reputation. May God grant it.*
>
> *Please excuse this hasty scrawl. Ill health & cramp in my hand forbid my revision or copying it.*

II

With Lincoln, despite his national responsibilities, so much always came back to Illinois—who he had met there, what he had learned there as a lawyer and state legislator. On Christmas Eve, Lincoln's close friend Orville Browning, the former senator from Illinois who was now a prominent Washington lawyer and lobbyist, called on him at the White House. Browning put to Lincoln a business proposition that involved cotton. From a point early in the war, after the Battle of Shiloh in April of 1862 and the subsequent Federal occupation of Memphis, enormous quantities of Southern-grown cotton fell into Union hands. The Northern war effort required continued supplies of cotton for the manufacture of uniforms, tents, and bandages, among many other items. Some Southern planters burnt thousands of bales of cotton rather than have their stocks of the valuable commodity aid the Confederacy's enemies, but they were in a minority. Many speculators and some government figures, both in the North and the South, saw the differing advantages to be gained by what became, in effect, trading with the enemy.

"Cotton contracts" sprang up everywhere, most involving middlemen. A Northern businessman who claimed to "control" a substantial number of bales of cotton would work out a deal with a United States Treasury purchasing agent to sell his cotton on a certain date for three-quarters of the price for cotton being quoted that day in New York City. When the cotton was delivered, the trader was allowed to return to the South with goods whose value equaled one-third of the cotton just sold. Similar arrangements existed for the sale of Southern-grown tobacco and other commodities.

From the outset, many in the War Department pointed out that, while the items permitted to be bought and taken south could not include weapons of war, such things as medicine and food would strengthen the Confederacy's ability to fight. By 1864, Lincoln felt that the North's need for cotton outweighed whatever advantages the trade might give the Confederate armies. (He also had a questionable theory that having Northern greenbacks flowing to the South was economically useful to the North.) Although Lincoln wanted all loyal citizens to be eligible to participate in this trade, most of the middlemen participating in it did not want Northern newspapers and the public to grasp the essence of the situation. Put simply, Northern and Southern speculators, many of them shady characters, were making a profit by feeding Confederate troops who continued to kill and wound Union soldiers.

The profits could be huge: a speculator could buy a 400-pound bale of cotton in the South for $100 in greenbacks and sell it in the North for $500; then, reinvesting the share of his profit allowed him for purchase of Northern goods to take south, he could buy bacon, at 22 cents a pound, for which Southerners would pay $6 a pound in Confederate currency. After every kind of discount, fee, and expense, the trader could make more than $2,000 in Northern greenbacks on his original purchase of a hundred-dollar bale of cotton. Should the Congress decide to launch an investigation of all these practices, that might stop the flow of cotton and the generation of profits from its sale. Thus, by its nature and the realities of public perception, this commerce had to exist in a grey area.

Although nothing indicated that to this point, late in 1864, Lincoln had ever made money for himself from this trade, he had often been one of the officials who signed the permits needed by traders, documents giving them freedom from Union military authorities who would otherwise have stopped these shipments from passing through their lines. In this, he had favored family and friends, signing permits for them and for the associates of such political allies as the New York Republican leader Thurlow Weed.

It was against this background that Orville Browning came to Lincoln on Christmas Eve. In this era when state legislatures rather than the popular vote decided who would represent a state in the Senate, when the Illinois legislature had returned to Democratic control in 1862, it replaced Browning. He had nonetheless remained in Washington, practicing law and lobbying; as an influence-peddler, he had a number of dubious figures as clients. What Browning now put before Lincoln involved a prospective deal with a Copperhead lawyer from Illinois named James W. Singleton. Born in Virginia, Singleton had a brother serving in the Confederate Congress and had met with leading Confederate agents in Canada. Some thought that he was involved in various peace overtures to the Confederacy, but on returning from a trip to Canada in late November, Singleton had talked with Browning about a purely commercial deal. He convinced Browning that there was a lot of money to be made, legally, if Lincoln would give him a pass through the Union lines to Richmond. Once there, Singleton could organize a massive purchase of cotton, tobacco, and other products of the South, to be sold profitably in the North. He would also require papers authorizing the goods to be brought north.

In his diary entry for Christmas Eve, Browning said that during his talk with Lincoln, he "submitted to him for consideration a written proposition." (In a later diary entry, made when Lincoln went ahead with the paperwork, Browning wrote more explicitly about their Christmas Eve conversation, saying that he "talked with him about permitting Singleton to go South to buy Cotton, tobacco, &c.[,] a scheme out of which he, Singleton, Judge Hughes of the Court of Claims, Senator Morgan myself and some others, hoped to make some money, and do the Country some service.")

So there it stood. Lincoln was entering into a deal that was legal but perhaps an unethical conflict of interest, to be arranged by the Copperhead Singleton. If it worked out, Singleton would get a handsome commission, and Lincoln and Browning, along with Senator Edwin D. Morgan of New York, the former chairman of the Republican National Committee, stood "to make some money." Judge James Hughes of the Federal Court of Claims, based in New York, would be a useful partner.

He had dealt with many cotton claims and knew a lot about the arrangements that Treasury agents constantly made with self-styled cotton importers; a favorite place for those government employees to sit down and do that—and possibly get a kickback—was at Manhattan's fashionable Astor House.

Browning had spoken of making "some money." Just what he meant by that became clear in another diary entry he made, just after Singleton, armed with the right authorization from Lincoln, returned from a trip to Richmond: "He brought back contracts for seven millions of dollars worth of Cotton, Tobacco, Rosin and Turpentine, which will make us rich if we can only get it out." (Browning's dream was not to be. Three months later, during the Confederate evacuation of Richmond, all the tobacco involved in the deal—200,000 pounds of it—was burned in a warehouse as Lee and his men left the city.)

This was more than enough for Lincoln to be discussing with Browning or anyone else on Christmas Eve, but Lincoln made a statement on another matter that varied from all else he had said on that subject. "During the evening," Browning noted, "the President showed me all the correspondence between him and Greel[e]y in regard to the negotiations [the past July] at Niagara . . . and assured me that he had been misrepresented and misunderstood and that he had never entertained the purpose of making the abolition of slavery a condition precedent to the termination of the war, and the restoration of the Union."

This was puzzling. On July 18, in his "To Whom It May Concern" letter sent to Greeley at Niagara Falls, Lincoln had spelled out the terms on which he would be willing to enter peace talks. In addition to making certain that the Confederate envoys had authority to negotiate, the preconditions set forth in that letter read, "the integrity of the Union, and the abandonment of slavery." Here, five months later, two lawyers, two men familiar with the issues and terminology, one a former senator and the other the president, were looking at "all the correspondence." Presumably, the documents in front of them included the copy of that letter of July 18, there in the "shop" and endorsed by Lincoln, that became a permanent part of Lincoln's presidential papers. Those had been the conditions for peace—the restoration of the Union and the ending of slavery. Perhaps on this Christmas Eve, Lincoln wished to believe that he had tried to hold out more of an olive branch to the Confederacy than he had.

III

The next morning, Washington began Christmas Day hearing the window-rattling sound of cannon booming away in celebration of a victory. The War Department Telegraph Office had received a wire from Sherman to Lincoln. Sent from Savannah on December 22 but arriving only now because of routing difficulties, it read, "I beg to present you as a Christmas gift the city of Savannah with 150 heavy guns & plenty of ammunition & also about 25000 bales of cotton." The general defending Savannah, William J. Hardee, had taken advantage of the escape route out of the city to the north that Sherman left open for him. It meant that Sherman's men would have to fight Hardee's troops, along with many more Confederate soldiers, at other places, but a beautiful city and its civilian population were left relatively undisturbed. Sherman would soon be leading his army north in a harsh campaign through the Carolinas, but he had begun a military occupation of Savannah that would be noted for its considerate treatment of the residents.

The day after Christmas, Lincoln sent Sherman a letter that became famous, one that displayed Lincoln's generosity of spirit and his eagerness to give his generals credit where it was due.

> *My dear General Sherman,*
> *Many, many thanks for your Christmas gift—the capture of Savannah.*
> *When you were about leaving Atlanta for the Atlantic coast, I was* anxious, *if not fearful; but feeling that you were the better judge, and remembering that "nothing risked, nothing gained" I did not interfere. Now, the undertaking being a success, the honor is all yours; for I believe that none of us went farther than to acquiesce. And, taking the work of Gen. Thomas into the count, as it should be taken, it is [all] indeed a great success. . . . But what next? I suppose it will be safer if I leave Gen. Grant and yourself to decide.*
>
> *Please make my grateful acknowledgments to your whole army, officers and men. Yours very truly*
>
> *A. Lincoln*

Grant fully appreciated Sherman's accomplishment in his March to the Sea from Atlanta to Savannah and warmly congratulated him "upon the splendid results of your campaign, the like of which is not read of in past history." Still, being Grant, he wanted to maximize every military movement: from City Point he wired Stanton his regret about Sherman's letting the troops that Hardee commanded retreat out of the city to the north. "I wish Hardee's fifteen to eighteen thousand of a garrison could have been added to the other captures," he told the secretary of war, but added that it was nevertheless "a good thing the way it stands and the country may well rejoice over it."

Grant was soon conferring by telegraph with Sherman about what would be Sherman's ruthless final march north through South and North Carolina, but another matter troubled him greatly. It came to the surface quickly, in an answer to a question Lincoln asked Grant in a telegram three days after Christmas. At five-thirty that afternoon, Lincoln inquired about B. F. Butler's move against Wilmington, North Carolina, the last port still held by the Confederacy. "If there be no objection," Lincoln said delicately, perhaps sensing that the silence about that operation could not be good, "please tell me what you now know of the Wilmington expedition, present & prospective."

Three hours later Grant replied from City Point with this:

The Wilmington expedition has proven a gross and culpable failure. Many of the troops are now back here. Delays and free talk of the object of the expedition enabled the enemy to move troops to Wilmington to defeat it. After the expedition sailed from Fort Monroe three days of fine weather was squandered, during which the enemy was without a force to protect himself. Who is to blame I hope will be known.

There could be no question as to who Grant thought was "to blame." Butler had failed earlier in 1864 in his assignment to advance inland from the Virginia coast and take Petersburg, allowing himself to be bottled up at Bermuda Hundred by a much smaller Confederate force. Now he had again been tentative and thrown away the chance to take Fort Fisher and close the port of Wilmington.

Among the things Butler had done this time, renewing memories of Union failures such as the Crater explosion at Petersburg, was to include in the attempted amphibious assault a "powder boat" loaded with 235 tons of explosives. Butler thought that "by bringing within four or five hundred yards of Fort Fisher a large mass of explosives" and setting the whole thing off at once, "the garrison would at least be so paralyzed as to enable, by a prompt landing of men, a seizure of the fort." The explosion had gone off harmlessly—Navy Secretary Welles reported that "the powder-ship was a mere puff of smoke, doing no damage so far as is known." The cannon from the navy's gunboats destroyed Fort Fisher's coast artillery, but Butler did not land his troops and the entire venture failed.

Grant understood that Lincoln wanted Butler, the most prominent figure appointed to the rank of general for political reasons, to be handled gently. Now he came to the end of his patience. While organizing a new expedition, not under Butler's command, that would succeed where Butler failed, Grant began a correspondence intended to end Butler's active service. A week after Lincoln's gentle "If there be no objection" question to Grant about Butler's Wilmington expedition, he sent Stanton a wire that came right to the point: "I am constrained to request the removal of Maj. Gen. B. F. Butler. . . . I do this with reluctance but the good of the service requires it." Stanton was away, so two days later Grant repeated the request, directly to Lincoln. The next day, Butler received an order from the War Department telling him that he was relieved "by direction of the President of the United States." He was told to "repair to Lowell, Mass."—the same method by which McClellan had been sent home to New Jersey, to await further orders that would never come. Butler fought the decision, getting his prominent Radical friends from the Committee on the Conduct of the War to conduct a hearing that in some ways cleared his name, but his days as a political general ended.

IN THESE LAST days of 1864, Lincoln continued to handle a remarkable variety of matters. He accepted the offer of the College of New Jersey, later to be known as Princeton University, to confer upon him the honorary degree of Doctor of Laws. In thanking the president of the college, he wrote this of the war and how he hoped it was perceived:

> *Thoughtful men must feel that the fate of civilization upon this continent is involved in the issue of our contest. Among the most gratifying proofs of this conviction is the hearty devotion everywhere exhibited by our schools and colleges to the national cause.*
>
> *I am most thankful if my labors have seemed to conduce to the preservation of those institutions under which alone we can expect good*

government and in its train sound learning and the progress of the liberal arts.

Some of the last letters he wrote before 1864 ended showed Lincoln once again acting sometimes as idealist, sometimes as politican, and sometimes as both simultaneously. Looking back on the accomplishments of the year, he wrote a delegation of black citizens of Louisiana a letter of thanks for sending him "the elegantly-mounted volume, commemorative of the celebration of the Ordinance of Emancipation of the State of Louisiana, held on the 11th of June, in New Orleans." In full political mode, he sent on to Stanton a letter from Grant's father, Jesse R. Grant, asking that an Alexander McKenzie of Kentucky be appointed as a quartermaster. "The writer of this is General Grant's father," Lincoln pointed out to Stanton. "Let Mr. McKenzie be appointed if his services are needed." (Stanton found a place for the man as an army captain and assistant quartermaster.) He also endorsed the application to West Point of William H. Lee of Rock Island, Illinois. In doing so, Lincoln wrote on it, "Mr. Lee, the father, was in the Ills. [Illinois] Legislature 1854–5."

On December 29, Lincoln wrote a letter to General B. F. Butler, who had at that time failed in his effort to take Wilmington but was not yet relieved of command. The subject was a matter of some delicacy and involved a sad tale that eventually came to a sad end. Lincoln identified a soldier named Frank R. Judd who was under Butler's jurisdiction and "is under arrest, and probably about to be tried for desertion." Lincoln explained his interest in this particular private.

> *He is the son of our present Minister to Prussia [Norman B. Judd], who is a close personal friend of Senator Trumbull [Lyman Trumbull of Illinois] and myself. We are not willing for the boy to be shot, but we think it as well that his trial go regularly on, suspending execution until further order from me & reporting to me.*

This matter remained unresolved; as Butler left his command and General Edward Ord took over, Lincoln followed up on the case, writing Ord that the prisoner "is the son of a friend so close that I must not let him be executed. Please let me know what is his present and prospective condition."

No reply from Ord was ever found, but once again the origins of the story were in Illinois. Norman Judd had been a state senator and Republican state chairman who supported Lincoln, and Lincoln eventually named him minister to Prussia as a consolation prize for not giving him a cabinet position. (Among those intriguing against Judd was Mary Lincoln, who behind Lincoln's back wrote his adviser David Davis, "Judd would cause trouble & dissatisfaction, & if Wall Street testified correctly, his business transactions, have not always borne inspection.") While Judd was serving as minister to Prussia, his son Frank, back in the United States and seventeen years old, was leading a life that Judd described in a troubled letter to Lincoln as a "course of dissipation more with women than with wine." He asked Lincoln to get him into Annapolis; as it developed, Lincoln gave young Frank Judd a presidential appointment to West Point, and things went badly from there. Frank had already enlisted in the army; he reported to West Point but did not take his entrance exams, disappeared, enlisted in another unit, and deserted. Then he enlisted again under a different name, and deserted again, this time being caught and held in the situation in which Lincoln was trying to save him from being shot.

Whatever may have happened to Frank Judd, he was not executed by a firing squad. The next thing known of him was this, from an item in the *New York Times* in 1882 that wrongly identified his father as having been minister to Russia rather than Prussia.

Chicago, April 13. — Frank R. Judd, 36 years old, the son of N. B. Judd, ex-Minister to Russia, was declared insane to-day and sent to an asylum. He was engaged in lead mines in Colorado, where he contracted lead poisoning, which caused paralysis of one side of his body and brain. His friends hope he will be cured.

III

On New Year's Eve, Lincoln closed out his momentous life during 1864 by writing letters that again demonstrated his flexibility, in this case moving from wise political leadership to his self-appointed role as guardian of soldiers in various kinds of trouble. In keeping with his vision for the nation, he wrote an executive order that was consistent with his policies and actions to develop the West. He designated seven offices—banks in Boston, Philadelphia, Baltimore, Cincinnati, and St. Louis, and railroad corporation offices in Chicago and New York—as the places authorized to sell stock in the Union Pacific Railroad Company.

After that, two of the last five letters he signed in 1864 involved clemency. In the first, he pardoned a Union Army lieutenant who had been convicted the previous June for "rape upon a colored girl." The man had been sentenced to ten years in prison; writing Stanton in these last hours of the year, Lincoln pointed out that when he had reviewed that case himself, "I thought there was some slight room for doubt on the question of personal indentification [sic]. I concluded, however, to let him suffer for a while, and then discharge him." Lincoln concluded with, "Let it be done now," but in fact no record of "the promulgation" of his order was ever found.

Lincoln's final communication of 1864 involved the case of an enlisted man named John Lennan, who was under sentence of death for desertion. Lincoln had already postponed the man's execution for ten days; unless other action occurred, Lennan was to be shot on New Year's morning. In the interim, Lincoln had learned that one of the officers serving on that court-martial board had recommended that Lennan be "pardoned and sent to his regiment." The day before this, Lincoln had fired off to that colonel, in Indianapolis, an urgent telegram about the case, asking him to reply "at once." Now, hours before midnight, Lincoln had the colonel's answer before him: "I do not advise that Jno Lenon [sic] be pardoned and sent to his regt he enlisted under a false name & I believe with the intention of deserting after drawing his bounty. In consideration however of his age & his conduct since his trial I could recommend that his sentence be commuted to hard labor for life."

The telegram Lincoln sent responding to this sprang from Lincoln the lawyer, Lincoln the commander-in-chief, Lincoln the man who spared lives when he could. "Suspend execution of John Lennan until further order from me & in the mean time send me the record of his trial."

SEVENTEEN

GOODBYE,
MR. LINCOLN

The traditional White House New Year's presidential reception took place on January 2, 1865. At noon, Lincoln and Mary began receiving the diplomatic corps, followed by his cabinet officers and their wives. Then came the justices of the Supreme Court; after they passed through, high-ranking army and navy officers and their staffs lined up to shake the president's hand and exchange a word with Mary. At 1 P.M., the public came pouring in, quickly creating the kind of crowd that had been present the year before; the *Washington Star* said, "At half past one the jam was terrible."

The reception went on until four. The previous year, four well-dressed black men had attended, invited by Lincoln. This year a reporter from the *New York Independent*, entering the White House, saw this, among the people outside:

> *I noticed groups of colored people gathered here and there, who seemed to be watching earnestly the in-pouring throng. For nearly two hours they hung around, until the crowd of white visitors began . . . to diminish. Then they summoned up courage, and began to approach the door. Some of them were richly and gayly dressed; some were in tattered garments, and others in the most fanciful and grotesque costume. All pressed eagerly forward. When they came into the presence of the President, doubting as to their reception, the feelings of the poor creatures overcame them, and here the scene baffles my powers of description.*

For two long hours Mr. Lincoln had been shaking the hands of the "sovereigns," and had become excessively weary, and his grasp languid, but here his nerves rallied and he welcomed this motley crowd with a heartiness that made them wild with exceeding joy. They laughed and wept, and wept and laughed, exclaiming through their blinding tears, "God bless you!" "God bless Abraham Lincoln!" "God bless Massa Linkum!"

Those who witnessed this scene will not soon forget it. A long distance down the Avenue, on my way home I heard fast [fashionable] young men cursing the President for this act; but all the way the refrain rang in my ears, — "God bless Abraham Lincoln!"

AFTER THE RECEPTION, Lincoln went up to his office. Exhausted though he was, he received a few visitors, and then sat alone. In the first weeks of 1865 immediately ahead of him, he had so many important actions to take, all stemming from the momentous events of 1864. The next day he would write Stanton that Sherman, still at Savannah, must not delay the start of his final march north through the Carolinas: sounding like Grant, Lincoln instructed Stanton to tell Sherman that "*time*, now that the enemy is wavering, is more important than ever." Accurately referring to the Confederate enemy as "being on the down-hill, & somewhat confused," he wanted everything thrown in, "keeping him going" on down the slope to defeat.

That expressed Lincoln's approach to the final phase of the war—Grant must finally break through Lee at Petersburg and Richmond, while Sherman had to slash and burn his way north through the Carolinas—but at the same time, he sought the chance to make or receive overtures for peace. Lincoln had already approved a secret mission in which Francis P. Blair, Sr., the man who had unsuccessfully offered Robert E. Lee the de facto command of the Union Army at the start of the war, went to Richmond for covert talks with Jefferson Davis. The Confederate president still tried for an accord on the basis of "a view to secure peace to the two countries"—the United States and the Confederate States of America—but Lincoln, while stating his readiness "to receive any agent" sent by Davis, reiterated that the goal must be that of "securing peace to the people of our one common country"—the United States of America.

These exchanges were leading Lincoln straight to a final personal effort—a clandestine meeting with prominent Confederates authorized by Jefferson Davis to discuss peace terms—but he also had ready for action his long-hoped-for Thirteenth Amendment to the Constitution, ending slavery with a finality the Emancipation Proclamation could never guarantee. In the next days, he had to engage in horse-trading to get reluctant Democrats to support this supremely important resolution when it came up for congressional approval on the last day of January. New York congressman Moses F. Odell, ready to vote against the measure to end slavery, switched his vote after Lincoln promised that he would receive the lucrative job of Navy Agent at New York when his congressional term ended.

On February 1, these matters started playing themselves out. Lincoln signed the resolution, passed by Congress the previous day, that sent the Thirteenth Amendment to the state legislatures of the Union to be ratified. That night, he gave an impromptu speech to a cheering crowd that offered him a "serenade" at the White House. As reported and in part paraphrased by the *New York Tribune*, he told them:

> *This amendment is a King's cure for all the evils [of slavery.] It winds the whole thing up . . . the consummation of the great game we are playing. He could not but congratulate all present, himself, the country and the whole world upon this great moral victory.*

Two days later, having arrived quietly aboard the presidential yacht *River Queen* at Hampton Roads, Virginia, Lincoln and Secretary of State Seward welcomed aboard the three men that Jefferson Davis had sent to discuss peace terms. Their leader was the diminutive Alexander Hamilton Stephens, vice president of the Confederate States of America, accompanied by Robert M. T. Hunter, one of the Confederacy's most prominent senators, and John A. Campbell, a former United States Supreme Court justice who had become the Confederacy's assistant secretary for war.

Despite having so much at stake, these men began their conference by chatting about the days when all of them except Campbell had been members of the Whig Party, which the Republicans had replaced. Then they turned to a number of topics—emancipation, the Thirteenth Amendment, whose passage in Congress the Southerners then first heard of, and even an idea earlier suggested by Lincoln's emissary Blair that Jefferson Davis give up slavery and Southern independence and march into Mexico to unseat Maximilian and become dictator of that fragile nation.

After four hours of polite, well-reasoned conversation, it became clear that nothing had changed on either side. The Confederate representatives would not give up on the issue of remaining an independent nation, and, despite the impression the Southerners had that Lincoln might give some concessions concerning slavery in return for immediate peace, they made no progress there. As Lincoln put it in a report to Congress, "The conference ended without result," but even on such a serious occasion his sense of humor made one of its sporadic appearances. The February weather on the waters of Hampton Roads was cold: when the southern commissioners first came aboard, Lincoln watched Stephens, who weighed only ninety pounds, enter the main saloon cabin of the *River Queen* so heavily bundled up that he looked like a man of average size. Then Stephens took off several shawls, a thick overcoat, and a long muffler, revealing himself as the small man he was. A corn farmer's image came to Lincoln from his days on the prairie. Shaking hands with Stephens, whom he had not seen for sixteen years, he smiled and told him, "Never have I seen so small a nubbin come out of so much husk"—a remark that Stephens evidently enjoyed and later repeated.

Returning to Washington, Lincoln reverted to an earlier idea he had entertained concerning a swift way to end the war. At an evening cabinet meeting on February 5, he put forward a proposal that he thought the Congress should consider. As Navy Secretary Welles described it in his diary, the Federal government would pay the "Rebel States" $400 million, "to be for the extinguishment of slavery, or for such purposes as the States were disposed." (This was the concept and figure put before him by Horace Greeley the previous summer.) Obviously, the payment was to be part of a broader arrangement for peace, but, as Welles noted, "It did not meet with favor. . . . The earnest desire of the President to conciliate and effect peace was manifest, but there may be such a thing as so overdoing as to cause a distrust or adverse feeling." Sorrowfully, Lincoln said to his cabinet, "You are all against me," and dropped his plan.

During these first weeks of 1865, John Wilkes Booth began changing his plot to kidnap Abraham Lincoln. Rather than try to stop a carriage in which the president was riding and drag him from it, Booth devised a remarkably bold scheme. Because he was well-known to the managers of

Washington's theaters, he and his guests were always welcome to come in through a stage door and sit in unused seats or stand in the back. Booth knew that Lincoln occasionally spent an evening at one of the city's theaters, and decided that he and his conspirators could grab him in the dark during a performance, somehow incapacitate him, and, before anyone could react, carry him out and into a carriage waiting outside a stage door.

On the evening of Wednesday, January 18, Lincoln was expected to attend Ford's Theatre for a performance of *Jack Cade*, a drama based on the British uprising in 1450 led by the Kentish rebel of that name. As Booth planned it, several of his gang would take part in abducting Lincoln that night. When his fellow conspirator John Surratt cut off the theater's gaslights, Booth and another man would enter the president's box. While his accomplice dealt with anyone who tried to interfere, Booth would knock Lincoln unconscious, gag him, and tie him up. Then they would lower Lincoln through the darkness to the side of the stage directly below the presidential box, where others in the plot would take hold of the president and carry him through the back door and into the alley where the carriage for their escape waited.

When Booth and his kidnappers arrived at Ford's, the State Box was festooned with flags and bunting, the sure sign that Lincoln was coming, probably with Mary and some guests, but business kept the president from appearing. The conspirators began to suspect that the authorities knew of their plot and that they were in a trap; they rapidly dispersed, to reorganize the following day.

The next chance that Booth had to get near Lincoln, he came as a spectator rather than as a man intent upon violence. He managed to get a free ticket that entitled him to stand in a large group of dignitaries during Lincoln's inauguration on Friday, March 4. On that day, the obsessed man who was to kill the president five weeks later, firing a pistol into the back of his head as he sat in the State Box at Ford's Theatre, was just another face in the crowd.

THIS HISTORIC INAUGURATION Day had in effect begun the night before. The Thirty-Eighth Congress was to remain in session until noon, and the press of business and last-minute signing of bills had kept everyone in the Capitol up until the final recess at eight in the morning. Lincoln, who issued a special order keeping the Senate in session through the ceremonies to come, spent all night working on documents in the office in the Capitol that he occasionally used. During those hours, Stanton came over from the War Department; he interrupted Lincoln's signing of bills into law, and showed him a communication that Grant had received from Robert E. Lee and immediately forwarded on from his headquarters at City Point. Lee wanted to stop the fighting: he used such language as "the possibility of arriving at a satisfactory adjustment of the present unhappy difficulties," but the essence of the matter was that Lee wanted a truce, and told Grant, "I propose to meet you at such convenient time and place as you may designate."

After conferring with Stanton, Lincoln had him send Grant instructions that he could meet with Lee only for the purpose of receiving the surrender of the Army of Northern Virginia or some other specifically "military matter." Stanton's wire to Grant added, "You are not to decide, discuss, or confer upon any political question. Such questions the President holds in his own hands; and will submit them to no military conferences or conventions. Meantime, you are to press to the utmost, your military advantages." This was not to be an armistice, or any form of peace treaty. Grant decided not to meet with Lee. Since Jefferson Davis intended to fight on, the door closed on any ending to the war other than the Confederacy's total defeat.

A few hours later, the ceremonies of Inauguration Day began. It had been raining for several days; in front of the Capitol the crowd gathered under a sea of umbrellas, with the hems of women's sodden long skirts dragging in the mud. While thousands waited for Lincoln to emerge from the building, Andrew Johnson's swearing-in as vice president took place in the Senate chamber. Johnson, tired after his long trip from Tennessee and recovering from an attack of typhoid fever, had taken some whiskey and was drunk. When he finally swore the oath after making a long, fumbling speech in which he bragged of coming from humble origins, a mortified Lincoln said quietly to the marshal responsible for arranging the next part of the program, "Do not let Johnson speak outside."

At noon, Abraham Lincoln appeared on the flag-draped platform erected for the occasion above the steps on the east side of the Capitol. A special guest, the Marquis de Chambrun, a descendant of Lafayette who thereby held both French and American citizenship, described what he saw from where he stood near the edge of the platform, looking down at the rain-soaked crowd under the scudding dark clouds.

> *The President issued alone from the Capitol, whereupon a thunder of shouts, hand-clappings and wild hurrahs rent the air . . . the grandeur of the scene before me was indescribable. . . . Thousands of colored folk, heretofore excluded from such reunions, were mingled for the first time with the white spectators. Further off, to right and left, infantry troops were drawn up. Among them was a Negro battalion.*

As Lincoln stepped forward to start his speech, something uncanny happened, something remarked upon by many witnesses to the moment. The sun began to break through the dark threatening sky; Welles noted, "the clouds disappeared and the day was beautiful."

As Lincoln began to speak, this was truly the moment that the year of 1864 ended. It was to reach this hour that the political maneuvers and battles leading to Lincoln's reelection had taken place; it was for this that Grant's and Sherman's and Sheridan's men had fought, suffered, and voted to continue fighting; it was to keep this building in Union hands that Washington's clerks had marched out to the rifle-pits to turn back Jubal Early, accompanied by wounded soldiers who left their hospital beds to join in defending the capital. And, to bring the nation to this moment of redemption, the tall, awkward man now speaking to his people had urged the lawmakers surrounding him to write into the Constitution of the United States the words that ended slavery.

Mary Lincoln sat near her husband, accompanied by their son Tad, listening to her husband as he made the shortest and most eloquent inaugural address in American history. Lincoln spoke of the day four years before, when he was sworn in during the period of crisis before the guns began firing: "Both parties deprecated war; but one of them would *make* war rather than let the nation survive; and the other would *accept* war rather than let it perish. And the war came."

Lincoln then spoke of the war as North and South had supposed it would be, and what they had actually experienced. "Neither party expected for the war, the magnitude, or the duration, which it has already attained. . . . Each looked for an easier triumph. . . ." Moving to the inconsistent spiritual dimensions of the conflict, he said of the North and South, "Both read the same Bible, and pray to the same God." Of slavery,

Lincoln observed, "It may seem strange that any men should ask a just God's assistance in wringing their bread from the sweat of other men's faces; but let us judge not that we be not judged."

With that, he moved to the transcendent plane. "The Almighty has His own purposes." God's will was not to be questioned. Lincoln expressed the desire of millions when he said, "Fondly do we hope— fervently do we pray—that this mighty scourge of war may speedily pass away," but he repeated that the nation's destiny, and the length of the war, lay in the hands of a higher power. "Yet, if God wills that it continue . . . until every drop of blood drawn with the lash, shall be paid by another drawn with the sword . . . so it still must be said, 'the judgments of the Lord, are true and righteous altogether.'"

Now Lincoln made his sublime summation. The man who wanted a just peace, the determined wartime leader who would have worked to avoid vindictive policies toward the soon-to-be-vanquished South, wanted everyone to act as he thought the omnipotent God he believed in would wish them to do. Here came the inspired words from the heart of a kind man, the perfect cadences from the poor frontier boy who loved Shakespeare.

With malice toward none; with charity for all; with firmness in the right, as God gives us to see the right, let us strive on to finish the work we are in; to bind up the nation's wounds; to care for him who shall have borne the battle, and for his widow, and his orphan—to do all which may achieve a just, and a lasting peace, among ourselves, and with all nations.

As soon as Lincoln finished speaking, he placed his right hand on the Bible that newly appointed Chief Justice Salmon P. Chase held before him, raised his left, and repeated the words of the presidential oath of office as Chase spoke them. It was a moment of great irony; Chase, the man who had yearned to be taking that oath, was administering it to Lincoln, who had rewarded him for his repeated duplicity by appointing him to a position that symbolized evenhanded integrity.

When Lincoln said "so help me, God," ending the oath, he bent and kissed the Bible. Chase, who later in the day presented that Bible to Mary Lincoln, marked with a pencil the place on the page of the Bible that Lincoln had kissed. For anyone thinking of what might lie immediately ahead of Lincoln, the words of one of the verses from Fifth Isaiah that his lips touched could be troubling. Describing those who could destroy a nation's peace, they said:

> *Whose arrows are sharp, and all their bows bent, their horses' hoofs shall be counted like flint, and their wheels like a whirlwind.*

As Lincoln raised his head after kissing the Bible, the crowd cheered again; several brass bands burst forth with patriotic airs; men in the crowd waved flags. At some distance, a cannon salute began to be fired, marking the orderly transfer of power in a democracy from one administration to the next. From time to time during the day, beginning at dawn, church bells had sounded throughout Washington, celebrating this day of hope and impending victory; bells had rung in cities, towns, and villages everywhere in the states that fought for the Union. As the cannons thundered, here in the capital all the bells started ringing again.

During the hours between the end of the ceremony and the beginning of the large public reception to begin at eight that evening, Lincoln and Mary ventured forth from the White House in an open carriage, being driven to the Willard Hotel so that she could visit a friend staying there. They enjoyed these infrequent outings, and Mary felt certain that they relaxed her constantly overworked husband. Thirty-five days later, to the hour, they would be taking what neither knew was their last ride together. By then, Lee had surrendered at Appomattox, and Lincoln, while visiting Grant and the Army of the Potomac at City Point, had walked the streets of conquered Richmond, stopping at what had been the Confederacy's White House to sit impulsively in the chair of Jefferson Davis, who was still eluding capture. Later that evening, they would go together to Ford's Theatre, where Booth, carrying a small concealed pistol, would use a pass issued by the friendly theater manager to gain access to the area of the box in which Mary and her husband sat, but on that last afternoon ride Lincoln was in good spirits. As they chatted, he talked quietly of the time when this next term in the White House would be finished. He would be sixty, and they could go back to Springfield, where he would resume practicing law.

• • •

THE RECEPTION CELEBRATING Lincoln's inauguration began at eight. Before it ended, 6,000 people would pass through the East Room; Welles said, "Such was the crowd that many were two hours before obtaining entrance after passing through the gates [of the White House grounds]. When I left, a little before eleven, the crowd was still going in." In contrast to the situation on New Year's Day when crowds of blacks were admitted, two policemen stopped the black leader Frederick Douglass, specially invited by Lincoln, as he first started to enter. Douglass told them that he knew the president, and eventually he was escorted in to where Lincoln and Mary stood in the receiving line greeting their guests. "Here comes my friend Douglass," Lincoln said on seeing him. Douglass wrote of what happened next:

> *As I approached him he reached out his hand, gave me a cordial shake, and said: "Douglass, I saw you in the crowd to-day listening to my inaugural address. There is no man's opinion that I value more than yours: what do you think of it?"*
>
> *I said: "Mr. Lincoln I cannot stop here to talk with you, as there are thousands here waiting to shake you by the hand"; but he said again: "What did you think of it?" I said: "Mr. Lincoln, it was a sacred effort," and then I walked off.*
>
> *"I am glad you liked it," he said. That was the last time I saw him to speak with him.*

At every one of Lincoln's receptions, something occurred that reflected Lincoln's generosity of spirit, his consideration for others, and in particular his appreciation for those who wore the uniform.

A nurse who served with the Army, Adelaide W. Smith, known to her friends as Ada, had come to the White House by herself to pass through the line and wish the president well. As she came through the door, she recognized a crippled lieutenant named Gosper, who had lost a leg and was hobbling forward on crutches as he made his way toward the East Room. Ada had been his nurse when he was brought in with his right leg shot away in the fighting around Petersburg, and they had become friends during the time she cared for him. They greeted each other and joined the long line waiting to shake hands with Lincoln.

From where he stood, Lincoln saw Gosper. He broke away from his place beside Mary and came striding from the other side of the big East

Room to greet him. He took Gosper's hand, and in what Ada remembered as "a voice unforgettable" said, "God bless you, my boy." As they left, Gosper said to Ada, "I'd lose another leg for a man like that!"

During the next days, completely exhausted, Lincoln took to his bed when he could. (One account had it that he held a cabinet meeting in his bedroom, sitting propped up in bed with pillows behind him.) All too soon, a grieving nation would have many separate memories of the moments and days after John Wilkes Booth struck—Mary Lincoln cradling her husband in her arms after he was shot, shrieking, "Why didn't he shoot me!"; cold and crusty Stanton sobbing loudly, his shoulders shaking convulsively as he watched the life ebbing from Lincoln, and then taking control of the situation, issuing orders, and finally saying quietly as Lincoln died, "Now he belongs to the ages"; Tad Lincoln staring out a window of the White House hours after his father's death, before turning to Welles, who was there with the new attorney general James Speed, both of them having yet to learn the assassin's identity, and weeping as he asked, "Mr. Welles, who killed my father?"—a moment that Welles recorded, saying, "Neither Speed nor myself could restrain our tears, nor give the poor boy an answer."

During the weeks of life left to Lincoln after his inauguration, a man who had seen him in more formal situations had a chance to observe a different side of Lincoln. During the president's long visit to Grant's headquarters at the end of March and into April, just before the final offensive that ended at Appomattox Court House, Grant's aide Lieutenant Colonel Horace Porter wrote of what he saw happen at the headquarters mess tent.

> *Three tiny kittens were crawling about the tent at the time. The mother had died, and the little wanderers were expressing their grief by mewing piteously. Mr. Lincoln picked them up, took them on his lap, and murmured: "Poor little creatures, don't cry, you'll be taken good care of," and turning to Bowers [a colonel of Grant's staff], said: "Colonel, I hope that you will see that these little motherless waifs are given plenty of milk and treated kindly." Bowers replied: "I will see, Mr. President, that they are taken in charge by the cook of our mess, and are well cared for."*
>
> *Several times during his stay Mr. Lincoln was found fondling these kittens. He would wipe their eyes tenderly with his handkerchief, stroke their smooth coats, and listen to them purring their gratitude to him. It*

was a curious sight, at an army headquarters, upon the eve of a great military crisis in the nation's history, to see the hand that had affixed the signature to the Emancipation Proclamation, and had signed the commissions of all the heroic men who had served the cause of the Union, from the general-in-chief to the lowest lieutenant, tenderly caressing three stray kittens.

That lay just ahead, but even as Lincoln climbed into bed as often as he could during these days after his inauguration, a letter was on its way to him from the little village of Hamilton, Massachusetts. It carried a subtle and profound tribute to all that he had accomplished, as symbolic in its way as the sunlight that had poured down on his magnificent Inaugural Address, opening the vista of the hard-earned peace to which this man who once steered flatboats on the Mississippi had led his nation.

Written on the morning that he took the oath of office to begin his second term, the letter came from Mary Abigail Dodge, a petite, brilliant journalist who used the pen name Gail Hamilton and was famous for her pieces, including antislavery and feminist articles, that appeared in newspapers and magazines. She had met Lincoln once, at the White House reception after his first inauguration, soon before the war began. On that occasion, approaching the man she felt could take the United States through what it had to face, she saw how many thousands of hands he had to shake, but felt compelled to say, "Mr. Lincoln, I am very sorry for you, but indeed I must shake hands with you." Lincoln had looked down at Mary Dodge, this lady who weighed 109 pounds, and said as he took her hand in his, "Ah! *your* hand doesn't hurt me."

As she wrote to her president on the morning he was sworn in for what she thought would be four more years of his leadership, Mary heard the bells throughout the New England countryside ringing in what she felt were happy, hopeful tones. Nonetheless, what she knew of the bitter feelings between North and South enabled her to understand that he still had to lead the country through a painful period of reconciliation. She told him this:

I only wish to thank you for being so good—and to say how sorry we all are that you have four years more of this terrible toil. But remember what a triumph it is for the right, what a blessing to the country—and then your rest shall be glorious when it does come!

You can't tell anything about it in Washington where they make a noise on the slightest provocation—but if you had been in this little speck of a village this morning and heard the soft, sweet music of unseen bells rippling through the morning silence from every quarter of the far-off horizon, you would have better known what your name is to this nation.

May God help you in the future as he has helped you in the past and a people's love and gratitude will be but a small portion of your exceeding great reward.

NOTES

In citing works in the notes, short titles have generally been used. Works frequently cited have been identified by the following abbreviations. The full citation appears in the bibliography, under the name of the author or editor.

CW   Roy Basler, ed., *The Collected Works of Abraham Lincoln*
NYT   *New York Times*
PUSG John Y. Simon, ed. *The Papers of Ulysses S. Grant*
W   John C. Waugh, *Reelecting Lincoln: The Battle for the 1864 Presidency*

CHAPTER ONE: THE BELEAGUERED GIANT

PAGE

1 *Description of White House, and this and other receptions*: Miers, *Lincoln Day by Day*, Vol. 3, 231; Brooks, *Mr. Lincoln's Washington*, 273–275; Brooks, *Washington in Lincoln's Time*, 68–70; Leech, *Reveille*, illustration of 1862 New Year's Day reception, following p. 388; Stoddard, *Inside the White House*, 47–53 et seq., 153–154.

1 *Lincoln's height*: Carpenter, *Six Months*, 217. Carpenter, the artist brought in to do the painting of Lincoln and his cabinet at the signing of the Emancipation Proclamation, says on that page that he measured Lincoln and found him to be "six feet three and three-quarter inches."

1 *stooped posture*: Stoddard, *Inside the White House*, 179.

1 *"coarse black hair"*: Donald, *Lincoln*, 237.

1 *"a bird's nest"*: W, 76.

1 *"canvassed hams"*: Carpenter, *Six Months*, 148.

2 *"a purple velvet dress"* and *"an immense train"*: Burlingame, ed., *Lincoln Observed*, 100.

2 *large white plume*: Fleishner, *Mrs. Lincoln and Mrs. Keckly*, 268. Note that in published sources there are variations in the spelling of Keckley.

2 *Lincoln kept shaking hands*: Burlingame, ed., *Lincoln Observed*, 100; and Brooks, *Washington in Lincoln's Time*, 69. In Stoddard, *Inside the White House*, 49, the author says that Lincoln usually stood between two of his private secretaries.

2 *using his left hand while he rested his right*: Leech, *Reveille*, 47.

2 *answering a remark in his high-pitched voice*: Goodwin, *Team of Rivals*, 165.

2 *"Howdy!"*: Hertz, ed., *The Hidden Lincoln*, 414.

2 *when he laughed*: Lincoln's laugh, in Leech, *Reveille*, 235.

2 *"the crushing of bonnets"*: Brooks, *Mr. Lincoln's Washington*, 274.

2 *cut little squares from curtains*: Brooks, *Mr. Lincoln's Washington*, 253. See also Stoddard, *Inside the White House*, 183.

2 *his right hand was swollen*: Stoddard, *Inside the White House*, p. 28, in which the author says that after one reception Lincoln's hand "was too lame to sign anything." Freidel, *The White House*, 70, speaking of raw with blisters. See also Stoddard, *Inside the White House*, 96–97.

2 *a wounded soldier, and his plainly dressed mother*: Carpenter, *Six Months*, 170.

3 *"four colored men"*: Donald, *Lincoln*, 475.

3 *He walked in an odd way*: Hertz, ed., *The Hidden Lincoln*, 413.

3 *"morning, afternoon, and evening"*: Bates, *Telegraph Office*, 7; includes subsequent description of hanging up grey plaid shawl, etc.

4 *Lincoln's invariable way of returning the salute* is described in Carpenter, *Six Months*, 169.

4 *"yellow tissue-paper telegraphic dispatch"*: Stoddard, *Inside the White House*, 132.

4 *"read over"*: Bates, *Telegraph Office*, 41.

4 *Message to Lincoln and his 3:30 P.M. reply*: CW, VII, 102–103.

5 *"He would there relax"* and *"spend hour after hour"*: Bates, *Telegraph Office*, 9.

5 *first draft of his Emancipation Proclamation*: Neely, in *The Last Best Hope*, 108–109, casts doubt on the idea that Lincoln spent any time developing the Proclamation in this office. One of the arguments he puts forward for this is that the man recalling this "was only a clerk in the telegraph office," for whom "to have witnessed the gestation of the Emancipation Proclamation would have been something of which to boast." In my estimation, David Homer Bates, author of *Lincoln in the Telegraph Office*, on 138–141 of which this account appears, was a straightforward young man whose assignment as one of several cipher-clerks happened to give him daily contact with Lincoln. Furthermore, the account in Bates's pages is that of then Major Thomas T. Eckert, chief of the War Department Telegraph Staff, in which the major says that Lincoln worked on this in the telegraph office "nearly every day for several weeks," handing the document back to him to be locked in a safe after each session. At the end of that period, Eckert says, "for the first time he told me that he had been writing an order giving freedom to the slaves in the South for the purpose of hastening the end of the war."

5 *"great black rings"*: Carpenter, *Six Months*, 30. Carpenter's description is on seeing Lincoln at the time of the battles of the Wilderness, but matches his initial impression, recorded on p. 18, of Lincoln being "haggard-looking" when he first met the president at a White House reception on Saturday, February 6, 1864.

5 *"Lines of care"*: Ibid., 12.

6 *"I now leave"*: Donald, *Lincoln*, 273.

6 *"the intellectual power of a giant"*: Harper, *Lincoln and the Press*, 55.

6 *"a national calamity"*: Mitgang, ed., *Abraham Lincoln: A Press Portrait*, 206.

6 *"a slang-whanging stump speaker"* and *"a fourth-rate lecturer"*: Harper, *Lincoln and the Press*, 56–57.

7 *more than 100,000 men had deserted*: Numbers of Union and Confederate troop

strength. In Boatner, *Civil War Dictionary*, these figures are to be found under "Numbers and Losses," 602; "Confederate Army," 169; and "Union Army," 858. Livermore, *Numbers and Losses*, has Union strength as 1,556,678, and Confederate strength 1,082,119. Other totals and estimates vary. The Library of Congress volume *Civil War Desk Reference*, 373, gives a total of 620,000 for those on both sides who "died in combat."

7   *"eight hundred or one thousand ruffians"*: Wilkeson, *Recollections*, 2–13.

7   *"At the commencement"*: Rowland, ed., *Jefferson Davis*, VI, 108. This is from Davis's Annual Message to the Confederate Congress, December 7, 1863, which begins as of that volume.

7   *Lee's regiments reenlist*: Tate, *Jefferson Davis*, 225.

9   *Morton's situation and actions in Indiana*: For a short description, see Catton, *The Army of the Potomac*, 121–125.

10 *"There is no backdown"*: Nevins, *Ordeal of the Union*, 153.

10 *closing arguments*: Donald, *Lincoln*, 151.

10 *We are a great empire*: *CW*, II, 364. The speech was made on August 27, 1856.

10 *I HAVE ORDERED*: *CW*, VII, 103n.

11 *Lincolns at supper*: Brooks, *Mr. Lincoln's Washington*, 257.

11 *"I know every step"*: Randall, *Lincoln's Sons*, 53–54.

11 *"completely overwhelmed"* through *"mysterious river of death"*: Keckley, *Behind the Scenes*, 102–104.

12 *The Lincolns spoiling both Willie and Tad*: See Hertz, ed., *The Hidden Lincoln*, 176–177, for one of many examples in that book.

12 *Emilie Todd Helm, and her stay at the White House*: Ross, *The President's Wife*, 147–149; Baker, *Mary Todd Lincoln*, 223–226; Randall, *Mary Lincoln*, 330–336; Randall, 336 and 495n, states that "the oath which the President carefully wrote out but Emilie did not sign is in the Lincoln Papers."

13 *"She seems very nervous"*: Turner, *Mary Todd Lincoln*, 156.

13 *"in regard to said restored rights"*: The three documents, all written in Lincoln's hand, referring to Emilie as "Emily T. Helm" and signed as "Emily T. Helm" in his handwriting on the oath, are in the Library of Congress. *CW*, VII, 63–64.

13 *"a struggling young lawyer"*: Helm, *The True Story of Mary*, 119–120.

13 *"I laugh because I must not weep"*: Tripp, *The Intimate World of Abraham Lincoln*, 38–39.

13 *"while Mary was courageous"*: Helm, *The True Story of Mary*, 119–120.

13 *Exchange with Senator Harris*: Ibid., 229–230. For a description of the Baltimore assassination plot, the thwarting of it, and the mob coming onto the train, see Donald, *Lincoln*, 277–278.

14 *Those fears never ceased*: The incident occurred on March 28, 1864. Miers, ed., *Lincoln Day by Day*, vol. 3, 248.

14 *Mary's accident*: Donald, *Lincoln*, 448.

14 *"business office"*: Stoddard, *Inside the White House*, 11.

14 *"two large draperied windows"*: Brooks, *Mr. Lincoln's Washington*, 255.

15 *"plain straw matting"*: Wilson, *Intimate Memories*, 559. Descriptions of Lincoln's of-

fice include Brooks, *Mr. Lincoln's Washington*, 255. Further descriptions of Lincoln's White House office: Stoddard, *Inside the White House*, 5; Donald, *Lincoln*, 310; sketch of office, Donald, *Lincoln*, following 224.

15 *"he shut himself up"*: Burlingame, ed., *At Lincoln's Side*, 110.

15 *"a biscuit, a glass of milk"*: Ibid.

15 *"I doubt if"*: Quotation from William O. Stoddard in Holzer, ed., *Dear Mr. Lincoln*, 1.

16 *"went into the political canvass"*: Stoddard, *Inside the White House*, x.

16 *"I avail myself"*: Holzer, *Dear Mr. Lincoln*, epigraph page.

16 *". . . every patriot"*: Ibid., 3.

16 *"Some days there will be less"*: Stoddard, *Inside the White House*, 14.

16 *"stories of partisan bitterness"*: Ibid., 15.

17 *"beggars' operas"*: Laas, *Wartime Washington*, 344.

17 *"public opinion baths"*: Carpenter, *Six Months*, 281.

17 *Lincoln throws man out of his office*: Burlingame, ed., *At Lincoln's Side*, xvii. A different version of what appears to be the same incident is in Carpenter, *Six Months*, 106.

18 *Lincoln removes wife from office*: Stephenson, *Lincoln*, 323–324.

18 *Lincoln and crying mother*: Burlingame, ed., *An Oral History of Abraham Lincoln: John G. Nicolay's Interviews and Essays*, 81–82, 1876 interview with James Speed. A different account of what may have been the same incident is in Carpenter, *Six Months*, 321.

19 *"If I don't suspend it tonight"*: Zall, *Abe Lincoln Laughing*, 113.

19 *"interruptious"*: Brooks, "Personal Reminiscences of Lincoln," *Scribner's Monthly* XV no. 5 (March 1878): 680.

20 *"slates, pencils"*: Burlingame, ed., *With Lincoln in the White House*, xii.

20 *"irregular and somewhat spasmodic"*: Ibid., xiii.

20 *"sour and crusty"*: Ibid., xvii.

20 *"The nicest looking man"*: Burlingame, ed., *At Lincoln's Side*, xxi. For the following descriptions and characterizations, see xii–xxii.

21 *Union Army's intimidation of Democratic voters*: Randall and Donald, *The Civil War and Reconstruction*, 459.

21 *"war power"*: The absence of this term in the Constitution is pointed out by James M. McPherson in his article "Any Measure Which May Best Subdue the Enemy," *Military History Quarterly* 19, no. 3 (Spring 2007): 34–40. As McPherson states, the term "war power" was used twice by Lincoln in his Message to Congress in Special Session of July 4, 1861, the text of which is in *CW*, IV, 421–441. This article also explores the question of Lincoln's authority regarding these other issues. Details of Vallandigham's exile, and votes for Governor of Ohio, in Klement, *Limits of Dissent*, 210–227, 252, 252n.

23 *"whose homes lie safely within"*: *CW*, VII, 103.

23 *"postoffices, landoffices, marshalships"*: Donald, *Lincoln*, 213.

23 *"rush to reap"*: Carman and Luthin, *Lincoln and the Patronage*, 4. Except where noted, all the examples of patronage cited in this passage are from Carman and Luthin's book. Further description of Lincoln's thinking on this subject, method of selection,

and specific examples of those chosen, can be found in Seitz, *Lincoln the Politician*, 245, 257–261.

24 *Six generals*: Smith, *Grant*, 113. Randall, *Lincoln the President*, vol. 1, 371–372, comes up with big Illinois totals for the whole war, and Randall, vol. 1, 371, cites Browning, *Diary*, pt. 1, 487–488, of Vol. XX of the Collections of the Illinois State Historical Library, 1925–1927, for a description of a caucus on this subject. This refers to a meeting of the Illinois congressional delegation on the evening of Saturday, August 27, 1861, at which seven names, including that of Ulysses S. Grant, were put forward for promotion to brigadier general.

24 Illinois Staats-Anzeiger: Baker, *Mary Todd Lincoln*, 157.

24 *Schimmelfennig*: Boritt, ed., *Lincoln, the War President: The Gettysburg Lectures*, 37, Lecture by James M. McPherson, "Lincoln and the Strategy of Unconditional Surrender."

25 *"shouldering the sleeping child"*: Brooks, *Washington in Lincoln's Time*, 250.

26 *a nurse to care for her*: Baker, *Mary Todd Lincoln*, 212.

26 *Mary and spiritualists*: Turner, *Mary Todd Lincoln*, 123–124; Baker, *Mary Todd Lincoln*, 217–222. Eight séances, Freidel and Pencak, eds., *The White House*, 67, in the essay *"This Damned Old House"* by David Donald.

26 *"He lives, Emilie!"*: The account is from Emilie Todd Helm's diary, as quoted in Helm, *The True Story of Mary*, 226–227.

27 *"She wishes to loom largely"*: Fleishner, *Mrs. Lincoln and Mrs. Keckly*, 160.

27 *"The First Lady"*: Baker, *Mary Todd Lincoln*, 180. Mary Todd Lincoln, writing to an editor, opining on matters of state and government personalities in Baker, *Mary Todd Lincoln*, 202–203, and Thomas, *Stanton*, 298.

27 *"that abolition sneak"*: Thomas, *Stanton*, 298.

27 *four hundred pairs of gloves*: Freidel and Pencak, eds., *The White House*, 71.

27 *The appropriation, and examples of Mary Todd Lincoln's spending* are from Baker, *Mary Todd Lincoln*, 182; Turner, *Mary Todd Lincoln: Her Life and Letters*, 88–89, 162–163; Thomas, *Abraham Lincoln*, 300. See also Ross, *The President's Wife*, 125–131; and Baker, *Mary Todd Lincoln*, 391n.

27 *"fatal to feminine nerves"*: Baker, *Mary Todd Lincoln*, 185.

27 *"black lace point shawls"*: Turner, *Mary Todd Lincoln*, 88, citing the *Philadelphia Dispatch*, n.d.

28 *flowers that never grew*: The itemization involving flowers and manure is from Burlingame, ed., *Honest Abe, Dishonest Mary* (Racine, WI: Lincoln Fellowship of Wisconsin, 1994), and is on 17 of no. 50 of that organization's *Historical Bulletin*. Further mention and documentation of fraudulent itemization is in Burlingame, ed., *At Lincoln's Side*, 194, 275 n. 46. The figure of more than a thousand dollars is from Baker, *Mary Todd Lincoln*, 191 and 392n. More on Mary Todd Lincoln's personal extravagances and fraudulent schemes: Turner, *Mary Todd Lincoln*, 88–89; Thomas, *Abraham Lincoln*, 300. The quotation from David Davis is from Burlingame, *The Inner World of Abraham Lincoln*, 304, citing a conversation that took place in 1873. In Randall, *Mary Lincoln*, 254 et seq., the account of Noah Brooks presents Mary as the gullible victim of the experienced Watt, an interpretation I find implausible considering her other machinations that had nothing to do with Watt.

Other biographies also tend to present Mary as an inexperienced novice in political matters and a naïve newcomer to the Washington scene. It must be noted that the biographies of her written by Baker, Randall, and the Turners, as well as the Thomas biography of Abraham Lincoln and numerous other studies of him that involved his wife, were all published before 1994, when the Illinois Stare Historical Library lifted the restrictions that had been placed on certain passages relating to Mary Todd Lincoln in the diary of Orville Browning when the complete manuscript was sold to that library in 1921. These passages, omitted from the version of *The Diary of Orville Hickman Browning* published in 1925, offer abundant evidence for the interpretations and connections involving fraud, deceit, and improper political influence on Mary Todd Lincoln's part, far greater than previously portrayed, that Burlingame draws from them. The greatest compilation of Mary's alleged or actual failings is in Burlingame, *The Inner World of Abraham Lincoln*. Chap. 9 of this work, titled *"The Lincolns' Marriage: 'A Fountain of Misery, of a Quality Absolutely Infernal,' "* 269–355, studies the subject in depth.

28 *"Union" letter:* Baker, *Mary Todd Lincoln*, 184; for Lincoln King, see Burlingame, *Honest Abe, Dishonest Mary*, 13, 33n, and Burlingame, *The Inner World of Abraham Lincoln*, 292 and 336n; Yates, ibid.; for Watt, ibid.

29 *gifts to herself:* Turner, *Mary Todd Lincoln*, 162.

29 *Keckley's estimate of bills owed by Mary:* Keckley, *Behind the Scenes*, 204; revised figure, Baker, *Mary Todd Lincoln*, 194.

29 *"Kreismann, she will not":* Burlingame, ed., *At Lincoln's Side*, 189.

29 *"My wife is as handsome":* Baker, *Mary Todd Lincoln*, 196.

30 *"probably in less than a year":* Burlingame, *The Inner World of Abraham Lincoln*, 268.

30 *Gettysburg Address:* There are five varying drafts, all in *CW*, VII, 17–23. The one beginning on p. 22 has the heading, "Final Text," followed by "Address delivered at the dedication of the Cemetery at Gettysburg." It is written in Lincoln's hand and is dated and signed by him. The sources and reports of these drafts are to be found in the notes in *CW*, VII, 17–23.

30 *"Grant is my man":* Williams, *Lincoln and His Generals*, 272, citing James F. Rusling, *Men and Things I Saw in Civil War Days*, 16–17.

31 *Jones as intermediary:* See *PUSG*, vol. 9, 541, and 542n., for an overture already made to Grant in a letter of December 7, 1863, by the Democratic politician Barnabas Burns, and Grant's rejection of the idea of running for any office, in his reply to Burns dated December 17, 1863. The evidence appears to be that as of January 1, 1864, Lincoln would have been unaware of that exchange, but the chronology of the soundings made by Jones is less clear. It is also worth noting that, in a number of works, references to Ida Tarbell's four-volume *The Life of Abraham Lincoln* erroneously cite an account of an important meeting on this matter between Jones and Lincoln as being in Vol. II, 187–189. It is in Vol. III, 187–189.

31 *"Fellow Citizens":* *CW*, V, 537.

32 *"The pilots on our Western rivers":* Donald, *Lincoln*, 15.

CHAPTER TWO: STEERING INTO A STORMY YEAR

PAGE

33 *"When the Blairs go in for a fight"*: This is from Riddle, *Recollections of War Times*, 273, and was said by Albert Gallatin Riddle to Lincoln in a conversation with Lincoln. In Lewis, *Sherman*, 152, the statement is given as if directly by Blair: "When we go in for a fight we go in for a funeral," but Lewis offers no documentation for this.

34 *"because he had no history"*: Goodwin, *Team of Rivals*, 495–496.

34 *"It is said that you are the power"*: Randall, *Mary Lincoln*, 239. For the effort to oust Seward from the cabinet in 1862, see Welles, *Diary*, I, 196–205.

34 *"lukewarmness in the conduct of the war"*: Goodwin, *Team of Rivals*, 490, citing Beale, ed., *The Diary of Edward Bates*, 269.

34 *"They wish to get rid of me"*: Hendrick, *Lincoln's War Cabinet*, 398, citing Browning, *Diary*, I, 600–601.

35 Seward, Lincoln, and the *"Proclamation of Thanksgiving"*: *CW*, VI, 496–497.

35 *"There is no administration"* and *"We have as little to do with it"*: W, 37.

35 *"that Seward exercised"*: Browning, *Diary*, I, 603.

35 *Chase and Seward's contest for patronage appointments*: Niven, *Salmon P. Chase*, 239–242.

35 *"I'm afraid Mr. Chase's head is turned"* Beale, ed., *The Diary of Edward Bates*, 310.

35 *"Presidency glaring out of both eyes"*: Hay, *Lincoln and the Civil War in the Diaries and Letters of John Hay*, 107.

35 *"No man knows"*: W, 39.

35 *Ten thousand Treasury Department employees*: W, 38.

36 *Chase and the forthcoming 1864 presidential campaign*: Niven, *Salmon P. Chase*, 316–317; 357–366.

36 *"Miss Chase is so busy"*: Burlingame, ed., *At Lincoln's Side*, 67.

36 *"I shall be glad to see you"*: Goodwin, *Team of Rivals*, 339, citing the story as being from the *Cincinnati Enquirer*, August 1, 1899, as found in Belden and Belden, *So Fell the Angels*, 4.

36 *"young and handsome"*: Ross, *The President's Wife*, 118.

36 *Mary Todd Lincoln does not attend Kate Chase's wedding*: Ross, *The President's Wife*, 197.

37 *Meeting at August Belmont's house*: W, 86–88.

37 *"an idiot"*: Sears, *George B. McClellan*, 103.

37 *"original gorilla"* and *"well-meaning baboon"*: Ibid., 132.

38 *"I can never regard him"*: Ibid., 236

38 *"to render it"*: Ibid.

38 *"He is an admirable engineer"*: Williams, *Lincoln and His Generals*, 176.

38 *"absolutely broken down from fatigue"*: Donald, *Lincoln*, 389, citing *CW*, V, 474–479.

39 *"I should regard such cases"*: Communications sent from Lincoln's office, January 23, 1864. *CW*, VII, 146–149.

39 *"I have a great respect"*: Brooks, "Personal Reminiscences of Lincoln," 566.

40 *"Please have the adjutant general"*: Thomas, *Abraham Lincoln*, 463.

40 *"public opinion baths"*: Donald, *Lincoln*, 391.

40 *"As I went into the Cabinet-meeting"*: Welles, *Diary*, I, 528, entry of February 19, 1864.

40 *Executions*: The incident described is from Eaton, *Grant, Lincoln, and the Freedmen*, 179–181. Lee, *Mr. Lincoln's City*, 79, has text and photograph concerning the Central Guardhouse, where prisoners sentenced to execution were held, and text concerning the circumstances of the executions.

41 *"These men have influence"*: Fleishner, *Mrs. Lincoln and Mrs. Keckly*, 276.

41 *"He glances at my rich dresses"*: Keckley, *Behind the Scenes*, 149–150.

41 *"Please say not a word"*: Turner, *Mary Todd Lincoln*, 181.

41 *"That lady"*: Ibid.

42 *"get hold of the particulars"* and *"almost crazy"*: Keckley, *Behind the Scenes*, 151.

42 *Situation regarding Sioux*: The problems existed well before January 29, 1864, but on that day Lincoln transmitted to the Senate the reply made on January 22 by Lord Lyons, the British ambassador in Washington, who said that he had sent to London what Lincoln termed "the proposed pursuit of hostile bands of Sioux Indians into the Hudson Bay Territories." *CW*, VII, 160. See also Nichols, *Lincoln and the Indians*, 120.

43 *"Sound policy"*: Annual Message to Congress, December 8, 1863. *CW*, VII, 36–53.

43 *Memorandum*: *CW*, VII, 151.

43 *"This war is eating my life out"*: Carpenter, *Six Months*, 17.

43 *"So you're the little woman"*: Hedrick, *Harriet Beecher Stowe*, vii.

44 *"Whichever way it ends"*: Mitgang, ed., *Abraham Lincoln: A Press Portrait*, 373.

44 *"I was . . . entirely"*: Stoddard, *Inside the White House*, xiii.

44 *"although made for her"*: Stoddard's account. Ibid., 99–100.

46 *"Nothing would induce me"*: *PUSG*, vol. 9, 543n.

46 *"I explained to him"*: Sherman, *Memoirs*, 210.

47 *"GENERAL WILLIAM T. SHERMAN INSANE"*: Headline in the *Cincinnati Daily Commercial*, December 11, 1861.

47 *"brothers, I the older in years"*: Ward, *"We Were as Brothers,"* 14.

48 *"jumped over the boxwood hedge"* and *"Lincoln and others"*: Miers, ed., *Lincoln Day by Day*, 239. Note, as in chapter notes for Chapter One, that the pagination for this book is as if for three volumes, of which this 239 is in the third. Further page references in Miers to events in 1864 will be cited as being in Volume 3. "Tad was in bitter tears" is found in Burlingame, ed., *With Lincoln in the White House*, 126. See also Carpenter, *Six Months*, 44–45.

48 *"Pomeroy Circular"*: See Randall, *Lincoln the President*, vol. 4, 98 et seq.; Donald, *Lincoln*, 482–483 et seq.; W, 116–117 et seq. This was an open letter printed above the signature of Radical Republican Senator Samuel C. Pomeroy of Kansas. In it, Pomeroy, who was acting on behalf of an array of Radical senators, representatives, and other prominent Radical sympathizers, opposed Lincoln's nomination and urged the public to support Secretary of the Treasury Chase for president.

48 *"I had no knowledge"*: The letter from Chase, including reference to "the use of my name," infra, was evidently written on January 21, 1864, and is in *CW*, VII, 200–201n.

49 *Public reaction to the Pomeroy Circular*: Donald, *Lincoln*, 481–482.

49 *nominated Grant for that promotion*: Miers, ed., *Lincoln Day by Day*, vol. 3, 241.

50 *slaves "will be made free?"*: *CW*, VII, 198n.

50 *"I am not prepared"*: Ibid., 198.

50 *"the extreme destitution"*: Ibid., 196n.

50 *I base this account of the patent*, and the circumstances leading to its invention, on displays at one of the two restored houses open to the public at the Lincoln Home National Historic Site, run by the National Park Service, in what was Lincoln's neighborhood in Springfield, Illinois. A photograph of a model of this, not on display there, is in Basler, *Lincoln*, 49, and a facsimile of the patent drawing of his invention is in Neely, *The Abraham Lincoln Encyclopedia*, 161–162, under "Inventions." Hertz, ed., *The Hidden Lincoln*, 396–397, has on 397 William H. Herndon's description of Lincoln's invention, which includes this: "That model is now in Washington, where it can be seen at any time. This invention was a perfect failure; the apparatus has never been put on any boat so far as known." It should be noted that Herndon died in 1891. A clue as to where the model may have been prior to that is in Burlingame, ed., *An Oral History*, 18, in which C. F. Smith of Springfield tells John Nicolay in 1875 that it, in Nicolay's words, "is preserved at Shurtleff College."

The original patent drawing submitted by Lincoln in 1846 was discovered at the United States Patent Office in 1997. A replica of the model is on display at the Smithsonian's National Museum of History in Washington, D.C.

51 *He thought that the Committee*: *CW*, VII, 197–198.

51 *"the worst speech I ever listened to"*: Miers, ed., *Lincoln Day by Day*, vol. 3, 231.

51 *Chase sent a letter*: March 5, 1864, to State Senator James C. Hall of Ohio, in Goodwin, *Team of Rivals*, 608, 858n.

51 *"The salmon is a queer fish"* and *"Mr. Chase's declination"*: Donald, *Lincoln*, 483, the last citing King, *Lincoln's Manager, David Davis*, 216–217.

CHAPTER THREE: LINCOLN JUGGLES IN THE "SHOP"; GRANT COMES EAST

PAGE

53 *Documents signed by Lincoln*, March 7, 1864: *CW*, VI, 225–231.

54 *"Order Designating"; Lincoln and railroads*: Ambrose, *Nothing Like It in the World*, 27–41 et seq.

54 *"His body seemed"*: Rice, *Reminiscences*, 345.

54 *... a tall, loose-jointed figure*: Wilson, *Intimate Memories*, 464–465.

55 *"If I had another face"*: *The Lion* (International Association of Lions Clubs), January 1952; 52–54. See also, Holzer, "'If I Had Another Face, Do You Think I'd Wear This One?'" *American Heritage*, no. 34 (February–March 1983): 56–63.

55 *"Mr. Lincoln settled back"*: Burlingame, ed., *An Oral History*, 52.

55 *"different parts of the room"*: Oakes, *The Radical and the Republican*, 213.

55 *"in sitting down on common chairs"*: Donald, *Lincoln*, 115.

55 *"sitting on his shoulders"*: Stephenson, *Lincoln*, 129.

55 *His favorite attitude*: Rice, *Reminiscences*, 340–341. Account of Benjamin Perley Poore.

56 *"with the exception"* and *"When he told"*: Ibid., 239 and 234.

56 *Cordelia Perrine Harvey*: Dexheimer, *Sketches of Wisconsin Pioneer Women*, 47–49.

57 *The Seventeenth [Corps] is largely composed*: Brooks, *Mr. Lincoln's Washington*, 479.

61 *Lincoln meets Grant*: Smith, *Grant*, p. 290, citing Porter, *Campaigning with Grant*, 19.

61 *the way Grant moved*: Thomas, *Abraham Lincoln*, 417.

61 *"The little, scared-looking man"*: Smith, *Grant*, 290.

61 *"all he wanted"*: Grant, *Memoirs*, 473.

62 *"first general I've had!"*: Stoddard, *Inside the White House*, 126, 125.

62 *"He was to go for Lee"*: Smith, *Grant*, 296.

62 *Haggard-looking . . . standing*: Carpenter, *Six Months*, 18. Unless otherwise noted, Carpenter's accounts of his time with Lincoln are from this memoir.

63 *"He received me pleasantly"*: This meeting, Carpenter's experiences in going to Brady's studio, and Lincoln on *Hamlet* are from Carpenter, *Six Months*, 18–20, 35–36, 49–52.

CHAPTER FOUR: ON THE VERGE OF THE GREAT COLLISION

PAGE

65 *Draft calls*: February 1, 1864. *CW*, VII, 164; March 14, ibid., 245.

65 *The wording of these proclamations*: See *CW*, VII, 245.

66 *"As a rule"*: *CW*, VII, 312, 312–313n.

66 *"So far, we feel sure"*: Long and Long, *The Civil War Day by Day*, 486; entry for April 15, 1864.

67 *"If there is one man"*: Freeman, *Lee*, II, 92.

67 *"Colonel, we have got to whip them"*: Ibid., III, 264.

67 *Lee analyzed*: Ibid., 265, 265n.

67 *Lincoln stood on the balcony*: Miers, ed., *Lincoln Day by Day*, 254.

67 *"old war worn clothing"*: Laas, ed. *Wartime Washington*, 372n.

67 *"banners flying"*: Brooks, *Mr. Lincoln's Washington*, 314.

67 *"large live Eagle"*: Hauptman, *Between Two Fires* 135. Other details of the parade: Leech, *Reveille*, 319.

67 *"If the South conquers you"*: Herek, *These Men Have Seen Hard Service*, 59.

68 *"their marching being absolutely perfect"*: Brooks, *Mr. Lincoln's Washington*, 314.

68 *We are coming, Father Abraham*: Ibid., 105.

68 *"It is as if the Earth looked at me"*: Epstein, *Lincoln and Whitman*, 163.

68 *Reference to George Whitman's wound*: Ibid., 86; Whitman and Burroughs on April 25, 1864, ibid., 216–217.

69 *"Woman Order"*: Boatner, *Civil War Dictionary*, 945.

70 *"doesn't object"* and *"I have for some time thought"*: Butler, *Butler's Book*, 631–632. It should be noted that all of this 1154-page book, published twenty-seven years after the Civil War ended, is marked by contentious and often questionable self-serving special pleading. Nonetheless, many of Butler's versions of events are supported by documents from other sources.

71 *"greatly delighted"* and *"your candidature"*: This and other quotations and details concerning Butler at this time are from Louis Taylor Merrill, "General Benjamin F. Butler in the Presidential Campaign of 1864," *Mississippi Valley Historical Review* 33, no. 4 (March 1947): 537–570. It should be noted that other accounts of the offer to

Butler have held that there is no proof that it was in fact made, or that Lincoln sent Cameron as a go-between, but, although some of the evidence is from Butler, writing years later, I find the article entirely persuasive.

71 *Cameron's role as emissary*: W, 388n, offers the various sources and studies concerning the veracity of this story. Lincoln sending Cameron: In Butler, *Butler's Book*, 634n, 635n, Butler quotes what he says "is a statement of the matter made by Mr. Cameron during his lifetime." The pertinent part of that statement is: ". . . Mr. Lincoln asked me to go to Fortress Monroe and ask General Butler if he would be willing to run, and, if not, to confer with him on the subject."

71 *die or resign*: Donald, *Lincoln*, 495, citing *Mississippi Valley Historical Review*, 33 (March 1947): 550. W, 162, states that Cameron visited Butler at Fort Monroe in March 1864.

72 *"his countenance is as serene"*: Longacre, *Army of Amateurs*, 63.

72 *"which I dread"*: Ibid., 65.

73 *"The men hung around him"*: Freeman, *Lee*, III, 267.

73 *"We must make up our minds"*: Smith, *Grant*, 301.

73 *"Not expecting to see you again"*: Lincoln to Grant, April 30, 1864. *CW*, VII, 324.

74 *A little after midnight*: Hay, *Letters of John Hay*, I, 190–191.

75 *"as intensely as he used to"*: Stoddard, *Inside the White House*, 106–107.

75 *"He read very little"*: Burlingame, ed., *At Lincoln's Side*, 110.

75 *"Your very kind letter"*: PUSG, vol. 10, 380.

76 *If he could do that*: This perspective is put forth in Smith, *Grant*, 316.

76 *"Our country demands"*: Freeman, *Lee*, III, 268.

77 *At times the wind*: Porter, *Campaigning*, 72–73.

77 *Page's description of stretcher-bearers*: Page, *Letters*, 50.

77 *"I never saw a man so agitated"*: Freeman, *Lee*, III, 298n.

78 *"We fought them"*: McWhiney, *Battle*, 45.

78 *"Who are you"*: Flood, *Lee*, 54–55, citing Freeman, *Lee*, III, 287–288; Freeman, *Lee's Lieutenants*, III, 357–359.

78 *Lee was led back from the front*: "Lee to the Rear," *Confederate Veteran* 11 (1903): 116.

79 *"Most of us thought"*: Smith, *Grant*, 337.

80 *"Our spirits rose"*: Ibid.

80 *Wild cheers*: Porter, *Campaigning*, 79.

80 *"Undismayed"*: Smith, *Grant*, 338–339.

81 *"We have been engaged"*: PUSG, vol. 10, 401.

81 *"as soon as our army"* Tarbell, *A Reporter for Lincoln*, 19.

81 *"Grant has gone"*: Lyman, *Civil War Quotations*, 156.

81 *"A man came into Union Mills"*: Tarbell, *A Reporter for Lincoln*, 5.

82 *. . . a crippled and wasted caricature of humanity*: Wing, *Raising the Old Boy*, 71–74.

83 *[I] said that I was coming out early*: Wing, *When Lincoln Kissed Me*, 12–13. In this version of his experience, Wing calls the horse Jesse.

84 *"Write your hundred words"*: Tarbell, *A Reporter for Lincoln*, 5–9. Except where otherwise noted, this account is taken from Tarbell.

84 *"no news direct from Grant"*: Bates, *Telegraph Office*, 244–249.

84 *"was a threat to arrest me"*: Ibid., 246.

84 *Mention of order made by Stanton*: Tarbell, *A Reporter for Lincoln*, 10.

85 *One person recognized him*: Ibid.

86 *Grant was again allowing journalists*: Times dispatch. *NYT*, May 9, 1864, p. 1. There seems no other explanation for the updated information in this story than that Grant had allowed this reporting to resume.

89 *"You are to tell me all you hear and see"*: Tarbell, *A Reporter for Lincoln*, 5–28.

89 *"There's many a night, Henry"*: Ibid., 53–54.

89 *The number of wounded*: *NYT*, May 9, 1864.

90 *"They couldn't hit"* and *"His loss to this army is greater"*; Smith, *Grant*, 346.

90 *"seemed like an orphaned household"*: Winslow, *General John Sedgwick*, 175.

91 *"We have now ended"*: *PUSG*, vol. 10, 422.

91 *"After eight days"*: McWhiney, *Battle in the Wilderness*, 88.

91 *"We have met a man"*: Long, *Civil War Day by Day*, 500.

91 *"I think General Grant has managed"*: Lyman, *Civil War Quotations*, 140.

92 *My dear Madam*: *CW*, VII, 331.

92 *"Kill the damned niggers!"*: Boatner, *Civil War Dictionary*, 296.

92 *There had been an outcry*: Welles, *Diary*, II, 24–25.

92 *Montana Appointments*: *CW*, VII, 371–372. This is noted as being circa June. Treaty with Delaware Indians, ibid., 403.

95 *Seward's maneuverings*: Randall, *Lincoln the President*, vol. 4, 66–67.

95 *"entirely refrain from intercourse"*: Ibid., 68.

96 *"a Monarchical government"*: Ibid., 69.

96 *You are already the great*: Seward, *Seward at Washington*, 200.

96 *"Hundreds of factories"*: Goodwin, *Team of Rivals*, 547.

97 *"see whether we cannot"*: This was Horace Greeley, quoted in W, 143.

97 *"strangely and disastrously remiss"*: *CW*, V, 389n.

97 *"Let us unite"*: Horner, *Lincoln and Greeley*, 341, citing the *New York Tribune* of February 23, 1864.

79 *"God bless the women of America!"*: *CW*, VII, 254, noting that the speech was in fact delivered on March 18, 1864, not on March 16 as reported in other sources.

CHAPTER FIVE: TROUBLED MILITARY AND POLITICAL CAMPAIGNS

PAGE

98 *"one damn blunder from beginning to end"*: Joiner, *One Damn Blunder*. Sherman's quotation, otherwise not attributed, is used as the title.

99 *"though in a position of great security"*: The quote here is from Randall, *Lincoln the President*, vol. 4, 147. In 147n, Randall comments on how, many years later, writing his *Memoirs*, Grant softened his words about this.

99 *"stationary advance"*: Long, *Civil War Day by Day*, 495.

100 *"One of my chief objects"*: Marszalek, *Commander of All Lincoln's Armies*, 205.

100 *". . . public sentiment"*: *CW*, III, 27.

100 *"My God! My God!"*: Brooks, *Washington in Lincoln's Time*, 57–58.

101 *It is inexpressibly sad*: Brooks, *Mr. Lincoln's Washington*, 323.

101 *There are anguished faces*: Ibid.

101 *"the whole city is more or less"*: Stoddard, *Inside the White House*, 93.

102 *The town is full of strangers*: Brooks, *Mr. Lincoln's Washington*, 321.

102 *"I tell you many a man"*: Smith, *Grant*, p. 361, citing Holmes, *Touched with Fire*, 149–150. The letter was written June 24, 1864.

102 *"I cannot bear it"*: Thomas, *Abraham Lincoln*, 423.

102 *Just beyond us, passed a well-dressed lady*: Brooks, *Washington in Lincoln's Time*, 19.

103 *It was the saddest face*; Carpenter, *Six Months*, 30–31.

103 *"a long-skirted"*: Rice, *Reminiscences*, 340, account of Benjamin Perley Poore.

103 *Lincoln's skull*: An Associated Press story in the *Bangor (ME) Daily News* on August 14, 2007, titled "Laser Scans Reveal Lincoln Facial Defect," notes this information as being in an article of the August, 2007 issue of the *Archives of Ophthalmology*. The condition is identified as being craniofacial microsomia.

104 *The account of Stuart's death*: taken from Morris, *Sheridan*, 168–169.

105 *"Gentlemen from VMI"*: Wikipedia, "Battle of New Market, 1." Other accounts and quotations are from this and Civil War. Battle of New Market, May 15, 1864, Porter Johnson Memoirs, New Market Collection, VMI Archives Manuscript #002.

106 *"I have read of the joy of battle"*: Online source, Civil War. Battle of New Market, May 15, 1864, Porter Johnson Memoirs at www.vmi.edu/archives.aspx?id=5591.

107 *Today, while passing through*: Brooks, *Mr. Lincoln's Washington*, 346.

108 *Some of Frémont's background* is taken from Neely, *The Lincoln Encyclopedia*, 118–120.

108 *"You are quite a female politician"*: Segal, *Conversations with Lincoln*, 132. See also Denton, *Passion and Principle*, 319.

109 *"open, shameless, and unrestrained patronage"*: W, 176.

109 *"immense in numbers"*: Ibid.

109 *"the rebels will sack Washington"*: Harper, *Women During the Civil War*, 352.

110 *"It is expected . . . [that] Chase"*: Donald, *Lincoln*, 496.

110 *softer positions*: See article on Manton Marble at the Web site Mr. Lincoln and New York, *www.mrlincolnandnewyork.org*.

110 *"a factious"*: W, 147.

110 *"gentlemen whose hair"*: W, 179, citing *New York World*, May 31, 1864.

110 *"motley set"*: *NYT*, June 2, 1864.

110 *"a conglomeration"*: *NYT*, June 3, 1864.

111 *"gentlemen who came"*: *NYT*, May 31, 1864.

111 *"But if Mr. Lincoln should be nominated"*: Thomas, *Abraham Lincoln*, 426. Cowles and Pettis reactions, ibid., 425.

112 *At one point we were losing*: *NYT*, June 9, 1864.

112 *Frank Wilkeson's account* is from Congdon, ed., *Combat*. The quoted portions of the account are from 487–494.

113 *four-thirty in the morning*: For the delay and some other details of the first attack, see Cleaves, *Meade of Gettysburg*, 250–251.

113 *"calmly writing their names"*: Smith, *Grant*, 362.

113 *"June 3. Cold Harbor. I was killed"*: Weber, *Copperheads*, 138.

113 *"It seemed more like a volcanic blast"*: Smith, *Grant*, 362.

113 *"We turned loose"*: Alexander, *Fighting for the Confederacy*, 406.

113 *McMahan's account*: Bradford, *Battles and Leaders*, Vol. IV, 213–14.

114 *Twenty minutes had not passed*: Wilkeson, *Recollections*, 132.

114 *"About 7 A.M."*: Alexander, *Fighting*, 406.

114 *fourteen successive attacks*: Freeman, *Lee*, III, 389.

114 *Wing's account*: Tarbell, *A Reporter for Lincoln*, 51.

114 *enemy officers exhorting*: Alexander, *Fighting*, 406; Freeman, *Lee*, III, 389.

114 *"at some places fifty yards"*: PUSG, 11, 9.

114 *By eleven in the morning*: Freeman, *Lee*, III, 389.

115 *Grant to Meade at 12:30 on June 3, 1864*: PUSG, vol. 11, 13. The language is: ". . . you may direct a suspension of further advance for the moment."

115 *The figure of more than 7,000 is from Freeman, Lee*, III, 391.

115 *"There can be no doubt"*: Alexander, *Fighting*, 497.

115 *. . . I heard the charging commands*: Wilkeson, *Recollections*, 134.

115 *Exchange between Lee and Reagan*, and Reagan's description of the sound of musketry: Freeman, *Lee*, III, 389.

116 *"I regret this assault"*: Smith, *Grant*, citing Porter, *Campaigning with Grant*, 179.

116 *"It was not war"*: Law's remark: Bradford, *Battles and Leaders of the Civil War*, IV, 141.

116 *Casualty figures*: Smith, *Grant*, 365n.

117 *"our loss was not severe"*: PUSG, vol. 11, 9.

117 *Grant's communications with Lee*: Ibid., 17–23.

117 *"[Grant] had the hardihood"*: This appeared in the *NYT* of June 15, 1864, attributed to the *Richmond Dispatch* of June 9. Mention of that story and a similar one in the Augusta paper is in Nelson, *Bullets, Ballots, and Rhetoric*, 50, 187n.

117 *"He loses two men to the enemy's one"*: Keckley, *Behind the Scenes*, 133.

CHAPTER SIX: TRIMMING THE POLITICAL TREE

PAGE

118 *Cameron's support of Lincoln*: McClure, *Lincoln and Men of War Times*, 142–156; Donald, *Lincoln*, 502; Neely, *The Lincoln Encyclopedia*, 46.

119 *"[He] always told only enough"*: Neely, *The Lincoln Encyclopedia*, 300.

119 *"was a trimmer"* and *"never trimmed his principles"*: Ibid.

119 *"will be unanimous"*: April 29, 1864, Lincoln Papers online at LOC.

119 *"without an exception"*: May 17, 1864, Lincoln Papers online at LOC.

119 *"are to a man"*: Ibid.

120 *"the great act of the age"*: Lincoln Encyclopedia, 136.

120 *Lincoln's views on having Hamlin or Johnson as his running mate*: W, 393n.

120 *Background on Lamon*: Lincoln Encyclopedia, 177–179.

120 *Lamon at the Chicago Convention*: Donald, *Lincoln*, 248, 267.

121 *"I saw and handled"*: W, 198.

122 *Lane on Johnson*: W, 197, citing Speer, *James H. Lane*, 284.

122 *He moved with masterly sagacity*: McClure, *Lincoln and Men of War Times*, 122–123. For the view that Lincoln preferred Hamlin, or at least did not favor Johnson, see Hamlin, *The Life and Times of Hannibal Hamlin*, 461–489. In evaluating that chapter, "The History of Johnson's Nomination," it seems relevant to point out that this book was written by Hamlin's grandson. In those pages, however, he marshals all the

evidence and arguments that might persuade the reader that Lincoln was in fact neutral in the matter. It should, however, be remembered that if Lincoln had preferred Hamlin, he had only to say so.

124 *For a day or two*: Hay, *Lincoln and the Civil War*, 185.

125 *"One of the first men I met"*: Nicolay to Hay, June 5, 1864, Lincoln Papers online at LOC.

125 *"Wish not to interfere"*: *CW*, VII, 376.

125 *The President wishes*: Hay, *Letters of John Hay*, Hay to Nicolay, June 6, 1864, 186.

126 *"Called on the President"*: Welles, *Diary*, II, 41.

127 *"information of high national importance"*: *CW*, VII, 379; and Rosecrans to Lincoln, June 2, 1864, Lincoln Papers online at LOC. See also Hay, *Letters of John Hay*, 199–200.

127 *"Northwest Conspiracy"*: Some reasons for the Copperheads' hopes for this are to be found in W, 210. Among them, Waugh speaks of these: "The 1860 census showed that 475,000 residents of Ohio, Indiana and Illinois had been born in the slave states. Four of every ten northwesterners in 1860 were of Southern birth or parentage. . . . The South and the Northwest had traditionally been tied together economically by their shared dependence on the Mississippi River." For additional information on the more militant Copperhead organizations, see Catton, *Army of the Potomac*, 125.

127 *"carefully investigated the matter"*: Hay, *Letters of John Hay*, 203–204.

127 *For a description of this strategy as it was reported to Jefferson Davis by Confederate agents in the North*, see Starr, *Colonel Grenfell's Wars*, 144–145. As set forth there, the added idea of the "Northwestern Confederacy" allying itself with the South was put forward by Clement Vallandigham.

127 *"a convocation"*: Hay, *Letters of John Hay*, 204.

128 *"Supreme Grand Commander"*: See Klement, *The Limits of Dissent*, 262.

128 *"an abject failure"* and *"the immediate inauguration"*: Klement, *The Limits of Dissent*, 267.

128 *United States Navy gunboat*: Ibid., 227.

128 *guns trained on the hotel*: Weber, *Copperheads*, 98.

128 *"watch Vallandigham and others"*: Seitz, *Lincoln the Politician*, 371.

129 *Plans for the Fourth of July attacks*: Starr, *Colonel Grenfell's Wars*, 152–156. Sources and interpretations concerning the details and extent of the militant Copperhead threat differ considerably. For different reasons, Confederate propagandists and self-serving Union officers had reason to exaggerate that threat. See Klement, *The Copperheads in the Middle West*, 170–205; Gray, *The Hidden Civil War*, 175–185. Weber, in *The Copperheads*, makes a solid case for the seriousness of the threat.

130 *"restive and inventive"*: Starr, *Colonel Grenfell's Wars*, 153.

130 *Stoddard at the Baltimore Convention*: Stoddard, *Inside the White House*, 136–138.

131 *[An] eloquent, powerful*: Ibid., 136.

132 *A UNITED STATES SENATOR*: Brooks, *Mr. Lincoln's Washington*, 316. In the text the words "a rencounter" appear; I am assuming that this is a misprint, and use "an encounter" in their place.

132 *Lane, conferring with Lincoln*: Miers, ed., *Lincoln Day by Day*, 262.

132 *"would go through a wall"*: Stoddard, *Inside the White House*, 137.

133 *"densely packed"*: Unless otherwise noted, these quotations or descriptions are from p. 1 of the *New York Times*, June 9, 1864, in a story datelined "Baltimore, Tuesday, June 7."

134 *"representatives of either of the old political parties"*: Donald, *Lincoln*, 504.

134 *"for such an amendment"*: W, 189.

134 *Morgan met with him*: Ibid., 188.

134 *"The Convention has just been called to order"*: Miers, ed., *Lincoln Day by Day*, 263.

135 *"I think to lose Kentucky"*: CW, IV, 190.

135 *"Show this letter to Robert"*: Townsend, *Lincoln and the Bluegrass*, 256.

135 *"As a Union party"*: W, 190.

135 *"The venerable speaker"*: Brooks, *Mr. Lincoln's Washington*, 330.

135 *"I was satisfied"*: Hamlin, *Life and Times of Hannibal Hamlin*, 474.

135 *"damned secessionist provinces"*: Donald, *Lincoln*, 504–505.

136 *Discussion of the seating of delegations*: NYT, June 9, 1864, p.1; W, 191–192.

136 *Gentlemen of the Convention*: NYT, June 9, 1864.

137 *"Enthusiastic unanimity"*: Miers, ed., *Lincoln Day by Day*, 263.

138 *Wording of the resolutions, and reaction of delegates*: NYT, June 9, 1864, p. 1; McClure, *Our Presidents and How We Make Them*, 187–188; and W, 193.

139 *"The mention of the name"*: NYT, June 9, 1864, p. 1.

139 *Montgomery Blair's views*: Neely, *The Lincoln Encyclopedia*, 31. For Lincoln's interest in colonization, see Donald, *Lincoln*, 343–344, and notes for 344 on 652; CW, VII, 417–418.

140 *Delegates' reactions to Lincoln's nomination*: NYT, June 9, 1864; Brooks, *Washington in Lincoln's Time*, 146; W, 193–196.

142 *"Can't you find"*: McClure, *Lincoln and Men of War Times*, 244.

142 *"What? Am I renominated?"*: W, 196; "Send it right over," in Bates, *Telegraph Office*, 267. For various accounts of the news reaching Lincoln, see W, 392n.

143 *"utterance to the almost universal voice"*: W, 202.

143 *"I will neither conceal"*: Ibid.

143 *"I have not permitted myself"*: CW, VII, 383–384.

143 *Comments of Bennett and Marble*: W, 201.

144 *"I am in active correspondence"*: CW, VII, 517–518n.

144 *"I told Mr. Lincoln"* and *"Lincoln is gone"*: W, 264, 262.

144 *Swett's letters to his wife*: Tarbell, *Life of Lincoln*, vol. 3, 200–203.

144 *This morning*: CW, VII, 514.

CHAPTER SEVEN: "I BEGIN TO SEE IT"—THE ELUSIVE "IT"

PAGE

145 *The descriptions of the relative situations of Grant and Sherman, Grant's plans and movements, and Lee's reactions* are based on Smith, *Grant*, 368–376.

147 *"The advance of our troops"*: PUSG, vol. 11, 39.

147 *Our forces will commence crossing*: Ibid., 45.

147 HAVE JUST READ YOUR DISPATCH: CW, VII, 393.

148 *Since Sunday*: PUSG, vol. 11, 55.

148 *"I wish"*: Brooks, *Washington in Lincoln's Time*, 138.

149 *"exhausted and discouraged troops"*: Wilkeson, *Recollections*, 174.

150 *"Petersburg at that time"*: Beauregard's estimate: Bradford, *Battles and Leaders*, IV, 541.

150 *"Its presence before our lines"*: Bradford, *Battles and Leaders*, IV, 542.

150 *"The Army of Northern Virginia"*: Ibid., 553.

151 *Lee's arrival at Petersburg*: Butler, *Butler's Book*, 703, telegram from Beauregard to Braxton Bragg, recorded as sent at 11:30 A.M,. saying in part, "General Lee has just arrived."

151 *"a mere question of time"*: Freeman, *Lee*, III, 398.

152 *"panting for peace"*: Laas, *Wartime Washington*, 145n. The woman was Elizabeth Blair Lee, daughter of Francis Preston Blair, Sr., and wife of Union naval captain Samuel Phillips Lee.

152 *"That night, while searching"*: Wilkeson, *Recollections*, 125.

152 *Sitting at the base*: Ibid., 175–176.

153 *Mistaken announcement of Petersburg being taken*: CW, VII, 399.

153 *Grant's losses*: W, 202.

153 *"as helpless as a child"*: Warner, *Generals in Blue*, 463.

153 *"The President in his intense anxiety"*: Welles, *Diary*, II, 55.

154 *The President came down*: Unless otherwise noted, all the description of this visit is from Porter, *Campaigning with Grant*, 217–224.

155 *... I came on the line*: Wilkeson, *Recollections*, 164.

156 *"sending Gen. Butler to another"* Grant to Halleck, July 1, 1865, *PUSG*, vol. 11, 155. In this letter, Grant notes that Butler is a good administrator, but, "not being a soldier by education or experience, is in the hands of his subordinates in all operations Military." Grant also says that Butler, while willing, has "a want of knowledge how to execute."

157 *"This country has more vitality"*: Neely, *The Lincoln Encyclopedia*, 43.

157 *Porter's observations*: Porter, *Campaigning with Grant*, 223.

157 *"a long summer's day"*: Hay, *The Letters of John Hay*, 195–196.

158 *"The President arrived"*: Stoddard, *Inside Lincoln's White House*, 310.

158 *"Just now the public feeling"*: Burlingame, ed., *Lincoln Observed*, 116.

158 *black troops should receive pay equal to whites'*: CW, II, 404–406.

159 *"deliver up to their owners"*: Donald, *Lincoln*, 136, citing *CW*, II, 20–22. See also Neely, *The Lincoln Encyclopedia*, 120.

160 *"We also discussed the negro question"*: Browning, *Diary*, I, 478.

160 *"a climate congenial to them"*: Stephenson, *Lincoln*, 202.

160 *Lincoln tells black leaders of bleak future*: CW, V, 372–375.

160 *"the greatest wrong inflicted"*: Blight, *Frederick Douglass' Civil War*, 138.

161 *"all his inconsistencies"*: Ibid., 139.

161 *Lincoln's interest in colonization*: See Donald, *Lincoln*, 343–344, and notes for 344 on 652; *CW*, VII, 417–418. See also Dennett, ed., *Lincoln and the Civil War*, 203, citing Nicolay and Hay, *History*, VI, 356–366.

162 *"rendition" [return] of fugitive slaves*: Miers, ed., *Lincoln Day by Day*, entry for June 28, 1864.

162 *"during the present rebellion"*: Neely, *The Lincoln Encyclopedia*, 135.

162 *"The supremacy of the military power"*: Simon, *Lincoln and Chief Justice Taney*, 246.

163 *"to superintend the fitting up"*: Burlingame, ed., *Lincoln Observed*, 125.

163 *"no financial or political standing"* Goodwin, *Team of Rivals*, 632.

163 *Barney and Hogeboom*: CW, VII, 413. For the correspondence leading to Lincoln's acceptance of Chase's resignation, see *CW*, VII, 412–413, 419.

163 *Nicolay's conference with Weed*: Donald, *Lincoln*, 495–496.

163 *Lincoln prepared to appoint Chase to Supreme Court*: Donald, *Lincoln*, 507; Nicolay and Hay, *History*, IX, 98; Donald, ed., *Inside Lincoln's Cabinet*, 224–225.

164 *I cannot help feeling*: The text of Chase's letter is in *CW*, VII, 414n.

164 *While we were talking*: Donald, ed., *Inside Lincoln's Cabinet*, 223. This is from Chase's diary entry of June 30, 1864. Further note: in the page cited, there is a period rather than a question mark after "resigned," and a bracketed single quote after "successor" where there is none in the original. I have also inserted the bracketed "Treasury."

165 *Your resignation*: CW, VII, 419. See also *CW*, VII, 412–414.

165 *"I had found a great deal of embarrassment"*: Donald, ed., *Inside Lincoln's Cabinet*, 223–224.

165 *"another Treasury imbroglio"*: Segal, *Conversations with Lincoln*, 330.

165 *"I thought I could not stand it any longer"*: Niven, *Salmon P. Chase*, 366, citing Dennett, ed., *Lincoln and the Civil War*, 199.

165 *"I put my pen into my mouth"*: Goodwin, *Team of Rivals*, 633.

165 *"I have nominated you"*: CW, VII, 420.

166 *"They not only objected"*: Nicolay and Hay, *History*, IX, 97, citing Hay's diary.

166 *Lincoln reads the Senate Finance Committee Chase's previous letters of resignation*: Goodwin, *Team of Rivals*, 634. See also Brooks, *Washington in Lincoln's Time*, 119–120.

166 *"The condition of my health"*: CW, VII, 420.

166 *"to communicate this information"*: Nicolay and Hay, *History*, IX, 99.

166 *"Start at once for the Senate"*: Ibid., 99. Since Nicolay was not in Washington at this time, the "secretary" referred to on p. 99 can only have been Hay.

167 *"The nomination was instantly confirmed"*: Dennett, ed., *Lincoln and the Civil War*, 201.

167 *Stanton's remark to Fessenden*: Goodwin, *Team of Rivals*, 636.

167 *"the crisis was such"*: Ibid.

167 *It is, and will be, my sincere desire*: CW, VII, 423.

167 *"the greatest financier of the century"*: Goodwin, *Team of Rivals*, 635.

167 *"the greatest financial secretary"*: Nicolay and Hay, *History*, IX, 103.

167 *"a delegation of New York bankers"*: Carpenter, *Six Months*, 183.

167 *"in high glee"*: Dennett, ed., *Lincoln and the Civil War*, 200–201.

168 *"dropped off like a rotten pear"*: Goodwin, *Team of Rivals*, 634.

168 *"they gave me to understand"*: Welles, *Diary*, II, 63.

168 *"Honest contracts are not fairly treated"*: Welles, *Diary*, II, 68, entry for July 7.

168 *"worse than another Bull Run defeat"*: Goodwin, *Team of Rivals*, 634.

168 *I will tell you how it is with Chase*: Ibid., 635.

168 *"So my official life closes"*: Donald, ed., *Inside Lincoln's Cabinet*, 225.

169 *"if the Democrats could only cut"*: Ibid., 233.

169 *"not willing now"*: Blue, *Salmon P. Chase*, 240.

169 "*No man knows what* that gnawing": W, 39.

170 *Sherman's casualties, supply line situation, and Johnston's corresponding advantages*: Marszalek, *Sherman*, 269.

170 "*Our enemy has gained strength*": Ibid.

171 *A solid line of blue*: Flood, *Grant and Sherman*, 254.

171 "*At all points*": Sherman, *Memoirs*, 531.

171 "*Hello, Johnny*": Lewis, *Sherman: Fighting Prophet*, 368.

172 *Description of the Crater plan*: Boatner, *Civil War Dictionary*, 647–649; see also Axelrod, *The Horrid Pit*, 46.

172 "*We could blow that damned fort*": Axelrod, *The Horrid Pit*, 36.

173 "*I authorized*" and "*lay the matter*": Ibid., 44–45.

CHAPTER EIGHT: A PRETTY PLACE FROM WHICH TO DROP INTO A DARK, DRAMATIC SUMMER

PAGE

175 "*most pleasing manners*": Pinsker, *Lincoln's Sanctuary*, 84. This and other information about Derickson comes from Pinsker, 57–58, 84–85.

176 "*made numerous inquiries*": Ibid., 57.

176 *Derickson's letter*: Ibid., 211n.

176 "*discussed points*": Ibid., 85.

176 *Lincoln signs the amended Pacific Railroad Act*. For the Union Pacific and the Central Pacific, see Ambrose, *Nothing Like It in the World*, 95 et seq.; and Randall, *Lincoln the President*, vol. 4, 180. Ambrose, 95, and Miers, vol. 3, 269, place this signing on July 1864. *CW*, VII, does not record this.

177 . . . *there is still a great deficiency*: *CW*, VII, 40.

178 *The rebels have demanded*: Hyman, *The Radical Republicans and Reconstruction*, 39.

179 "*I certainly expected you to retreat*": Jones, *Personal Reminiscences*, 240–241.

179 "*I have taken command of all these troops*": PUSG, vol. 11, 166n.

179 *Exchanges between Halleck and Grant*: Ibid., 166–169.

181 "*went on with the other work*": Nicolay and Hay, *History*, IX, 120.

181 *In spite of all the efforts*: Ibid., 114.

181 "*mercy to traitors*": Neely, *The Lincoln Encyclopedia*, 321.

182 "*Several prominent members*" This and following exchanges: Nicolay and Hay, *History*, IX, 120.

183 "*of possible* reconstruction with slavery": Ibid., 124. The italics are mine.

183 "*our boys got the Fourth of July dinner*": Cooling, *Jubal Early's Raid on Washington*, 27.

184 "*idle scare*": Ibid., 83.

184 "*We are doing as well as we can*": Donald, *Lincoln*, 518.

185 "*Proclamation Suspending Writ of Habeas Corpus*": *CW*, VII, 425–427.

185 *Letter and enclosures from Greeley*: Horner, *Lincoln and Greeley*, 298 et seq.

186 "*I have to inform you*": Ibid., 315.

187 "*In compensation*": Ibid., 296.

187 "*Come here, my boy*": Carpenter, *Six Months*, 319–320. The description of this incident has also been ascribed to an unidentified reporter of the *New York Times*. The

particular incident is spoken of as occurring "November last," but it is difficult to establish the year in which it happened. It is placed here as an additional example of Lincoln's willingness to receive those who wished to see him.

188 *"Proclamation Concerning Reconstruction"*: *CW*, VII, 433.

188 *"Pale with wrath"*: Donald, *Lincoln*, 512.

188 *"dictatorial usurpation"*: Neely, *The Lincoln Encyclopedia*, 322.

189 *"Cannon was heard here"*: Laas, *Wartime Washington*, 401–402.

189 *"There could no longer be"*: Cooling, *Jubal Early's Raid on Washington*, 47.

190 *"Surrender, you son of a bitch!"*: Ibid., 78.

190 *"private soldiers of our brigade"*: Ibid., 73.

190 *"amounted almost to a martial delirium"*: Ibid.

191 *Lincoln's exchanges with Garrett*: *CW*, VII, 434–435.

191 *"A fact that has just been reported"*: Thomas, *Abraham Lincoln*, 433.

191 *"tonight," and other details of these measures for Lincoln's security*: Randall, *Lincoln the President*, vol. 4, 200.

191 *"I am directed"*: *CW*, VII, 435n.

191 *"Baltimore is in great peril"*: Ibid., 438n.

191 *"I have not a single soldier"*: Ibid., 437–438, 438n.

192 *"How an army so great"*: Beale, ed., *The Diary of Edward Bates*, entry of July 10, 1864, 384.

192 *There had been no information*: Welles, Diary, II, 71, 73.

192 *"I regret his passion for the service"* and *"I have tried to dissuade"*: Ibid., 71, 82.

193 *The truth is*: Ibid., 72.

193 *. . . the Black Horse Cavalry*: Cramer, *Lincoln Under Enemy Fire*, 40.

194 *"Force enough to defeat"*: *PUSG*, vol. 11, 198.

194 *Your despatch to Gen. Halleck*: *CW*, VII, 437, 437n.

194 *". . . where the remainder of Hunter's army"*: *PUSG*, vol. 11, 200n.

194 *"I think on reflection"*: Ibid., 202.

195 *"The news of the approach"*: Brooks, *Washington in Lincoln's Time*, p. 159.

195 *"In Georgetown one nest of secessionists"*: Ibid., 161.

195 *"It seems funny to hear the rumbling"*: Doster, *Lincoln and Episodes of the Civil War*, 253.

195 *Lincoln's move back into the White House*: Dennett, ed., *Lincoln and the Civil War*, 208.

195 *Details of the arrival of the reinforcements*: Cooling, *Jubal Early's Raid on Washington*, 121.

195 *"an immense throng"*: Bidwell, *History of the Forty-Ninth New York Volunteers*, 129.

196 *"I must go to my boys"*: Cooling, *Jubal Early's Raid on Washington*, 122.

197 *"The enemy is within"*: Ibid., 118.

197 *"within range"*: Cramer, *Lincoln Under Enemy Fire*, 51.

198 *"Some of our boys"*: Ibid., 41.

198 *"Get down, you fool!"*: Cramer, *Lincoln Under Enemy Fire*, 22. Cramer's book is in essence a compilation of accounts of Lincoln's actions at Fort Stevens on the days of July 10, 11, and 12, 1864, and an analysis of their authenticity. Cooling, *Jubal Early's Raid on Washington*, 143 et seq., offers similar varying accounts and perspectives.

198 *". . . just as Mr. Lincoln was quitting the fort"*: Ibid., 103. It should again be noted that

everything about Lincoln's visits to Fort Stevens and what occurred during them has been the subject of many different versions and interpretations.

198 *At three o'clock P.M.*: Dennett, ed., *Lincoln and the Civil War*, 208.

199 *"Hextry Staar"*: Doster, *Lincoln and Episodes of the Civil War*, 250.

199 *The President is in very good feather*: Dennett, ed., *Lincoln and the Civil War*, 209.

200 *"Vague rumors"*: *CW*, VII, 438.

200 *"are confusingly conflicting"*: Cooling, *Jubal Early's Raid on Washington*, 135.

200 *"to be brought forward"*: Welles, *Diary*, II, 74.

201 *President Lincoln and his wife*: Stevens, *Three Years in the Sixth Corps*, 374. See also Cramer, *Lincoln Under Enemy Fire*, 28–29.

201 *Salmon P. Chase at Fort Stevens*: Cooling, *Jubal Early's Raid on Washington*, 144.

202 *"stationed with about one hundred and twenty men"*: Bidwell, *History of the Forty-Ninth New York Volunteers*, 130–131.

202 *"Not a man was visible"*: Cooling, *Jubal Early's Raid on Washington*, 146.

203 *"I certainly gave my approbation"*: Ibid., 145.

203 *"with such great sacrifice"*: Ibid., 136.

204 *"accompanied by Senator Zack Chandler"*: Cramer, *Lincoln Under Enemy Fire*, 43 et seq.

204 *"Lincoln with a hole in his coat sleeve"*: Cooling, *Jubal Early's Raid on Washington*, 144.

204 *"I saw the President standing"*: Ibid., 144.

204 *Soon a sharpshooter fired*: Cramer, *Lincoln Under Enemy Fire*, 44. Once again, there are different versions of the circumstances under which Lincoln was fired at for the second day in a row, but virtually all accounts agree on the identity of the man hit.

205 *"Mary entreated"*: Ibid., 77.

205 *"the summit of the road"*: Welles, *Diary*, II, 74–75.

205 *"as fine a bayonet charge"*: Cooling, *Jubal Early's Raid on Washington*, 148.

205 *". . . our men ran to the charge"*: Welles, *Diary*, II, 75.

205 *Civilians applauding*: Leech, *Reveille in Washington*, 343.

206 *"fell back, rallied again"*: Cooling, *Jubal Early's Raid on* Washington, 149.

206 *"went up beautifully"*: Ibid.

206 *"On all the floors"*: Ibid., 151.

207 *As we came out of the fort*: Welles, *Diary*, II, 75.

CHAPTER NINE: TRYING TO PICK UP THE MILITARY AND POLITICAL PIECES

PAGE

208 *. . . we proceeded through the encampment*: Dennett, ed., *Lincoln and the Civil War*, 210.

209 *"Boldness is all that is wanted"*: *PUSG*, vol. 11, 228 et seq. Grant's telegram, marked in its text as being sent at 2:30 P.M. on July 13, is noted as being received at 1 A.M. the next morning.

209 *"Wright telegraphs that he thinks"*: Dennett, ed., *Lincoln and the Civil War*, 210.

209 *"Mrs. Lincoln, I intend"*: Randall, *Mary Lincoln*, 341.

209 *"the Rebel Invasion"*: Welles, *Diary*, II, 77.

210 *"the great noodles"* and *"stumping the States"*: W, 244.

210 *Now Uncle Abe*: Lee, *Mr. Lincoln's City*, 9.

210 *"In conversation with him"*: Browning, *Diary*, I, 676.

210 *"To day, I spoke my mind"*: Beale, ed., *The Diary of Edward Bates*, 385.

211 *"Met the President"*: Browning, *Diary*, I, 676.

211 *prewar acts of hospitality and friendship*: See Brooks, *Mr. Lincoln's Washington*, 358; W, 243; Smith, *The Francis Preston Blair Family*, II, 272–273; Cooling, *Jubal Early's Raid on Washington*, 178–179.

211 *". . . the officers in command about Washington"*: *CW*, VII, 440 n.1.

211 *"it should be known"*: *CW*, VII, 440n.

212 *I must be the judge*: *CW*, VII, 439.

212 *"that 30,000"*: Browning, *Diary*, I 676.

212 *"In my opinion"* and *Yours of yesterday*: *PUSG*, vol. 11, 280, 280n.

212 *"a recurrence of what has just taken place"*: Grant to Halleck, July 18, 1864. *PUSG*, vol. 11, 274.

212 *"I shall make a desperate effort"* and *". . . I am glad to hear"*: *CW*, VII, 444, 444n.

213 *"You misconceive . . . "*: *CW*, VII, 445, 445n.

213 *"put himself south of the enemy"* and *This, I think, is exactly right*: *CW*, VII, 476, 476n.

213 *"clothed with full power"*: *CW*, VII, 451n.

214 *"To Whom It May Concern"*: Ibid., 451.

215 *We will go on*: Kirkland, *The Peacemakers of 1864*, 94–95.

215 *The men of the South*: *CW*, VII, 461.

216 *"prepared a Platform and an Address"*: This and the other quotations from this memorandum are in *CW*, VII, 459–460. The letter to Waksman is in *CW*, VII, 461.

218 *"read us all the letters"*: Bates, *Diary*, 388–389.

219 *No one who has not witnessed it*: This and the following quotations from Doster are in Doster, *Lincoln and Episodes of the Civil War*, 136–146, 152.

221 *"six months' incessant labor"*: This and the subsequent quotations and descriptions of Carpenter's final days at the White House are from Carpenter, *Six Months*, 350–353. The cabinet meeting referred to is that of July 22.

223 *'War Powers of the President'*: The book referred to is *War Powers Under the Constitution of the United States* by William Whiting, a lawyer working for the War Department. Its first edition appeared in 1862, with subsequent chapters added in the 1870 edition.

225 *General Burnside wanted*: Unless otherwise noted, this and subsequent quotations concerning the events of July 30 in front of Petersburg are from the study of the Battle of the Crater, sometimes known as the Petersburg Mine Assault, by Alan Axelrod, cited here as Axelrod, *The Horrid Pit*, 99 et seq.

226 *"unlucky victim"*: This quotation comes from the account of Major William H. Powell, in Bradford, *Battles and Leaders*, IV, 563. The wording there is: "Upon his arrival General Burnside determined that the three commanders of his white divisions should 'pull straws,' and Ledlie was (as he thought) the unlucky victim."

229 *"This caused them to break and scatter"*: Ibid., 551.

230 *"on the right and left of the crater"*: Ibid., 555.

230 *"the whole scene of the explosion"*: Ibid., 551.

231 *"Every organization melted away"*: Ibid., 553.

233 *General Grant now began*: Porter's account, ending with "unofficerlike and ungentle-manly," is from Porter, *Campaigning with Grant*, 266–268.

236 *Some details of Lee's participation* are in Freeman, *Lee*, III, 467–477.

237 *Some details of the Confederate artillery* in action, including the gunners smiling at how little powder the mortars required for this mission, are in ibid., 470–476.

237 *The major-general commanding*: Axelrod, *The Horrid Pit*, 192.

239 *Union casualty figures*: Ibid., 238.

240 *"He has suffered severely"*: Dowdey, ed., *The Wartime Papers of R. E. Lee*, 828.

240 *"uncertain and confused"*: Welles, *Diary*, II, 89.

240 *"desperate attempt,"* the other terms, and the subheadline: *NYT*, August 2, 1864.

240 *"The shameful slaughter"*: Ibid., August 8, 1864.

240 *"Gen. Grant and Porter returned"*: All the quotations from the individuals at City Point at this time are to be found in *PUSG*, vol. 11, 361–364.

241 *Court of Inquiry, and Burnside's approaches to Grant and Lincoln*: Axelrod, *The Horrid Pit*, 239–242.

241 *"failed to obey"*: Ibid., 240.

242 *"I sometimes feel very nervous"*: Flood, *Grant and Sherman*, 373. The description of the committee's prejudices is from 371.

242 *"gave me an even more favorable opinion"*: Grant, *Memoirs*, 470.

242 *Chandler, Wilkinson, and Wade visit Lincoln*: Trefousse, *The Radical Republicans*, 244.

243 *Chandler and Wilkinson visit headquarters*: Cleaves, *Meade of Gettysburg*, 272.

243 *"I had a great fondness"*: Smith, *Grant*, 292.

243 *"stupendous failure"*: Grant, *Memoirs*, 613.

243 *Grant suggests a court-martial for Burnside*: Marvel, *Burnside*, 416.

243 *"He is not competent"*: Cleaves, *Meade of Gettysburg*, 282.

243 *"the Indians showed"*: Herek, *These Men Have Seen Hard Service*, 226.

244 *"If the Indian is so willing"*: Ibid., 234.

CHAPTER TEN: AUGUST: THE DARKEST MONTH

PAGE

246 *"Who shall revive"*: Lewis, *Sherman*, 398.

246 *"Copperhead Convention"*: Randall, *Lincoln the President*, vol. 4, 202–203.

247 *"We seized this morning"*: Tarbell, *Life of Lincoln*, III, 200–201.

247 *The dollar at 37 cents*: Smith, *Grant*, 378.

247 *"the worst thing I have noticed"*: Hay to Nicolay, August 26, 1864. In Dennett, ed., *Lincoln and the Civil War*, 213.

248 *Invention of the word "miscegenation"*: Croly, *Miscegenation*, II.

248 *"When the President proclaimed"*: Ibid., 49.

248 *"If any fact is well established"*: Ibid., 8.

248 *"The Blending of Diverse Bloods"*: Ibid., 14.

248 *"the most perfect and highest type of manhood"*: Ibid., 65.

248 *According to the census*: Kaplan, "The Miscegenation Issue in the Election of 1864," 318.

249 *The fusion, whenever it takes place*: Croly, *Miscegenation*, 31.

249 *"The Love of the Blonde for the Black"*: Ibid., 27.

249 *"The mothers and daughters"*: Ibid., 43.

249 *The next step will be:* Ibid., 19.

250 *"doctrine and dogma"*: Long, *The Jewel of Liberty*, 164.

250 *Fill with mulattoes and mongrels:* Long, Ibid., 165.

250 *Does the Republican party:* The entire text of "The Lincoln Catechism" is in Hyman, "Election of 1864," with this exchange appearing on 1237. It is identified by Hyman only as being published in New York in 1864; in Long, *Jewel of Liberty*, it is quoted from and commented upon on 173–174, and on 355 it appears in the bibliography in the section, "Election Pamphlets," under this entry: Democratic Campaign Document. *The Lincoln Catechism, Wherein the Eccentricities & Beauties of Despotism are Fully Set Forth*. New York: 1864.

250 *"a war for the negro"*: Croly, *Miscegenation*, 18.

250 *"until Mr. Lincoln's time is out"*: Kaplan, "The Miscegenation Issue," 277.

251 *I have seen your despatch: CW*, VII, 499.

251 *"The president has more nerve"*: Porter, *Campaigning*, 279.

252 *"the defeat of my army"*: Morris, *Sheridan*, 183.

252 *"will probably not survive the night"*: *CW*, VII, 484n. See also Welles's diary entry of August 6, Welles, *Diary*, II, 94.

252 *"I shall be glad to have this done"*: *CW*, VII, 484.

253 *"erase some of the lamentations"*: Welles, *Diary*, II, 94.

253 *"was undoubtedly an adroit party move"*: ibid., p. 110.

253 *"mere oligarchies"* and *"A more studied outrage"*: Williams, *Lincoln and the Radicals*, 324–325.

253 *"an infinity of party and personal intrigue"*: Welles, *Diary*, II, 95.

254 *I am a War Democrat: CW*, VII, 501.

254 *"The President was free and animated"*: *CW*, VII, 506–507. This diary entry was written by Mills in an abbreviated style, an example being "Aye said the President, 3 weeks would do me no good." I have changed this into a more readable form, as seen in the text.

257 *"As President"*: Randall, *Lincoln the President*, vol. 4, 209, and Donald, *Lincoln*, 524, both citing the *New York Herald* of August 6, 1864.

257 *"The people of the loyal states"*: Donald, *Lincoln*, 523.

257 *"It would be difficult to determine"*: Harper, *Lincoln and the Press*, 308.

258 *"my lieutenant general in Congress"* and *"does not exactly pronounce him,"* W, 309.

258 *"His election was a rash experiment"*: Dudley, "The Election of 1864," 500–518. The quotation is from 516.

258 *"The fact begins to shine out"*: W, 262.

258 *"Reviewing the history"*: Harper, *Lincoln and the Press*, 304.

258 *"little mac will be president"* and *quotations from other soldiers*: Davis, *Lincoln's Men*, 200–201.

259 *Weed's calling on Lincoln*: Stoddard, *Horace Greeley*, 227.

259 *"Lincoln is gone"*: W, 262.

259 *Weed and the Crittenden resolution*: Donald, *Lincoln*, 528.

259 *"A friend of mine just in from the West"*: J. H. Puleston to John G. Nicolay, [August

1864] [Political Affairs], Abraham Lincoln Papers, Manuscript Division, Library of Congress.

259 *"took from a corner of his desk"*: McClure, *Lincoln and Men of War Times*, 125.

260 *"You are wearing yourself down"*: Sandburg, *Storm over the Land*, 313.

260 *"They can't do it!"*: Donald, *Lincoln*, 525.

261 *"I suppose you think"*: Simon, ed., *The Personal Memoirs of Julia Dent Grant*, 147.

261 "One denounces": W, 264.

261 *For the meeting at Opdyke's house and the composition of this group*, see Randall, *Lincoln the President*, vol. 4, 211–213; W, 270–271.

261 *"I doubt not"*: Welles, *Diary*, II, 120.

261 *"Mr. Lincoln is already beaten"*: W, 270.

261 *"The People are wild for Peace"*: Donald, *Lincoln*, 528.

262 *"to get rid of"*: Ibid., 525.

262 *"Tell Clark"*: Rankin, *Intimate Character Sketches*, 33.

262 *"the nation is worth fighting for"*: CW, VII, 512.

263 *"I don't make the stories mine"*: Brooks, "Personal Reminiscences of Lincoln," *Scribner's Monthly*, XV, no. 5 (March, 1878): 673–681. This and the other quotations from Lincoln in talking with Brooks are from this issue of *Scribner's Monthly*, or from XV, no. 4 (February 1878): 564.

265 *On one occasion* and *"began to talk of the functions"*: Bates, *Lincoln in the Telegraph Office*, 218–222.

266 *"bareheaded"* and other quotations from Nichols, and conversation with Lamon: Pinsker, *Lincoln's Sanctuary*, 163 et seq.

267 *"neither of whom"*: Donald, *Lincoln*, 548.

267 *The* Tribune *story in March*: Pinsker, *Lincoln's Sanctuary*, 163.

267 *"If you value your life!"* and the Tribune's mention of a kidnapping plot: Donald, *Lincoln*, 548–549.

267 *"We hope that a bold hand"*: Randall, *Lincoln the President*, vol. 4, 368–369.

267 *Booth in Baltimore*: Tidwell, *Come Retribution*, 263.

268 *"Abe's contract is nearly up"*: Beschloss, *Presidential Courage*, 106.

270 *"been able to persuade myself"*: Donald, *Lincoln*, 528.

270 *"There is not much hope"*: Tarbell, *Life of Lincoln*, III, 201.

270 *"We are in the midst of conspiracies"*: Ibid., 203.

270 *"There are no Lincoln men"*: Thomas, *Abraham Lincoln*, 433.

270 *"a disastrous panic"*: Burlingame, ed., *With Lincoln in the White House*, 153.

270 *"No, sir . . . "*: W, 267.

271 *I feel compelled*: Ibid., 264.

271 *"entirely respectful terms"*: CW, VII, 517.

272 *This morning, as for some days past*: Ibid., 514.

273 *"very readily concurred"*: Burlingame, ed., *With Lincoln in the White House*, 153.

273 *encouraged and cheered*: Ibid., 154.

273 *"Hell is to pay"*: Ibid., 152.

273 *"the largest and most enthusiastic"* W, 279. Unless otherwise noted, this and other quotations, some used only in part, are from W, 279–293, on which much of my account of the Democratic Party convention of 1864 is based.

273 "express wish": Thomas, *Abraham Lincoln*, 444.

273 *"much excitement in our city"*: *NYT*, August 28, 1864.

275 *The administration cannot save*: Thomas, *Abraham Lincoln*, 444.

275 *We demand no conditions*: *NYT*, August 30, 1864. This wording is slightly different from that in W, which cites the convention's official proceedings.

278 *"In short, if Mr. Jeff. Davis"*: Dudley, "The Election of 1864," 500–518. This quotation is on 513.

278 *"not insinuate even a little war"*: Ibid.

CHAPTER ELEVEN: SIX WORDS FROM SHERMAN

279 *"Atlanta is ours, and fairly won"*: Marszalek, *Commander of All Lincoln's Armies*, 213. The chronology of initial communications about this victory can be understood by reading *PUSG*, vol. 12, 121–127.

279 *"in honor of your great victory"*: *PUSG*, vol. 12, 127.

279 Lincoln's "Proclamation of Thanksgiving and Prayer" and "Order of Thanks to William T. Sherman and Others": And dated the same day, *CW*, VII, 532, Lincoln issued an "Order of Thanks to David G. Farragut and Others."

279 *"I feel you have"*: *PUSG*, vol. 12, 155.

280 *"Union men!"* W, 297.

280 *"We have suffered a great disaster"* Ibid., 298.

280 *"to carry the presidential election"*: Flood, *Grant and Sherman*, 255.

280 *"An armistice!"*: W, 308.

280 *The skies begin to brighten*: *NYT*, September 7, 1864.

281 *"prepare to pass"*: W, 300.

281 *"Oh, he's intrenching"*: Ibid.

281 *"the eve of the Presidential election"*: W, citing the *NYT*, August 16, 1864. The citation of the Detroit paper is from Williams, *Lincoln and the Radicals*, 327, 327n.

281 *The list of publications* is taken from Williams, *Lincoln and the Radicals*, 326–327, 326–327n.

282 *"I could not look in the face"*: Sears, *George B. McClellan*, 375–376.

282 *"the effect thus far has been electric"*: Ibid.

283 *"not to aid in the triumph"*: W, 306.

283 *"poltroons"*: Cited, above, as *CW*, VII, 440 n . 1.

284 *If Frémont would pull out*: Denton, *Passion and Principle*, 344, sets forth the offer in these words: "If *Frémont* withdrew, the president would assign him to a high military command and would dismiss Montgomery Blair from his administration."

285 *"The latter part of the proposition"*: Ibid.

285 *You have generously said*: *CW*, VIII, 18.

285 *"I can not take leave of you"*: Ibid., 18n.

285 *"Mr. Blair has resigned"*: Ibid., 20.

285 *"for a better man"*: W, 308.

286 *"We MUST re-elect him"*: Ibid.

286 *"I shall fight"*: Ibid., 307.

286 *"Presidential pygmy"*: Previously cited as W, 201.

286 *"Two men of mediocre talent"*: Neely, *The Lincoln Encyclopedia*, 23.

286 *"We shall soon see them skedaddling"*: W, 307.

286 *"all make tracks for Old Abe's plantation"* and ... *crowing and blowing*: Williams, *Lincoln and the Radicals*, 328.

286 *"seems to me to be"*: W, 308–309.

287 *"blazed with anger"*: Blanton and Cook, *They Fought Like Demons*, 94. Other facts and references regarding Mary Ellen Wise are on pp. 17, 93, 150–151, 155. Also see Miers, ed., *Lincoln Day by Day*, 281, for mention of Wise's meeting with Lincoln in the *Washington Chronicle* of September 11, 1864.

288 *"had been ordered away"*: Carpenter, *Six Months*, 296–298.

289 *"I believe the prayer"*: *CW*, VII, 536n, 535.

290 *"For those appealing to me"*: Ibid.

CHAPTER TWELVE: SHERIDAN GOES IN; LINCOLN GETS OUT THE VOTE

PAGE

292 *"possessed an excessive caution"*: Morris, *Sheridan*, 189.

292 *"eat out Virginia clear and clean"*: Ibid., 184.

292 *"it is desirable"*: Ibid.

293 *"Watch closely"*: Ibid., 191.

293 *"when he moves"*: Hergesheimer, *Sheridan*, 197.

293 *Sheridan and Early*: Lincoln's suggestion and Grant's reply: *CW*, VII, 548.

294 *I have no communication*: This text and the facts concerning both Thomas Laws and Rebecca Wright are taken from Morris, *Sheridan*, 192–193; see also Wert, *From Winchester to Cedar Creek*, 41–42.

294 *"Could you be ready"*: Morris, *Sheridan*, 194, and Wert, *From Winchester to Cedar Creek*, 41–42.

294 *Numbers engaged at Winchester*: Freeman, *Lee's Lieutenants*, III, 577, places Early's force at 12,150, while Livermore, *Numbers and Losses*, 141, gives the Confederate strength as 17,030. Also on 141, Livermore has Sheridan's Union total as 37,711.

295 *"A glaring and blood-red sun"*: Wert, *From Winchester to Cedar Creek*, 48.

295 *"stupid, mischievous clutter"*: Ibid., 50.

296 *"walked death in our ranks"*: Ibid., 56.

296 *"Charge them, boys!"*: Ibid., 66.

296 *"Because I know"*: Ibid., 67.

296 *"Every man was fighting"*: Ibid., 87.

297 *"Damn close"*: Ibid., 94.

297 *"happy as a schoolboy"*: Ibid., 93.

297 *"Boys the only way"*: Ibid., 94.

297 *"Press them, General"*: Ibid.

297 *In action ... the whole man*: Ibid., 93–94.

298 *"Every man's saber"*: Ibid., 95.

298 *"I never seen any men Run faster"*: Ibid.

298 *"Hurrah for this loyal girl!"* and *"Winchester, 7:30 P.M.":* Morris, *Sheridan,* 201.

299 *"Familiar as I was":* Wert, *From Winchester to Cedar Creek,* 102.

299 *"... taking up the charge":* Boatner, *Civil War Dictionary,* 281, citing Pond, *The Shenandoah Valley,* 177.

299 *"Run boys, run!":* Morris, *Sheridan,* 203.

300 *"astonishment and chagrin":* Ibid.

300 *"My troops are very much shattered"* and *"I lament those disasters":* Wert, *From Winchester to Cedar Creek,* 137.

300 *"Our success was very great":* Sheridan, *Memoirs,* II, 40.

300 *"Have just heard of your great victory":* CW, VIII, 13.

300 *"I have just received news"* and *I congratulate you: PUSG,* vol. 12, 177 and 191.

301 *The price of gold:* The figure of 20 percent is extrapolated from the *Journal of Political Economy* 6, no. 2: 287. See also George T. McCandless, "Money, Expectations, and the Civil War." *American Economic Review* 86, no. 3 (August 1996): 661–671.

301 *... some Rebel refugees:* Welles, *Diary,* II, 151–152.

302 *"He is always"* and *I remarked:* Ibid., 152–153. For more on Welles's view of Stanton, see Goodwin, *Team of Rivals,* 668.

302 *"the flurry was pretty well over":* Welles, *Diary,* II, 152.

302 *"the enemy's property":* *"Conspiracy in Canada"* Central Intelligence Agency Publications, found on the Web at https://www.cia.gov/library/publications/additional -publications/civil-war/p37.htm.

302 *"proceed at once to Canada":* This and other quotations and the majority of facts concerning this incident are from the Ohio Historical Society Publication "Rebels on Lake Erie—Chapter IX—The Lake Erie Conspiracy," as carried on the Web site Middle Bass on the Web http://middlebass2.org.Frohman_ix.shtml. See also Gray, *The Hidden Civil War,* 167–169, 179, 187–188.

304 *"I am looking for a young man":* Facts concerning John Staples are from Emerson Reck, "President Lincoln's 'Substitute' ", the *Lincoln Herald* 80, no. 3 (Fall 1978): 137–139.

306 *"America"* and other songs: Bernard, *Lincoln and the Music of the Civil War,* 92.

307 *Aunt Mary, from Mrs. Lincoln:* Anna L. Boyden, *War Reminiscences* (Boston: Lothrop, 1887), 228–229.

307 *It was all planned out:* Pinsker, *Lincoln's Sanctuary,* 180.

307 *"humiliating failure":* Donald, *Lincoln,* 540. See also 549.

307 *"make a dash":* Pinsker, *Lincoln's Sanctuary,* 134.

308 *"The party carrying the state":* W, 333.

308 *"are entering into this contest"* Ibid., 311.

309 *"Henry,"* Lincoln said: Ibid., 343.

309 *Details concerning the pressure from Governor Morton, the role of Lincoln and Stanton, and the figure of 9,000* are from Stampp, *Indiana Politics During the Civil War,* 251–252.

309 *The State election of Indiana: CW,* VIII, 11. Morton's request is Ibid., 11n.

309 *Sherman influenced by Hood's moves:* Lewis, *Sherman,* 413–414.

310 *"In performing this sacred duty": PUSG,* vol. 12, 212–215.

310 *"Quite a form has to be gone through":* Commager, *The Blue and the Gray,* I, 298.

311 *"had gathered two or three hundred workmen":* Welles, *Diary,* II, 123.

311 *"a majority of the men"*: Ibid., 143–145.

312 *Raymond has in party matters*: Ibid., 142.

312 *Lincoln's overtures to Bennett and Greeley*: W, 304. See also Carman and Luthin, *Lincoln and the Patronage*, 286.

313 *"refused to recognize me"*: Ibid., 283–284.

313 *"asked an appointment"*: Ibid., 282. See also Dennett, ed., *Lincoln and the Civil War*, 181n.

314 *The figure of $250 is from Thomas*, *Abraham Lincoln*, 451.

314 *The National Republican Committee*: Carman and Luthin, *Lincoln and the Patronage*, 287.

314 *a million documents*: Ibid., 286.

314 *"an average three per cent"* and *"will be found"*: Ibid., 289.

315 *The 5 percent figure is from Thomas*, *Abraham Lincoln*, 451.

315 *"the Committee, presuming you will esteem"*: Carman and Luthin, *Lincoln and the Patronage*, 293.

315 *"We are now sending"*: Randall, *Lincoln the President*, vol. 4, 239.

315 *Lincoln doing nothing concerning removal from office of those who did not contribute*: Carman and Luthin, *Lincoln and the Patronage*, 288.

315 *Political allegiance influencing military promotions*: Ibid., 299.

315 *"all for McClellan."* Dennett, ed., *Lincoln and the Civil War*, 229.

316 *"I reduced"*: Ibid. The account is a diary; "and" is rendered as "&."

316 *"McClellan's Platform"* and other details concerning Stanton's actions: Sears, *George B. McClellan*, 363–364.

316 *In all my experience*: Wilson, *Intimate Memories of Lincoln*, 577.

317 *Stanton had the commissioners jailed*: Pratt, *Stanton*, 390.

317 *"eloquent Teuton"*: W, 311.

317 *"The Republicans have sent out"*: Randall, *Lincoln the President*, vol. 4, 239.

317 *"would do pretty well"*: Ibid., 238.

317 *"Rebels expelled from Kentucky"* and "hundreds of thousands of dollars": *NYT*, October 10, 1864.

318 *"the largest ever assembled"*: W, 312.

318 *"the leader of the Confederate forces"*: Ibid., 315.

318 *"I take it for granted"*: Carman and Luthin, *Lincoln and the Patronage*, 290–291.

318 *"Please remit"*: Ibid.

318 *"I enclose check"*: Ibid., 291.

319 *"came from the rebel lines"*: CW, VII, 526–527.

319 *The poll taken on a train*: Ibid., 3. The date is given as circa September 13.

320 *"A vigorous policy"*: Ibid., VIII, 99.

321 *I presume it is no secret*: Ibid., VIII, 41, 42n.

321 *"seemed to be in a great hurry"*: Hay, *Letters of John Hay*, I, 233.

321 *Lincoln and Walborn*: CW, VII, 402.

321 *Information on Forney*: Neely, *The Lincoln Encyclopedia*, 114.

322 *"must be paid the bounty or discharged"*: Welles, *Diary*, II, 174.

322 *I was present*: CW, VIII, 42, 43n.

323 *"relative to New York voters in the Navy"*: Welles, *Diary*, II, 175. See also *CW*, VIII, 43.

323 *"The subject is one"*: Welles, *Diary*, II, 175.

323 *Stanton locks War Department door*: Some details of this evening are based on W, 334.

324 *"gave the heaviest opposition vote"*: Dennett, ed., *Lincoln and the Civil War*, 228.

324 *"That's hard on us"*: Ibid.

324 *Vote of Company K*: Ibid.

324 *"several chapters"*: Hay, *Letters of John Hay*, 235.

324 *Some of Nasby's letters*: Bates, *Lincoln in the Telegraph Office*, 186.

325 *Am leaving office to go home*: *CW*, VIII, 43.

325 *"So good night, Mr. Cox."*: W, 335.

325 *"Bravo, for Indiana"*: *CW*, VIII, 46.

326 *"Better late than never"*: W, 338.

326 *That he had many good qualities*: Welles, *Diary*, II, 177.

327 *"Seward thought it was his duty"*: Ibid., 176–177.

327 *He was a man of great and varied talent*: Beale, ed., *The Diary of Edward Bates*, 418. It should be noted that some details of Taney's record, death, and funeral arrangements are from Simon, *Lincoln and Chief Justice Taney*.

328 *"It is a matter of the greatest importance"*: Dennett, ed., *Lincoln and the Civil War*, 230.

328 *"If you can deem it proper"*: Carman and Luthin, *Lincoln and the Patronage*, 174.

328 *"I think that the President"*: Ibid., 315.

329 *"I think Montgomery's unswerving"*: Ibid., 317.

329 *"Of course you will accept"* and *"it is certainly not wrong"*: Schuckers, *Life and Public Services of Salmon Portland Chase*, 512.

329 *"Mr. Blair, Chase and his friends"*: Randall, *Lincoln the President*, vol. 4, 272.

329 *"File this with his other recommendations"*: Thomas, *Abraham Lincoln*, 492.

330 *Already (before his poor old clay is cold)*: Dennett, ed., *Lincoln and the Civil War*, 231.

330 *". . . we could not fail"*: David Bates, *Lincoln in the Telegraph Office*, 280–281; following 280 is what is described in this edition, published in 1907, as "Facsimile of Lincoln's autographic estimate of the electoral vote of 1864."

331 *"We now look upon"*: W, 339.

331 *I therefore say*: *CW*, VII, 52.

332 *"that all is favorable"*: Sears, *George B. McClellan*, 384.

332 *"the fire demon"*: Wert, *From Winchester to Cedar Creek*, 144.

332 *"to let the burning of the crops"*: Ibid., 143.

333 *"If you can come here"*: Ibid., 169.

333 *"you had better move against him"*: Ibid., 173.

333 *"With your united force"*: Ibid.

335 *". . . the long gray line"*: Ibid., 176.

336 *"You have to feel it"*: Ibid., 185.

336 *"a disorganized, routed,"* *"simply insane with fear,"* and *"That these men were brave"*: Ibid., 187.

336 *"make your position strong"*: Ibid., 173.

337 *"the appalling spectacle"*: Morris, *Sheridan*, 212.

337 *"Come on back, boys!"*: Ibid., 213.

338 *"Men, by God"*: Ibid., 214.

338 *"Hope and confidence"*: Ibid.

338 *"a deafening cheer"*: Wert, *From Winchester to Cedar Creek*, 224.

339 *"The men were inspired"*: Ibid., 230.

339 *"Give 'em hell!"*: Ibid., 237.

339 *"the grandest stampede"*: Ibid., 234.

339 *"Regiment after regiment"*: Ibid.

339 *"The state of things"*: Morris, *Sheridan*, 218.

339 *"I have labored faithfully to gain success"*: Wert, *From Winchester to Cedar Creek*, 246,

339 *"we believe that"*: Ibid., 225.

340 *"I have the honor*: PUSG, vol. 12, 327n.

340 *"For ten miles"* and *"My loss in killed and wounded"*: Ibid., 334n, 335n.

340 *"I had a salute"*: Ibid., 327.

340 *[A torchlight parade] passed through*, and *Lincoln's remarks*: CW, VIII, 57–58, 58n.

341 *"With great pleasure"*: Ibid., 73.

341 *"I was struck"*: Dana, *Recollections*, 218–219.

342 *"Sheridan's Ride"*: Lounsbury, *Yale Book of American Verse*, 339–341.

343 *"The thing they seem"* and *"Your genius has put"*: Brian Brehm, article titled "Sheridan's Ride," *Winchester (Va.) Star*, n.d.

CHAPTER THIRTEEN: THE FINAL MILE TO THE POLLS: ROCKS, SMOOTH PLACES, PUZZLES

PAGE

345 *"more disaffection and disloyalty"*: PUSG, vol. 12, 341n.

345 *"asking me to send more troops"*: Ibid., 370n.

345 *"Will start in an hour"*: Ibid.

345 *"the troops sent to preserve peace"*: This and the following quotations concerning Butler's activities in Manhattan are from Butler, *Butler's Book*, 758–771. It should be noted that in these memoirs Butler unfailingly presents himself in a favorable light, but his activities during this time in New York appear to be consistent with other accounts.

347 *"No, Mr. Lyons"*: Ibid., 767. Butler is the only authority for this conversation.

347 *"Approval of First Hundred Miles"*: CW, VIII, 89.

347 *"Your complimentary little poem"*: Ibid., 77.

347 *"It is said"*: Ibid., 75.

349 *"Proclamation Admitting Nevada into the Union"*: Ibid., 83.

349 *"opposition policy"*: CW, VIII, 49.

349 *"There is imminent"*: W, 337.

349 *"on the part of persons claiming to represent"*: Myer S. Isaacs to Abraham Lincoln, October 26, 1864, Abraham Lincoln Papers, Manuscript Division, Library of Congress.

350 *Yesterday a deputation*: Burlingame, ed., *Lincoln Observed*, 138–139. It should be noted that there is a possibility that Brooks had the date of this meeting wrong, or that another similar meeting may have occurred.

351 *You are in error*: Burlingame, ed., *At Lincoln's Side*, 98; see also notes 148 and 149 on p. 256.

351 *"We propose to give—not to take:"* Samuel A. Lewis to Abraham Lincoln, October 26, 1864, ibid.

352 *Letter to Zacharie from Lincoln, with salutation of "Dear Sir."*: A photostat of this letter is found in the online Jewish Virtual Library presentation "Judaic Treasures of the Library of Congress: President Lincoln's Friends." http://jewishvirtuallibrary.org/jsource/intro.html. In the paragraph preceding a printed text, a sentence referring to this letter says in part, "There are thirteen letters from Zacharie to Lincoln, and one dated September 19, 1864, apparently as yet unpublished, from Lincoln to Zacharie." It cites this letter as Abraham Lincoln to Isachar Zacharie, September 19, 1864. Abraham Lincoln Papers, Manuscript Division, Library of Congress.

352 *Dear Friend*: The text of Zacharie's reply is in the online article cited in the previous note and is also on p. 237 of this useful study: Bertram W. Korn, *American Jewry and the Civil War* (Philadelphia: Jewish Publication Society of America, 1951).

352 *I just returned to this city*: Isachar Zacharie to Abraham Lincoln, November 3, 1864, Abraham Lincoln Papers, Manuscript Division, Library of Congress.

353 *Sojourner Truth and Washington streetcars*: See Painter, *Sojourner Truth*, 210–211, and Gilbert, *Narrative of Sojourner Truth*, 184–187.

353 *"And ain't I a woman?"* Sojourner Truth, Speech at the women's convention in Akron, Ohio, Dec. 1851. Halsall, Paul, ed., Modern History Sourcebook. http://www.fordham.edu/halsall/mod/sojtruth-woman.html.

354 *Upon entering his reception room*: Gilbert, *Narrative of Sojourner Truth*, 177. The same account of Sojourner Truth's meeting with Lincoln is in Carpenter, *Six Months*, 201–203.

355 *For Aunty Sojourner Truth*: Gilbert, *Narrative of Sojourner Truth*, 179

355 *"'Aunty' . . . as he would"*: Painter, *Sojourner Truth*, 207, presents different views on whether Lincoln's attitude was condescending.

355 *As I was taking my leave*: Gilbert, *Narrative of Sojourner Truth*, 179.

356 *"This man wants to go home"*: CW, VIII, 88. Miers, ed., *Lincoln Day by Day*, III, 293, has under its entry for November 3, citing a *Washington Chronicle* story, the information that the soldier intended to vote for McClellan.

356 *the Republican elephant*: A picture of this cartoon and a history of how the elephant became the party symbol is to be found in the online offering of *Harper's Weekly*, under www.elections.harpweek.com/1864/cartoon-1864-Medium.asp?UniqueID=4&Year=1864.

358 *The day has come*: W, 346.

358 *"Sherman's army"*: Long and Long, *The Civil War Day by Day*, 571.

358 *"Friends are drawn together"*: Ibid., 573.

359 *"will give him their strength"*: Ibid., 579.

359 *"free and independent"*: Ibid., 580.

359 *"There are no vital points"*: Ibid., 593.

360 *"We have been denying all along"*: Cleland, "Jefferson Davis and the Confederate Congress."

361 *"Mr. Lincoln was highly gratified"*: Entry for November 7, 1864, in Miers, ed., *Lincoln*

Day by Day, III, 293. Some details concerning Elizabeth Comstock and her activities in Washington are to be found in Beale, ed., *The Diary of Edward Bates*, 423–426.

CHAPTER FOURTEEN: THE FORTY-EIGHT-HOUR ELECTION DAY

PAGE

362 *"The streets"*: Donald, *Lincoln*, 667.

362 *"Everybody in Washington"*: Dennett, ed., *Lincoln and the Civil War*, 232.

363 *"Mammoth Ox"* and *"upwards of Three Thousand"*: CW, VIII, 96, 96n.

363 *"What business has the turkey"*: W, 348.

363 *"singularly deserted"*: Randall, *Lincoln the President*, vol. 4, 259.

364 *"just enough of a politician"*: Ibid.

364 *"two unfurled flags of his country"*: CW, VIII, 118n.

364 *Thousands of bits*: W, 348.

365 *This day, fraught with so deep an interest*: Denney, *The Civil War Years*, 484.

365 *"under that challenge"*: Butler, *Butler's Book*, 770.

365 *"sick abed"* and *"shut up with New York financiers"*: Brooks, *Mr. Lincoln's Washington*, 385. For some of Fessenden's concerns and activities at this time, see Fessenden, *Life and Public Services of William Pitt Fessenden*, I, 352–356.

366 *McClellan resigned his commission as major general*: Sears, *George B. McClellan*, 385, 455 n. 17.

366 *The night was rainy, steamy, and dark*: Dennett, ed.. *Lincoln and the Civil War*, 233. Subsequent quotations are from this account by Hay, unless otherwise noted.

366 " *'As Pennsylvania goes' "*: Burlingame, ed., *Lincoln Observed*, 143.

367 *"I don't believe that"*: Ibid.

367 *"in solid phalanx"*: W, 350.

367 *WE ARE COMING*: Ibid., 351.

368 *"enjoyed them scarcely less"*: Cited, above, as Bates, *Lincoln in the Telegraph Office*, 186. It should be noted that there are some discrepancies concerning the events of November 8, 9, and 10 among the three principal eyewitness accounts of those days, those of Brooks, Dana, and Hay. Of the three, those from Hay that are diary entries are the ones written nearest to the time, but these may have been revised by him prior to publication. It is also difficult to establish the chronology of the arrival of various individuals and messages at the War Department Telegraph Office.

368 *"No, Sir"*: Dana's account is in Wilson, *Intimate Memories*, 577–578.

368 *"Show him in!"*: Ibid., 578.

369 *"gone in favor of Lincoln"*: Ibid.

369 *"I cannot at this hour"*: CW, VII, 96.

369 *"thanks and congratulations"*: Dana, in Wilson, *Intimate Memories*, 578.

369 *"By midnight"*: Burlingame, ed., *Lincoln Observed*, 144.

369 *"We had supper"* Dennett, ed., *Lincoln and the Civil War*, 236.

369 *"We got later in the evening"*: Ibid., 236. This also mentioned victory in Michigan.

370 *"About two o'clock in the morning"*: Burlngame, ed., *Lincoln Observed*, 144. It should be noted that Hay's account of this evening, in Dennett, ed., *Lincoln and the Civil War*, 236, leaves open the possibility that the speech Lincoln made early in the morning

of November 9 was actually made from a window of the War Department, not the White House.

370 *"All who have labored to-day"*: *CW*, VIII, 96.

370 *He took a glass of whiskey*: Dennett, ed., *Lincoln and the Civil War*, 236.

371 *"This poor soldier"*: *CW*, VIII, 97.

371 *"to give laborers at the White House a holiday"*: Ibid., 98.

371 *"Butler wants to grab"*: Dennett, ed., *Lincoln and the Civil War*, 236.

371 *"reports a splendid"*: Ibid., 237.

371 *"Nicolay sent a superb"*: Ibid.

371 *"The smoke has cleared away"*; *"the heaviest calamity"*; *"The ballot-box has spoken"*; *"The Yankee nation"*: W, 356–358.

372 *"We accept it"*: Ibid.

372 *"VICTORY!"*: Donald, *Lincoln in the Times*, 212.

372 *The election results and percentage figure* are from W, 354.

373 *... an impromptu procession*: Burlingame, ed., *Lincoln Observed*, 145.

373 *"It has long been" through "And now"*: *CW*, VIII, 100–101.

374 *"Thank you, Elizabeth"*: Keckley, *Behind the Scenes*, 157.

374 *"I was well tired out"*: Burlingame, ed., *Lincoln Observed*, 206.

375 *... the President took*: Burlingame and Ettlinger, *Inside Lincoln's White House*, 247.

376 *"In himself"*: Mitgang, ed., *Abraham Lincoln*, 419.

376 *"one of the greatest"* and *"Seldom in history"*: W, 356–357.

376 *I see the President often*: Online, The Civil War—Classroom Materials, under the heading "Walt Whitman, Patriot Poet" at www.pbs.org/civilwar/classroom/lesson_whitman.html.

376 *Dear Sir.*: Holzer, ed., *Dear Mr. Lincoln*, 273.

377 *"The nomination of McClellan"* and *There were in the Western Army*: W, 342.

377 *"We must have the man"*: Ibid., 343.

378 *"Congratulate the President"*: PUSG, vol. 12, 398.

378 *"He took it very calmly"*: Burlingame, ed., *Lincoln Observed*, 144.

378 *"Being only mortal"*: W, 359.

378 *"I am here by the blunders"*: Ibid.

CHAPTER FIFTEEN: AN EPIC YEAR BEGINS ITS DRAMATIC CLOSE

PAGE

379 *"Behind us lay Atlanta"*: Simpson and Berlin, eds. *Sherman's Civil War*, 147.

380 *"anxious, if not fearful"*: *CW*, VIII, 181. A detailed description of the differences between Grant and Sherman concerning this movement, and their resolution, is in Flood, *Grant and Sherman*, 263–265.

380 *"I can make the march"*: Simpson, *Sherman's Civil War*, 147.

380 *Grant's wish for Sherman to "settle" Hood*: PUSG, vol. 12, 370.

380 *"even without a battle"*: Simpson, *Sherman's Civil War*, 751.

381 *"the utter destruction"*: Ibid., 731.

381 *"I say, then, go on as you propose"*: PUSG, vol. 12, 190.

381 *"what rations of hard bread"*: Smith, *Grant*, 244.

381 *"Started this morning"*: Hanson, *The Soul of Battle*, 150.

382 *It may be a matter of interest*: Brooks, *Mr. Lincoln's Washington*, 397.

382 *I feel how weak and fruitless*: CW, VIII, 116–117, 117n.

383 *Castleman* and *"Northwestern Insurrection"*: Ibid., 123, 123n.

383 *"Sam, this is for you"*: Ibid., 123n.

384 *Seth Kinman*: Kimmel, *Mr. Lincoln's Washington*, 157.

385 Liberty! Freedom!: The description of this part of Booth's activities, including the choice of Brutus's speech, is from Kauffman, *American Brutus*, 149 et seq.

386 *"Hood is a bold fighter"*: Wagner, Gallagher, and Finkelman, eds. *Civil War Desk Reference*, 413.

387 *"My satisfaction"*: Simon, ed., *The Personal Memoirs of Julia Dent Grant*, 326.

388 *"for three more days,"* and *"The slightest mistake"*: Groom, *Shrouds of Glory*, 162. The accounts here of the battles of Franklin and Nashville, including most of the quotations, are based in good part on those in Groom, principally from pp. 169–235 and 251–265.

388 *"I don't like the looks"* and *"I would prefer to fight"*: Ibid., 169.

388 *"the line moved forward"*: Ibid., 172.

388 *"Nearer and nearer"*: Ibid., 180.

389 *"It was a grand sight"*: Ibid., 183.

389 *As forerunners well in advance*: Ibid.

389 *"thrust a fence rail"* and *"At every discharge"*: Ibid., 198–199.

391 *"A complete silence pervaded"*: Brooks, *Mr. Lincoln's Washington*, 396.

391 *Precisely at one o'clock*: Ibid., 395.

391 *"reasonably satisfactory"*: This and the following quotations from Lincoln's Annual Message are taken from CW, VIII, 136–152.

393 *"I was thinking"*: McClure, *Lincoln's Yarns and Stories*, 152.

394 *"We must conclude"*: CW, VIII, 148n.

394 *"rang out clarion-like"*: Brooks, *Mr. Lincoln's Washington*, 396.

396 *"When the noble sentences"*: Ibid.

396 *"the message is the best"*: Ibid.

396 *"I nominate Salmon P. Chase"*: CW, VIII, 154.

396 *"Be assured that I prize"*: Ibid.

397 *"His appointment"*: Donald, *Lincoln*, 552.

397 *"he would sooner have"*: Ibid.

397 *"The President told"*: Welles, *Diary*, II, 196.

397 *"I have no good news"*: CW, VIII, 154.

397 *"Grant has the bear"*: Lewis, *Sherman*, 485.

398 *"I know that in the beginning"*: Ibid., 442. It should be noted that much of this description of Sherman's March to the Sea is from Flood, *Grant and Sherman*, 267–276. In some cases, I have used entire sentences from that text.

398 *"They regard us"*: Simpson, *Sherman's Civil War*, 792.

398 *"wild-animal stare"*: Lewis, *Sherman*, 448.

398 *"sub-terra shells"*: Long and Long, *The Civil War Day by Day*: 599.

399 *"Anything and Everything"*: Glatthaar, *The March to the Sea and Beyond*, 79.

399 *"The prevailing feeling"*: Hanson, *The Soul of Battle*, 160.

399 *It was very touching*: Lewis, *Sherman*, 440.

400 *"the negro should be a free race"*: Simpson, *Sherman's Civil War*, 522.

400 *"A nigger as such"*: Kennett, *Sherman*, 107.

400 *"we have confidence"*: Merrill, *Sherman*, 278. This statement was made to Stanton when he met with this group in Savannah early in 1865.

401 *"Is Fort McAllister taken?"*: Lewis, *Sherman*, 463.

402 *"The President feels solicitous"*: PUSG, vol. 13, 50n.

402 *"in a few more days"*: Ibid., 54n. Several of the subsequent quotations concerning the days immediately prior to the Battle of Nashville are in Groom, *Shrouds of Glory*, 233–235, and PUSG, vol. 13, 54n et seq.

402 *"Hood should be attacked"*: PUSG, vol. 13, 67.

402 *"Attack at once . . . "*: Ibid., 77.

402 *"Thomas seems unwilling"*: Ibid., 99n.

403 *"You probably saw my order"*: Ibid., 78.

403 *"If Thomas has not struck yet"*: Ibid., 83.

403 *"If you wish Genl Thomas"*: Ibid., 84n.

403 *"Why not attack at once?"*: Ibid., 87–88.

404 *"Many officers here"*: Groom, *Shrouds of Glory*, 234.

404 *"Please telegraph orders"*: PUSG, vol. 13, 90.

404 *I had nearly completed*: Ibid., 88n.

404 *"suspend the order"*: Ibid., 90–91.

404 *"If you delay attack longer"*: Ibid., 107.

405 *"I am unexpectedly called away"*: Ibid., 120.

405 *"The ice having melted away"*: Groom, *Shrouds of Glory*, 239.

405 *"I attacked the enemy's left"*: Ibid., 251.

406 *"although the battle"* PUSG, vol. 13, 125n.

406 *"Mister Secretary"*: This part of the account of the receipt of the news from Nashville and Lincoln's reaction to it is from Bates, *Lincoln in the Telegraph Office*, 315–318.

407 *Thomas's victory*: Ibid.

407 *"I guess we will not"*: Ibid., 318.

407 *"I was just on my way"*: PUSG, vol. 13, 124.

407 *"I congratulate you"*: Ibid., 124n.

407 *"Please accept for yourself"*: CW, VIII, 169.

408 *At 12 P.M.*: Groom, *Shrouds of Glory*, 255.

408 *"Five color-bearers"*: Ibid.

408 *"every move, attack or retreat"*: Ibid., 261.

408 *"shooting as fast"* and *"I now felt"*: Ibid.

408 *It was more like a scene*: Groom, *Shrouds of Glory*, 264.

409 *"I beheld for the first and only time"*: Ibid.

409 *"mud roads completely sogged"*: Groom, *Shrouds of Glory*, 268.

409 *"Hood is dead"*: Ibid., 274.

CHAPTER SIXTEEN: LINCOLN'S LAST CHRISTMAS

PAGE

410 *"Can't you and others"*: Donald, *Lincoln*, 550.

411 *"to serve for one, two, and three"*: *CW*, VIII, 171.

411 *Enrollment statistics*: Murdock, *One Million Men*. For a table of cumulative statistics, including entries, see p. 356. The categories include "Did Not Report; Exempted; Commuted; Furnished Substitutes."

412 *"is one of the best men"* and . . . *I feel fully conscious*: *CW*, VIII, 179, 179–180n.

412 *"Cotton contracts"*: Johnson, "Beverly Tucker's Canadian Mission," 88–99. Both the description of Civil War cotton-trading and Lincoln's specific involvement with it are based on this article. See also Surdam, "Traders or Traitors."

413 *The example of the hundred-dollar bale of cotton* is from Surdam, "Traders or Traitors," 302.

413 *one of the officials who signed the permits*: Johnson, "Beverly Tucker's Canadian Mission," 90, says of Lincoln's role regarding these permits: "In the execution of this policy he was willing to give his personal and political friends special privileges. An investigator attempting to trace the skein of favoritism repeatedly encounters Lincoln's intimates or, alternatively, the associates of the old wizard, Thurlow Weed, whose fine Italian hand appears in more than one dubious transaction." Surdam states, "Although Lincoln also approved permits or issued orders on behalf of people not identified as friends or family, of those he denied no one was identified as friends or family."

414 *"submitted to him for consideration"*: Browning, *Diary*, II, 699.

414 *"talked with him about"*: Ibid., 1.

415 *"He brought back contracts"*: Ibid., 4.

415 *The fate of the tobacco*: Ibid., 10–11.

415 *"During the evening"*: Browning, *Diary*, II, 699.

415 *"the integrity of the Union"*: Previously cited as *CW*, VII, 451.

416 *My dear General Sherman*: Ibid., VIII, 181.

416 *"upon the splendid results"* and *"I wish Hardee's"*: *PUSG*, vol. 13, 130, 163.

417 *"If there be no objection"*: *CW*, VIII, 187.

417 *The Wilmington expedition*: Ibid., 187n.

417 *"by bringing within four or five hundred yards"*: This account of Butler's failure and removal is based on Randall, *Lincoln the President*, vol. 4, 290–295.

418 *"the powder-ship"*: Welles, *Diary*, II, 213.

418 *"I am constrained to request"*: *PUSG*, vol. 13, 223.

418 *Grant directly to Lincoln*: Telegram, January 6, 1865, ibid., 223n.

418 *"By direction of the President"* and *"repair to Lowell, Mass."*: Ibid.

418 *Thoughtful men*: *CW*, VIII, 183–184.

419 *"the elegantly-mounted volume"*: Ibid., 179. This is dated December 24, 1864.

419 *"The writer of this"*: Ibid., 189, 189n.

419 *"Mr. Lee, the father"*: Ibid., 184; 184n says, "No record of Lee's appointment has been found."

419 *"is under arrest"*: Ibid., 189.

419 *"is the son of a friend so close"*: Ibid., 224.

420 *"Judd would cause trouble & dissatisfaction"*: Entry of Norman B. Judd from online site Mr. Lincoln and Friends, *www.mrlincolnandfriends.org* or *http://www.mrlincolnand-friends.org/inside_search.asp?pageID=68&subjectID=5&searchWord=judd*.

420 *"course of dissipation"*: Ibid.

420 Times *item on Frank R. Judd*: *NYT*, April 13, 1882.

421 *"rape upon a colored girl"*: *CW*, VIII, 193, 193n. In 193n, this appears: "No record of the promulgations of Lincoln's order has been found."

421 *be "pardoned and sent"* through *"record of his trial"*: The pertinent communications are in *CW*, VIII, 177, 177–178n, 192, 192n, 194, 194n.

CHAPTER SEVENTEEN: GOODBYE, MR. LINCOLN

PAGE

423 *"time, now that the enemy is wavering"*: *CW*, VIII, 201.

423 *"a view to secure peace to the two countries"*: Ibid., 275.

423 *"securing peace to the people of our one common country"*: Ibid., 221. See also 274–285.

424 *"This amendment"*: Ibid., 254–255.

425 *For the Southern commissioners' perception that Lincoln might have some concessions in mind*, see Donald, *Lincoln*, 559–560.

425 *"The conference ended without result"*: *CW*, VIII, 285.

425 *"Never have I seen"*: Sandburg, *Abraham Lincoln*, 652.

425 *"Rebel States"* Welles, *Diary*, II, 237.

425 *"You are all against me"*: Donald, *Lincoln*, 561.

425 *Booth at Ford's Theatre on January 18, 1865*: John Wilkes Booth: The Story of Abraham Lincoln's Murderer: *http://www.crimelibrary.com/terrorists_spies/assassins/booth/10.html*.

427 *"the possibility of arriving"*: This exchange is to be found in *CW*, VIII, 330–331.

427 *"Do not let Johnson speak"*: Donald, *Lincoln*, 565.

428 *The President issued alone*: Chambrun, *Impressions of Lincoln*, 38–39.

428 *"the clouds disappeared"*: Welles, *Diary*, II, 252. Donald, *Lincoln*, 680n, says: "Most observers said that the sun came out when Lincoln began to speak. Chase, as usual self-centered, thought it burst forth when he stepped forward to administer the oath of office."

428 *"Both parties deprecated war"*: The entire text of Lincoln's Second Inaugural Address is in *CW*, VIII, 332–333.

430 *Whose arrows are sharp*: The words from Isaiah 5 are noted in Sandburg, *Abraham Lincoln*, 665.

431 *"Such was the crowd"*: Welles, *Diary*, II, 252.

431 *"Here comes my friend Douglass"*: Rice, *Reminiscences*, 322–325.

432 *"God bless you, my boy"*: Sandburg, *Abraham Lincoln*, 665.

432 *Lincoln in bed*: Donald, *Lincoln*, 568, says, "Lincoln was so exhausted after the inauguration ceremonies that he took to his bed for a few days." He cannot have been constantly in his bedroom—for example, he and his wife attended the Inaugural Ball

the evening after he was inaugurated—but Lincoln was long overdue for some sort of concession to cumulative fatigue.

432   *"Why didn't he shoot me!"*: Kauffman, *American Brutus*, 7.

432   *"Now he belongs to the ages"* Donald, *Lincoln*, 599.

432   *"Mr. Welles, who killed my father?"* Welles, *Diary*, II, 290.

432   *Three tiny kittens*: Porter, *Campaigning with Grant*, 410.

433   *"Mr. Lincoln, I am very sorry"*: This quotation and most of the facts concerning Mary Abigail Dodge, and the text of her letter, are from Sandburg, *Abraham Lincoln*, 665–666.

BIBLIOGRAPHY

Alexander, Edward Porter. *Fighting for the Confederacy*. Chapel Hill: University of North Carolina Press, 1989.

Ambrose, Stephen E. *Halleck: Lincoln's Chief of Staff*. Baton Rouge: Louisiana State University Press, 1962.

———. *Nothing Like It in The World: The Men Who Built the Transcontinental Railroad, 1863–1869*. New York: Simon & Schuster, 2000.

Anastaplo, George. *The Amendments to the Constitution: A Commentary*. Baltimore: John Hopkins University Press, 1995.

Anderson, William M., ed. *We Are Sherman's Men: The Civil War Letters of Henry Obendorff*. Western Illinois Monograph Series No. 6. Macomb, IL: Western Illinois University, 1986.

Angle, Paul M., ed. *New Letters and Papers of Lincoln*. Boston: Houghton Mifflin, 1930.

Axelrod, Alan. *The Horrid Pit: The Battle of the Crater, the Civil War's Cruelest Mission*. New York: Carroll & Graf, 2007.

Ayers, Edward L. *What Caused the Civil War?: Reflections on the South and Southern History*. New York: W. W. Norton, 2005.

Bacon, Benjamin W. *Sinews of War: How Technology, Industry, and Transportation Won the Civil War*. Novato, CA: Presidio Press, 1997.

Baker, Jean H. *Mary Todd Lincoln*. New York: W. W. Norton, 1987.

Ballard, Colin R. *The Military Genius of Abraham Lincoln*. Cleveland: World Publishing Co., 1952.

Baringer, William E. *Lincoln's Rise to Power*. Boston: Little, Brown, 1937.

Barnes, Thurlow Weed. *Memoir of Thurlow Weed*. 2 vols. Boston: Houghton Mifflin, 1884.

Barrett, John G. *Sherman's March Through the Carolinas*. Chapel Hill: University of North Carolina Press, 1956.

Basler, Roy P. *Lincoln*. New York: Octagon Books, 1975.

Basler, Roy P., ed. *The Collected Works of Abraham Lincoln*. 8 vols. New Brunswick, NJ: Rutgers University Press, 1953.

Bates, David Homer. *Lincoln in The Telegraph Office*. New York: Century Co., 1907.

———. *Lincoln Stories Told by Him in the Military Office in the War Department During the Civil War*. New York: William Edwin Ridge, 1926.

Battles and Leaders of the Civil War. 4 vols. Edited by Neal Bradford. Secaucus, NJ: Castle Books, 1982.

Baxter, Maurice G. *Orville H. Browning: Lincoln's Friend and Critic*. Bloomington: Indiana University Publications, Social Science Series No. 16, 1957.

Beale, Howard K., ed., *The Diary of Edward Bates, 1859–1866*. New York: Da Capo Press, 1971.

Belden, Thomas G., and Marva Robins Belden. *So Fell the Angels*. Boston: Little, Brown, 1986.

Belz, Herman. *Reconstructing the Union: Theory and Policy During the Civil War*. Ithaca, NY: Cornell University Press, 1969.

Beringer, Richard E., et al. *The Elements of Confederate Defeat: Nationalism, War Aims, and Religion*. Athens: University of Georgia Press, 1988.

———. *Why the South Lost the Civil War*. Athens: University of Georgia Press, 1986.

Bernard, Kenneth A. *Lincoln and the Music of the Civil War*. Caldwell, ID: Caxton Printers, 1966.

Berry, Stephen William. *House of Abraham: Lincoln and the Todds, a Family Divided by War*. Boston: Houghton Mifflin, 2007.

Beschloss, Michael R. *Presidential Courage*. New York: Simon & Schuster, 2007.

Bidwell, Frederick David. *History of the Forty-Ninth New York Volunteers*. Albany, NY: J. B. Lyon & Co., 1916.

Bishop, Jim. *The Day Lincoln Was Shot*. New York: Harper, [1955].

Blanton, DeAnne, and Lauren M. Cook. *They Fought Like Demons: Women Soldiers in the American Civil War*. Baton Rouge: Louisiana State University Press, 2002.

Bleser, Carol K., and Lesley T. Gordon, eds. *Intimate Strategies of the Civil War: Military Commanders and Their Wives*. New York: Oxford University Press, 2001.

Blight, David W. *Frederick Douglass' Civil War*. Baton Rouge: Louisiana State University Press, 1989.

Blue, Frederick. *Salmon P. Chase: A Life in Politics*. Kent, OH: Kent State University Press, 1987.

Boatner, Mark Mayo, III. *The Civil War Dictionary*. New York: David McKay, 1987.

Bogue, Allan G. *The Earnest Men: Republicans of the Civil War Senate*. Ithaca, NY: Cornell University Press, 1981.

Boorstin, Daniel J. *The Genius of American Politics*. Chicago and London: University of Chicago Press, 1953.

Boritt, Gabor S., ed. *The Lincoln Enigma*. New York: Oxford University Press, 2001.

———. *Lincoln, the War President*. New York: Oxford University Press, 1992.

Bowman, John S., ed. *The Civil War Day by Day*. Greenwich, CT: Dorset Press, 1989.

Brady, Kathleen. *Ida Tarbell: Portrait of a Muckraker*. New York: Seaview/Putnam, 1984.

Brooks, Noah. *Abraham Lincoln, and the Downfall of American Slavery*. New York: Putnam, 1925.

———. *Mr. Lincoln's Washington*. Edited by P. J. Staudenraus. South Brunswick, NJ: T. Yoseloff, 1967.

———. "Personal Reminiscences of Lincoln." *Scribner's Monthly* XV, no. 5, (March 1878): 673–681.

———. *Washington in Lincoln's Time*. Edited with an introduction by Herbert Mitgang. New York: Rinehart & Co., 1958.

Brown, Kent Masterson. *Cushing of Gettysburg: The Story of a Union Artillery Commander.* Lexington: University of Kentucky Press, 1993.

———. *Retreat from Gettysburg: Lee, Logistics, and the Pennsylvania Campaign.* Chapel Hill: University of North Carolina Press, 2005.

Browning, Orville Hickman. *The Diary of Orville Hickman Browning.* Springfield: Trustees of the Illinois State Historical Library, 1925.

Bruce, Robert V. *Lincoln and the Tools of War.* Westport, CT: Greenwood Press, 1973.

Bundy, Carol. *The Nature of Sacrifice; A Biography of Charles Russell Lowell, Jr., 1835–64.* New York: Farrar, Straus & Giroux, 2005.

Burkhimer, Michael. *100 Essential Lincoln Books.* Nashville: Cumberland House, 2003.

Burlingame, Michael. *Honest Abe, Dishonest Mary.* Racine: Lincoln Fellowship of Wisconsin, 1994.

———. *The Inner World of Abraham Lincoln.* Urbana, IL: University of Illinois Press, 1994.

Burlingame, Michael, ed. *At Lincoln's Side: John Hay's Civil War Correspondence and Selected Writings.* Carbondale, IL: Southern Illinois University Press, 2000.

———. *Dispatches from Lincoln's White House: The Anonymous Civil War Journalism of Presidential Secretary William O. Stoddard.* Lincoln: University of Nebraska Press, 2002.

———. *Lincoln Observed: Civil War Dispatches of Noah Brooks.* Baltimore: Johns Hopkins University Press, 1998.

———. *An Oral History of Abraham Lincoln: John G. Nicolay's Interviews and Essays.* Carbondale, IL: Southern Illinois University Press, 1996.

———. *With Lincoln in the White House: Letters, Memoranda, and Other Writings of John G. Nicolay, 1860–1865.* Carbondale, IL: Southern Illinois University Press, 2000.

———, and John R. Turner Ettlinger, eds., *Inside Lincoln's White House: The Complete Civil War Diary of John Hay.* Carbondale, IL: Southern Illinois University Press, 1997.

Burne, Alfred H. *Lee, Grant, and Sherman: A Study in Leadership in the 1864–1865 Campaign.* New York: Scribner, 1939.

Bush, Bryan S. *Lincoln and the Speeds.* Morley, MO: Acclaim Press, 2008.

Butler, Benjamin F. *Butler's Book.* Boston: A. M. Thayer & Co., 1892.

Carman, Harry J., and Reinhard H. Luthin. *Lincoln and the Patronage.* New York: Columbia University Press, 1943.

Carpenter, F. B. *Six Months at the White House with Abraham Lincoln.* New York: Hurd & Houghton, 1867. Reprint: Michigan Historical Reprint Series, 2006.

Carter, Samuel, III. *The Siege of Atlanta, 1864.* New York: St. Martin's Press, 1973.

Carter, Susan B., et al., *Historical Statistics of the United States: Earliest Times to the Present.* 5 vols. New York: Cambridge University Press, 2006.

Carwardine, Richard. *Lincoln: A Life of Purpose and Power.* New York: Knopf, 2006.

Castel, Albert E. *Winning and Losing in the Civil War: Essays and Stories.* Columbia, SC: University of South Carolina Press, 1996.

Catton, Bruce. *Glory Road: The Bloody Route from Fredericksburg to Gettysburg.* Garden City, NY: Doubleday, 1952.

———. *Grant Moves South.* Boston: Little, Brown, 1960.

———. *Grant Takes Command.* Boston: Little, Brown, 1968.

Chambrun, Adolphe de Pineton, Marquis de. *Impressions of Lincoln and the Civil War, a Foreigner's Account*. New York: Random House, 1952.

Chase, Salmon P. *Diary and Correspondence of Salmon P. Chase*. New York: Da Capo Press, 1971.

———. *Inside Lincoln's Cabinet: The Civil War Diaries of Salmon P. Chase*. Edited by David Donald. New York: Longmans Green, 1954.

Cincinnati Daily Commercial. Cincinnati: M. D. Potter & Co.

Cleaves, Freeman. *Meade of Gettysburg*. Norman: University of Oklahoma Press, 1960.

Cleland, Robert Glass, "Jefferson Davis and the Confederate Congress," *Southwestern Historical Quarterly Online* 019, no. 3: 213–231.

Commager, Henry Steele. *The Blue and the Gray: The Story of the Civil War as Told by Participants*. 2 vols. Indianapolis: Bobbs-Merrill, 1950.

Confederate Veteran, Harrisburg, PA: National Historical Society.

Congdon, Don, ed. *Combat: The Civil War*. Secaucus, NJ: Blue and Gray Press, 1967.

Conrad, Earl. *The Governor and His Lady*. New York: Putnam, 1960.

Cooling, B. Franklin. *Jubal Early's Raid on Washington, 1864*. Baltimore: Nautical & Aviation Publishing Co. of America, 1989.

Corry, John A. *Lincoln at Cooper Union: The Speech That Made Him President*. [Philadelphia]: Xlibris Corp., 2003.

Cottrell, John. *Anatomy of an Assassination*. New York: Funk & Wagnalls, 1966.

Cox, Samuel S. *Eight Years in Congress, from 1857 to 1865: Memoir and Speeches*. New York: Appleton, 1865.

Cramer, John Henry. *Lincoln Under Enemy Fire: The Complete Account of His Experiences During Early's Attack on Washington*. Baton Rouge: Louisiana State University Press, 1948.

Crippen, Lee F. *Simon Cameron: Ante-Bellum Years*. Oxford, OH: Mississippi Valley Press, 1942.

Croly, David Goodman [and George Wakeman]. *Miscegenation: The Theory of the Blending of the Races, Applied to the White Man and the Negro*. New York: 1864. Reprint, Upper Saddle River, NJ: Literature House/Gregg Press, 1970. (Also available through the Cornell University Library Digital Collections, *www.library.cornell.edu*).

Cuomo, Mario M., and Harold Holzer, eds. *Lincoln on Democracy*. New York: HarperCollins, 1990.

Dabbs, Jack Autrey. *The French Army in Mexico, 1861–1867*. The Hague: Mouton, 1963.

Dana, Charles A. *Recollections of the Civil War*. New York: Collier Books, 1963.

Davis, Cullom, et al., *The Public and Private Lincoln*. Carbondale, IL: Southern Illinois University Press, 1979.

Davis, William C. *The Cause Lost: Myths and Realities of the Confederacy*. Lawrence: University Press of Kansas, 1996.

———. *Lincoln's Men: How President Lincoln Became Father to an Army and a Nation*. New York: Free Press, 1999.

Dawson, George Francis. *Life and Services of Gen. John A. Logan, as Soldier and Statesman*. Chicago and New York: Belford, Clarke & Co. 1887.

Dell, Christopher. *Lincoln and the War Democrats: The Grand Erosion of Conservative Tradition*. Rutherford, NJ: Fairleigh Dickinson University Press, 1975.

Dennett, Tyler, ed. *Lincoln and the Civil War in the Diaries and Letters of John Hay*. New York: Dodd-Mead, 1939. (Also listed under Hay.)

Denney, Robert E. *The Civil War Years: A Day-by-Day Chronicle of the Life of a Nation*. New York: Sterling Publishing Co., 1992.

Denton, Sally. *Passion and Principle: John and Jessie Frémont, the Couple Whose Power, Politics, and Love Shaped Nineteenth-Century America*. New York: Bloomsbury, 2007.

Dexheimer, Florence Chambers. *Sketches of Wisconsin Pioneer Women*. Fort Atkinson, WI: W. O. Hoard & Sons, 1925.

DiLorenzo, Thomas J. *Lincoln Unmasked*. New York: Crown Forum, 2006.

Dodge, Grenville M. *Personal Recollections of President Abraham Lincoln, General Ulysses S. Grant, and General William T. Sherman*. Denver: Sage Books, 1965.

Donald, David, ed. *Inside Lincoln's Cabinet: The Civil War Diaries of Salmon P. Chase*. New York: Longmans, Green, 1954. (Also listed under Chase.)

Donald, David Herbert. *Lincoln*. New York: Simon & Schuster, 1995.

———. *Lincoln in the Times*. New York: St. Martin's Press, 2005.

———. *Lincoln Reconsidered*. New York: Knopf, 1966.

———. *"We Are Lincoln Men": Abraham Lincoln and His Friends*. New York: Simon & Schuster, 2003.

Dornbusch, C. E. *Military Bibliography of the Civil War*. 3 vols. New York: New York Public Library, 1971–.

Doster, William E. *Lincoln and Episodes of the Civil War*. New York: Putnam, 1915.

Dowdey, Clifford. *Lee's Last Campaign: The Story of Lee and His Men Against Grant—1864*. Boston: Little, Brown, 1960.

———, ed. *The Wartime Papers of R. E. Lee*. Boston: Little, Brown, 1961.

Duberman, Martin. *Charles Francis Adams, 1807–1886*. Stanford, CA: Stanford University Press, 1960.

Dudley, Harold M. "The Election of 1864." *Mississippi Valley Historical Review*, 18, no. 4. (March 1932): 500–518.

Dufour, Charles L. *Nine Men in Gray*. Garden City, NY: Doubleday, 1963.

Eaton, John. *Grant, Lincoln, and the Freedmen: Reminiscences of the Civil War, with Special Reference to the Work for the Contrabands and Freedmen of the Mississippi Valley*. New York: Negro Universities Press, 1969.

Eckenrode, H. J., and Bryan Conrad. *George S. McClellan: The Man Who Saved the Union*. Chapel Hill: University of North Carolina Press, 1941.

Epstein, Daniel Mark. *Lincoln and Whitman: Parallel Lives in Civil War Washington*. New York: Random House, 2004.

Fehrenbacher, Don E. *The Leadership of Abraham Lincoln*. New York: Wiley, 1970.

Fellman, Michael. *Citizen Sherman: A Life of William Tecumseh Sherman*. New York: Random House, 1995.

Fessenden, Francis. *Life and Public Services of William Pitt Fessenden*. 2 vols. New York: Da Capo Press, 1970.

Findley, Paul. *A. Lincoln: The Crucible of Congress*. New York: Crown, 1979.

Fleishner, Jennifer. *Mrs. Lincoln and Mrs. Keckly*. New York: Random House, 2003.

Fleming, Thomas J. *West Point: The Men and Times of the United States Military Academy*. New York: Morrow, 1969.

Flood, Charles Bracelen. *Grant and Sherman: The Friendship That Won the Civil War*. New York: Farrar, Straus & Giroux, 2005.

———. *Lee: The Last Years*. Boston: Houghton Mifflin, 1998.

Flower, Frank Abial. *Edwin McMasters Stanton*. Akron: Saalfield Publishing Co., 1905.

Foner, Eric. *Frederick Douglass: A Bibliography*. New York: Citadel Press, 1950.

———. *Reconstruction: America's Unfinished Revolution, 1863–1877*. New York: Harper & Row, 1988.

Foote, Shelby. *The Civil War: A Narrative*. 14 vols. Alexandria, VA: Time-Life Books, 1999.

Frassanito, William A. *Grant and Lee: The Virginia Campaigns, 1864–1865*. New York: Scribner, 1983.

Freeman, Douglas Southall. *Lee's Lieutenants: A Study in Command*. 3 vols. New York: Scribner, 1942–1944.

———. *R. E. Lee: A Biography*. 4 vols. New York: Scribner, 1949.

Freidel, Frank, and William Pencak, eds. *The White House: The First Two Hundred Years*. Boston: Northeastern University Press, 1994.

Frost, Lawrence A. *The Phil Sheridan Album: A Pictorial Biography of Phillip Henry Sheridan*. Seattle: Superior Publishing Co., 1968.

Fuller, Major General J. F. C. *Grant and Lee: A Study in Personality and Generalship*. New York: Scribner, 1955.

Gilbert, Oliver. *Narrative of Sojourner Truth: A Bondswoman of Olden Time*. Battle Creek, MI, 1878.

Gilmore, James R. *Personal Recollections of Abraham Lincoln and the Civil War*. L. C. Page & Co., 1898.

Glatthaar, Joseph T. *Forged in Battle: The Civil War Alliance of Black Soldiers and White Officers*. New York: Meridian Publishers, 1991.

———. *The March to the Sea and Beyond: Sherman's Troops in the Savannah and Carolinas Campaigns*. New York: New York University Press, 1985.

———. *Partners in Command: The Relationships Between Leaders in the Civil War*. New York: Free Press, 1994.

Goodwin, Doris Kearns. *Team of Rivals: The Political Genius of Abraham Lincoln*. New York: Simon & Schuster, 2005.

Grant, Ulysses S. *Memoirs and Selected Letters*. New York: Library of America, 1990.

Gray, Wood. *The Hidden Civil War: The Story of the Copperheads*, New York: Viking, 1942.

Groom, Winston. *Shrouds of Glory: Atlanta to Nashville: The Last Great Campaign of the Civil War*. New York: Atlantic Monthly Press, 1995.

Gurowski, Adam. *Diary: 1863–'64–'65*. 3 vols. New York: Burt Franklin, 1968.

Hall, James O. "John Wilkes Booth: The Money Trail." *Lincoln Herald* 105, no. 1 (Spring 2003): 7–14.

Hamilton, Charles, and Lloyd Ostendorf. *Lincoln in Photographs: An Album of Every Known Pose*. Norman: University of Oklahoma Press, 1963.

Hamlin, Charles Eugene. *The Life and Times of Hannibal Hamlin*. 2 vols. Port Washington, NY: Kennikat Press, 1899.

Handlin, Oscar, and Lilian Handlin. *Abraham Lincoln and the Union*. Boston: Little, Brown, 1980.

Hanson, Victor Davis. *The Soul of Battle: From Ancient Times to the Present Day: How Three Great Liberators Vanquished Tyranny.* New York: Free Press, 1999.

Harper, Judith E. *Women During the Civil War: An Encyclopedia.* New York: Routledge, 2004.

Harper, Robert S. *Lincoln and the Press.* New York: McGraw-Hill, 1951.

Harris, William C. *Lincoln's Last Months.* Cambridge, MA: Harvard University Press, 2004.

Harvard Memorial Bibliographies. 2 vols. Cambridge, MA: Sever & Francis, 1867.

Haslip, Joan. *The Crown of Mexico.* New York: Holt, Rinehart & Winston, 1971.

Hassler, Warren W., Jr. *General George B. McClellan: Shield of the Union.* Baton Rouge: Louisiana State University Press, 1957.

Hauptman, Laurence M. *Between Two Fires: American Indians in the Civil War.* New York: Free Press, 1995.

Hay, John. *Letters of John Hay and Extracts from Diary.* Vol. 1. New York: Gordian Press, 1969.

———. *Lincoln and the Civil War in the Diaries and Letters of John Hay.* Edited by Tyler Dennett. New York: Da Capo Press, 1988.

Heatwole, John L. *The Burning: Sheridan in the Shenandoah Valley.* Charlottesville, VA: Howell Press, 1998.

Hedrick, Joan D. *Harriet Beecher Stowe: A Life.* New York: Oxford University Press, 1994.

Heidler, David S., and Joanne T. Heidler. *Encyclopedia of the American Civil War: A Political, Social, and Military History.* Santa Barbara, CA: ABC-CLEO, 2000.

Helm, Katherine. *The True Story of Mary, Wife of Lincoln.* New York: Harper, 1928.

Hendrick, Burton J. *Lincoln's War Cabinet.* Gloucester, MA: Peter Smith, 1965.

———. *Statesmen of the Lost Cause: Jefferson Davis and His Cabinet.* New York: Literary Guild of America, 1939.

Herek, Raymond J. *These Men Have Seen Hard Service: The First Michigan Sharpshooters in the Civil War.* Detroit: Wayne State University Press, 1998.

Hergesheimer, Joseph. *Sheridan: A Military Narrative.* Boston: Houghton Mifflin, 1931.

Herndon, William H. *Herndon's Lincoln: The True Story of a Great Life.* Indianapolis: Bobbs-Merrill, 1970.

———, and Jesse W. Weik. *Herndon's Life of Lincoln.* Cleveland: World Publishing Co., 1943.

Hernon, Joseph M, Jr. *Celts, Catholics, and Copperheads: Ireland Views the American Civil War.* Athens: Ohio State University Press, 1968.

Hertz, Emanuel, ed. *The Hidden Lincoln: from the Letters and Papers of William H. Herndon.* New York: Viking, 1938.

Hess, Earl J. *The Union Soldier in Battle: Enduring the Ordeal of Combat.* Lawrence: University of Kansas Press, 1997.

Hirshson, Stanley P. *Grenville M. Dodge: Soldier, Politician, Railroad Pioneer.* Bloomington: Indiana University Press, 1967.

———. *The White Tecumseh: Biography of General William T. Sherman.* New York: Wiley, 1997.

Hitchcock, Henry. *Marching with Sherman.* New Haven, CT: Yale University Press, 1927.

Hofstadter, Richard. *The American Political Tradition and the Men Who Made It.* New York: Vintage, 1954.

——. *Great Issues in American History: A Documentary Record.* Vol. 1. New York: Vintage, 1958.

——. *Ten Major Issues in American Politics.* New York: Oxford University Press, 1968.

Holmes, Oliver Wendell, Jr. *Touched with Fire: Civil War Letters and Diary of Oliver Wendell Holmes, Jr., 1861–1864.* New York: Da Capo Press, 1969.

Holzer, Harold. "How the Printmakers Saw Lincoln: Not-So-Honest Portraits of 'Honest Abe.' " *Winterthur Portfolio* 14, no. 2 (Summer 1979): 143–170.

——. " 'If I Had Another Face, Do You Think I'd Wear This One?' " *American Heritage,* 34 (February–March 1983): 56–63.

Holzer, Harold, ed. *Dear Mr. Lincoln: Letters to the President.* Reading, MA: Addison-Wesley, 1993.

Horgan, Paul. *Citizen of New Salem.* New York: Farrar, Straus & Cudahy, 1961.

Horner, Harlan Hoit. *Lincoln and Greeley.* Urbana: University of Illinois Press, 1953.

Hubbell, John T., and James W. Geary. *Biographical Dictionary of the Union: Northern Leaders of the Civil War.* Westport, CT: Greenwood Press, 1995.

Hunt, Harry Draper. *Hannibal Hamlin of Maine.* Syracuse, NY: Syracuse University Press, 1969.

Hutton, Paul Andrew. *Phil Sheridan and His Army.* Lincoln: University of Nebraska Press, 1995.

Hyman, Harold M. "Election of 1864." In *History of American Presidential Elections, 1789–1968,* vol. 2. Edited by Arthur M. Schlesinger Jr., Fred L. Israel, and William P. Hansen. New York: Chelsea House Publishers/McGraw-Hill, 1971.

——. *The Radical Republicans and Reconstruction, 1861–1870.* Indianapolis: Bobbs-Merrill, 1967.

"John Wilkes Booth: The Story of Abraham Lincoln's Murderer." http://www.crime library.com/terrorists_spies/assassins/booth/10.html.

Johnson, Ludwell H. "Beverly Tucker's Canadian Mission, 1864–1865." *Journal of Southern History* 29, no. 1. (February 1963): 88–99.

Johnston, Richard Malcolm, and William Hand Browne. *Life of Alexander H. Stephens.* Philadelphia: Lippincott, 1879.

Joiner, Gary Dillard. *One Damn Blunder from Beginning to End: The Red River Campaign of 1864.* Wilmington, DE: Scholarly Resources, 2003.

Jones, J. William. *Personal Reminiscences, Anecdotes, and Letters of Gen. Robert E. Lee.* Richmond: United States Historical Society Press, 1989.

Jones, Katharine M. *When Sherman Came: Southern Women and the "Great March."* Indianapolis: Bobbs-Merrill, 1969.

Julian, George Washington. *Political Recollections.* Chicago: Jansen, McClurg & Co., 1884.

Kaplan, Sidney. "The Miscegenation Issue in the Election of 1864." *Journal of Negro History,* 34 (July 1949): 273–343.

Kauffman, Michael W. *American Brutus: John Wilkes Booth and the Lincoln Conspiracies.* New York: Random House, 2004.

Keckley, Elizabeth. *Behind the Scenes; or, Thirty Years a Slave and Four Years in the White House*. New York: Arno Press, 1968.

Keller, Julia. *Mr. Gatling's Terrible Marvel: The Gun That Changed Everything and the Misunderstood Genius Who Invented It*. New York: Viking, 2008.

Keneally, Thomas. *Abraham Lincoln*. New York: Lipper/Viking, 2003.

Kennett, Lee. *Marching Through Georgia: The Story of Soldiers and Civilians During Sherman's Campaign*. New York: HarperCollins, 1995.

————. *Sherman: A Soldier's Life*. New York: HarperCollins, Perennial Edition, 2002.

Kerner, Fred, ed. *A Treasury of Lincoln Quotations*. Garden City, NY: Doubleday, 1965.

Key, William. *The Battle of Atlanta and the Georgia Campaign*. Atlanta: Peach Tree Publishers, 1981.

Kimmel, Stanley. *Mr. Lincoln's Washington*. New York: Coward-McCann, 1954.

King, Willard Leroy. *Lincoln's Manager, David Davis*. Cambridge, MA: Harvard University Press, 1960.

Kirkland, Edward Chase. *The Peacemakers of 1864*. New York: Macmillan, 1927.

Kirschberger, Joe H. *The Civil War and Reconstruction: An Eyewitness History*. New York and Oxford: Facts on File, 1991.

Klement, Frank L. *The Copperheads in the Middle West*. Chicago: University of Chicago Press, 1960.

————. *The Limits of Dissent*. Lexington: University Press of Kentucky, 1970.

Klingaman, William K. *Abraham Lincoln and the Road to Emancipation, 1861–1865*. New York: Viking, 2001.

Kollonitz, Countess Paula. *The Court of Mexico*. London: Sanders, Otley, & Co., 1868.

Korn, Bertram W. *American Jewry and the Civil War*. Philadelphia: Jewish Publication Society of America, 1951.

Kunhardt, Dorothy Meserve. *Twenty Days: A Narrative in Text and Pictures of the Assassination of Abraham Lincoln and the Twenty Days and Nights That Followed the Nation in Mourning, the Long Trip Home to Springfield*. New York: Harper & Row, 1965.

Laas, Virginia Jean, ed. *Wartime Washington: The Civil War Letters of Elizabeth Blair Lee*. Urbana, IL: University of Illinois Press, 1991.

Lamers, William M. *The Edge of Glory: A Biography of General William S. Rosecrans, USA*. New York: Harcourt, Brace, 1961.

Lash, Jeffrey N. *Destroyer of the Iron Horse: General Joseph E. Johnston and Confederate Rail Transport, 1861–1865*. Kent, OH: Kent State University Press, 1991.

Lee, Richard M. *Mr. Lincoln's City: An Illustrated Guide to the Civil War Sites of Washington*. McLean, VA: EPM Publications, 1981.

Leech, Margaret. *Reveille in Washington: 1860–1865*. New York: Harper, 1941.

Leonard, Elizabeth D. *All the Daring of the Soldier*. New York: Penguin, 2001.

Lewis, Lloyd. *Sherman: Fighting Prophet*. New York: Harcourt Brace, 1932.

Lewis, Thomas A. *The Guns of Cedar Creek*. New York: Harper & Row, 1988.

Library of America. *Memoirs of General W. T. Sherman*. New York: Penguin, 1990.

Library of Congress Manuscript Collections. *Index to the Abraham Lincoln Papers*. Washington, D.C.: 1960.

Liddell-Hart, B. H. *Sherman: Soldier, Realist, American*. New York: Praeger, 1958.

Lincoln, Abraham. *Speeches and Writings, 1859–1865*. New York: Library of America, 1989.

Lincoln Institute. Mr. Lincoln and Friends. http://www.mrlincolnandfriends.org. (Accessed May 4, 2008)

Lincoln Studies Center. Abraham Lincoln Papers at the Library of Congress. http://memory.loc.gov/ammem/alhtml/malhome.html.

Lind, Michael. *What Lincoln Believed.* New York: Doubleday, 2004.

Livermore, Thomas L. *Numbers and Losses in the Civil War in America, 1861–1865.* New York: Kraus Reprint Co., 1969.

Logan, Mary. *Reminiscences of the Civil War and Reconstruction.* Carbondale, IL: Southern Illinois University Press, 1970.

Logsdon, Joseph. *Horace White, Nineteenth Century Liberal.* Westport, CT: Greenwood Publishing Corp., 1971.

Long, David E. *The Jewel of Liberty: Abraham Lincoln's Re-Election and the End of Slavery.* Mechanicsburg, PA: Stackpole Books, 2008.

Long, E. B., with Barbara Long. *The Civil War Day by Day: An Almanac, 1861–1865.* Garden City, NY: Doubleday, 1971.

Longacre, Edward G. *Army of Amateurs: General Benjamin F. Butler and the Army of the James, 1863–1865.* Mechanicsburg, PA: Stackpole Books, 1997.

Lounsbury, Thomas R. *Yale Book of American Verse.* New Haven, CT: Yale University Press, 1912.

Lyman, Darryl. *Civil War Quotations.* Conshohocken, PA: Combined Books, 1995.

Markle, Donald E. *Spies and Spymasters of the Civil War.* New York, Hippocrene Books, 1994.

Marszalek, John F. *Commander of All Lincoln's Armies: A Life of General Henry W. Halleck.* Cambridge, MA: Harvard University Press, 2004.

———. *Sherman: A Soldier's Passion for Order.* New York: Free Press, 1993.

Marvel, William. *Burnside.* Chapel Hill, NC: University of North Carolina Press, 1991.

———. *Mr. Lincoln Goes to War.* Boston: Houghton Mifflin, 2006.

Massey, Mary Elizabeth. *Bonnet Brigades.* New York: Knopf, 1966.

Matter, William D. *If It Takes All Summer: The Battle of Spotsylvania.* Chapel Hill: University of North Carolina Press, 1988.

Maurice, Major General Sir Frederick. *Statesmen and Soldiers of the Civil War: A Study of the Conduct of the War.* Boston: Little, Brown, 1926.

McClure, Alexander K. *Lincoln and Men of War Times.* Philadelphia: Rolley & Reynolds, 1962.

———. *Lincoln's Yarns and Stories.* Chicago: John C. Winston Co., n.d.

———. *Our Presidents and How We Make Them.* New York: Harper, 1900.

McCrary, Peyton. *Abraham Lincoln and Reconstruction: The Louisiana Experiment.* Princeton, NJ: Princeton University Press, 1978.

McFeely, William S. *Grant: A Biography.* New York: W. W. Norton, 1981.

———. *Frederick Douglass.* New York: W. W. Norton, 1991.

McPherson, James M. "Any Measure Which May Best Subdue the Enemy," *MHQ: The Quarterly of Military History* (Spring 2007): 34.

———. *Drawn with the Sword: Reflections on the American Civil War.* New York: Oxford University Press, 1996.

———. *Ordeal by Fire: The Civil War and Reconstruction.* New York: Knopf, 1982.

McWhiney, Grady. *Battle in the Wilderness: Grant Meets Lee.* Forth Worth, TX: Ryan Place Publishers, 1995.

———, ed. *Grant, Lee, Lincoln, and the Radicals.* Evanston, IL: Northwestern University Press, 1964.

Mearns, David Chambers. *Largely Lincoln.* New York: St. Martin's Press, 1961.

Merrill, James M. *William Tecumseh Sherman.* Chicago: Rand McNally, 1971.

Merrill, Louis Taylor. "General Benjamin F. Butler in the Presidential Campaign of 1864," *Mississippi Valley Historical Review*, 33 (March 1947): 537–570.

Meserve, Frederick Hill, and Carl Sandburg. *The Photographs of Abraham Lincoln.* New York: Harcourt Brace, 1944.

Middle Bass on the Web. *Rebels on Lake Erie Chapter IX–The Lake Erie Conspiracy.* Reprinted with permission of the Ohio Historical Society, 2001. *http://www.middlebass2 .org/Frohman_IX.shtml.*

Miers, Earl S., ed. U.S. Lincoln Sesquicentennial Commission. *Lincoln Day by Day: A Chronology, 1809–1865.* 3 vols. Dayton, OH: Morningside, 1991.

Milton, George Fort. *Abraham Lincoln and the Fifth Column.* New York: Vanguard Press, 1942.

Mitgang, Herbert, ed. *Abraham Lincoln: A Press Portrait.* Athens: University of Georgia Press, 1989.

Morris, Roy, Jr. *Sheridan: The Life and Wars of General Philip Sheridan.* New York: Crown, 1992.

Murdock, Eugene C. *One Million Men: The Civil War Draft in the North.* Madison, WI: State Historical Society of Wisconsin, 1971.

Neely, Mark E., Jr. *The Abraham Lincoln Encyclopedia.* New York: McGraw-Hill, 1982.

———. *The Fate of Liberty: Abraham Lincoln and Civil Liberties.* New York: Oxford University Press, 1991.

———. *The Last Best Hope of Earth: Abraham Lincoln and the Promise of America.* Cambridge, MA: Harvard University Press, 1993.

Nelson, Larry E. *Bullets, Ballots, and Rhetoric: Confederate Policy for the United States Presidential Contest of 1864.* Tuscaloosa: University of Alabama Press, 1980.

Nevins, Allan. *The Emergence of Lincoln.* New York: Scribner, 1950.

———. *Ordeal of the Union: Selected Chapters.* New York: Scribner, 1973.

———. *The Statesmanship of the Civil War.* New York: Collier Books, 1962.

New York Times. New York [H. J. Raymond & Co.], 1857–

Nichols, David A. *Lincoln and the Indians: Civil War Policy and Politics.* Columbia, MO: University of Missouri Press, 1978.

Nichols, George Ward. *The Story of the Great March.* Williamstown, MA: Corner House Publishers, 1972.

Nicolay, John G., and John Hay. *Abraham Lincoln: Complete Works.* 2 vols. New York: Century Co., 1894.

———. *Abraham Lincoln: A History.* 10 vols. New York: Century Co., 1914.

Niven, John. *Salmon P. Chase: A Biography.* New York: Oxford University Press, 1995.

Oakes, James. *The Radical and the Republican.* New York: W. W. Norton, 2007.

Oates, Stephen B. *Abraham Lincoln: The Man Behind the Myths.* New York: Harper & Row, 1984.

———. *With Malice Toward None: The Life of Abraham Lincoln.* New York: Harper & Row, 1977.

Page, Charles A. *Letters of a War Correspondent.* Boston: L. C. Page & Co., 1899.

Painter, Nell Irvin. *Sojourner Truth: A Life, A Symbol.* New York: W. W. Norton, 1996.

Paolino, Ernest N. *The Foundations of the American Empire.* Ithaca, NY: Cornell University Press, 1973.

Pease, Theodore Calvin, ed. *The Diary of Orville Hickman Browning.* 2 vols.: I, 1850–1864; II, 1865–1881. Springfield: Illinois State Historical Library, 1925, 1932.

Perry, James M. *Touched with Fire: Five Presidents and the Civil War Battles That Made Them.* New York: Public Affairs, 2003.

Phisterer, Frederick. *Statistical Record of the Armies of the United States.* Carlisle, PA: John Kallmann, 1996.

Pinkerton, Allan. *The Spy of the Rebellion.* Lincoln: University of Nebraska Press, 1989.

Pinsker, Matthew. *Lincoln's Sanctuary: Abraham Lincoln and the Soldiers' Home.* New York: Oxford University Press, 2003.

Piston, William Garrett. *Lee's Tarnished Lieutenant.* Athens: University of Georgia Press, 1987.

Pond, George E. *The Shenandoah Valley in 1864.* New York: Scribner, 1883.

Porter, General Horace. *Campaigning with Grant.* Edited with an introduction by Wayne C. Temple. New York: Bonanza Books, 1961.

Pratt, Fletcher. *Stanton: Lincoln's Secretary of War.* New York: W. W. Norton, 1953.

Randall, J. G. *Lincoln the President.* 4 vols. New York: Dodd-Mead, 1945–1955.

———, and David Donald. *The Civil War and Reconstruction.* Boston: Little, Brown, 1969.

Randall, Ruth Painter. *Lincoln's Sons.* Boston: Little, Brown, 1955.

———. *Mary Lincoln: Biography of a Marriage.* Boston: Little, Brown, 1953.

Rankin, Henry B. *Intimate Character Sketches of Abraham Lincoln.* Philadelphia: Lippincott, 1924.

Raymond, Henry J. *The Life and Public Services of Abraham Lincoln....* New York: Derby & Miller, 1865.

———. *Lincoln: His Life and Times.* New York: Hurst & Co., 1891.

Reck, Emerson, "President Lincoln's Substitute," *Lincoln Herald* 80, no. 3 (Fall 1978): 137–139.

Reed, Robert. *Old Washington, D.C. in Early Photographs, 1846–1932.* New York: Dover, 1980.

Reep, Thomas P. *Lincoln at New Salem.* (Written for the Old Salem Lincoln League) [Chicago]: c1927.

Rice, Allen Thorndike, ed. *Reminiscences of Abraham Lincoln by Distinguished Men of His Time.* New York: Harper, 1909.

Riddle, Albert Gallatin. *Recollections of War Times: Reminiscences of Men and Events in Washington, 1860–1865.* New York: Putnam, 1895.

Robertson, William Glen. *Back Door to Richmond: The Bermuda Hundred Campaign, April–June, 1864.* Newark: University of Delaware Press, 1987.

Roland, Charles P. *An American Iliad: The Story of the Civil War.* Lexington: University Press of Kentucky, 1991.

Ross, Ishbel. *First Lady of the South: The Life of Mrs. Jefferson Davis.* New York: Harper, 1958.

———. *The General's Wife: The Life of Mrs. Ulysses S. Grant.* New York: Dodd-Mead, 1959.

———. *The President's Wife: Mary Todd Lincoln.* New York: Putnam, 1973.

Rowland, Dunbar, ed. *Jefferson Davis, Constitutionalist: His Letters, Papers, and Speeches.* 10 vols. Jackson: Mississippi Department of Archives and History, 1923.

Rusling, James Fowler. *Men and Things I Saw in Civil War Days.* New York: Eaton & Mains; Cincinnati: Curts & Jennings, 1899.

Sandburg, Carl. *Abraham Lincoln: The Prairie Years and The War Years.* 1-vol. ed. New York: Harcourt Brace, 1954.

———. *Abraham Lincoln: The War Years.* 4 vols. New York: Harcourt Brace, 1939.

———. *Storm over the Land: A Profile of the Civil War.* New York: Harcourt, Brace, 1942.

Sanger, Colonel Donald Bridgman, and Thomas Robson Hay. *James Longstreet: I. Soldier; II. Politican, Officerholder, and Writer.* Baton Rouge: Louisiana State University Press, 1968.

Schuckers, J. W. *Life and Public Services of Salmon Portland Chase.* New York: Da Capo Press, 1970.

Scott, Robert Garth. *Into the Wilderness with the Army of the Potomac.* Bloomington: Indiana University Press, 1985.

Sears, Stephen W. *George B. McClellan: The Young Napoleon.* New York: Ticknor & Fields, 1988.

Segal, Charles M. *Conversations with Lincoln.* New York: Putnam, 1961.

Seitz, Don C. *Lincoln the Politician: How the Rail-Splitter and Flatboatman Played the Great American Game.* New York: Coward-McCann, 1931.

Sellers, John R., compiler. *Civil War Manuscripts: A Guide to Collections in the Manuscript Division of the Library of Congress.* Washington, D.C.: Library of Congress, 1986.

Severance, Frank H. "The Peace Conference at Niagara Falls in 1864." Buffalo, NY: Buffalo Historical Society, 1914, 79–94.

Seward, Frederick W. *Seward at Washington as Senator and Secretary of State.* New York: Derby & Miller, 1891.

Shaw, William L. "The Confederate Conscription and Exemption Acts:" *American Journal of Legal History* 6, no. 4 (October 1962): 368–405.

Shenk, Joshua Wolf. *Lincoln's Melancholy: How Depression Challenged a President and Fueled His Greatness.* Boston: Houghton Mifflin, 2005.

Sheridan, Philip Henry. *Personal Memoirs of P. H. Sheridan, General, United States Army.* New York: C. L. Webster & Co., 1888.

Sherman, William Tecumseh. *Marching Through Georgia.* Edited by Mills Lane. New York: Arno Press, 1978.

———. *Memoirs of General W. T. Sherman.* New York: Library of America, 1990.

———. *William T. Sherman Papers*. Library of Congress Manuscript Collections.

Simon, James F. *Lincoln and Chief Justice Taney*. New York: Simon & Schuster, 2006.

Simon, John Y., ed. *The Papers of Ulysses S. Grant*. 28 vols. Carbondale: Southern Illinois University Press, 1967–2005.

———, ed. *The Personal Memoirs of Julia Dent Grant (Mrs. Ulysses S. Grant)*. Carbondale: Southern Illinois University Press, 1988.

Simon, Paul. *Lincoln's Preparation for Greatness: The Illinois Legislative Years*. Urbana: University of Illinois Press, 1971.

Simpson, Brooks D. *Let Us Have Peace: Ulysses S. Grant and the Politics of War and Reconstruction, 1861–1868*. Chapel Hill: University of North Carolina Press, 1991.

———, and Jean V. Berlin, eds. *Sherman's Civil War: Selected Correspondence of William T. Sherman, 1860–1865*. Chapel Hill: University of North Carolina Press, 1999.

Smith, Carter, ed. *1863: The Crucial Year*. Brookfield, CT: Millbrook Press, 1993.

Smith, George Wilson, and Charles Judah. *Life in the North During the Civil War: A Source History*. Albuquerque: University of New Mexico Press, 1966.

Smith, Jean Edward. *Grant*. New York: Simon & Schuster, 2001.

Smith, William Ernest. *The Francis Preston Blair Family in Politics*. 2 vols. New York: Macmillan, 1933.

Speer, John. *Life of General James H. Lane*. Garden City, KS: John Speer, 1896.

Stackpole, Edward J. *Sheridan in the Shenandoah: Jubal Early's Nemesis*. New York: Bonanza Books, 1961.

Stampp, Kenneth M. *Indiana Politics During the Civil War*. Bloomington: Indiana University Press, 1978.

Stanchak, John E., ed. *Leslie's Illustrated Civil War*. Jackson: University Press of Mississippi, 1992.

Starr, Stephen Z. *Colonel Grenfell's Wars: The Life of a Soldier of Fortune*. Baton Rouge: Louisiana State University Press, 1971.

Steere, Edward. *The Wilderness Campaign*. New York: Bonanza Books, 1960.

Stephenson, Nathaniel W. *Lincoln*. Indianapolis: Bobbs-Merrill, 1922.

Stern, Philip Van Doren. *The Life and Writings of Abraham Lincoln*. New York: Modern Library, 1940.

———. *The Man Who Killed Lincoln: The Story of John Wilkes Booth and His Part in the Assassination*. New York: Literary Guild of America, 1939.

Stevens, George Thomas. *Three Years in the Sixth Corps*. New York: Time-Life Books, 1984.

Stevens, Joseph E. *1863: The Rebirth of a Nation*. New York: Bantam, 1999.

Stevenson, Nathaniel W. *The Day of the Confederacy: A Chronicle of the Embattled South*. New Haven, CT: Yale University Press, 1920.

Stoddard, Henry L. *Horace Greeley, Printer, Editor, Crusader*. New York: Putnam, 1946.

Stoddard, William O. *Inside the White House in War Times: Memoirs and Reports of Lincoln's Secretary*. Edited by Michael Burlingame. Lincoln: University of Nebraska Press, 2000.

———. *Lincoln at Work; Sketches from Life*. Boston and Chicago: United Society of Christian Endeavor, 1900.

Strode, Hudson, ed. *Jefferson Davis: Private Letters, 1823–1889*. New York: Harcourt, Brace, 1966.

Surdam, David G., "Traders or Traitors: Northern Cotton Trading During the Civil War." *Business and Economic History*. 28, no. 2. (Winter 1999), 301–312.

Swank, Walbrook D. *Old Abe's Jokes: Humorous Stories Told of and by Abraham Lincoln*. Shippensburg, PA: Burd Street Press, 1996.

Symonds, Craig L.. *Joseph E. Johnston: A Civil War Biography*. New York: W. W. Norton, 1992.

Tarbell, Ida M. *The Life of Abraham Lincoln*. . . . New York: Lincoln Historical Society, 1909.

———. *A Reporter for Lincoln*. New York: Macmillan, 1927.

———, ed. *Selections from the Letters, Speeches, and State Papers of Abraham Lincoln*. Boston: Ginn & Co., 1911.

Tate, Allen. *Jefferson Davis: His Rise and Fall*. New York: Minton, Balch, 1929.

Thayer, William Roscoe. *Life and Letters of John Hay*. 2 vols. Boston and New York: Houghton Mifflin, 1916.

Thomas, Benjamin P. *Abraham Lincoln*. New York: Knopf, 1952.

———. *Lincoln's New Salem*. Springfield, IL: Abraham Lincoln Association, 1934.

———. *Stanton; the Life and Times of Lincoln's Secretary of War*. New York: Knopf, 1962.

Thomas, Benjamin P., and Harold M. Hyman. *Stanton: The Life and Times of Lincoln's Secretary of War*. New York: Knopf, 1962.

Thorndike, Rachel Sherman, ed. *The Sherman Letters: Correspondence Between General Sherman and Senator Sherman from 1837 to 1891*. New York: Da Capo Press, 1969.

Tidwell, William A. *Come Retribution: The Confederate Secret Service and the Assassination of Lincoln*. Jackson: University Press of Mississippi, 1988.

Tomkins, Mary E. *Ida M. Tarbell*. New York: Twayne Publishers, 1974.

Townsend, William H. *Lincoln and the Bluegrass: Slavery and the Civil War in Kentucky*. Lexington: University Press of Kentucky, 1955.

Trefousse, Hans L. *The Radical Republicans: Lincoln's Vanguard for Racial Justice*. New York: Knopf, 1969.

Tripp, C. A. *The Intimate World of Abraham Lincoln*. New York: Free Press, 2005.

Turner, Justin G., and Linda Levitt Turner. *Mary Todd Lincoln: Her Life and Letters*. New York: Knopf, 1972.

Turner, Kathleen J., ed. *Doing Rhetorical History: Concepts and Cases*. Tuscaloosa: University of Alabama Press, 1998.

United States Central Intelligence Agency. Library Publications. *https://www.cia.gov/library/publications/additional-publications/civil-war/p37.htm*.

United States Park Service. *The Civil War Defenses of Washington, D.C. http://www.nps.gov/history/history/online_books/civilwar/hrs1-4.htm* (Accessed May 5, 2008.)

Vinovaskis, Marisa, ed. *Toward a Social History of the American Civil War: Exploratory Essays*. Cambridge: Cambridge University Press, 1990.

Wagner, Margaret E., Gary W. Gallagher, and Paul Finkelman, eds. *Civil War Desk Reference*. New York: Simon & Schuster, 2002.

Ward, Geoffrey C. "We Were as Brothers." *American Heritage*, November 1990, p. 14.

Warner, Ezra J. *Generals in Blue: Lives of the Union Commanders*. Baton Rouge: Louisiana State University Press, 1972.

———. *Generals in Gray: Lives of the Confederate Commanders*. Baton Rouge: Louisiana State University Press, 1959.

Waugh, John C. *Reelecting Lincoln: The Battle for the 1864 Presidency*. Cambridge, MA: Da Capo Press, 2001.

Webb, Willard. *Crucial Moments of the Civil War*. New York: Bonanza Books, 1961.

Weber, Jennifer L. *Copperheads: The Rise and Fall of Lincoln's Opponents in the North*. Oxford and New York: Oxford University Press, 2006.

Weed, Harriet A. *Autobiography of Thurlow Weed*. 2 vols. Boston: Houghton Mifflin, 1883.

Welles, Gideon. *Diary of Gideon Welles*. 3 vols. Boston: Houghton Mifflin, 1911.

Wert, Jeffry D. *From Winchester to Cedar Creek: The Shenandoah Campaign of 1864*. Carlisle, PA: South Mountain Press, 1987.

Wheeler, Tom. *Mr. Lincoln's T-Mails*. New York: HarperCollins, 2006.

Whiting, William. *War Powers Under the Constitution of the United States*. New York: Da Capo Press, 1972.

Wilentz, Sean. *The Rise of American Democracy: Jefferson to Lincoln*. New York: W. W. Norton, 1954.

Wilkeson, Frank B. *Recollections of a Private Soldier in the Army of the Potomac*. Freeport, NY: Books for Libraries Press, 1972.

Williams, A. Dana. *The Praise of Lincoln: An Anthology*. Indianapolis: Bobbs-Merrill, 1911.

Williams, Kenneth P. *Lincoln Finds a General: A Military Study of the Civil War*. 2 vols. New York: Macmillan, 1949.

Williams, T. Harry. *Lincoln and His Generals*. New York: Knopf, 1952.

———. *Lincoln and the Radicals*. University of Wisconsin Press, 1941.

———. *McClellan, Sherman, and Grant*. New Brunswick, NJ: Rutgers University Press, 1962.

Wilson, Douglas L. *Honor's Voice: The Transformation of Abraham Lincoln*. New York: Vintage, 1998.

———. *Lincoln's Sword: The Presidency and the Power of Words*. New York: Knopf, 2007.

Wilson, Rufus Rockwell. *Intimate Memories of Lincoln*. Elmira, NY: Primavera Press, 1945.

Wilson, Rufus Rockwell, et al., eds. *Uncollected Works of Abraham Lincoln: His Letters, Addresses, and Other Papers*. 2 vols. (A supplement to and revision of *The Complete Works of Lincoln* by Nicolay and Hay.) Elmira, NY: Primavera Press, 1947.

Wing, Henry Ebeneser. *Raising the Old Boy*. New York: Abingdon Press, 1923.

———. *When Lincoln Kissed Me: A Story of the Wilderness Campaign*. New York: Eaton & Mains, 1913.

Winik, Jay. *April 1865: The Month That Saved America*. New York: HarperCollins, 2001.

Winkle, Kenneth J. *The Young Eagle: The Rise of Abraham Lincoln*. Dallas: Taylor Trade Publishing, 2001.

Winn, Ralph B. *A Concise Lincoln Dictionary*. New York: Wisdom Library, 1959.

Winslow, Richard E. *General John Sedgwick: The Story of a Union Corps Commander*. San Rafael, CA: Presidio Press, 1981.

Wood, Forrest G. *Black Scare: The Racist Response to Emancipation and Reconstruction*. Berkeley: University of California Press, 1968.

Wood, Gray. *The Hidden Civil War: The Story of the Copperheads*. New York: Viking, 1942.

Woodward, C. Vann, ed., *Mary Chesnut's Civil War*. New Haven, CT: Yale University Press, 1981.

Woodworth, Steven E. *Davis and Lee at War*. Lawrence: University Press of Kansas, 1995.

———. *Jefferson Davis and His Generals: The Failure of Confederate Command in the West*. Lawrence: University Press of Kansas, 1990.

———. *Nothing but Victory: The Army of the Tennessee, 1861–1865*. New York: Knopf, 2005.

Zall, P. M., ed. *Abe Lincoln Laughing*. Berkeley: University of California Press, 1982.

———. *Lincoln on Lincoln*. Lexington: University Press of Kentucky, 1999.

Zornow, William Frank. *Lincoln and the Party Divided*. Norman: University of Oklahoma Press, 1954. Reprint: Westport, CT: Greenwood Press, 1972.

ACKNOWLEDGMENTS

I wish first to express my loving thanks to my wife, Katherine Burnam Flood, for her unwavering support of my efforts as I worked on this large project. I am also deeply appreciative of the useful readings given the manuscript by my daughter, Lucy, herself a published writer, and by my sons, Caperton and Curtis.

Before mentioning the various scholars who have generously shared with me their time and thoughts about this book as it came into being, I want to pay special tribute to my friend Carol Tudor Thomas, who works in Government Documents in the Crabbe Library of Eastern Kentucky University. I will have more to say about that excellent library in which I work daily, and its exceedingly able and helpful staff, but on her own time Carol has acted as my assistant throughout every step of the development of this book, taking home work on hundreds of nights. In addition to her greatly superior secretarial and organizational skills, she has been unfailingly encouraging, and has developed that sense of the hunt that marks the determined researcher, joining those of us who have discovered that the last place you look, tired as you may be, produces the little-known apt quotation, or the vivid description from an obscure source.

As has been the case in the development of several of my books, I owe a particular debt to my old and close friend Thomas Fleming, the author of more than forty works of history, biography, and fiction. In the summer of 2006, when I had written what I thought was a good, comprehensive proposal of the idea for this book to submit to publishers, I sent it to him for his review, and got back what can only be called a whistle-blowing letter. As a result, I refocused many of my ideas, and changed certain emphases. Whatever the failings of this book, Tom's efforts, which later included an insightful reading of large portions of the manuscript, have improved it significantly.

The next person to whom I owe many thanks is my friend Dwight Taylor, of San Francisco. I met Dwight in the autumn of 1947, when I was a seventeen-year-old freshman at Harvard and he, the proctor in charge of one wing of my dormitory, was a twenty-six-year-old graduate of Harvard, returning to complete his studies at the Law School after several years of service in the South Pacific during World War II. Going far beyond his duties, Dwight not only befriended me, but—"scolded" would be too gentle a word—talked to me about my mediocre first mid-semester academic showing, using language that would motivate almost anyone. Over the years, he has taken time from a distinguished legal and corporate career to read my manuscripts, bringing to the task the same intellectual ability that won him one of Harvard's prestigious Sheldon Traveling Fellowships, given at a time when only one a year was awarded to a member of the senior class. So here we are, sixty-one years later as I write this, I bringing out my twelfth book and Dwight telling me to amplify a description here, and delete a comma there.

Yet another friend who has brought his talents to bear on my behalf is my cousin by marriage, Edward H. Pulliam, of Alexandria, Virginia, who has frequently published articles in magazines of American history. As in the past, he has given drafts of my work careful and sensitive readings, and has been extremely helpful in confirming details of Civil War sites in and around Washington.

Turning to noted Civil War experts who have been good enough to help me, my editor at Simon & Schuster, the legendary Alice Mayhew, enlisted the eminent author and Lincoln scholar, Harold Holzer, to read my manuscript. His excellent suggestions also included a bit of whistle-blowing, as a result of which, among other things, I added important facts about the miscegenation issue in the 1864 presidential campaign. In addition, he has been good enough to share his encyclopedic knowledge of photographs and other illustrations involving Lincoln.

Several scholars who helped me greatly with my *Grant and Sherman: The Friendship That Won the Civil War*, published in 2005, have continued to help me in my writing of this book. John F. Marszalek, the W. L. Giles Distinguished Professor Emeritus of History at Mississippi State University and the author of *Sherman: A Soldier's Passion for Order* and *Commander of All Lincoln's Armies: A Life of General Henry J. Halleck*, has answered queries and remained interested in my work. Similar help has been given me by Charles P. Roland, alumni professor of history at the

University of Kentucky and the author, among other books, of that fine one-volume history, *An American Iliad: The Story of the Civil War.* Also at the University of Kentucky, where I have had the support of Carol Diedrichs, Dean of the University of Kentucky Libraries, I have been fortunate to have the continuing wise counsel of Civil War expert, William J. Marshall. Bill, who was for many years the director of Special Collections and Archives at the University of Kentucky and is now Curator of Manuscripts, is the perennial secretary of the Kentucky Civil War Round Table of Lexington, Kentucky, the nation's largest such organization. I also want to include among those who have helped me, Professor Marshall Myers of Eastern Kentucky University's Department of English and Theater, who has served as president of the Madison County Civil War Round Table.

Although he had no direct contact with this book, I wish to add my tribute to the late Professor John Y. Simon of Southern Illinois University, the editor of *The Papers of Ulysses S. Grant,* one of the monumental feats of American scholarship. He helped guide me into my *Grant and Sherman,* and throughout the writing of my present work one or another of the twenty-eight volumes of *The Papers of Ulysses S. Grant* was always at my side.

No writer has better conditions in which to work than those available to me in the main library of Eastern Kentucky University. I have done my research and writing in libraries all over the world, and, in relation to its mission, I consider it to be the best library in which I have worked. I am there so much of the time that I regard the staff as my friends, and herewith express my thanks to all of them for their efficient service and constant encouragement and support.

This interest in helping me begins at the top: Carrie Cooper, the most impressive young Dean of Libraries, has continued the practice of assisting me in every way started in 1975 by the late Dean Ernest E. Weyhrauch, who greeted me on my first visit to his office by saying, "We'd like to help you in every way we can." He and I became close friends, and that immensely cooperative attitude was continued by his successors, the late Marcia Myers, and Lee Van Orsdel, with Carrie Cooper now presiding over a library that under her direction is constantly expanding its facilities and services. Among those working in her office I wish to thank Kari Martin, with whom I have had the pleasure of renewing the activities of the Friends of the EKU Libraries, and Jo Lane, Verna Freer, and Pam

Bennett. I have already spoken of the special role in my work played by Carol Tudor Thomas of Government Documents, and wish to thank that department's leader, my friend Linda Sizemore, for helping me on this project as she did with my *Grant and Sherman*. I also appreciate the assistance given me by Linda Witt. In a different area of the library's activity, I wish to thank for his help on the second book in a row, Chuck Hill, the University Archivist and head of University Archives.

Whenever I exhaust the resources of this million-volume library, I turn gratefully to Interlibrary Loan, which is run by Pat New. Pat has done a literally perfect job of getting me materials of all kinds, sometimes so swiftly that I think she has some secret courier service, and is almost psychic in anticipating my needs for new books, as well as in renewing books in such a timely fashion that I am never left without a copy of whatever I need. She is ably assisted by René McGuire and Ashley Wray, and I also wish to thank Mia Fields Thomas for her help during the time she worked in that office. I often turn for assistance to the Reference Services, presided over by Julie George. As it has developed, Kevin Jones and Rob Sica of that department, whose reference skills I came to appreciate some years ago, have been the ones on whom I have most relied to provide accurate, helpful answers to questions large and small, but I would also like to mention the others who have always been ready to help, and have frequently done so: Karen Gilbert, Brad Marcum, Victoria Koger, Leah Banks, Nancy McKenney, Christine Gearhart, and Zhou Ning.

Most of my in-house social life is provided by the staffers whose area is opposite to that of the Reference Desk. This involves a combination of individuals from the Public Services Division and Circulation/Periodicals, who have been good enough, in addition to keeping track of the many books from the collection that I use, to include me in their daily sandwich lunches, brief but lively gatherings held in a room not far from the circulation desk. Shifting in and out of this area while always keeping people on duty during the lunch hour, this group of able, dedicated workers includes the Coordinator of Public Services, Betina Gardner, with whom I have had many interesting conversations, and her assistant, Kate Montgomery. From Circulation/Periodicals there is its leader, Carol Lawson as well as Anna Boggs, Stefanie Brooks, Chandra Chaffin, Eric Hall, Sandra Kessler, Jeremy Turner, and Judy Warren. They are often joined by Beverly Hisel, who is in charge of Shelving/Stack Maintenance. More than these pleasant and entertaining people probably realize, my time with them enables this writer to go back to his work space better able to face more hours alone with books, screens, and keyboards. My thanks to others in the library extend to Cindi Trainor, who, in addition to her duties as Coordinator of Technology and Data Services, is the fine photographer who took the picture of me that appears on the jacket of this book, to Systems Administrator Todd King, and to Shirley Dickerson of Custodial Services.

Although they are in a separate category, I would like to thank my friends Ashley, Brenda, and Pumpkin (yes, Pumpkin), who greet me every morning from behind the counter of the little Java City Café in the entrance atrium of the library. Their friendly smiles and excellent coffee lattes smooth my transition into the working day.

When it came time to offer the finished manuscript to publishers, this was done in his usual masterful fashion by my literary agent, John Taylor ("Ike") Williams, who has as his assistant the invaluable, Hope Denekamp. Ike's excellent efforts on my behalf resulted in my book finding the best possible home, Simon & Schuster, the publisher of so many highly regarded Civil War books, with my editor being the justly famous Alice Mayhew, the house's Editorial Director and the gifted editor of more than a score of books dealing with Lincoln and various aspects of his life. As the manuscript has moved through the various phases of production under Alice's experienced guidance, I have come to know and appreciate the efforts of a number of individuals involved in the process, including Roger Labrie and Alice's assistant, Karen Thompson. Fred Wiemer, the outside copy editor and a man who previously worked on such important Simon & Schuster Lincoln books as David Donald's *Lincoln*, brought special expertise to the task, and I have thoroughly enjoyed working with Gypsy da Silva, Associate Director of Copyediting, who turned what is sometimes a tedious task into a pleasure. I have had a productive meeting with Simon & Schuster's Executive Director of Publicity Victoria Meyer, and look forward to working with her, and I also appreciate the chance to have met and exchanged ideas with the book's designer, Dana Sloan.

During the course of my research, in my travels I have had pleasant and efficient cooperation from several admirable institutions. While in Springfield, Illinois, I received help from the Abraham Lincoln Presidential Library. Across the past few years, I have consulted with Dr. Russell Flinchum, Archivist of the Century Association in New York City, and this has led me to the vast holdings of the nearby main building of the

New York Public Library, whose staff has always been able to guide me to what I needed to find.

In closing this long list of those who have helped me, I think of a number of people who have made additional contributions of various kinds, ranging from insightful readings to the gift or loan of valuable materials. My sister, Mary Ellen Reese, of Washington, D.C., herself an author, read the manuscript and offered suggestions and encouragement, as did her husband Mitch. Carl M. Schencker of Washington, who has drawn my attention to Civil War topics about which he has written. My friends Jerry and Mimi Gordon of Corte Madera, California, also gave me ideas, as did Clayton and Barbara Pluff, of Brunswick, Maine. My friend, the author Thomas Parrish, of Berea, Kentucky, has for years acted as reader, friend, and artistic conscience. Others in Kentucky who have been helpful are Gerald Toner and David O. Watson, both of Louisville. The Reverend Charles Lawrence of Lexington, Kentucky, most generously gave me his own two-volume copy of *Harvard Memorial Biographies*, a remarkable collection of obituaries and tributes to the Harvard men who died in the Civil War, including accounts of the manner in which many of these men met their deaths. This work, assembled and published within two years of the war's end, speaks to Harvard's sense of history and tradition, as does the fact that it was presented to Charles Lawrence by his grandfather Bishop William Lawrence, Bishop of Western Massachusetts, upon his graduation from Harvard in 1938. Yet another gift for which I am grateful came from Diana Jeanne Beck of Brooksville, Maine, who gave me a copy of an interesting and useful document she had privately printed: *History of the 49th Regiment, New York Volunteers*, in which her ancestor, Private William A. Bartlett served. My friend Dwight L. Eaton of Brooksville has loaned me valuable Civil War materials.

I cannot finish these many acknowledgments without mentioning the constant interest in my work shown by my dear friend Sidney Offit, whom I first met in 1960, when we were both working on novels in the Frederick Lewis Allen Room of the New York Public Library at 42nd Street and Fifth Avenue. His combination of high-hearted laughter and deep interest in and knowledge of the creative process has been an inspiration to so many of us, as it will always be to this old friend.

INDEX

ABOUT THE AUTHOR

Charles Bracelen Flood is the author of eleven previous books, most recently *Grant and Sherman: The Friendship That Won the Civil War* (Farrar, Straus and Giroux, 2005). He is the past president of PEN American Center and has served on the governing bodies of the Authors League and Authors Guild.